F. R. McMillan

12/22/39

# REINFORCED CONCRETE DESIGN HANDBOOK

OF THE

AMERICAN CONCRETE INSTITUTE

DETROIT, MICHIGAN

•

Reported by

COMMITTEE 317

A. J. Boase, Author-Chairman

H. P. Bigler
Harry Ellsberg
L. E. Grinter
Mogens Ipsen
A. E. Lindau
F. E. Richart

•

Published Cooperatively by

AMERICAN CONCRETE INSTITUTE
PORTLAND CEMENT ASSOCIATION
CONCRETE REINFORCING STEEL INSTITUTE
RAIL STEEL BAR ASSOCIATION

First Edition—Price $2.00

# Foreword

THE committee charged with the task of preparing this handbook on reinforced concrete design recognizes that throughout the United States there are many codes and specifications covering a multitude of uses of reinforced concrete. In these codes various types of static and moving loads are anticipated for use under numerous conditions; consequently there are many combinations of unit stresses needed for general design.

One of the important objectives of the committee has been to prepare tables covering as large a range of unit stresses as may be met in general practice.

A second and equally important aim has been to reduce the design of members under combined bending and axial load to the same simple form as is used in the solution of common flexural problems.

The committee necessarily has consulted and studied many authorities—too many to list—and acknowledges its gratitude to all of those writers who have, from the beginning, contributed so generously of their time and energy to make possible this report.

The committee has had the valuable suggestions and able assistance of L. H. Corning, H. L. Flodin, Thor Germundsson, J. T. Howell, C. E. Morgan, J. P. Thompson and J. E. Zyka. Without their efforts this report would have presented a problem too great for committee accomplishment.

Mogens Ipsen, one of the committee members, died after completion of the report, but prior to its publication.

Committee 317 on
Reinforced Concrete Design Handbook

## Symbols and Notation

$a$ : coefficient used in $A_s = \frac{M}{ad}$ and in $A_s = \frac{NE}{adi}$
$a_f$ : same as $a$ but for flange only of T-section
$a_w$ : same as $a$ but for web only of T-section
$A_c$ : core area based on diameter out to out of spiral
$A_g$ : gross area of concrete section
$A_s$ : area of tensile reinforcement or of column bars
$A'_s$ : area of compressive reinforcement in flexural members
$A_{sf}$ : that part of tensile steel in T-beams corresponding to compression in flange
$A_{sw}$ : that part of tensile steel in T-beams required to balance compression in web
$A_v$ : area of web reinforcement
$b$ : width of rectangular beam or width of flange of T-beam
$b'$ : width of web in T-beams (used in flexural computations)
$B$ : $\sin x + \cos x$; used in connection with inclined web reinforcement
$c$ : coefficient used in $A'_s = \frac{M - KF}{cd}$ and in $A'_s = \frac{NE - KF}{cd}$; also size of bar reinforcement
$C$ : resultant of compressive stresses
$d$ : effective depth of flexural members; also diameter of spiral core
$d'$ : distance from extreme fiber to compressive reinforcement
$d''$ : distance from centerline of concrete section to tensile reinforcement
$D$ : $t^2/2R^2$; used in investigation of eccentrically loaded columns
$e$ : eccentricity measured from tensile steel axis (in.)
$e'$ : eccentricity measured from gravity axis (in.)
$E$ : eccentricity measured from tensile steel axis (ft.)
$E_c$ : modulus of elasticity of concrete
$E_s$ : modulus of elasticity of steel
$f_c$ : compressive stress in extreme fiber
$f'_c$ : ultimate compressive strength of concrete
$f_p$ : allowable stress in eccentrically loaded columns
$f_a$ : average stress in axially loaded columns
$f_s$ : stress in tensile reinforcement or in column reinforcement
$f'_s$ : stress in compressive reinforcement in flexural members
$f_r$ : stress in column reinforcement
$f_v$ : stress in web reinforcement
$F$ : $\frac{bd^2}{12{,}000}$; used in determination of resisting moment of concrete sections
$F_f$ : same as $F$ but for flange only of T-section
$F_w$ : same as $F$ but for web only of T-section
$g$ : ratio of diameter of circle ($gt$) through bar centerlines, or distance ($gt$) between bars at opposite faces of column to over-all dimension ($t$)
$G$ : $\frac{7bd}{8000}$; used for calculation of shear

$i$ : $\dfrac{1}{1 - \dfrac{jd}{e}}$; used in sections subject to bending and axial load

$i_f$ : same as $i$ but for flange only of T-section

$i_w$ : same as $i$ but for web only of T-section

$I$ : moment of inertia

$j$ : ratio of distance ($jd$) between resultants of compressive and tensile stresses to effective depth

$k$ : ratio of distance ($kd$ or $kt$) between extreme fiber and neutral axis to effective depth or to total depth

$K$ : $\frac{1}{2} f_c jk$

$K_f$ : same as $K$ but for flange only of T-section

$K_w$ : same as $K$ but for web only of T-section

$L$ : width of square footing; also length of span

$m$ : $np + (n - 1)p'$; used in determination of $k$

$M$ : external moment (ft.kips)

$M_r$ : resisting moment of concrete stresses

$n$ : ratio of modulus of elasticity of steel ($E_s$) to that of concrete ($E_c$)

$N$ : external force or load (kips); also number of stirrups

$N.A.$ : neutral axis

$\Sigma o$ : sum of perimeters of bars

$p$ : ratio of tensile reinforcement in beams; also ratio of longitudinal reinforcement in columns

$p'$ : ratio of compressive reinforcement in beams; also ratio of spiral reinforcement in columns

$P$ : external concentric load on columns or piles

$q$ : $np + (n - 1)p'\dfrac{d'}{d}$; used in determination of $k$

$Q$ : $\dfrac{f_p A_g}{1000N}$; used in design of eccentrically loaded columns

$r$ : radius of round columns

$R$ : radius of gyration

$s$ : spacing of stirrups (in.)

$S$ : base length of shear diagram (ft.)

$t$ : over-all dimension of columns; also depth of flange

$T$ : resultant of tensile stresses

$u$ : bond stress

$v$ : shearing stress

$v'$ : shearing stress taken by web reinforcement

$V$ : total shear

$w$ : permissible soil pressure; also uniformly distributed load

$W$ : concentrated load on flexural members

$x$ : angle between tensile and web reinforcement

$y$ : ratio of distance ($yt$) between extreme fiber and resultant of stresses in flange to flange depth ($t$)

$z$ : ratio of distance ($zkd$) between extreme fiber and resultant of compressive stresses to distance $kd$

# LIST OF EXAMPLES

## DESIGN OF FLEXURAL MEMBERS



## INVESTIGATION OF FLEXURAL MEMBERS



## STIRRUPS



## COLUMNS—CONCENTRICALLY LOADED



## COLUMNS—ECCENTRICALLY LOADED



## FOOTINGS

# LIST OF TABLES AND DIAGRAMS

# Reinforced Concrete Design Handbook

## Design of Flexural Members

## Simple Bending and Bending Combined with Axial Load

DETERMINATION of the required depth of slabs having balanced reinforcement and subject to simple bending involves only the use of Table 2 from which the effective depth can be selected when the allowable working stresses and the value of $n$ are known (*see Example 1*). Table 2 applies also to combined bending and axial load.

The dimensions of rectangular beams with similar information given can be obtained by using Tables 1 and 4. Take $K$ from Table 1, compute $F$* and enter Table 4, from which $b$ and $d$ may be selected (*see Example 1*).

Example 1 may be considered preliminary to the examples which follow and has been carried only to the point of determining the slab and beam dimensions. The method of determining the reinforcement is illustrated in succeeding examples.

The problem of determining the tensile and compressive reinforcement in a double-reinforced beam, as in Example 2, is solved by computing

$A'_S$** $= \dfrac{M - KF}{cd}$ and $A_S$† $= \dfrac{M}{ad}$. The numerator in the expression for $A'_S$

represents that part of the external moment which the concrete section is unable to carry when stressed to the allowable limit. This part of the moment must therefore be taken by compressive reinforcement. Values of $c$** are obtained from Table 7 and the values of $a$† for rectangular beams from Table 1. The tabular values of $a$ are based upon average values of $j$ in the usual range of working stresses. While the use of the value $a$, in general, gives more accurate results than the often used value of $j = 7/8$ for both single and double-reinforced beams, it should be realized in the latter case that the value of $A_S$ thus obtained is approximate as stated in the footnote to Example 2.

The design of T-sections subject to simple bending and neglecting the stress in the stem is essentially the same as the design of a rectangular beam except that values of $K$ and $a$ are obtained from Table 8 instead of Table 1 (*see Example 3*).

When the stress in the stem of a T-section is included and compressive reinforcement is or is not required, the design procedure is similar to that

*See page 46, Equation 8.
**See page 47, Equation 9.
†See page 45, Equation 4.

of a rectangular beam, considering the web and the flange separately (*see Example 4*). When considering the web, values of $K$, $a$ and $F$ are taken from Tables 1 and 4, and when considering the flange, the values of $K$ and $a$ are taken from Table 8.

There is no fundamental difference in the design of flexural members for simple bending and for those cases of combined bending and axial load in which tension exists over a considerable part of the cross section. In the design equations for simple bending, $M$ (ft.kips) is replaced by $NE$ in which $N$ (kips) is the axial load on the section and $E$ (ft.) the distance from the resultant of tensile stresses to the equivalent eccentric load $N$ which may be substituted for $M$ and $N$. For example, the equation $A_S = \frac{M}{ad}$ for simple bending becomes $A_S{}^* = \frac{NE}{adi}$ for combined bending where $i = \frac{1}{1 - \frac{jd}{e}}$. When these substitutions are made, all equations customarily used for simple bending are applicable to combined bending and axial load. Values of $a$ are taken from Tables 1 or 8, depending on whether the member is a rectangular or T-section, and values of $i$ are taken from Table 10. Examples 5 to 8 illustrate in detail the design procedure for members subject to combined bending and axial load when the eccentricity is relatively large. When the eccentricity is relatively small, the procedure for design of eccentrically loaded columns should be used (*see Examples 32 to 36*).

**Example 1. Rectangular Section, Simple Bending**

For a rectangular section subject to bending moment $M$, determine the least concrete dimensions allowed without compressive reinforcement. Consider (1) slab section; (2) beam web.

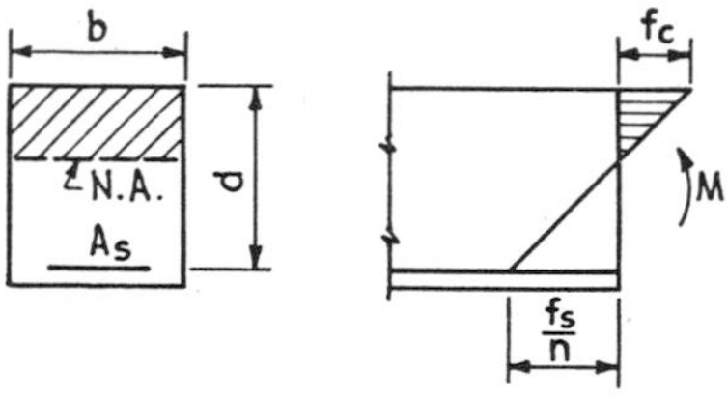

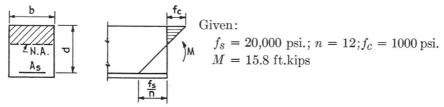

Given:

$f_S = 20{,}000$ psi.; $n = 12$; $f_C = 1000$ psi.
$M = 15.8$ ft.kips

(1) *Slab section.* ($M$ is moment per foot of width.)
From Table 2, for 20,000/12/1000: $d = 10$ in. (Resisting moment = 16.4 ft.kips)

(2) *Beam web.* ($M$ is moment on beam)
From Table 1, for 20,000/12/1000, $K = 164$, therefore

$$\frac{M}{K} = \frac{15.8}{164} = 0.096 = F$$

From Table 4, select $b \times d = 7\tfrac{1}{2} \times 12\tfrac{1}{2}$ in. ($F = 0.098$)

*See page 45, Equation 5.

## Example 2. Rectangular Section, Simple Bending, Compressive Reinforcement

For a rectangular section subject to bending moment $M$, determine (1) whether concrete section is adequate without compressive reinforcement, $A'_S$; (2) $A'_S$, if required; (3) tensile reinforcement, $A_S$.

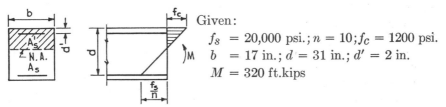

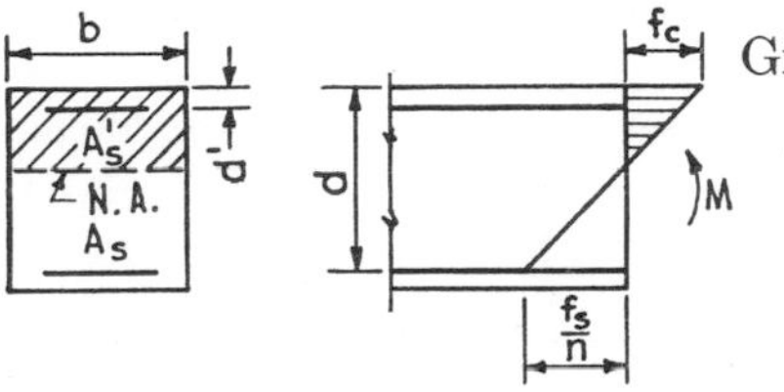


Given:

$f_S = 20{,}000$ psi.; $n = 10$; $f_C = 1200$ psi.
$b = 17$ in.; $d = 31$ in.; $d' = 2$ in.
$M = 320$ ft.kips

(1) From Table 1, for 20,000/10/1200: $K = 197$
From Table 4, for $b \times d = 17.0 \times 31.0$: $F = 1.36$
then

$$\begin{aligned} M & & = 320 \\ KF &= 197 \times 1.36 &= \underline{268} \\ M - KF & &= 52 \end{aligned}$$

Compressive reinforcement is required when $(M - KF)$ is positive, since this is the residual moment not taken by the concrete.

(2) From Table 7, for 20,000/10/1200 and $\dfrac{d'}{d} = 0.065$: $c = 0.70$, therefore

$$A'_S{}^{*} = \frac{M - KF}{cd} = \frac{52}{0.70 \times 31.0} = 2.40 \text{ sq.in.}$$

(3) From Table 1, for $f_S = 20{,}000$: $a = 1.44$, therefore

$$A_S{}^{**} = \frac{M}{ad} = \frac{320}{1.44 \times 31.0} = 7.17 \text{ sq.in.}\dagger$$

With $u$ = allowable bond stress, compute $\Sigma o = \dfrac{8000V\dagger\dagger}{7ud}$, select bars from Table 5, and check width of web required to accommodate bars from Table 6. This note applies in general to other similar examples.

For tensile reinforcement choose two 1¼-in. sq. bars plus three 1⅛-in. sq. bars with an area of $A_S = 6.93$ sq.in. as shown in Table 5. Enter Table 5 with two 1¼-in. sq. bars at the left hand margin, proceed horizontally to the group marked 1⅛-in. sq., and select the value in column headed

---

*See page 47, Equation 9.
**See page 45, Equation 4.
†By using the value of $a = 1.44$ based upon $j$ for beams reinforced with tension steel only, the value of $A_S$ as computed is approximate but sufficiently accurate for most cases. In some instances, such as in relatively deep beams with large amounts of compressive reinforcement, it may be desirable to determine $A_S$ with greater accuracy, as follows:

Obtain $p$ from Table 1 for 20,000/10/1200
Then tensile reinforcement to balance concrete =
$pbd = 0.0113 \times 17 \times 31 =$ 5.96 sq.in.
and tensile reinforcement to balance compressive steel =
$\dfrac{(M - KF)12{,}000}{f_S(d - d')} = \dfrac{52 \times 12{,}000}{20{,}000 \times 29} =$ 1.08 sq.in.
Total tensile reinforcement, $A_S =$ 7.04 sq.in.

††$V$ is in kips

"3". $A_S = 6.93$ sq.in. is shown in bold type. The companion figure, $\Sigma o = 23.5$ in light type, is the perimeter of two 1¼-in. sq. bars plus three 1⅛-in. sq. bars. The minimum width of web required to accommodate these bars is given in Table 6 for two types of bar spacing as indicated.

For further illustration of Table 5, consider the problem of selecting $A_S$ and $\Sigma o$ for four 1¼-in. sq. bars. Enter from the left with four 1¼-in. sq. bars and proceed horizontally to the first group marked 1¼-in. sq. In the column headed "0", select $A_S = 6.24$ and $\Sigma o = 20.0$.

As a third example, select $A_S$ and $\Sigma o$ for seven 1¼-in. sq. bars. When the number of bars exceeds five, subtract five from the number of bars, which in this case gives two. Consider the seven bars as the combination of two 1¼-in. sq. bars plus five 1¼-in. sq. bars. Enter from the left with two 1¼-in. sq. bars and proceed horizontally to the group marked 1¼-in. sq. In the column headed "5" select $A_S = 10.92$ and $\Sigma o = 35.0$.

**Example 3. T-Section, Simple Bending, Stress in Stem Neglected**

For a T-section subject to bending moment $M$, determine (1) whether concrete section is adequate without compressive reinforcement; (2) tensile reinforcement, $A_S$. Neglect compressive stresses below flange.

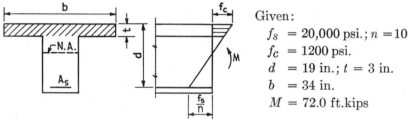

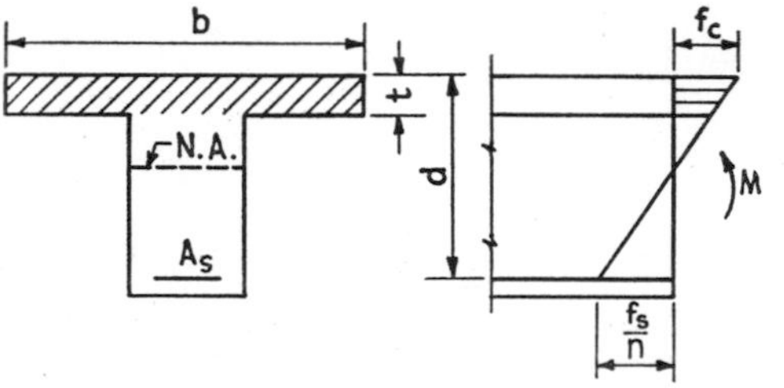


Given:

$f_S = 20{,}000$ psi.; $n = 10$
$f_C = 1200$ psi.
$d = 19$ in.; $t = 3$ in.
$b = 34$ in.
$M = 72.0$ ft.kips

(1) From Table 8, for 20,000/10/1200 and $\frac{t}{d} = 0.16$: $K = 140$

From Table 4, for $b \times d = 34.0 \times 19.0$: $F = 1.02$
then

$$\begin{aligned} M & = 72.0 \\ KF = 140 \times 1.02 & = \underline{142.8} \\ M - KF & = -70.8 \end{aligned}$$

No compressive reinforcement is required when $(M - KF)$ is negative.

(2) From Table 8, for $f_S = 20{,}000$ and $\frac{t}{d} = 0.16$: $a = 1.55$, therefore

$$A_S = \frac{M}{ad} = \frac{72.0}{1.55 \times 19.0} = 2.44 \text{ sq.in.}$$

**Example 4. T-Section, Simple Bending, Stress in Stem Included, Compressive Reinforcement**

For a T-section subject to bending moment $M$, determine (1) whether concrete section is adequate without compressive reinforcement, $A'_S$; (2) $A'_S$, if required; (3) tensile reinforcement, $A_S$. Include compressive stresses below flange.

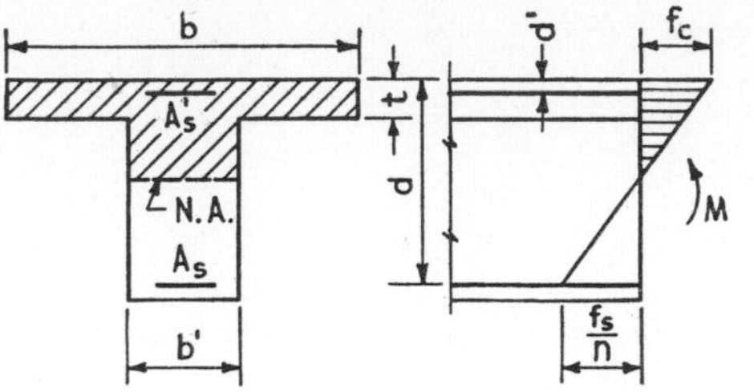


Given:

$f_s$ = 20,000 psi.; $n$ = 12
$f_c$ = 1000 psi.
$d$ = 31 in.; $t$ = 3.5 in.
$d'$ = 2 in.
$b$ = 27 in.; $b'$ = 17 in.
$M$ = 320 ft.kips

(1) *Web* From Table 1, for 20,000/12/1000: $K_w = 164$
From Table 4, for $b'd = 17.0 \times 31.0$: $F_w = 1.36$

*Flange* From Table 8, for $\frac{t}{d} = 0.11$: $Kf = 89$
From Table 4, for $(b - b')d = 10.0 \times 31.0$: $Ff = 0.801$

then

$$\begin{aligned} M &= 320 \\ K_wF_w = 164 \times 1.36 &= 223 \\ KfFf = 89 \times 0.801 &= \underline{71} \\ M - \Sigma(KF) &= 26 \end{aligned}$$

Compressive reinforcement is required since $[M - \Sigma(KF)]$ is positive.

(2) From Table 7, for $\frac{d'}{d} = 0.065$: $c = 0.71$, therefore

$$A'_s{}^* = \frac{M - \Sigma(KF)}{cd} = \frac{26}{0.71 \times 31.0} = 1.18 \text{ sq.in.}$$

(3) *Web.* From Table 1, for $f_s$ = 20,000: $a_w = 1.44$, therefore

$$A_{sw}{}^{**} = \frac{K_wF_w}{a_wd} = \frac{223}{1.44 \times 31.0} = 5.00$$

*Flange.* From Table 8, for $\frac{t}{d} = 0.11$: $af = 1.58$, therefore

$$A_{sf}{}^{**} = \frac{M - K_wF_w}{afd} = \frac{320 - 223}{1.58 \times 31.0} = \underline{1.98}$$

$$A_s = A_{sw} + A_{sf} = 6.98 \text{ sq.in.}$$

**Example 5. Rectangular Section, Combined Bending and Axial Load, Compressive Reinforcement**

For a rectangular section subject to bending moment $M$ combined with axial load $N$, determine (1) whether concrete section is adequate without compressive reinforcement, $A'_s$; (2) $A'_s$, if required; (3) $A_s$.

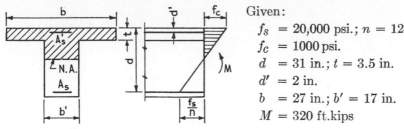

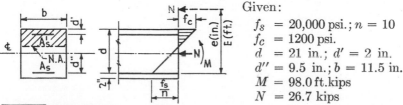

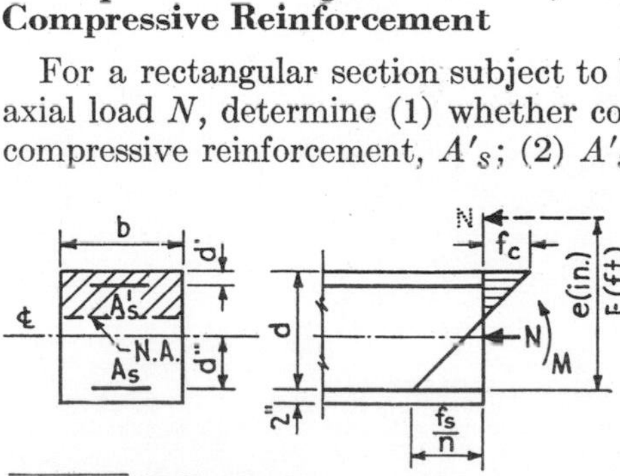


Given:

$f_s$ = 20,000 psi.; $n$ = 10
$f_c$ = 1200 psi.
$d$ = 21 in.; $d'$ = 2 in.
$d''$ = 9.5 in.; $b$ = 11.5 in.
$M$ = 98.0 ft.kips
$N$ = 26.7 kips

*See page 47, Equation 9.
**See page 45 and 46, Equations 4 and 8.

Eccentricity measured from tensile reinforcement: $e$ in in., $E$ in ft.:

$$e^* = \frac{12M}{N} + d'' = \frac{12 \times 98.0}{26.7} + 9.5 = 53.5 \text{ in.}; \frac{e}{d} = \frac{53.5}{21.0} = 2.55$$

$$E = \frac{e}{12} = \frac{53.5}{12} = 4.46 \text{ ft.}$$

(1) In this example it can be shown that the sum of $A_S + A'_S$ decreases when $f_S$ is reduced below 20,000**. The design based upon $f_S = 20,000$ will be illustrated:

From Table 1, for 20,000/10/1200: $K = 197$
From Table 4, for $bd = 11.5 \times 21.0$: $F = 0.423$
then

$$NE = 26.7 \times 4.46 = 119.1$$
$$KF = 197 \times 0.423 = 83.3$$
$$NE - KF = 35.8$$

Compressive reinforcement is required, since $(NE - KF)$ is positive†.

(2) From Table 7, for $\frac{d'}{d} = 0.095$: $c = 0.60$, therefore

$$A'_S{}^{\dagger\dagger} = \frac{NE - KF}{cd} = \frac{35.8}{0.60 \times 21.0} = 2.84 \text{ sq.in.}$$

(3) From Table 10, for $\frac{e}{d} = 2.55$ and $j = 0.875$ (*see Table 1*): $i = 1.52$

From Table 1, for $f_S = 20,000$: $a = 1.44$, therefore

$$A_S{}^* = \frac{NE}{adi} = \frac{119.1}{1.44 \times 21.0 \times 1.52} = 2.59 \text{ sq.in.}$$

**Example 6. T-Section, Combined Bending and Axial Load, Stress in Stem Neglected**

For a T-section subject to bending moment $M$ combined with axial load $N$, determine (1) whether concrete section is adequate without compressive reinforcement; (2) tensile reinforcement, $A_S$. Neglect compressive stresses below flange.

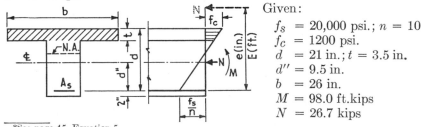

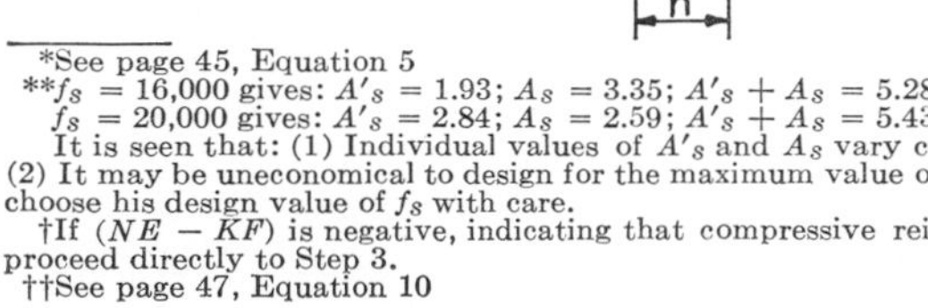


Given:

$f_S = 20,000$ psi.; $n = 10$
$f_C = 1200$ psi.
$d = 21$ in.; $t = 3.5$ in.
$d'' = 9.5$ in.
$b = 26$ in.
$M = 98.0$ ft.kips
$N = 26.7$ kips

*See page 45, Equation 5
**$f_S = 16,000$ gives: $A'_S = 1.93$; $A_S = 3.35$; $A'_S + A_S = 5.28$ sq.in.
$f_S = 20,000$ gives: $A'_S = 2.84$; $A_S = 2.59$; $A'_S + A_S = 5.43$ sq.in.
It is seen that: (1) Individual values of $A'_S$ and $A_S$ vary considerably more than the sum $A'_S + A_S$; (2) It may be uneconomical to design for the maximum value of $f_S$ allowed. The designer should therefore choose his design value of $f_S$ with care.
†If $(NE - KF)$ is negative, indicating that compressive reinforcement is not required, omit Step 2 and proceed directly to Step 3.
††See page 47, Equation 10

Eccentricity measured from tensile reinforcement: $e$ in in., $E$ in ft.

$$e^* = \frac{12M}{N} + d'' = \frac{12 \times 98.0}{26.7} + 9.5 = 53.5 \text{ in.}; \quad \frac{e}{d} = \frac{53.5}{21.0} = 2.55$$

$$E = \frac{e}{12} = \frac{53.5}{12} = 4.46 \text{ ft.}$$

(1) From Table 8, for $20{,}000/10/1200$ and $\dfrac{t}{d} = 0.17$: $K = 145$

From Table 4, for $b \times d = 26 \times 21$: $F = 0.96$
then

$$NE = 26.7 \times 4.46 = 119.1$$
$$KF = 145 \times 0.96 = 139.2$$
$$NE - KF = -20.1$$

No compressive reinforcement is required, since $(NE - KF)$ is negative.

(2) From Table 10, for $\dfrac{e}{d} = 2.55$ and $j = 0.925$ (Table 9 for $\dfrac{t}{d} = 0.17$ and assumed $k = 0.40$); $i = 1.57$

From Table 8, for $f_s = 20{,}000$ and $\dfrac{t}{d} = 0.17$: $a = 1.54$, therefore

$$A_s^* = \frac{NE}{adi} = \frac{119.1}{1.54 \times 21.0 \times 1.57} = 2.35 \text{ sq.in.}$$

## Example 7. T-Section, Combined Bending and Axial Load, Stress in Stem Included, Compressive Reinforcement

For a T-section subject to bending moment $M$ combined with axial load $N$, determine (1) whether concrete section is adequate without compressive reinforcement, $A'_s$; (2) $A'_s$, if required; (3) tensile reinforcement, $A_s$. Include compressive stresses below flange.

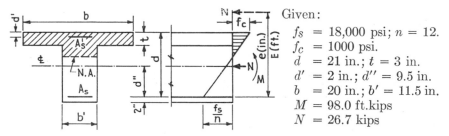

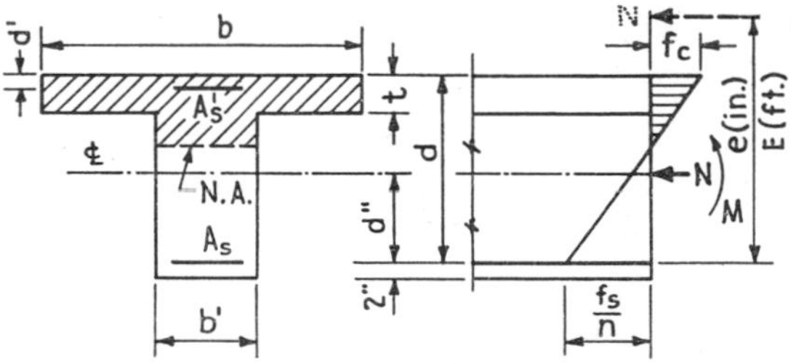

Given:

$f_s = 18{,}000$ psi; $n = 12$.
$f_c = 1000$ psi.
$d = 21$ in.; $t = 3$ in.
$d' = 2$ in.; $d'' = 9.5$ in.
$b = 20$ in.; $b' = 11.5$ in.
$M = 98.0$ ft.kips
$N = 26.7$ kips

As in Example 6: $e = 53.5$ in.; $\dfrac{e}{d} = 2.55$; $NE = 119.1$ ft.kips

(1) Web $\begin{cases} \text{From Table 1, for } 18{,}000/12/1000: \qquad K_w = 173 \\ \text{From Table 4, for } b \times d = 11.5 \times 21.0: \; F_w = 0.423 \end{cases}$

Flange $\begin{cases} \text{From Table 8, for } 18{,}000/12/1000 \text{ and } \dfrac{t}{d} = 0.14: \; K_f = 108 \\ \text{From Table 4, for } (b - b')d = 8.5 \times 21.0: \qquad F_f = 0.313 \end{cases}$

*See page 45, Equation 5.

$$
\begin{aligned}
NE & & = 119.1 \\
K_wF_w &= 173 \times 0.423 &= 73.2 \\
K_fF_f &= 108 \times 0.313 &= 33.8 \\
NE - \Sigma(KF) & &= 12.1
\end{aligned}
$$

Compressive reinforcement is required, since $[NE - \Sigma(KF)]$ is positive.

(2) From Table 7, for $\frac{d'}{d} = 0.095$: $c = 0.63$, therefore

$$A'_s{}^* = \frac{NE - \Sigma(KF)}{cd} = \frac{12.1}{0.63 \times 21.0} = 0.91 \text{ sq.in.}$$

(3)

*Web*

From Table 1, for 18,000/12/1000: $j = 0.867$

From Table 10, for $\frac{e}{d} = 2.55$: $i_w = 1.51$

From Table 1, for $f_s = 18{,}000$: $a_w = 1.29$

$$A_{sw}{}^{**} = \frac{K_wF_w}{a_wdi_w} = \frac{73.2}{1.29 \times 21.0 \times 1.51} = 1.79 \text{ sq.in.}$$

*Flange*

From Table 9, for $\frac{t}{d} = 0.14$ and assumed $k = 0.40$: $j = 0.93$

From Table 10, for $\frac{e}{d} = 2.55$: $i_f = 1.58$

From Table 8, for $f_s = 18{,}000$ and $\frac{t}{d} = 0.14$: $a_f = 1.40$

$$A_{sf}{}^{**} = \frac{NE - K_wF_w}{a_fdi_f} = \frac{119.1 - 73.2}{1.40 \times 21.0 \times 1.58} = 0.99 \text{ sq.in.}$$

$$A_s = A_{sw} + A_{sf} = 1.79 + 0.99 = 2.78 \text{ sq.in.}$$

## Example 8. Rectangular Section, Combined Bending and Axial Load (Tension), Compressive Reinforcement

For a rectangular section subject to bending moment $M$ combined with axial tension $N$, determine (1) whether concrete section is adequate without compressive reinforcement, $A'_s$; (2) $A'_s$, if required; (3) tensile reinforcement, $A_s$.

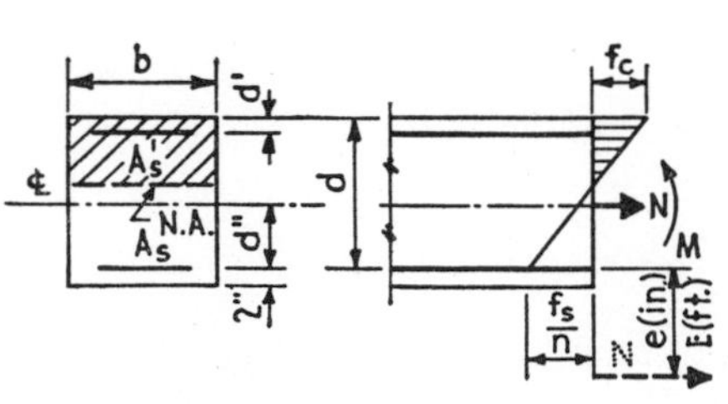


Given:

$f_s = 20{,}000$ psi.; $n = 12$
$f_c = 1000$ psi.
$d = 21$ in.; $d' = 2$ in.
$d'' = 9.5$ in.
$b = 11.5$ in.
$M = 98.0$ ft.kips; $N = -26.7$ kips (negative because axial tension)

---

*See page 47, Equation 10
**See page 45 and 46, Equations 5 and 8

$$e = \frac{12M}{N} + d'' = \frac{12 \times 98.0}{-26.7} + 9.5 = -44.0 + 9.5 = -34.5 \text{ in.}$$

$$E = \frac{e}{12} = \frac{-34.5}{12} = -2.88 \text{ ft.}$$

(1) From Table 1, for 20,000/12/1000: $K = 164$
From Table 4, for $b \times d = 11.5 \times 21.0$: $F = 0.423$
then

$$\begin{aligned} NE &= (-26.7) \times (-2.88) = 76.9 \\ KF &= 164 \times 0.423 = 69.4 \\ NE - KF &= 7.5 \end{aligned}$$

Compressive reinforcement is required when $(NE - KF)$ is positive.

(2) From Table 7, for 20,000/12/1000 and $\frac{d'}{d} = 0.095$: $c = 0.62$, therefore

$$A'_s{}^* = \frac{NE - KF}{cd} = \frac{7.5}{0.62 \times 21.0} = 0.58 \text{ sq.in.}$$

(3) From Table 1: $j = 0.875$, therefore

$$i = \frac{1}{1 - \frac{jd}{e}} = \frac{1}{1 - \frac{0.875 \times 21.0}{-34.5}} = 0.652$$

The value of $i$ cannot be taken from Table 10 because $e$ is negative, and $i$ therefore must be computed.

From Table 1, for $f_s = 20{,}000$: $a = 1.44$, therefore

$$A_s{}^{**} = \frac{NE}{adi} = \frac{76.9}{1.44 \times 21.0 \times 0.652} = 3.90 \text{ sq.in.}$$

*See page 47, Equation 10.
**See page 45, Equation 5.

# Investigation of Flexural Members

## Simple Bending and Bending Combined with Axial Load

Procedures presented here for investigation of flexural members are fundamentally alike for simple bending and for combined bending and axial load. The procedure is to determine (1) value of $k$, (2) value of $j$, and (3) stresses.

For rectangular sections subject to simple bending, values of $k$ and $j$ can be taken from Tables 11 and 13, respectively, when the quantities of tensile and compressive reinforcement are known. For the purpose of entering Table 11 to obtain $k$, two quantities designated as $m$* and $q$* must be computed (*see Examples 9 and 10*). In order to obtain $j$ from Table 13, the value of $z$**, which locates the resultant of the compressive forces, is first obtained from Table 12. Having the values of $k$ and $j$, stresses in the concrete and reinforcement are computed by the usual formulas†.

In the investigation of T-sections subject to simple bending when the stress in the stem is neglected, the value of $k$†† is computed directly without use of tables. With $k$ determined, $j$ is obtained from Table 9 and the stresses can then be computed (*see Example 11*).

When the stress in the stem of a T-section is taken into consideration, the problem is similar to that of a rectangular section except that the formulas for $m$, $q$ and $j$ are modified to take into account the dimensions of the flange and web (*see Examples 12 and 13*). Note that the value of $j$ is computed and not taken from Table 13 as in the case of rectangular sections.

The procedure for investigating rectangular and T-sections subject to combined bending and axial load is essentially the same as for simple bending. It is necessary to make a preliminary estimate of the value of $j$ in order to obtain the value of $i$‡ from Table 10, which is subsequently used in computing $m$ and $q$. A zigzag line in Table 10 serves as a guide in estimating $j$. Having computed $m$ and $q$, the value of $k$ can be obtained from Table 11 and then the actual value of $j$ can be taken from Table 13 as in the case of simple bending. With the actual value of $j$, Table 10 is re-entered to obtain the correct value of $i$ necessary for computing the tension steel stress.

---

*See page 50, Equations 18 and 19.
**See page 51, Equation 20.
†See pages 52 and 53, Equations 24, 25, 26 and 27
††See page 52, Equations 22 and 23.
‡See page 45, Equation 5.

## Example 9. Investigation, Rectangular Section, Simple Bending

In a given rectangular section subject to bending, determine stresses $f_s$ and $f_c$.



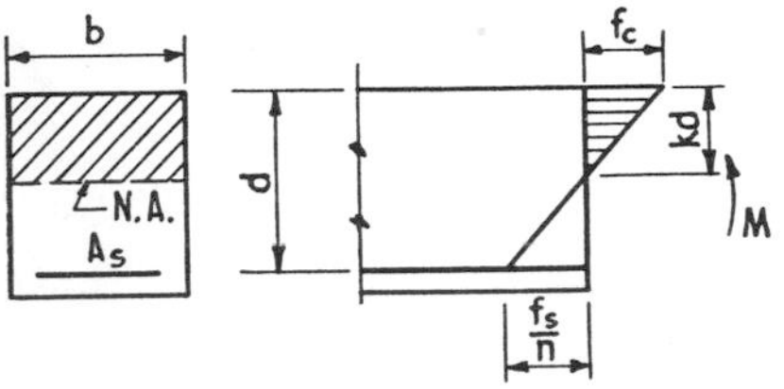

Given:

$b = 17$ in.; $d = 31$ in.
$A_s = 6.93$ sq.in.; $n = 10$
$M = 320$ ft.kips

$$m^* = q^* = \frac{nA_s}{bd} = \frac{10 \times 6.93}{17.0 \times 31.0} = 0.131$$

From Table 11, for $m = 0.13$** and $q = 0.131$: $k = 0.398$
From Table 13, for $z = 0.33$ and $k = 0.398$: $j = 0.87$

$$f_s\dagger = \frac{12{,}000M}{jdA_s} = \frac{12{,}000 \times 320}{0.87 \times 31.0 \times 6.93} = 20{,}500 \text{ psi.}$$

$$f_c\dagger\dagger = \frac{f_s}{n} \times \frac{k}{1-k} = \frac{20{,}500}{10} \times \frac{0.398}{0.602} = 1360 \text{ psi.}$$

## Example 10. Investigation, Rectangular Section, Simple Bending, Compressive Reinforcement

In a given rectangular section with compressive reinforcement and subject to bending, determine stresses $f_s$ and $f_c$.

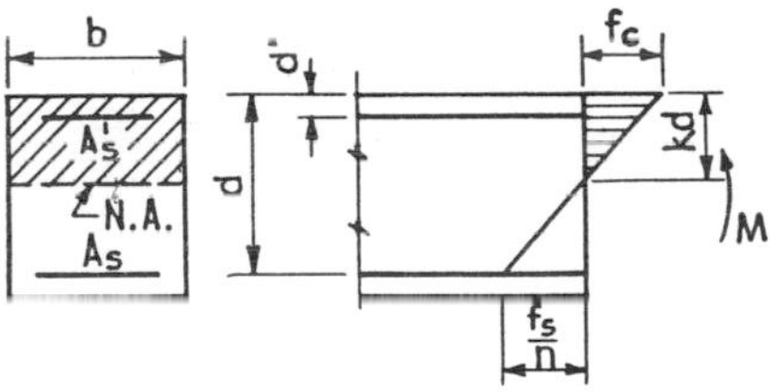

Given:

$b = 17$ in.; $d = 31$ in.; $d' = 2$ in.
$A_s = 6.93$ sq.in.; $n = 10$
$A'_s = 2.37$ sq.in.
$M = 320$ ft.kips

$$m^* = \frac{nA_s}{bd} + \frac{(n-1)A'_s}{bd} = \frac{10 \times 6.93}{17.0 \times 31.0} + \frac{9 \times 2.37}{17.0 \times 31.0}$$

$$= 0.131 + 0.040 = 0.171$$

$$q^* = \frac{nA_s}{bd} + \frac{(n-1)A'_s}{bd} \times \frac{d'}{d} = \frac{10 \times 6.93}{17.0 \times 31.0} + \frac{9 \times 2.37}{17.0 \times 31.0} \times \frac{2.0}{31.0}$$

$$= 0.131 + 0.003 = 0.134$$

From Table 11, for $m = 0.17$** and $q = 0.134$: $k = 0.375$
For entering Table 12 determine

---

*See page 50, Equations 18 and 19.
**The value of $k$ is not sensitive to small variations in $m$ so the computed value of $m$ is rounded to two decimal places to avoid a double interpolation in Table 11.
†See page 52, Equation 24.
††See page 53, Equation 26.

$$\frac{1}{k} \times \frac{(n-1)A'_s}{bd} = \frac{0.040}{0.375} = 0.11 \qquad \frac{1}{k} \times \frac{d'}{d} = \frac{1}{0.375} \times \frac{2.0}{31.0} = 0.17$$

From Table 12: $z = 0.31$
From Table 13, for $z = 0.31$ and $k = 0.375$: $j = 0.88$

$$f_s{}^* = \frac{12{,}000M}{jdA_s} = \frac{12{,}000 \times 320}{0.88 \times 31.0 \times 6.93} = 20{,}300 \text{ psi.}$$

$$f_c{}^{**} = \frac{f_s}{n} \times \frac{k}{1-k} = \frac{20{,}300}{10} \times \frac{0.375}{0.625} = 1220 \text{ psi.}$$

$f'_s$ is always less than $nf_c$.

### Example 11. Investigation, T-Section, Simple Bending, Stress in Stem Neglected

In a given T-section subject to bending, determine stresses $f_s$ and $f_c$. Neglect compressive stresses below flange.

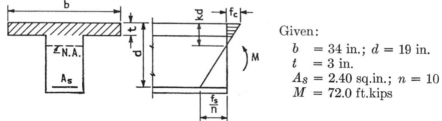

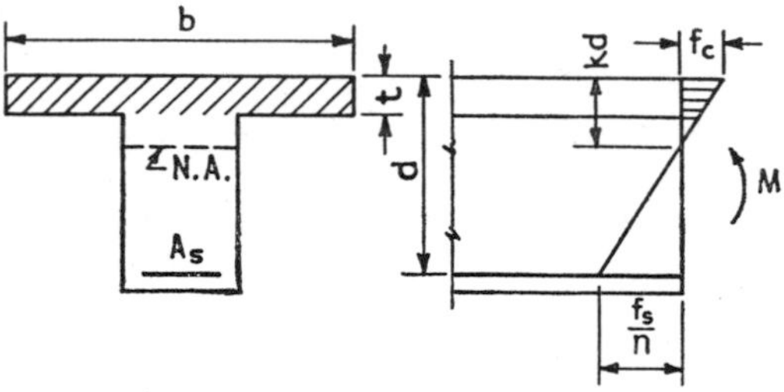


Given:
$b = 34$ in.; $d = 19$ in.
$t = 3$ in.
$A_s = 2.40$ sq.in.; $n = 10$
$M = 72.0$ ft.kips

$$k\dagger = \frac{\frac{nA_s}{bt} + \frac{1}{2}\frac{t}{d}}{\frac{nA_s}{bt} + 1.000} = \frac{\frac{10 \times 2.40}{34.0 \times 3.0} + \frac{1}{2} \times \frac{3.0}{19.0}}{\frac{10 \times 2.40}{34.0 \times 3.0} + 1.000} = \frac{0.235 + 0.079}{0.235 + 1.000} = 0.254$$

From Table 9, for $\frac{t}{d} = 0.16$ and $k = 0.254$: $j = 0.93$

$$f_s{}^* = \frac{12{,}000M}{jdA_s} = \frac{12{,}000 \times 72.0}{0.93 \times 19.0 \times 2.40} = 20{,}400 \text{ psi.}$$

$$f_c{}^{**} = \frac{f_s}{n} \times \frac{k}{1-k} = \frac{20{,}400}{10} \times \frac{0.254}{0.746} = 690 \text{ psi.}$$

### Example 12. Investigation, T-Section, Simple Bending, Stress in Stem Included

In a given T-section with all concrete in compression considered effective and subject to bending, determine stresses $f_s$ and $f_c$.

*See page 52, Equation 24.
**See page 53, Equation 26.
†See page 52, Equation 22.

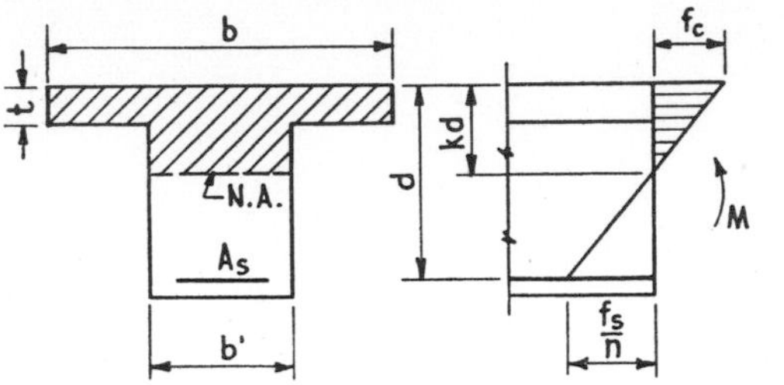


Given:

$b = 27$ in.; $b' = 17$ in.
$d = 31$ in.; $t = 3.5$ in.
$A_s = 6.93$ sq.in.; $n = 12$
$M = 320$ ft.kips

$$m^* = \frac{nA_s}{b'd} + \frac{(b-b')t}{b'd} = \frac{12 \times 6.93}{17.0 \times 31.0} + \frac{(27-17) \times 3.5}{17.0 \times 31.0}$$

$$= 0.158 + 0.066 = 0.224$$

$$q^* = \frac{nA_s}{b'd} + \frac{(b-b')t}{b'd} \times \frac{yt^{**}}{d} = 0.158 + 0.066 \times \frac{0.47 \times 3.5}{31.0}$$

$$= 0.158 + 0.004 = 0.162$$

From Table 11, for $m = 0.22$ and $q = 0.162$: $k = 0.390$

For entering Table 12 compute

$$\frac{1}{k}\frac{(b-b')t\dagger}{b'd} = \frac{0.066}{0.390} = 0.17 \qquad \frac{1}{k} \times \frac{yt\dagger}{d} = \frac{1}{0.390}\frac{0.47 \times 3.5}{31.0} = 0.14$$

From Table 12: $z = 0.29$

From Table 13, for $z = 0.29$ and $k = 0.390$: $j = 0.89$

$$f_s = \frac{12{,}000M}{jdA_s} = \frac{12{,}000 \times 320}{0.89 \times 31.0 \times 6.93} = 20{,}100 \text{ psi.}$$

$$f_c = \frac{f_s}{n} \times \frac{k}{1-k} = \frac{20{,}100}{12} \times \frac{0.390}{0.610} = 1070 \text{ psi.}$$

## Example 13. Investigation, T-Section, Simple Bending, Stress in Stem Included, Compressive Reinforcement

In a given T-section with compressive reinforcement and subject to bending, determine stresses $f_s$ and $f_c$. Include compressive stresses below flange.

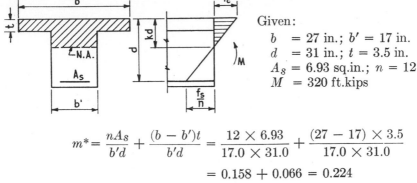

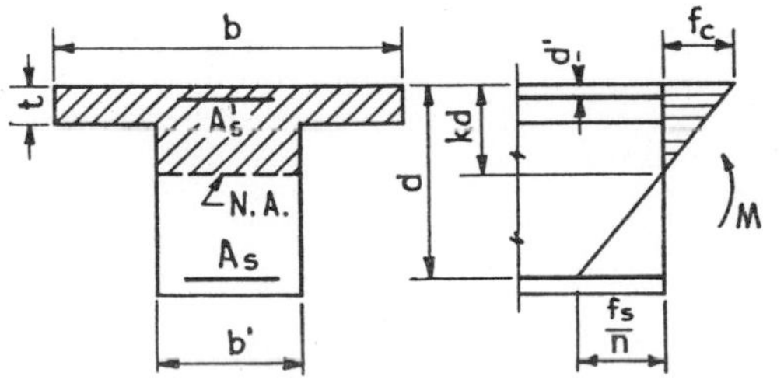


Given:

$b = 27$ in.; $b' = 17$ in.
$d = 31$ in.; $d' = 2$ in.
$t = 3.5$ in.
$A_s = 6.93$ sq.in.
$A'_s = 1.20$ sq.in.
$n = 12$
$M = 320$ ft.kips

*See page 50, Equations 18 and 19.
**$yt$ is depth to resultant of compressive stresses in flange. From Table 9, for $k = 0.40$ (estimated): $y = 0.47$.
†See page 51, derivation of Equation 21.

$$m^* = \frac{nA_s}{b'd} + \frac{(n-1)A'_s}{b'd} + \frac{(b-b')t}{b'd}$$

$$= \frac{12 \times 6.93}{17.0 \times 31.0} + \frac{11 \times 1.20}{17.0 \times 31.0} + \frac{(27-17) \times 3.5}{17.0 \times 31.0}$$

$$= 0.158 + 0.025 + 0.066 = 0.249$$

$$q^* = \frac{nA_s}{b'd} + \frac{(n-1)A'_s}{b'd} \times \frac{d'}{d} + \frac{(b-b')t}{b'd} \times \frac{yt^{**}}{d}$$

$$= \frac{12 \times 6.93}{17.0 \times 31.0} + \frac{11 \times 1.20}{17.0 \times 31.0} \times \frac{2.0}{31.0} + \frac{(27-17) \times 3.5}{17.0 \times 31.0} \times \frac{0.47 \times 3.5}{31.0}$$

$$= 0.158 + 0.002 + 0.004 = 0.164$$

From Table 11, for $m = 0.25$ and $q = 0.164$: $k = 0.375$

The general equation for $j$ is:

$$j\dagger = 1 - \frac{\frac{k^2}{6} + \frac{(n-1)A'_s}{b'd}\frac{d'}{d}\left(1 - \frac{d'}{kd}\right) + \frac{(b-b')t}{b'd}\frac{yt}{d}\left(1 - \frac{yt}{kd}\right)}{\frac{k}{2} + \frac{(n-1)A'_s}{b'd}\left(1 - \frac{d'}{kd}\right) + \frac{(b-b')t}{b'd}\left(1 - \frac{yt}{kd}\right)}$$

The equation includes two elements: one for compressive steel, the other for flange:

For compressive steel: $1 - \frac{d'}{kd} = 1 - \frac{2.0}{0.375 \times 31.0} = 0.83$

For flange: Compute $\frac{t}{kd} = 0.30$ and select $y = 0.47$ (*Table 9*)

$$1 - \frac{yt}{kd} = 1 - 0.47 \times 0.30 = 0.86$$

Other factors in equation for $j$ are already computed under $m$ and $q$:

$$j = 1 - \frac{\frac{0.375^2}{6} + 0.002 \times 0.83 + 0.004 \times 0.86}{\frac{0.375}{2} + 0.025 \times 0.83 + 0.066 \times 0.86} = 1 - \frac{0.029}{0.265} = 0.89$$

$$f_s = \frac{12{,}000M}{jdA_s} = \frac{12{,}000 \times 320}{0.89 \times 31.0 \times 6.93} = 20{,}100 \text{ psi.}$$

$$f_c = \frac{f_s}{n} \times \frac{k}{1-k} = \frac{20{,}100}{12} \times \frac{0.375}{0.625} = 1010 \text{ psi.}$$

---

*See page 50, Equations 18 and 19.

**$yt$ is depth to resultant of compressive stresses in flange. From Table 9, for $k = 0.40$ (estimated): $y = 0.47$.

†See page 51, Equations 20 and 21.

### Example 14. Investigation, Rectangular Section, Combined Bending and Axial Load

In a given section subject to bending moment $M$ combined with axial load $N$, determine $f_s$ and $f_c$.

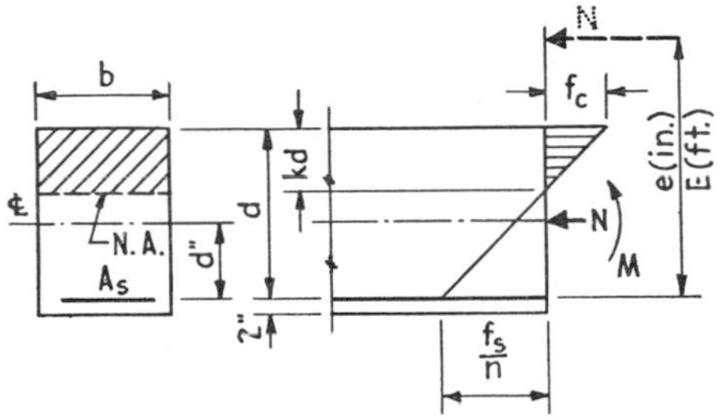


Given:
$b = 11.5$ in.; $d = 21$ in.
$d'' = 9.5$ in.
$A_s = 3.33$ sq.in.; $n = 10$
$M = 98.0$ ft.kips
$N = 26.7$ kips

$$e = \frac{12M}{N} + d'' = \frac{12 \times 98.0}{26.7} + 9.5 = 53.5 \qquad \frac{e}{d} = \frac{53.5}{21.0} = 2.55$$

From Table 10, for $\frac{e}{d} = 2.55$ and $j = 0.87$ (estimated): $i = 1.52$

$$m^* = q^* = \frac{nA_si}{bd} = \frac{10 \times 3.33 \times 1.52}{11.5 \times 21.0} = 0.210$$

From Table 11, for $m = 0.21$ and $q = 0.210$: $k = 0.471$
From Table 13, for $z = 0.33$ and $k = 0.471$: $j = 0.84$ (actual)

From Table 10, for $\frac{e}{d} = 2.55$ and $j = 0.84$: $i = 1.50$

$$f_s\dagger = \frac{1000N}{jA_si}\frac{e}{d} = \frac{26{,}700 \times 2.55}{0.84 \times 3.33 \times 1.50} = 16{,}200 \text{ psi.}$$

$$f_c\dagger\dagger = \frac{f_s}{n} \times \frac{k}{1-k} = \frac{16{,}200}{10} \times \frac{0.471}{0.529} = 1440 \text{ psi.}$$

### Example 15. Investigation, Rectangular Section, Combined Bending and Axial Load, Compressive Reinforcement

In a given rectangular section with compressive reinforcement and subject to bending moment $M$ combined with axial load $N$, determine $f_s$ and $f_c$.

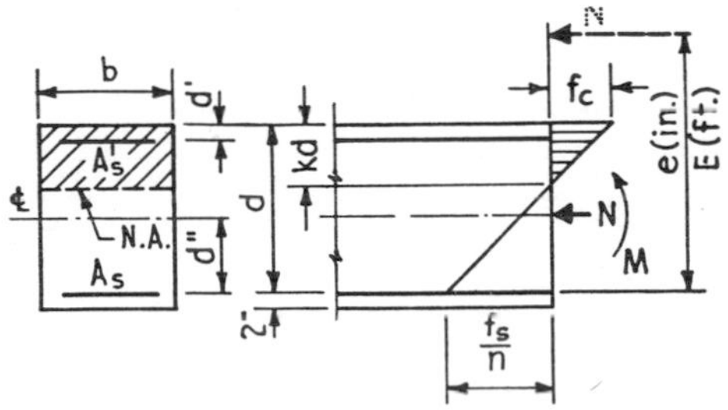


Given:
$b = 11.5$ in.; $d = 21$ in.
$d' = 2$ in.; $d'' = 9.5$ in.
$A_s = 3.33$ sq.in.; $n = 10$
$A'_s = 1.92$ sq.in.
$M = 98.0$ ft.kips
$N = 26.7$ kips

---

*See page 50, Equations 18 and 19.
**See footnote Example 9.
†See page 52, Equation 25.
††See page 53, Equation 26.

$$e = \frac{12M}{N} + d'' = \frac{12 \times 98.0}{26.7} + 9.5 = 53.5$$

$$\frac{e}{d} = \frac{53.5}{21.0} = 2.55$$

From Table 10, for $\frac{e}{d} = 2.55$ and $j = 0.87$ (estimated): $i = 1.52$

$$m^* = \frac{nA_si}{bd} + \frac{(n-1)A'_s}{bd} = \frac{10 \times 3.33 \times 1.52}{11.5 \times 21.0} + \frac{9 \times 1.92}{11.5 \times 21.0}$$

$$= 0.210 + 0.072 = 0.282$$

$$q^* = \frac{nA_si}{bd} + \frac{(n-1)A'_s}{bd} \times \frac{d'}{d} = \frac{10 \times 3.33 \times 1.52}{11.5 \times 21.0} + \frac{9 \times 1.92}{11.5 \times 21.0} \times \frac{2.0}{21.0}$$

$$= 0.210 + 0.007 = 0.217$$

From Table 11, for $m = 0.28$ and $q = 0.217$: $k = 0.436$
For entering Table 12, compute

$$\frac{1}{k} \times \frac{(n-1)A'_s}{bd} = \frac{0.072}{0.436} = 0.17 \quad \text{and} \quad \frac{1}{k} \times \frac{d'}{d} = \frac{1}{0.436} \times \frac{2.0}{21.0} = 0.22$$

From Table 12: $z = 0.31$
From Table 13, for $z = 0.31$ and $k = 0.436$: $j = 0.86$

From Table 10, for $\frac{e}{d} = 2.55$ and $j = 0.86$ (actual): $i = 1.50$

$$f_s = \frac{1000N}{jA_si}\frac{e}{d} = \frac{26{,}700 \times 2.55}{0.86 \times 3.33 \times 1.50} = 15{,}800 \text{ psi.}$$

$$f_c = \frac{f_s}{n} \times \frac{k}{1-k} = \frac{15{,}800}{10} \times \frac{0.436}{0.564} = 1220 \text{ psi.}$$

$f'_s$ is always less than $nf_c$.

### Example 16. Investigation, T-Section, Combined Bending and Axial Load, Stress in Stem Neglected

In a given T-section subject to bending moment $M$ combined with axial load $N$, determine stresses $f_s$ and $f_c$. Neglect compressive stresses below flange.

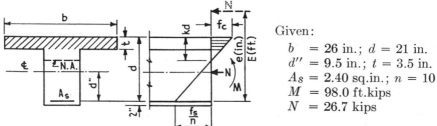

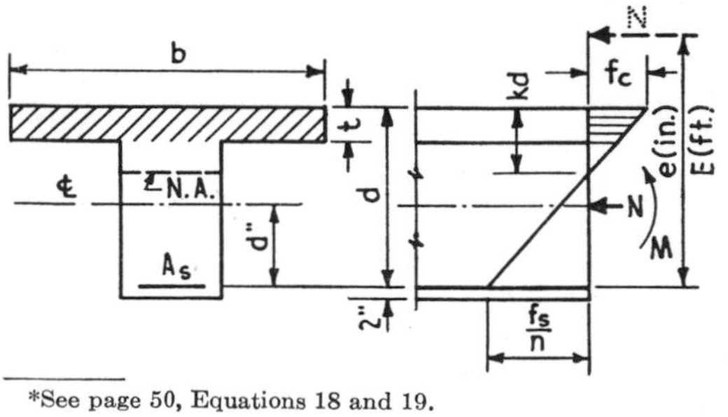


Given:

$b = 26$ in.; $d = 21$ in.
$d'' = 9.5$ in.; $t = 3.5$ in.
$A_s = 2.40$ sq.in.; $n = 10$
$M = 98.0$ ft.kips
$N = 26.7$ kips

*See page 50, Equations 18 and 19.

$$e = \frac{12M}{N} + d'' = \frac{12 \times 98.0}{26.7} + 9.5 = 53.5$$

$$\frac{e}{d} = \frac{53.5}{21.0} = 2.55$$

From Table 9, for $\frac{t}{d} = \frac{3.5}{21.0} = 0.17$, estimate $j = 0.93$

From Table 10, for $\frac{e}{d} = 2.55$ and $j = 0.93$ (estimated): $i = 1.58$

$$k^* = \frac{\frac{nA_si}{bt} + \frac{1}{2}\frac{t}{d}}{\frac{nA_si}{bt} + 1.000} = \frac{\frac{10 \times 2.40 \times 1.58}{26.0 \times 3.5} + \frac{1}{2} \times \frac{3.5}{21.0}}{\frac{10 \times 2.40 \times 1.58}{26.0 \times 3.5} + 1.000} = \frac{0.417 + 0.083}{0.417 + 1.000}$$

$$= 0.353$$

From Table 9, for $k = 0.353$ and $\frac{t}{d} = 0.17$: $j = 0.93$ (actual)

From Table 10, for $\frac{e}{d} = 2.55$ and $j = 0.93$: $i = 1.58$

$$f_s{}^{**} = \frac{1000N}{jA_si}\frac{e}{d} = \frac{26{,}700 \times 2.55}{0.93 \times 2.40 \times 1.58} = 19{,}300 \text{ psi.}$$

$$f_c{}^{\dagger} = \frac{f_s}{n} \times \frac{k}{1-k} = \frac{19{,}300}{10} \times \frac{0.353}{0.647} = 1050 \text{ psi.}$$

**Example 17. Investigation, T-Section, Combined Bending and Axial Load, Stress in Stem Included**

In a given T-section subject to bending combined with axial load, determine stresses $f_s$ and $f_c$.

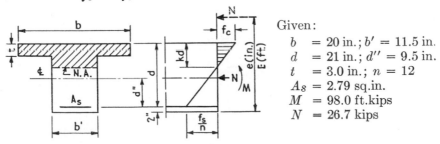

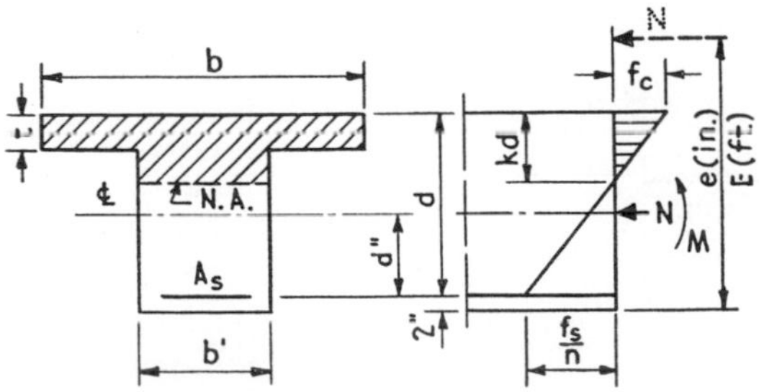


Given:

$b$ = 20 in.; $b'$ = 11.5 in.
$d$ = 21 in.; $d''$ = 9.5 in.
$t$ = 3.0 in.; $n$ = 12
$A_s$ = 2.79 sq.in.
$M$ = 98.0 ft.kips
$N$ = 26.7 kips

*See page 52, Equation 23.
**See page 52, Equation 25.
†See page 53, Equation 26.

From Example 15: $\frac{e}{d} = 2.55$ and $i = 1.52$ (estimating $j = 0.87$)

$$m^* = \frac{nA_s i}{b'd} + \frac{(b - b')t}{b'd} = \frac{12 \times 2.79 \times 1.52}{11.5 \times 21.0} + \frac{8.5 \times 3.0}{11.5 \times 21.0}$$
$$= 0.211 + 0.106 = 0.317$$

$$q^* = \frac{nA_s i}{b'd} + \frac{(b - b')t}{b'd} \times \frac{yt^{**}}{d} = 0.211 + 0.106 \times \frac{0.46 \times 3.0}{21.0}$$
$$= 0.211 + 0.007 = 0.218$$

From Table 11, for $m = 0.32\dagger$ and $q = 0.218$: $k = 0.413$
For entering Table 12, compute

$$\frac{1}{k} \times \frac{(b - b')t\dagger\dagger}{b'd} = \frac{0.106}{0.413} = 0.26, \text{ and}$$

$$\frac{1}{k} \times \frac{yt\dagger\dagger}{d} = \frac{1}{0.413} \times \frac{0.46 \times 3.0}{21.0} = 0.16$$

From Table 12: $z = 0.28$
From Table 13, for $z = 0.28$ and $k = 0.413$ : $j = 0.88$ (actual)

From Table 10, for $\frac{e}{d} = 2.55$ and $j = 0.88$: $i = 1.53$

$$f_s = \frac{1000N}{jA_s i}\frac{e}{d} = \frac{26{,}700 \times 2.55}{0.88 \times 2.79 \times 1.53} = 18{,}100 \text{ psi.}$$

$$f_c = \frac{f_s}{n} \times \frac{k}{1 - k} = \frac{18{,}100}{12} \times \frac{0.413}{0.587} = 1060 \text{ psi.}$$

### Example 18. Investigation, T-Section, Combined Bending and Axial Load, Stress in Stem Included, Compressive Reinforcement

In a given T-section with compressive reinforcement and subject to bending combined with axial load, determine stresses $f_s$ and $f_c$. Include compressive stresses below flange.

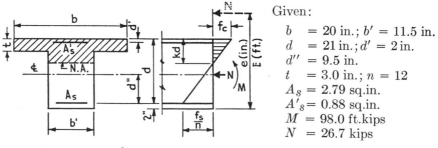

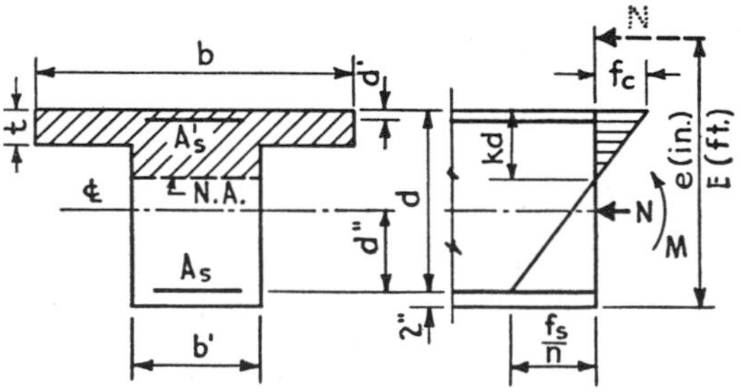


Given:

$b = 20$ in.; $b' = 11.5$ in.
$d = 21$ in.; $d' = 2$ in.
$d'' = 9.5$ in.
$t = 3.0$ in.; $n = 12$
$A_s = 2.79$ sq.in.
$A'_s = 0.88$ sq.in.
$M = 98.0$ ft.kips
$N = 26.7$ kips

From Example 15: $\frac{e}{d} = 2.55$ and $i = 1.52$ (estimating $j = 0.87$)

---

*See page 50, Equations 18 and 19.
**See footnote Example 12.
†See footnote Example 9.
††See page 51, derivation of equation 21.

$$m^* = \frac{nA_{s}i}{b'd} + \frac{(n-1)A'_s}{b'd} + \frac{(b-b')t}{b'd}$$

$$= \frac{12 \times 2.79 \times 1.52}{11.5 \times 21.0} + \frac{11 \times 0.88}{11.5 \times 21.0} + \frac{8.5 \times 3.0}{11.5 \times 21.0}$$

$$= 0.211 + 0.040 + 0.106 = 0.357$$

$$q^* = \frac{nA_{s}i}{b'd} + \frac{(n-1)A'_s}{b'd} \times \frac{d'}{d} + \frac{(b-b')t}{b'd} \times \frac{yt}{d}^{**}$$

$$= \frac{12 \times 2.79 \times 1.52}{11.5 \times 21.0} + \frac{11 \times 0.88}{11.5 \times 21.0} \times \frac{2}{21.0} + \frac{8.5 \times 3.0}{11.5 \times 21.0} \times \frac{0.46 \times 3.0}{21.0}$$

$$= 0.211 + 0.004 + 0.007 = 0.222$$

From Table 11, for $m = 0.36$† and $q = 0.222$: $k = 0.397$

The general equation for $j$ is:

$$j\dagger\dagger = 1 - \frac{\dfrac{k^2}{6} + \dfrac{(n-1)A'_s}{b'd}\dfrac{d'}{d}\left(1 - \dfrac{d'}{kd}\right) + \dfrac{(b-b')t}{b'd}\dfrac{yt}{d}\left(1 - \dfrac{yt}{kd}\right)}{\dfrac{k}{2} + \dfrac{(n-1)A'_s}{b'd}\left(1 - \dfrac{d'}{kd}\right) + \dfrac{(b-b')t}{b'd}\left(1 - \dfrac{yt}{kd}\right)}$$

The equation includes two elements: one for compressive steel, the other for flange:

For compressive steel: $1 - \dfrac{d'}{kd} = 1 - \dfrac{2.0}{0.397 \times 21.0} = 0.76$

For flange: Compute $\dfrac{t}{kd} = 0.36$ and select $y = 0.46$ (*Table 9*)

$$1 - \frac{yt}{kd} = 1 - 0.46 \times 0.36 = 0.83$$

Other factors in equation for $j$ are already computed under $m$ and $q$:

$$j = 1 - \frac{\dfrac{0.397^2}{6} + 0.004 \times 0.76 + 0.007 \times 0.83}{\dfrac{0.397}{2} + 0.040 \times 0.76 + 0.106 \times 0.83} = 1 - \frac{0.035}{0.317} = 0.89$$

From Table 10, for $\dfrac{e}{d} = 2.55$ and $j = 0.89$ (actual): $i = 1.54$

$$f_s = \frac{1000N}{jA_{s}i}\frac{e}{d} = \frac{26{,}700 \times 2.55}{0.89 \times 2.79 \times 1.54} = 17{,}800 \text{ psi.}$$

$$f_c = \frac{f_s}{n} \times \frac{k}{1-k} = \frac{17{,}800}{12} \times \frac{0.397}{0.603} = 980 \text{ psi.}$$

---

*See page 50, Equations 18 and 19.
**See footnote Example 12.
†See footnote Example 9.
††See page 51, Equations 20 and 21.

**Example 19. Investigation, Rectangular Section, Combined Bending and Axial Load (Tension)**

In a given section subject to bending moment $M$ combined with axial tension $N$, determine stresses $f_s$ and $f_c$.

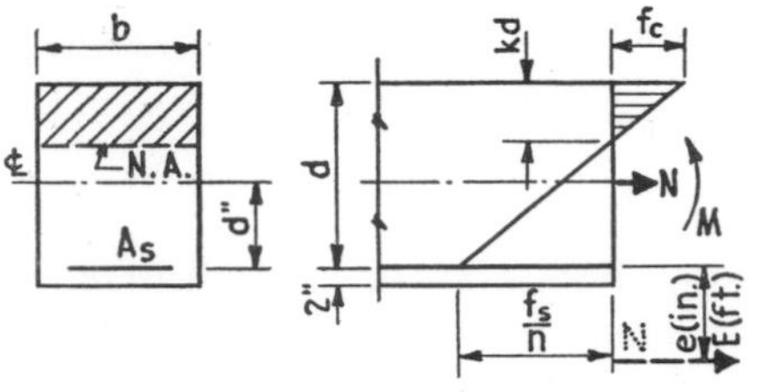


Given:

$b = 11.5$ in.; $d = 21$ in.
$d'' = 9.5$ in.
$A_s = 3.91$ sq.in.
$n = 12$
$M = 98.0$ ft.kips
$N = -26.7$ kips (negative because axial tension)

$$e = \frac{12M}{N} + d'' = \frac{12 \times 98.0}{-26.7} + 9.5 = -34.5 \qquad \frac{e}{d} = \frac{-34.5}{21.0} = -1.64$$

Estimate $j = 0.90$ and determine: $i^* = \dfrac{1}{1 - \dfrac{jd}{e}} = \dfrac{1}{1 - \dfrac{0.90}{-1.64}} = 0.65$

$$m^{**} = q^{**} = \frac{nA_s i}{bd} = \frac{12 \times 3.91 \times 0.65}{11.5 \times 21.0} = 0.126$$

From Table 11, for $m = 0.13$ and $q = 0.126$: $k = 0.388$
From Table 13, for $z = 0.33$ and $k = 0.388$: $j = 0.87$

For $j = 0.87$ (actual), determine $i = \dfrac{1}{1 - \dfrac{jd}{e}} = \dfrac{1}{1 + 0.53} = 0.654$

$$f_s = \frac{1000N}{jA_s i}\frac{e}{d} = \frac{(-26{,}700)(-1.64)}{0.87 \times 3.91 \times 0.654} = 19{,}700 \text{ psi.}$$

$$f_c = \frac{f_s}{n} \times \frac{k}{1-k} = \frac{19{,}700}{12} \times \frac{0.388}{0.612} = 1040 \text{ psi.}$$

**Example 20. Investigation, Rectangular Section, Combined Bending and Axial Load (Tension), Compressive Reinforcement**

In a given rectangular section with compressive reinforcement and subject to bending moment $M$ combined with axial tension $N$, determine stresses $f_s$ and $f_c$.

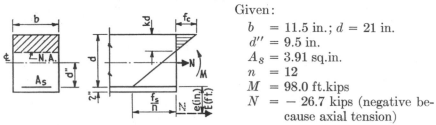

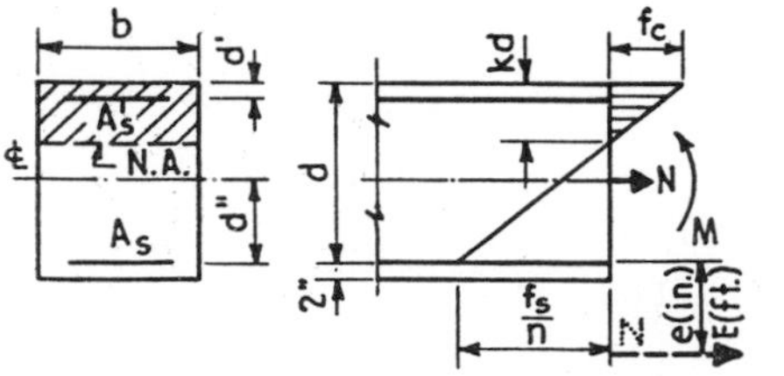


Given:

$b = 11.5$ in.; $d = 21$ in.
$d' = 2$ in.; $d'' = 9.5$ in.
$A_s = 3.91$ sq.in.
$A'_s = 0.62$ sq.in.; $n = 12$
$M = 98.0$ ft.kips
$N = -26.7$ kips (negative because axial tension)

*The value of $i$ cannot be taken from Table 10 because $e$ is negative.
**See page 50, Equations 18 and 19.

From Example 19: $\frac{e}{d} = -1.64$ and $i = 0.65$

$$m^* = \frac{nA_s i}{bd} + \frac{(n-1)A'_s}{bd} = \frac{12 \times 3.91 \times 0.65}{11.5 \times 21.0} + \frac{11 \times 0.62}{11.5 \times 21.0}$$

$$= 0.126 + 0.028 = 0.154$$

$$q^* = \frac{nA_s i}{bd} + \frac{(n-1)A'_s}{bd} \times \frac{d'}{d} = \frac{12 \times 3.91 \times 0.65}{11.5 \times 21.0} + \frac{11 \times 0.62}{11.5 \times 21.0} \times \frac{2.0}{21.0}$$

$$= 0.126 + 0.003 = 0.129$$

From Table 11 for $m = 0.15$** and $q = 0.129$: $k = 0.380$

For entering Table 12 compute

$$\frac{1}{k} \times \frac{(n-1)A'_s}{bd} = \frac{0.028}{0.380} = 0.07 \qquad \frac{1}{k} \times \frac{d'}{d} = \frac{1}{0.380} \times \frac{2.0}{21.0} = 0.25$$

From Table 12: $z = 0.33$

From Table 13, for $z = 0.33$ and $k = 0.380$: $j = 0.87$

For $j = 0.87$ (actual), determine: $i = \dfrac{1}{1 - \dfrac{jd}{e}} = \dfrac{1}{1 + 0.53} = 0.654$

$$f_s = \frac{1000N}{jA_s i} \frac{e}{d} = \frac{(-26{,}700)(-1.64)}{0.87 \times 3.91 \times 0.654} = 19{,}700 \text{ psi.}$$

$$f_c = \frac{f_s}{n} \times \frac{k}{1-k} = \frac{19{,}700}{12} \times \frac{0.380}{0.620} = 1010 \text{ psi.}$$

*See page 50, Equations 18 and 19.
**See footnote Example 9.

## Design of Stirrups

Determination of number and spacing of stirrups depends upon the shape and area of that part of the shear diagram for which stirrups are required by code. The area of the shear diagram determines the number of stirrups required, while the stirrup spacing depends also on the shape of the diagram. Shear diagrams may be considered of three types—rectangular, trapezoidal and triangular. Only trapezoidal and triangular shear diagrams offer problems in stirrup spacing as the spacing is constant for rectangular diagrams.

The procedure illustrated in the following examples requires:

(1) selection of type of stirrup (vertical or inclined); size, $A_v$ ($A_v$ = area of two stirrup legs); and allowable steel stress, $f_v$;

(2) calculation of the reciprocal of the spacing of stirrups at large and at small ends of shear diagram;

(3) calculation of number of stirrups required; and

(4) determination of stirrup spacing so that each stirrup receives its full allowable stress.

Step 1 is preliminary, of course, to the general problem.

Steps 2 and 3 are made by computations involving length, $S$, of the base, and the end ordinates of that part of the shear diagram taken by the stirrups—maximum unit shear (max.$v'$) at large end of diagram and minimum unit shear (min.$v'$) at small end. Min.$v'$ equals zero for triangular diagram. The following expressions are used, $s$ being spacing in inches:

For triangular shear diagrams:

$$\text{At point of min.}s\text{: max.}\frac{1}{s}^{*} = \frac{(\text{max.}v')b}{A_v f_v}$$

$$\text{Number of stirrups required, } N^{**} = 6S\left(\text{max.}\frac{1}{s}\right)$$

$$\text{Index} = \frac{1.5S \text{ (in ft.)}}{\left(\text{max.}\frac{1}{s}\right)}$$

For trapezoidal shear diagrams:

$$\text{At point of min.}s\text{: max.}\frac{1}{s}^{*} = \frac{(\text{max.}v')b}{A_v f_v}$$

$$\text{At point of max.}s\text{: min.}\frac{1}{s}^{*} = \frac{(\text{min.}v')b}{A_v f_v}$$

$$\text{Number of stirrups required, } N\dagger = 6S\left(\text{max.}\frac{1}{s} + \text{min.}\frac{1}{s}\right)$$

$$\text{Index} = \frac{1.5S \text{ (in ft.)}}{\text{max.}\frac{1}{s} - \text{min.}\frac{1}{s}}$$

*See page 53, Equation 30.
**See page 53, Equation 31.
†See page 53, Equation 32.

Step 4 in the procedure—the spacing and grouping of stirrups—is made by entering Diagram 17 with the proper "Index" value and reading the number of stirrups at the various spacings, beginning at the max. $\frac{1}{s}$-value and stopping at the min. $\frac{1}{s}$-value, or at the right margin of the diagram for shear triangles. Examples will illustrate the procedure.

Diagram 17 consists of 36 horizontal scales, each marked at the left margin by an index value ranging from 10 to 160. Each scale has numbered dots, representing stirrups, which were located as follows.

A shear triangle on a base of arbitrary length was laid out. The triangle was divided into equal areas by means of lines perpendicular to the base. The center of gravity of each area was taken as the position of one stirrup. The positions of these points were transferred to a horizontal scale in Diagram 17 and the number of areas chosen was recorded as the index value. This was repeated for 36 shear triangles. On the diagram each shear triangle is represented by a horizontal scale which covers the range between $\frac{1}{s} = 0.50$ and $\frac{1}{s} = 0$. The $\frac{1}{s}$-scale is shown at the top and bottom of the diagram.

The index value, by which the proper stirrup scale is chosen, is the number of stirrups theoretically needed in the shear triangle represented by the particular scale. Note that this is the number required only when the shear triangle has a maximum ordinate, $v'$, corresponding to $\frac{1}{s} = 0.50$ or $s = 2$ in. Parts of the same stirrup scale may also be used for other shear triangles or trapezoids into which the basic triangle may be divided by vertical lines. Each stirrup scale is useful, then, for many shear diagrams.

For illustration consider the shear triangle with Index = 36 and max. $\frac{1}{s} = 0.50$. Choosing arbitrary values of $\frac{1}{s} = 0.35$ and $0.22$, divide the triangle into three parts:

(a) a trapezoid extending from $\frac{1}{s} = 0.50$ to $\frac{1}{s} = 0.35$

(b) a trapezoid extending from $\frac{1}{s} = 0.35$ to $\frac{1}{s} = 0.22$

(c) a triangle extending from $\frac{1}{s} = 0.22$ to $\frac{1}{s} = 0$

Enter Diagram 17 with Index = 36 and select those stirrups which lie in the ranges indicated. The number and spacing of the stirrups are:

(a): 13 @ 2 in., 5 @ 3 in. (11 − 6 = 5)
(b): 6 @ 3 in., 5 @ 4 in. (6 − 1 = 5)
(c): 1 @ 4 in., 3 @ 6 in., 2 @ 8 in., 2 @ 12 in.

It is seen that each scale on Diagram 17 is useful for a multitude of shear diagrams, the only limitation being that the minimum spacing that can be used with this diagram is 2 in.

Diagram 17 may be used for stirrups with any number of legs if values of $\frac{1}{s}$ are determined from the equations that follow:

$$\text{Two-leg (U) stirrups: } \frac{1}{s} = \frac{v'b}{A_v f_v}$$

$$\text{Four-leg (W) stirrups: } \frac{1}{s} = \frac{v'b}{2A_v f_v}$$

$$n\text{-leg stirrups: } \frac{1}{s} = \frac{v'b}{\left(\frac{n}{2}\right) A_v f_v}$$

$A_v f_v$ is in all cases taken from table in Diagram 17.

The stirrup spacing diagram is divided into groups marked Spacing: 2 in., 3 in., 4 in., 6 in., 8 in., 12 in. These groups have been chosen in accordance with good design practice but, if desired, readjustment of groups can easily be made on the diagram. If a 5-in. spacing group were to be inserted between the 4-in. and the 6-in. groups, block out the heavy vertical line at $\frac{1}{s} = 0.20$ ($s = 5$ in.) and substitute two new heavy lines, one at $\frac{1}{s} = 0.222$ ($s = 4\frac{1}{2}$ in.), the other at $\frac{1}{s} = 0.182$ ($s = 5\frac{1}{2}$ in.). The dots marking the position of stirrups remain as they are but must be renumbered beginning at the right hand edge of the 5-in. and 4-in. groups.

The diagram may also be used for spacings, say, twice as large as those shown. In this case, proceed as follows:

(1) Compute $\frac{1}{s}$ and Index as for stirrups with $n$ legs;

(2) Use stirrups with $2n$ legs; also $N_{2n} = \frac{N_n}{2}$;

(3) Count only half the stirrups of each group taken from Diagram 17;

(4) Use twice the spacing shown in the diagram.

### Example 21. Vertical Stirrups, Triangular Shear Diagram

For the shear triangle shown, determine number and spacing of vertical stirrups required:

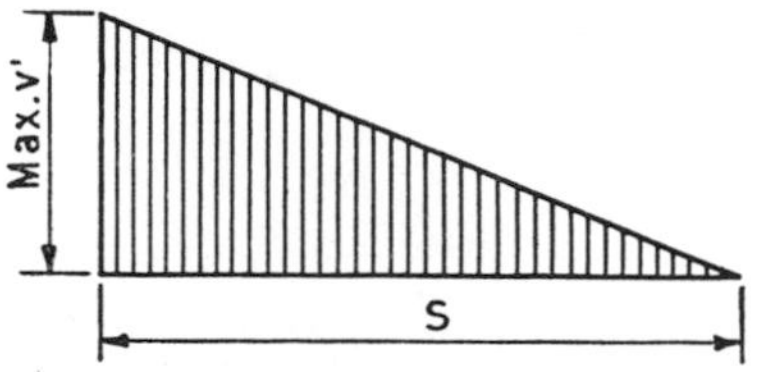


Given:
Max. $v' = 108$ psi.
$S = 8$ ft. 3 in.; $b = 13$ in.
$d = 20$ in.;
$f_v = 20{,}000$ psi.; $f'_c = 2500$ psi.
$\frac{3}{8}$-in. U-stirrups

From Diagram 17, for $f_v = 20{,}000$ and $\frac{3}{8}$-in. U-stirrups: $A_v f_v = 4400$.

$$\text{max. } \frac{1}{s} = \frac{(\text{max. } v')b}{A_v f_v} = \frac{108 \times 13.0}{4400} = 0.319$$

$$N = 6S(\text{max. } \frac{1}{s}) = 6 \times 8.25 \times 0.319 = 16 \text{ stirrups}$$

$$\text{Index} = \frac{1.5S}{\text{max. } \frac{1}{s}} = \frac{1.5 \times 8.25}{0.319} = 38.8, \text{ say } 38.$$

In Diagram 17, use line marked Index = 38, and select those stirrups only which lie between $\frac{1}{s}$ equal to 0.319 and zero:

3 @ 3 in., 6 @ 4 in., 3 @ 6 in., 1 @ 8 in., 3 @ 12 in. Total = 16 stirrups (check). Refer to Table 15 for ⅜-in. round stirrups with $f'_c$ = 2500 psi. and $f_v$ = 20,000 psi. and ascertain that stirrups have sufficient embedment: $d$ = 19.6 in. required.

### Example 22. Vertical Stirrups, Trapezoidal Shear Diagram

For the shear trapezoid shown, determine number and spacing of vertical stirrups.

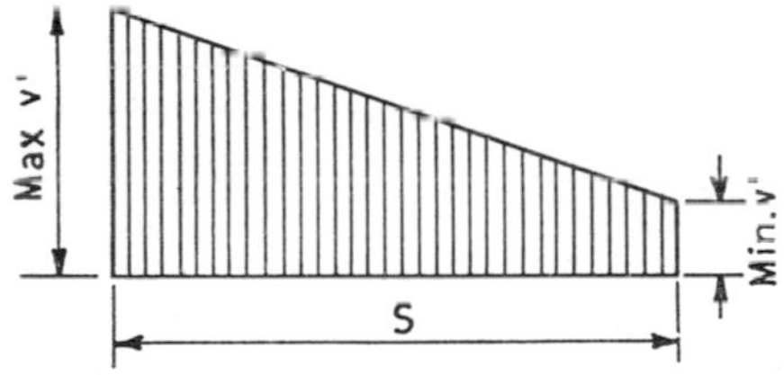


Given:

Max.$v'$ = 120 psi.; min.$v'$ = 17 psi.
$S$ = 8 ft. 3 in.; $b$ = 13 in.
$d$ = 20 in.
$f_v$ = 20,000 psi.; $f'_c$ = 2500 psi.
⅜-in. U-stirrups.

From Diagram 17, for $f_v$ = 20,000 and ⅜-in. U-stirrups: $A_v f_v$ = 4400

$$\text{max.} \frac{1}{s} = \frac{(\text{max.} v')b}{A_v f_v} = \frac{120 \times 13.0}{4400} = 0.355$$

$$\text{min.} \frac{1}{s} = \frac{(\text{min.} v')b}{A_v f_v} = \frac{17 \times 13.0}{4400} = 0.050$$

$$N = 6S\ (\text{max.} \frac{1}{s} + \text{min.} \frac{1}{s}) = 6 \times 8.25(0.355 + 0.050) = 20 \text{ stirrups}$$

$$\text{Index} = \frac{1.5S}{\text{max.} \frac{1}{s} - \text{min.} \frac{1}{s}} = \frac{1.5 \times 8.25}{0.355 - 0.050} = 40.6, \text{ say, } 40$$

In Diagram 17, use line marked Index = 40, and select those stirrups only which lie between $\frac{1}{s}$ equal to 0.355 and 0.050:

7 @ 3 in., 7 @ 4 in., 3 @ 6 in., 1 @ 8 in., 2 @ 12 in. Total = 20 stirrups (check). Refer to Table 15 and ascertain that stirrups have sufficient embedment, as in Example 21.

**Example 23. Inclined Stirrups, Triangular Shear Diagram**

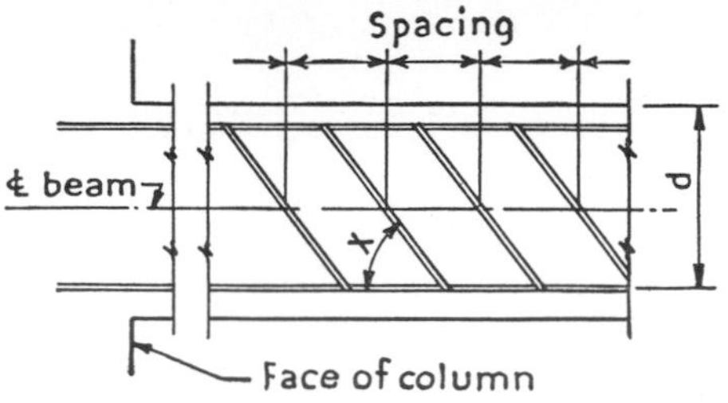


Same data as in Example 21 except assume $f'_c = 2000$, and note from Table 15 that for 3/8-in. U-stirrups and $f_v = 20{,}000$, an effective depth, $d$, of 23.4 in. is required. The actual depth, $d$, of 20 in. is less than the minimum required depth so stirrups must be inclined. Determine number and spacing of inclined stirrups.

$$\text{Compute } \sin x = \frac{\text{actual } d}{\text{min. } d} = \frac{20.0}{23.4} = 0.85$$

From Table 16, for $\sin x = 0.85$: $x = 58$ deg. and $B = 1.38$

Also, $\dfrac{\text{max. } s}{d}$ for inclined stirrups $= 0.81$

Maximum spacing allowed $= 0.81 \times 20 = 16.2$ in.

$$\text{max.}\frac{1}{s} = \frac{(\text{max.}v')\,b}{BA_vf_v} = \frac{108 \times 13.0}{1.38 \times 4400} = 0.231$$

$$N = 6S\,(\text{max.}\frac{1}{s}) = 6 \times 8.25 \times 0.231 = 11 \text{ stirrups}$$

$$\text{Index} = \frac{1.5S}{\text{max.}\frac{1}{s}} = \frac{1.5 \times 8.25}{0.231} = 53.6, \text{ say, } 52$$

In Diagram 17, use line marked Index = 52, and select those stirrups only which lie between $\frac{1}{s}$ equal to 0.231 and zero:

3 @ 4 in., 4 @ 6 in., 2 @ 8 in., 3 @ 12 in. Total = 12 stirrups.*
These stirrups are to be placed at an angle of 58 deg. with the horizontal.

**Example 24. Inclined Stirrups, Trapezoidal Shear Diagram**

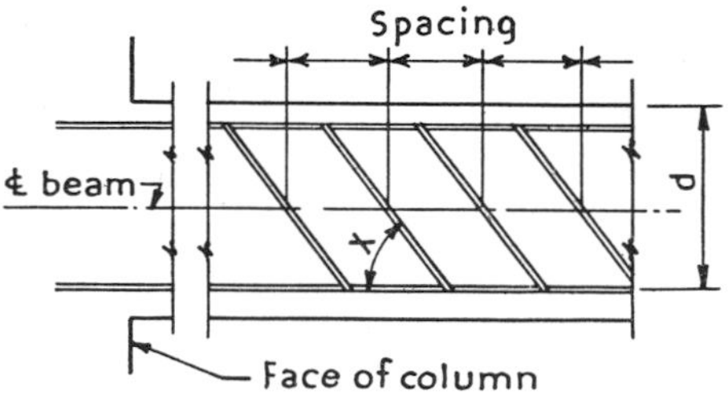


Same data as in Example 22 except assume $d = 17$ in. Minimum effective depth, $d$, required for stirrup embedment is 19.6 in. (*see Table 15*). Determine number and spacing of inclined stirrups.

$$\text{Compute } \sin x = \frac{\text{actual } d}{\text{min. } d} = \frac{17.0}{19.6} = 0.87$$

*Note that 12 stirrups are used although approximately 11 are theoretically required. This is due to the maximum spacing being 12 in. in Diagram 17 which makes it possible to get one or two extra stirrups within the space $S$.

From Table 16, for sin $x = 0.87$: $x = 60$ deg. and $B = 1.37$

Also from Table 16, maximum spacing allowed:

$$0.79d = 0.79 \times 17.0 = 13.4 \text{ in.}$$

$$\text{max.}\frac{1}{s} = \frac{(\text{max.}v')b}{BA_v f_v} = \frac{120 \times 13.0}{1.37 \times 4400} = 0.259$$

$$\text{min.}\frac{1}{s} = \frac{(\text{min.}v')b}{BA_v f_v} = \frac{17 \times 13.0}{1.37 \times 4400} = 0.037$$

$$N = 6S\,(\text{max.}\frac{1}{s} + \text{min.}\frac{1}{s}) = 6 \times 8.25(0.259 + 0.037) = 15 \text{ stirrups}$$

$$\text{Index} = \frac{1.5S}{\text{max.}\frac{1}{s} - \text{min.}\frac{1}{s}} = \frac{1.5 \times 8.25}{0.259 - 0.037} = 55.7, \text{ say, } 56$$

In Diagram 17, use line marked Index = 56, and select those stirrups only which lie between $\frac{1}{s}$ equal to 0.259 and 0.037:

6 @ 1 in., 1 @ 6 in., 3 @ 8 in., 2 @ 12 in. Total = 15 stirrups (check).

## Design of Columns—Concentrically Loaded

The capacity of a concentrically loaded column according to the column formulas in the codes for which design tables are given in this book consists basically of two elements: (1) the load carried by the concrete, and (2) the load carried by the reinforcement. This fact makes possible a general procedure for design applicable to tied and spiral columns under all the codes except (a) spiral columns, American Concrete Institute Code 1928, and (b) spiral columns, New York Code 1938.

The general procedure is: (1) enter the table for the type of column being designed and for the code under which the design is made and select the load carried by the concrete; (2) subtract the load on the concrete from the total load to determine the load which must be carried by the reinforcement; (3) enter that part of the table giving the number and size of bars and select bars required to carry the load taken by the reinforcement.

It will be noted that each table except (a) and (b) mentioned above gives minimum and maximum load on bars or load on column. The values shown are dependent upon the number of bars that can be placed in a single ring or upon the percentage of reinforcement which varies from a minimum to a maximum depending upon the code used. The total load carried by the column or the load carried by the bars should fall between the limits shown.

Examples 25 to 28 illustrate the general procedure for design of tied and spiral columns.

### Example 25. Tied Columns, Joint Committee Code 1940 (Proposed), American Concrete Institute Code 1936, and Chicago Code 1937

Given:

$P$ = 300 kips; $f'_c$ = 3000 psi.; $f_s$ = 16,000 (intermediate grade bars). Design a square column.

#### *Joint Committee Code 1940—Table 18*

Assume column size 18x18 in.

| | |
|---|---|
| Column load, $P$: | 300 kips |
| Load on concrete from Table 18, Part 1 for 18-in. square column and $f'_c$ = 3000: | 175 kips |
| Remainder of load to be carried by longitudinal bars: | 125 kips |

In Table 18, Part 1 for $f_s$ = 16,000, the value of 125 kips is between the minimum and maximum load on bars; therefore the column size assumed is satisfactory. Enter Table 18, Part 2, select ten 1-in. sq. bars, load 128 kips. Use ¼-in. ties @ 12-in. centers.

#### *American Concrete Institute Code 1936—Table 19*

Design procedure under this code using Table 19 is the same as that under the Joint Committee Code using Table 18.

### *Chicago Code 1937—Table 22*

Design procedure under this code using Table 22 is the same as that under the Joint Committee Code 1940 using Table 18.

## Example 26. Tied Columns, American Concrete Institute Code 1928 and New York Code 1938

Given:

$P$ = 300 kips; $f'_c$ = 3000 psi.; $f_s$ = 16,000 (intermediate grade bars).
Design a square column.

### *American Concrete Institute Code 1928—Table 20*

Design procedure under this code using Table 20 differs from that under the American Concrete Institute Code 1936 with Table 19 or the Joint Committee Code 1940 with Table 18 in that the column size need not be assumed but can be selected by entering the table in the column headed "Maximum load on column." Opposite the total load to be carried obtain the size of column having that capacity.

From the column headed "Maximum load on column" for $f'_c$ = 3000 it will be seen that the smallest square column that will carry a load of 300 kips is 20x20 in.

| | |
|---|---|
| Column load, $P$: | 300 kips |
| Load on concrete from Table 20, Part 1 for 20-in. square column and $f'_c$ = 3000: | 270 kips |
| Remainder of load to be carried by longitudinal bars: | 30 kips |

Enter Table 20, Part 2, select four 1⅛-in. sq. bars, load 31 kips. Use ¼-in. ties @ 12-in. centers.

### *New York Code 1938—Table 21*

Design procedure under this code using Table 21 is the same as that under the American Concrete Institute Code 1928 using Table 20.

## Example 27. Spiral Columns, Joint Committee Code 1940 (Proposed) and American Concrete Institute Code 1936

Given:

$P$ = 540 kips; $f'_c$ = 3000 psi.; $f_s$ = 16,000 psi. (intermediate grade bars); hot rolled spirals; 2-in. protection.
Design a square column.

### *Joint Committee Code 1940—Tables 23, 25 and 26*

Assume column size 24x24 in.

| | |
|---|---|
| Column load, $P$: | 540 kips |
| Load on concrete from Table 23 for 24-in. square column and $f'_c$ = 3000: | 389 kips |
| Remainder of load to be carried by longitudinal bars: | 151 kips |

In Table 23 for $f_s = 16{,}000$, the value of 151 kips is between the minimum and maximum load on bars; therefore the column size assumed is satisfactory. Enter Table 25, select ten 1-in. sq. bars, load 160 kips. Number of 1-in. sq. bars not to exceed fourteen in one ring for 20-in. core diameter (*see Table 25*). Spiral from Table 26 for 2-in. protection and 24-in. sq. column: ⅝-in. round, 2-in. pitch.

### *American Concrete Institute Code 1936—Tables 24, 25 and 26*

Design procedure for spiral columns under this code using Tables 24, 25 and 26 is the same as that under the Joint Committee Code 1940 using Tables 23, 25 and 26.

## Example 28. Spiral Columns, Chicago Code 1937

The column formula in this code (*see heading of Table 29*) involves the load carried by the spiral as well as that carried by the concrete and the longitudinal bars; therefore a tabular arrangement of design data slightly different from that in Tables 23 to 26 has been used. The design procedure as illustrated below, however, is essentially the same as that under the Joint Committee Code 1940 and the American Concrete Institute Code 1936.

Given:

$P = 540$ kips; $f'_c = 3000$ psi.; $f_r$ (stress in reinforcement) $= 15{,}000$ psi.; hot rolled spirals; 2-in. protection.

Design a square column.

Assume column size 24x24 in.

| | |
|---|---|
| Column load, $P$: | 540 kips |
| Load on concrete core from Table 29, Part 1 for $d = 20$ in. and $f'_c = 3000$: | 212 kips |
| Remainder of load to be carried by reinforcement: | 328 kips |

In Table 29, Parts 2 and 5, the minimum and maximum load that may be carried on the bars and the minimum that may be carried by the spiral are given, and the maximum number of bars allowed in a single ring is given in Part 4. Many combinations of longitudinal bars and spirals will fulfill the code requirements. The following combination is satisfactory:

| | |
|---|---|
| Load on ten 1-in. sq. bars, from Part 3: | 150 kips |
| Remainder to be carried by spiral: | 178 kips |

From Part 6, select spiral: ½-in. rd., 2-in. pitch, allowable load: 189 kips

Note that load on bars is between the minimum and maximum allowed, that as many as sixteen 1-in. sq. bars in a single ring are permitted, that the minimum load to be carried by the spiral is 76 kips and the maximum ($4/3 \times$ load on bars, *see Part 6*), 200 kips, is not exceeded.

Examples 29 and 30 will illustrate use of Tables 27 and 28. It will be seen by comparison of the spiral column formulas in the American Concrete

Institute Code 1928 and the New York Code 1938 with those in the Joint Committee Code 1940 and the American Concrete Institute Code 1936, each of which is given at the head of the respective design tables, that the first two do not lend themselves readily to the same tabular arrangement of design data nor to the same general procedure as used for the two latter ones.

**Example 29. Spiral Columns, American Concrete Institute Code 1928**

Given:

$P = 540$ kips; $f'_c = 3000$ psi.; 2-in. protection.

Design a square column.

Assume column size 24x24 in. Core diameter $d = 20$ in.

From Table 27, Part 1: $A_c = 314$ sq.in.

Compute $\frac{P}{A_c} = \frac{540}{314} = 1.72$ kips per sq.in.

From Table 27, Part 2, for $f'_c = 3000$ and $\frac{P}{A_c} = 1.72$: percentage of longitudinal bars, $100p = 5.0$ and $A_s = 15.7$ sq.in.; and percentage of spiral, $100p' = 1.25$. From Table 27, Part 3 obtain number of bars: Ten $1\frac{1}{4}$ in. sq., and check maximum number of bars permitted in one ring in Part 4. Number and size selected are satisfactory. With $d = 20$ in. and $100p' = 1.25$, obtain from Part 5 size and pitch of spiral: $\frac{3}{8}$-in. rd., $1\frac{3}{4}$ in. pitch.

**Example 30. Spiral Columns, New York Code 1938**

Given:

$P = 540$ kips; $f'_c = 3000$ psi.; 2-in. protection.

Design a square column.

Determine required sum of core area of concrete plus transformed area of longitudinal bars and spiral as $\frac{1000P}{f_c} = \frac{540{,}000}{750} =$ 720 sq.in.*

Assume column size 24x24 in. Core diameter $d = 20$ in.

From Table 28, Part 1, $A_c$: 314 sq.in.

Remainder of total area for which reinforcement must be provided: 406 sq.in.

From Table 28, Part 3, note that transformed area of longitudinal bars for 24-in. sq. column must be between 65 and 346 sq.in., and from Part 4 that as many as fourteen 1-in. sq. bars are allowed in one ring. Choose ten 1-in. sq. bars.

From Table 28, Part 2, transformed area of bars: 150 sq.in.

Area to be provided by spiral: 256 sq.in.

From Table 28, Part 5, transformed area of spiral, $\frac{1}{2}$-in. rd., $2\frac{1}{4}$-in. pitch: 279 sq.in.

*Gross area of concrete to be not less than $\frac{1000P}{2f_c} = 360$ sq.in. Minimum column size $= \sqrt{360} = 19$ in. sq

# Example 31. Tier of Columns for Given Concentric Loads ($P$, kips) Extending Through Ten Stories. Design in Accordance with Joint Committee Code 1940, Chicago Code 1937, New York Code 1938

Given: $f'_c = 3000$ psi.; intermediate grade bars; hot rolled spirals

Minimum protection required: 1½ in. for J.C. 1940 and Chicago 1937; 2 in. for N.Y. 1938

| Story and Size | | J.C. 1940 Table 18 | Chicago 1937 Table 22 | N.Y. 1938 Table 21 | Story and Size | | J.C. 1940 Tables 23, 25, 26 | Chicago 1937 Table 29 | N. Y. 1938 Table 28 |
|---|---|---|---|---|---|---|---|---|---|
| | | | $P$: 290 | $P$: 290 | | | | | |
| | | $P$: 290 | Min.: 294 | Min.: 315 | | | $P$: 540 | $P$: 540 | $1000P/f_c$ 720 |
| 10 | Conc. | 20x20 216 | 20x20 240 | 20x20 300 | 5 | Conc. | 24x24 389 | 21″φ 234 | 20″φ 314 |
| | | 74 | 54 | 15 | | | 151 | 306 | 406 |
| 20x20 | Bars | 6–1 □ 77 | 4–1 □ 54 | 4–⅞φ 18 | 24x24 | Bars | 10–1 □ 160 | 10–1 □ 150 | 10–1 □ 150 |
| | | | | | | | | 156 | 256 |
| | Ties | ¼φ @12″ | ¼φ @12″ | ¼φ @12″ | | Spiral | ⅝φ–2½″ | ½φ–2½″ 158 | ½φ–2¼″ 279 |
| | | $P$: 340 | $P$: 340 | $P$: 340 | | | $P$: 590 | $P$: 590 | $1000P/f_c$ 787 |
| 9 | Conc. | 20x20 216 | 20x20 240 | 20x20 300 | 4 | Conc. | 24x24 389 | 21″φ 234 | 20″φ 314 |
| | | 124 | 100 | 40 | | | 201 | 356 | 473 |
| 20x20 | Bars | 10–1 □ 128 | 8–1 □ 108 | 6–1 □ 45 | 24x24 | Bars | 10–1⅛ □ 203 | 10–1⅛ □ 191 | 10–1⅛ □ 191 |
| | | | | *** | | | | 165 | 282 |
| | Ties | ¼φ @12″ | ¼φ @12″ | ¼φ @7½″ | | Spiral | ⅝φ–2½″ | ½φ–2¼″ 176 | ½φ–2¼″ 279 |
| | | Tables 23, 25, 26 | Table 29 | Table 28 | | | | | |
| | | $P$: 390 | $P$: 390 | *$1000P/f_c$ 520 | | | $P$: 640 | $P$: 640 | $1000P/f_c$ 853 |
| 8 | Conc. | 20x20 270 | 17″φ 153 | 16″φ 201 | 3 | Conc. | 24x24 389 | 21″φ 234 | 20″φ 314 |
| | | 120 | 237 | 319 | | | 251 | 406 | 539 |
| 20x20 | Bars | 8–1 □ 128 | 8–1 □ 120 | 8–1 □ 120 | 24x24 | Bars | 10–1¼ □ 250 | 10–1¼ □ 234 | 10–1¼ □ 234 |
| | | | 117 | 199 | | | | 172 | 305 |
| | Spiral | ⅝φ–2¾″ | ½φ–2¾″ 117 | ½φ–2½″ 201 | | Spiral | ⅝φ–2½″ | ½φ–2¼″ 176 | ½φ–2″ 314 |
| | | $P$: 440 | $P$: 440 | $1000P/f_c$ 587 | | | $P$: 690 | $P$: 690 | $1000P/f_c$ 920 |
| 7 | Conc. | 24x24 389 | 21″φ 234 | 20″φ 314 | 2 | Conc. | 28x28 529 | 25″φ 331 | 24″φ 452 |
| | | ** 51 | 206 | 273 | | | ** 161 | 359 | 468 |
| 24x24 | Bars | 8–1 □ 128 | 8–1 □ 120 | 8–1 □ 120 | 28x28 | Bars | 10–1¼ □ 250 | 10–1¼ □ 234 | 10–1¼ □ 234 |
| | | | 86 | 153 | | | | 125 | 234 |
| | Spiral | ⅝φ–2½″ | ⅜φ-2½″ 87 | ⅜φ–2¼″ 154 | | Spiral | ⅝φ–2¼″ | ⅜φ–2″ 130 | ½φ–3¼″ 232 |
| | | $P$: 490 | $P$: 490 | $1000P/f_c$ 653 | | | $P$: 740 | $P$: 740 | $1000P/f_c$ 987 |
| 6 | Conc. | 24x24 389 | 21″φ 234 | 20″φ 314 | 1 | Conc. | 28x28 529 | 25″φ 331 | 24″φ 452 |
| | | ** 101 | 256 | 339 | | | ** 211 | 409 | 535 |
| 24x24 | Bars | 8–1 □ 128 | 8–1 □ 120 | 8–1 □ 120 | 28x28 | Bars | 10–1¼ □ 250 | 10–1¼ □ 234 | 10–1¼ □ 234 |
| | | | 136 | 219 | | | | 175 | 301 |
| | Spiral | ⅝φ–2½″ | ½φ–2¾″ 144 | ½φ–2¾″ 229 | | Spiral | ⅝φ–2¼″ | ½φ–2½″ 189 | ½φ–2½″ 302 |

*N. Y. Code design is based upon $\frac{1000\,P}{f_c}$ in which $f_c = 0.25f'_c$, therefore, $\frac{390{,}000}{750} = 520$ sq.in.

**Bars have been chosen so that load on bars in a column is not less than load on bars in column immediately above.

***N. Y. Code specifies: The total cross-sectional area of lateral and cross ties per foot of length of column shall be at least one-fifteenth of the area of the vertical reinforcement. The 7½-in. spacing is based on total cross-sectional area of ties = 5 × 0.05 sq.in.

# Design and Investigation of Columns—Eccentrically Loaded

Eccentrically loaded columns are designed and investigated by use of Diagrams 30 to 32, which are applicable to any concrete stress and eccentricity within the limits of the values of $Q$* and $\frac{e'}{t}$ shown on the diagrams. Under most codes it is necessary to determine the allowable concrete stress for any given column section and loading conditions. Tables 33 and 34 are provided to facilitate determination of allowable stresses for Joint Committee Code 1940 as illustrated in Example 36.

For design, the column size is estimated, if the dimensions have not been determined on the basis of a concentric load or otherwise established; then $\frac{e'}{t}$ and $Q$ are computed as in Examples 32 and 33 for the purpose of entering the diagrams to obtain values of $np$. Because of the uncertainty of the value of $n$, and since the use of $np$ for the tension side of the member and $(n - 1)p$ for the compression side would result in practical difficulties in plotting the curves in Diagrams 30 to 32 without improved accuracy, $np$ has been used throughout.** Having obtained $np$ from the proper diagram, the area of steel required is computed by the equation, $A_s$† $= \frac{np}{n} A_g$. The area of steel determined is the total required and is arranged symmetrically about the centerline of the section as indicated in the figures included in the diagrams.

Investigation of an eccentrically loaded column is similar to design except that the value of $np$ is computed from the equation $np = \frac{nA_s}{A_g}$ and values of $Q$ and $k$ are taken from the diagrams. With these values, the concrete and steel stresses are determined from the equations $f_c = \frac{1000N}{A_g} Q$ and $f_s = nf_c\left(\frac{1 + g}{2k} - 1\right)$

Under the Joint Committee Code 1940, determine the allowable axial load which can be carried on the column by the column formula for concentric load. Next compute the average stress for the axially loaded column, $f_a$†† $= \frac{1000P}{A_g + (n - 1)A_s}$. Note that $(n - 1)$ is used in the expression $f_a$ because the term appears in the formula for allowable stress in the code, whereas $n$ is used in Diagrams 30 to 32 for the reason previously explained. No error of consequence results from this seeming inconsistency as can be

*See page 59, Equation 34.
**See "The Resistance of Reinforced Concrete Columns to Eccentric Loads," by F. E. Richart and T. A. Olson, *Journal of American Concrete Institute*, March-April, 1938.
†See page 59, Equation 35.
††See pages 59 and 60, Equations 36 and 37.

ascertained by using values of $np$ instead of $(n-1)p$ in Table 33. Finally, the value of $D$* is obtained from Table 33 and $f_p$ (the allowable stress) is taken from Table 34. With the allowable stress determined, the balance of the design procedure is the same as that already discussed (*see Example 32*).

**Example 32. Rectangular Column, Eccentric Load—Design**

For a rectangular section subject to combined bending and axial load, determine area of longitudinal bars, $A_s$.

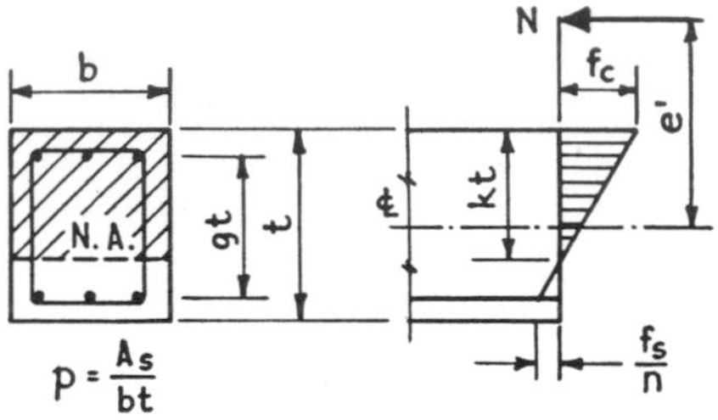


Given:

$b = 15$ in.; $t = 24$ in.; $g = 0.78$

$f_p$** $= 1200$ psi.; $n = 12$

$M = 109$ ft.kips; $N = 118$ kips

$$e' = \frac{12M}{N} = \frac{12 \times 109}{118} = 11.1 \text{ in.}; \quad \frac{e'}{t} = \frac{11.1}{24.0} = 0.46$$

Compute $Q\dagger = \dfrac{bt}{1000N} f_p = \dfrac{15 \times 24}{118{,}000} 1200 = 3.66$

For $\dfrac{e'}{t} = 0.46, Q = 3.66$, and $g = 0.78$, determine $np = 0.14$ from Diagram 30

$$A_s = \frac{np}{n} bt = \frac{0.14}{12} \times 15 \times 24 = 4.20 \text{ sq.in.}$$

Use ten ¾-in. rd. bars (4.40), five at each face.

**Example 33. Circular Column, Eccentric Load—Design**

For a circular section subject to combined bending and axial load, determine area of longitudinal bars, $A_s$.

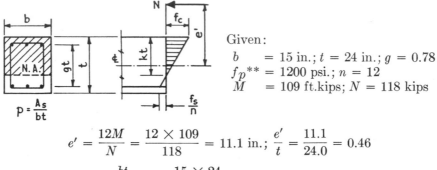

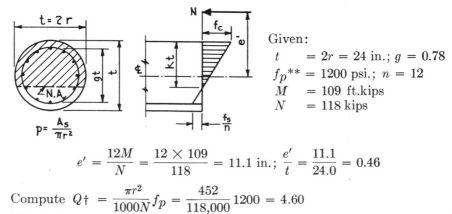

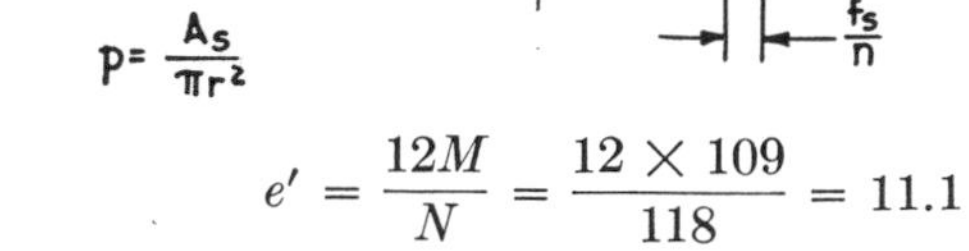


Given:

$t = 2r = 24$ in.; $g = 0.78$

$f_p$** $= 1200$ psi.; $n = 12$

$M = 109$ ft.kips

$N = 118$ kips

$$e' = \frac{12M}{N} = \frac{12 \times 109}{118} = 11.1 \text{ in.}; \quad \frac{e'}{t} = \frac{11.1}{24.0} = 0.46$$

Compute $Q\dagger = \dfrac{\pi r^2}{1000N} f_p = \dfrac{452}{118{,}000} 1200 = 4.60$

---

*See pages 59 and 60, Equations 36 and 37.

***fp*: Allowable stress in eccentrically loaded columns (see Example 36).

†See page 59, Equation 34

For $\frac{e'}{t} = 0.46, Q = 4.60$, and $g = 0.78$, determine $np = 0.25$ from Diagram 32.

$$A_s = \frac{np}{n}\pi r^2 = \frac{0.25}{12}452 = 9.42 \text{ sq.in.}$$

Use ten 1-in. sq. bars (10.0)

**Example 34. Rectangular Column, Eccentric Load—Investigation**

For a rectangular section symmetrically reinforced as shown, and subject to combined bending and axial load, determine stresses $f_c$ and $f_s$.

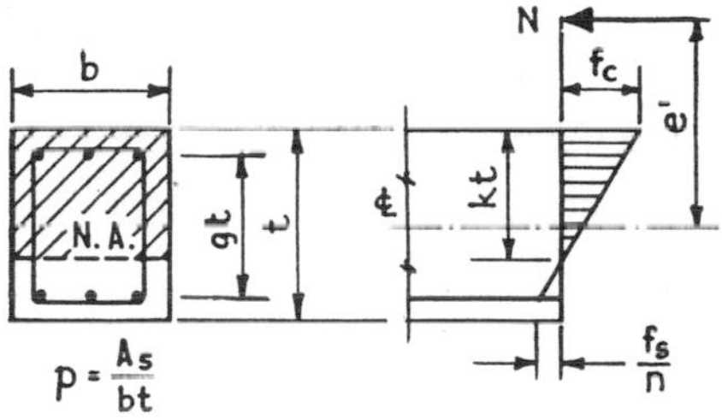


Given:
$b = 15$ in.; $t = 24$ in.; $g = 0.78$
$A_s = 4.40$ sq.in.; $n = 12$
$M = 109$ ft.kips; $N = 118$ kips

$$e' = \frac{12M}{N} = \frac{12 \times 109}{118} = 11.1 \text{ in.}; \quad \frac{e'}{t} = \frac{11.1}{24.0} = 0.46$$

Compute $np = \frac{nA_s}{bt} = \frac{12 \times 4.40}{15 \times 24} = 0.15$

For $\frac{e'}{t} = 0.46$, $np = 0.15$, and $g = 0.78$, determine $Q = 3.6$ and $k = 0.54$ from Diagram 30.

$$f_c = \frac{1000N}{bt}Q = \frac{118{,}000}{15 \times 24} \times 3.6 = 1180 \text{ psi.}$$

$$f_s = nf_c\left(\frac{1+g}{2k} - 1\right) = 12 \times 1180\left(\frac{1.78}{1.08} - 1\right) = 9200 \text{ psi.}$$

**Example 35. Circular Column, Eccentric Load—Investigation**

For a circular section subject to combined bending and axial load, determine stresses, $f_c$ and $f_s$.

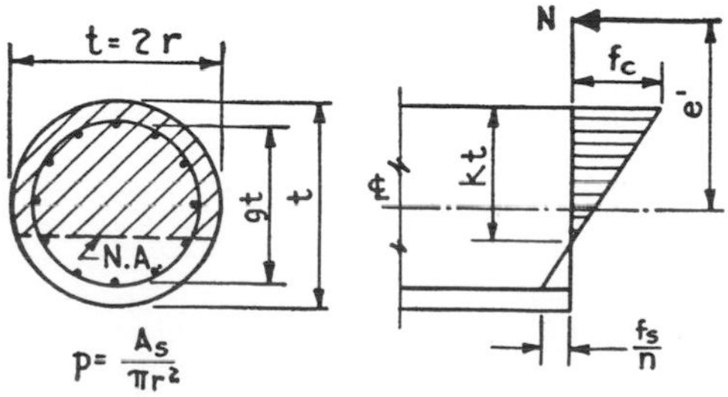


Given:
$t = 2r = 24$ in.; $g = 0.78$
$A_s = 10.0$ sq.in.; $n = 12$
$M = 109$ ft.kips
$N = 118$ kips

$$e' = \frac{12M}{N} = \frac{12 \times 109}{118} = 11.1 \text{ in.}; \quad \frac{e'}{t} = \frac{11.1}{24.0} = 0.46$$

Compute $np = \frac{nA_s}{\pi r^2} = \frac{12 \times 10.0}{452} = 0.27$

For $\frac{e'}{t} = 0.46$, $np = 0.27$, and $g = 0.78$, determine $Q = 4.5$ and $k = 0.51$ from Diagram 32.

$$f_c = \frac{1000N}{\pi r^2}Q = \frac{118{,}000}{452} 4.5 = 1170 \text{ psi.}$$

$$f_s = nf_c\left(\frac{1 + g}{2k} - 1\right) = 12 \times 1170\left(\frac{1.78}{1.02} - 1\right) = 10{,}500 \text{ psi.}$$

**Example 36. Circular Column, Eccentric Load—Allowable Stress**

For the column section and data given in Example 35, determine the allowable stress $f_p$ in extreme fiber in accordance with Joint Committee Code 1940.

Compute allowable axial load $P$ on the column section, using concentric load Tables 23 and 25 for Joint Committee Code 1940 ($f'_c = 2500$, $f_s = 16{,}000$, hot rolled spiral).

| | | |
|---|---|---|
| Load on gross area | = | 254 kips** |
| Load on bars | = | 160 kips |
| Allowable axial load, $P$ | = | 414 kips |

$$\text{Compute } f_a = \frac{1000P}{A_g + (n-1)A_s} = \frac{414{,}000}{452 + 11 \times 10.0} = 740$$

From Table 33, for $g = 0.78$ and $(n - 1)p = \frac{11 \times 10.0}{452} = 0.24$: $D = 7.6$

therefore

$$D\frac{e'}{t} = 7.6 \times 0.46 = 3.50$$

From Table 34, for $\frac{f_a}{f'_c} = \frac{740}{2500} = 0.30$ and $D\frac{e'}{t} = 3.50$: $f_p = 1010$ psi.

Redesign column section for $f_p = 1010$ psi.

$$Q^* = \frac{\pi r^2}{1000N} f_p = \frac{452}{118{,}000} 1010 = 3.87$$

For $\frac{e'}{t} = 0.46$, $Q = 3.87$, and $g = 0.78$, determine $np = 0.38$ from Diagram 32.

$$A_s = \frac{np}{n}\pi r^2 = \frac{0.38}{12} 452 = 14.3 \text{ sq.in.}$$

Use fourteen 1-in. sq. bars.

*See page 59, Equation 34.
**Provided spiral is not less than ½-in. rd., 3¼-in. pitch, when concrete protection is 1½ in.

## Design of Spread Footings

Since determination of footing dimensions and reinforcement is not subject to precise analysis and column loads are only approximate, it is satisfactory to give design data for footings in fairly large increments.

Table 35 is a condensed tabulation of footings designed according to the American Concrete Institute Code 1936 for allowable soil pressures ranging between 2000 and 8000 lb. per sq.ft. Sufficient column loads are given for each soil pressure to permit selection of an adequate footing. A small and a large column size are given for most column loads to cover the usual variation in sizes. The effect these column sizes have on footing dimensions is so small that it is possible to give one set of footing dimensions and reinforcement for all column sizes in the particular range. It should be noted that the footings are designed for the smallest column size given, the footing being adequate, of course, for all of the larger columns as long as the load is not increased. Table 35 may thus be used without interpolation for column loads and column sizes not recorded by using the footing dimensions for the next larger column load. To use Table 35 for round columns enter the table with a square column of equivalent area.

### Example 37. Design of Spread Footing

Given, a 22-in. square column carrying a load of 600 kips, and a maximum allowable soil pressure of 6000 lb. per sq.ft.

Enter Table 35 under "Soil Pressure—6000 lb/sq.ft." and proceed down left margin to column load equal to or just greater than 600 kips. Note that the footing dimensions for that load are for column sizes between 18 and 24 in., satisfactory for a 22-in. column. Required footing data:

| | |
|---|---|
| Width of footing: | 10 ft. 4 in. |
| Total depth: | 30 in.* |
| Reinforcement, each way: | Thirty ⅝-in. rd. bars |

## Design of Pile Footings

Variables involved in the design of pile footings include pile arrangement or "pattern", load capacity of piles, column load, and footing dimensions and reinforcement.

The arrangement of piles in compact groups of different numbers has been standardized to a certain extent, resulting in great simplification of design. For a given column load and predetermined load capacity of pile, the required number of piles is computed. Arrangement of piles and footing plan dimensions may then be taken from tables. Table 36 supplies these data and also permits quick calculation of footing depth and reinforcement based

*Where total depth is insufficient to allow bond for column dowel bars equal to 24 bar diameters, calculate total area of dowels needed and use a greater number of bars having smaller diameters.

on requirements given in American Concrete Institute Code 1936. Important requirements from other codes or specifications are also observed.

**Example 38. Design of Pile Footing**

Design a pile footing to support a 14-in. square column (or round column of equivalent area) carrying a load of 80 kips. Assume that 23 kips is allowed on each pile.

From Table 36, select tentatively a 4-pile footing with a depth of 2 ft. 0 in. and a weight per pile of 1.9 kips.

$$\text{Load on pile from column: } \frac{80}{4} = 20.0 \text{ kips}$$

$$\text{Load on pile from footing: } \quad 1.9 \text{ kips}$$

$$\text{Total load on pile: } \quad 21.9 \text{ kips}$$

The footing selected is satisfactory because 21.9 kips is smaller than the load, 23.0 kips, allowed on each pile and also smaller than the load $P$ = 31.5 kips, allowed on the footing itself.

Footing dimensions are taken from the sketch, and reinforcement is computed based on the load, 20.0 kips, which is transferred from column to pile:

$$A_S \text{ (each way)} = 0.039 \times 20.0 = 0.78 \text{ sq.in.}$$

$$\Sigma o \text{ (each way)} = 0.51 \times 20.0 = 10.2 \text{ in. (controls)}$$

Use nine 3/8-in. rd. bars each way, uniformly spaced, supplying

$$A_S = 0.99 \text{ sq.in.* and } \Sigma o = 10.6 \text{ in.}$$

*For low pile capacities, ascertain that cross-sectional area of reinforcement is not less than 0.20 sq.in. per ft. in each direction, a frequent code requirement.

# Summary and Derivations of Equations*

## A1. Flexural Members—Design of Rectangular Sections

### *Section Coefficients*

(1) $$K = f_s pj \text{ or } \tfrac{1}{2} f_c kj \text{ or } \frac{M_r}{bd^2}$$ *See Table 1*

in which $M_r$ is resisting moment of concrete stresses

(2) $$k = \sqrt{2np + (np)^2} - np \text{ or } \frac{1}{1 + \frac{f_s}{nf_c}}$$ *See Table 1*

(3) $$j = 1 - \frac{k}{3}$$ *See Table 1*

### *Tensile Reinforcement*

(4) $$A_s = \frac{M(\text{in.lb.})}{f_s jd} = \frac{M(\text{ft.kips})}{\frac{f_s jd}{12{,}000}} = \frac{M(\text{ft.kips})}{ad} \text{(simple bending)}$$

in which $$a = \frac{f_s j}{12{,}000}$$ *For* a, *see Tables 1 and 3*

(5) $$A_s = \frac{NE}{adi} \text{ (combined bending and axial load)}$$ *For* i, *see Table 10*

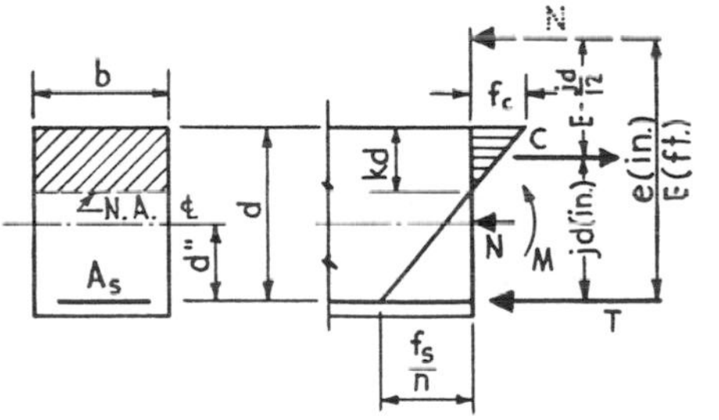


$M$: external moment in ft.kips

$N$: axial load in kips; also equivalent eccentric load located a distance of $E$ (ft.) from $T$**

$C$: resultant of compressive stresses

$T$: resultant of tensile stresses $= A_s f_s$

Moments about $T$ of moment $M$ and axial load $N$: $M + N\frac{d''}{12}$

Moment about $T$ of equivalent eccentric load $N$: $NE$

Since $$NE = M + N\frac{d''}{12}$$

$$E = \frac{M}{N} + \frac{d''}{12}, \text{ or } e = \frac{12M}{N} + d''$$

Moments about $C$: $$-N\left(E - \frac{jd}{12}\right) + \frac{A_s f_s jd}{12{,}000} = 0, \text{ therefore}$$

$$A_s = \frac{12{,}000NE}{f_s jd}\left(1 - \frac{jd}{12E}\right)$$

*In this section only those derivations will be given that are not readily found in standard textbooks on reinforced concrete design.

**"Equivalent eccentric load" means load which may be substituted for and which will produce the same stresses as "bending moment $M$ and axial load $N$."

Substitute $e$ for $12E$ in parentheses and $a$ for $\frac{f_s j}{12{,}000}$, then:

$$A_s = \frac{NE}{adi} \qquad \text{in which} \qquad i = \frac{1}{1 - \frac{jd}{e}}$$ *See Table 10*

For simple bending: $E$ = infinity, $NE = M$ and $i$ = unity; therefore the equation $A_s = \frac{NE}{adi}$ applies to both simple bending and bending combined with axial load.

Since $A_s$ and $i$ must be positive, Equation 5 is applicable only when $e$ is greater than $jd$. For small values of $\frac{e}{d}$, reference is made to the section on eccentrically loaded columns.

## *Balanced steel ratio*

(6) $$p = \frac{A_s}{bd} \text{ or } \frac{1}{\frac{2f_s}{f_c}\left(1 + \frac{f_s}{nf_c}\right)} \text{ or } \frac{f_c k}{2f_s} \text{ (simple bending)}$$ *See Table 1*

(7) $$p = \frac{f_c k}{2f_s i} \text{ (combined bending and axial load)}$$ *See Table 10*

In the equation

$$p = \frac{A_s}{bd}$$

substitute for $A_s$:

$$\frac{NE}{adi} = \frac{12{,}000NE}{jf_s di}$$

which gives

$$p = \frac{12{,}000NE}{jf_s bd^2 i}$$

Since $p$ is "balanced steel ratio",

$$12{,}000NE = M_r = Kbd^2, \text{ therefore}$$

$$p = \frac{Kbd^2}{jf_s bd^2 i} = \frac{K}{jf_s i}$$

Substitute $\frac{1}{2}f_c kj$ for $K$. Then:

$$p = \frac{\frac{1}{2}f_c kj}{jf_s i} = \frac{f_c k}{2f_s i}$$

## *Resisting Moment of Concrete Stresses*

(8) $$M_r = KF \text{ (ft.kips)}$$

in which

$$F = \frac{bd^2}{12{,}000}$$ *See Table 4*

For rectangular sections:

$$K = \tfrac{1}{2}f_c kj$$ *See Table 1*

Moment of compressive concrete stresses about tensile reinforcement:

$$M_r = \tfrac{1}{2}f_c bkd \times jd = \tfrac{1}{2}f_c kj \times bd^2 \text{(in.lb.) or}$$

$$M_r = K\frac{bd^2}{12{,}000}\text{(ft.kips)}$$

Values of $\frac{bd^2}{12{,}000} = F$ are given in Table 4.

### *Compressive Reinforcement*

(9) $$A'_s = \frac{M - KF}{cd} \text{ (simple bending)}$$

(10) $$A'_s = \frac{NE - KF}{cd} \text{ (combined bending and axial load)}$$

in which $$c = \frac{f_s}{12{,}000} \times \frac{n-1}{n} \times \frac{\left(1 - \frac{d'}{d}\right)\left(k - \frac{d'}{d}\right)}{1 - k}$$ *See Table 7*

Compressive reinforcement is required when external moment exceeds resisting moment of concrete stresses, that is, when $M > KF$ or $NE > KF$.

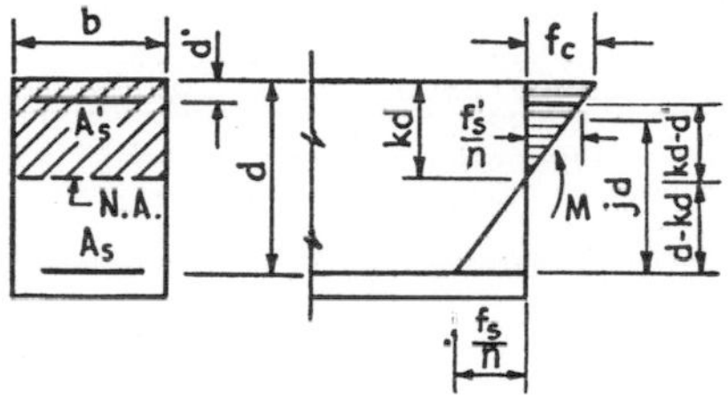


Take moments about tensile reinforcement:

$$M \text{ (in.lb.)} = \tfrac{1}{2} f_c bkdjd + \frac{n-1}{n} A'_s f'_s (d - d')$$

$$= Kbd^2 + \frac{n-1}{n} A'_s f'_s (d - d')$$

$$M \text{ (ft.kips)} = \frac{Kbd^2}{12{,}000} + \frac{A'_s f'_s}{12{,}000} \times \frac{n-1}{n} \times \left(1 - \frac{d'}{d}\right) d$$

Substitute $F$ for $\frac{bd^2}{12{,}000}$ and use the relation of similar triangles:

$$\frac{\frac{f'_s}{n}}{\frac{f_s}{n}} = \frac{kd - d'}{d - kd} \quad \text{or} \quad f'_s = \frac{f_s\left(k - \frac{d'}{d}\right)}{1 - k}$$

Therefore, $$M \text{ (ft.kips)} = KF + \frac{A'_s f_s}{12{,}000} \times \frac{k - \frac{d'}{d}}{1 - k} \times \frac{n-1}{n} \times \left(1 - \frac{d'}{d}\right) d$$

Set $$c = \frac{f_s}{12{,}000} \times \frac{n-1}{n} \times \frac{\left(1 - \frac{d'}{d}\right)\left(k - \frac{d'}{d}\right)}{1 - k}$$

and solve for $A'_s$: $$A'_s = \frac{M - KF}{cd} \text{ (simple bending)}$$ *See Table 7*

For combined bending, the total external moment about tensile reinforcement is:

$$M + N\frac{d''}{12} \text{ or } N\left(\frac{M}{N} + \frac{d''}{12}\right) \text{ or } NE.$$ *See derivation of Equation 5*

The algebraic expression for moment of compressive stresses about tensile reinforcement is the same as for simple bending. The only difference between simple bending and combined bending is in the external moment. $M$ is simply replaced by $NE$, which gives Equation 10. Values of $c$ given in Table 7 apply in both types of bending.

### *Tensile Reinforcement in Sections Having Compressive Reinforcement*

Usually Equation 4 for simple bending and Equation 5 for combined bending give satisfactory accuracy, but if a great degree of accuracy is desired and both $d$ and $p'$ are relatively large, use the following equations:

$$\text{(11)} \qquad A_s = pbd + \frac{12{,}000(M - KF)}{f_s(d - d')} \text{ (simple bending)}$$

$$\text{(12)} \quad A_s = \frac{pbd}{i} + \frac{12{,}000(NE - KF)}{f_s(d - d')i} \text{ (combined bending and axial load)}$$

$p$ is taken from Table 1.

The first term in both equations is the tensile steel area required to balance the compressive concrete stresses, the moment of which is $KF$. The second term provides tensile reinforcement for the differential moment $M - KF$ (simple bending) or $NE - KF$ (combined bending). The introduction of the factor $i$ for combined bending has been explained elsewhere.

## A2. Flexural Members—Design of T-Sections with Compression in Stem Neglected

### *Resisting Moment of Concrete Stresses*

$$M_r = K\frac{bd^2}{12{,}000} = KF \text{ (ft.kips)}$$

in which

$$\text{(13)} \qquad K = \frac{f_c}{2}\frac{t}{d}\left(2 - \frac{t}{d} - \frac{t}{kd} + \frac{2t^2}{3kd^2}\right) \qquad \textit{See Table 8}$$

The stress diagram for concrete in compression is a trapezoid. Subdivide it into two stress triangles, and take moments of each triangle about tensile reinforcement:

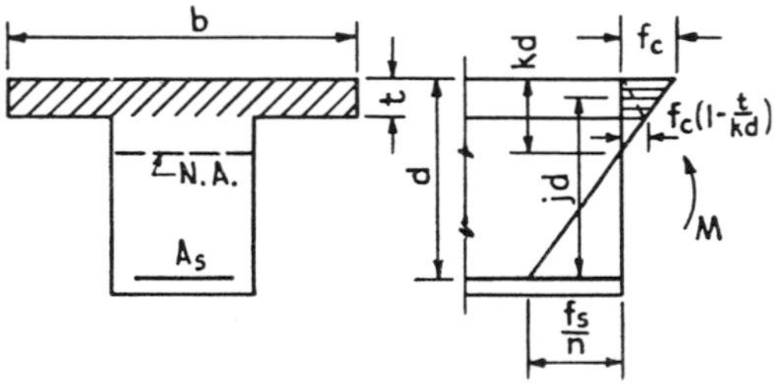


$$M_r = \tfrac{1}{2}f_cbt\left(d - \frac{t}{3}\right) + \tfrac{1}{2}f_c\left(1 - \frac{t}{kd}\right)bt\left(d - \frac{2t}{3}\right)$$

Therefore ,

$$M_r = \tfrac{1}{2}f_cbt\left(2d - t - \frac{t}{k} + \frac{2t^2}{3kd}\right)$$

Divide by $bd^2$ and set $\frac{M_r}{bd^2} = K$:

$$K = \frac{f_c}{2}\frac{t}{d}\left(2 - \frac{t}{d} - \frac{t}{kd} + \frac{2t^2}{3kd^2}\right)$$

***Ratio of Distance* (jd) *between Tensile Reinforcement and Center of Gravity of Compressive Stresses in Flange to Effective Depth* (d)**

(14) $$j = 1 - \frac{yt}{d} = 1 - \frac{k - \frac{2t}{3d}}{2k - \frac{t}{d}} \times \frac{t}{d}$$ *See Table 9*

***Ratio of Distance* (yt) *between Extreme Fiber and Center of Gravity of Compressive Stresses in Flange to Flange Depth* (t)**

(15) $$y = \frac{1 - \frac{2t}{3kd}}{2 - \frac{t}{kd}}$$ *See Table 9*

Determine the distance $jd$ between resultants $C$ and $T$ from the fundamental equation:

$$M_r = C \times jd, \text{ therefore}$$

$$j = \frac{M_r}{Cd}$$

in which $M_r$ has been derived under Equation 13 and $C$ equals sum of compressive stresses in flange:

$$C = \tfrac{1}{2}f_c bt + \tfrac{1}{2}f_c\left(1 - \frac{t}{kd}\right)bt = \tfrac{1}{2}f_c bt\left(2 - \frac{t}{kd}\right)$$

Substitute values of $M_r$ and $C$, which gives:

$$j = \frac{\tfrac{1}{2}f_c bt\left(2d - t - \frac{t}{k} + \frac{2t^2}{3kd}\right)}{\tfrac{1}{2}f_c bt\left(2 - \frac{t}{kd}\right)d} = \frac{2 - \frac{t}{kd} - \frac{t}{d} + \frac{2t^2}{3kd^2}}{2 - \frac{t}{kd}}$$

therefore

$$j = 1 - \frac{1 - \frac{2t}{3kd}}{2 - \frac{t}{kd}} \times \frac{t}{d}$$

Multiply numerator and denominator by $k$, which gives Equation 14.

$$j = 1 - \frac{yt}{d} \text{ gives } y = \frac{1 - \frac{2t}{3kd}}{2 - \frac{t}{kd}} \text{ which is Equation 15}$$

Values of both $j$ and $y$ are given in Table 9.

### *Area of Reinforcement*

For $A_s$ use Equations 4 and 5. For $A'_s$ use Equations 9 and 10. Select values of $a$ from Table 8. Both $c$ and $i$ are selected from the same tables as used for rectangular sections.

## B1. Flexural Members—Investigation of Rectangular Sections

### *Ratios of Reinforcement*

(16) $$p' = \frac{A'_s}{bd}$$

(17) $$p = \frac{A_s}{bd} \times i \begin{cases} \text{simple bending} & i = 1 \\ \text{combined bending} & i = \dfrac{1}{1 - \dfrac{jd}{e}} \end{cases}$$ *See Table 10*

From Equation 4:

$$A_s = \frac{M(\text{in.lb.})}{f_s jd} \text{ (simple bending)}$$

From Equation 5:

$$A_s = \frac{NE}{adi} = \frac{1000Ne}{f_s jdi} \text{ (combined bending)}$$

$$\text{or } A_s i = \frac{1000Ne}{f_s jd}$$

The general expression covering all cases of bending is:

$$A_s i = \frac{\text{Moment(in.lb.)}}{f_s jd}$$

In the special case of simple bending, $i$ = unity and $p = \frac{A_s}{bd}$. For combined bending, it has been shown that the customary design relations hold, provided $A_s$ is introduced together with the factor $i$. The product $A_s i$ must then be introduced also in the customary equations for investigation. Therefore, the general equation for ratio of tensile reinforcement is:

$$p = \frac{A_s i}{bd}$$

### *Ratio of Distance* (kd) *between Extreme Fiber and Neutral Axis to Effective Depth* (d)

(18) $$k = \sqrt{m^2 + 2q} - m$$

in which:

$$m = np + (n-1)p'$$

$$q = np + (n-1)p'\frac{d'}{d}$$

(19) $$q = k\left(\frac{k}{2} + m\right)$$ *See Table 11*

Equation 18 results from substitution of $m$ and $q$ in the customary equation:

$$k = \sqrt{[np + (n-1)p']^2 + 2\left[np + (n-1)p'\frac{d'}{d}\right]} - [np + (n-1)p']$$

Therefore,

$$k = \sqrt{m^2 + 2q} - m$$

Equation 19 may be derived from Equation 18 as follows:

$$k + m = \sqrt{m^2 + 2q}$$

$$(k+m)^2 = m^2 + 2q$$

$$k^2 + 2mk + m^2 = m^2 + 2q$$

$$q = \frac{k^2}{2} + mk = k\left(\frac{k}{2} + m\right)$$

***Ratio of Distance* (zkd) *between Extreme Fiber and Center of Gravity of Compressive Stresses to Depth* (kd)**

**(20)**
$$z = \frac{\frac{1}{6} + \frac{(n-1)A'_s}{kbd} \times \frac{d'}{kd} \times \left(1 - \frac{d'}{kd}\right)}{\frac{1}{2} + \frac{(n-1)A'_s}{kbd} \times \left(1 - \frac{d'}{kd}\right)}$$
*See Table 12*

from which

**(21)**
$$j = 1 - zk$$
*See Table 13*

Let $C$ denote the resultant of concrete and steel compressive stresses and $zkd$ the distance from $C$ to the extreme fiber. Then, $zkd$ equals moment of $C$ about extreme fiber divided by $C$:

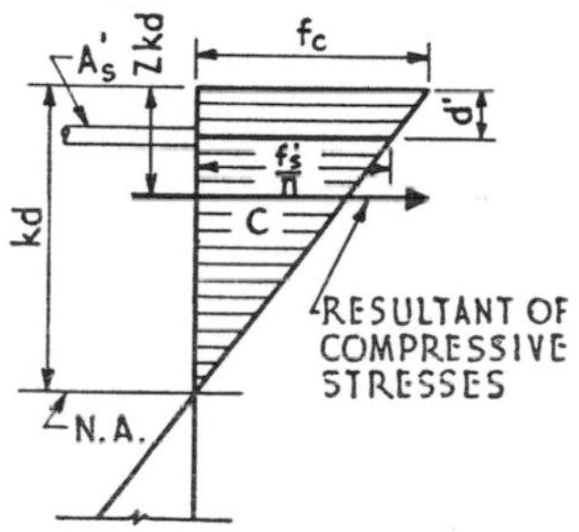


$$zkd = \frac{\frac{1}{2}f_c kdb \times \frac{kd}{3} + A'_s f'_s \frac{(n-1)}{n} \times d'}{\frac{1}{2}f_c kdb + A'_s f'_s \frac{(n-1)}{n}}$$

From similar triangles: $f'_s = nf_c\left(1 - \frac{d'}{kd}\right)$

Substitute values of $f'_s$:

$$zkd = \frac{\frac{1}{6}f_c bk^2d^2 + A'_s \times \frac{(n-1)}{n} \times d' \times nf_c\left(1 - \frac{d'}{kd}\right)}{\frac{1}{2}f_c bkd + A'_s \times \frac{(n-1)}{n} \times nf_c\left(1 - \frac{d'}{kd}\right)}$$

$$= \frac{f_c bk^2d^2\left[\frac{1}{6} + \frac{(n-1)A'_s}{kbd} \times \frac{d'}{kd}\left(1 - \frac{d'}{kd}\right)\right]}{f_c bkd\left[\frac{1}{2} + \frac{(n-1)A'_s}{kbd} \times \left(1 - \frac{d'}{kd}\right)\right]}$$

Divide both sides of equation by $kd$ and cancel $f_c bkd$, which gives equation 20.

The distance between $C$ and the tensile reinforcement equals $jd = d - zkd$, therefore:

$$j = 1 - zk$$

Substitute value of $z$:

$$j = 1 - \frac{\frac{k}{6} + \frac{(n-1)A'_s}{bd} \times \frac{d'}{kd} \times \left(1 - \frac{d'}{kd}\right)}{\frac{1}{2} + \frac{(n-1)A'_s}{kbd} \times \left(1 - \frac{d'}{kd}\right)}$$

$$j = 1 - \frac{\frac{k^2}{6} + \frac{(n-1)A'_s}{bd} \times \frac{d'}{d}\left(1 - \frac{d'}{kd}\right)}{\frac{k}{2} + \frac{(n-1)A'_s}{bd} \times \left(1 - \frac{d'}{kd}\right)}$$

For determination of $k$ and $j$ in T-beams in which compressive stresses in the stem are included, the procedure is to convert the flange area into an equivalent transformed area of compressive reinforcement. When the width of flange projecting beyond the web is $b - b'$, and its depth is $t$, then its area is $(b - b')t$ and the depth from extreme fiber to resultant of stresses in flange is $yt$. These two quantities correspond to the quantities of $(n-1)A'_s$ and $d'$ used for compressive reinforcement, and they may be introduced as shown for compressive reinforcement in the determination of $p'$, $k$ and $j$. The flange quantities shall, of course, be kept separate from quantities due to compressive reinforcement.

## B2. Flexural Members—Investigation of T-Sections with Compression in Stem Neglected

***Ratio of Distance* (kd) *between Extreme Fiber and Neutral Axis to Effective Depth* (d)**

(22) $$k = \frac{\dfrac{nA_s}{bt} + \dfrac{1}{2}\dfrac{t}{d}}{\dfrac{nA_s}{bt} + 1.00} \quad \text{(simple bending)}$$

(23) $$k = \frac{\dfrac{nA_si}{bt} + \dfrac{1}{2}\dfrac{t}{d}}{\dfrac{nA_si}{bt} + 1.00} \quad \text{(combined bending and axial load)}$$

Area of concrete which is considered effective equals $bt$ (flange area). Transformed area of tensile reinforcement equals $nAsi$ ($i = 1$ for simple bending). The neutral axis is located at the center of gravity of these combined areas:

$$bt\left(kd - \frac{t}{2}\right) = nA_si(d - kd)$$

Divide by $btd$:

$$k - \frac{1}{2}\frac{t}{d} = \frac{nA_si}{bt}(1 - k)$$

Solve for $k$, which gives Equation 23.

***Ratio of Distance* (jd) *between Tensile Reinforcement and Center of Gravity of Compressive Stresses in Flange to Effective Depth* (d)**

Use Equation 14 in conjunction with Table 9.

## B3. Flexural Members—Stress Determination

***Tensile Stresses***

(24) $$f_s = \frac{M(\text{in.lb.})}{jdA_s} = \frac{12{,}000M(\text{ft.kips})}{jdA_s} \quad \text{(simple bending)}$$

(25) $$f_s = \frac{1000N}{jA_si}\frac{e}{d} \quad (N \text{ in kips}) \quad \text{(combined bending and axial load)}$$

See Derivation of Equation 5:

$$A_s = \frac{NE}{adi} \text{ in which } \begin{cases} E = \dfrac{e}{12} \\ a = \dfrac{f_sj}{12{,}000} \end{cases}$$

Therefore,

$$A_s = \frac{N \times \dfrac{e}{12}}{\dfrac{f_sj}{12{,}000} \times di} = \frac{1000Ne}{f_sjdi}$$

which is the same as Equation 25.

*Compressive Stresses*

(26)
$$f_c = \frac{f_s}{n} \times \frac{k}{1-k}$$

(27)
$$f'_s = f_s \times \frac{k - \frac{d'}{d}}{1-k}$$ *See derivation of Equation 10*

## C. Shearing and Bond Stresses

*Shearing Stress*

(28)
$$v = \frac{V(\text{kips})}{G}$$

Unit shearing stress, $v = \frac{V(\text{lb.})}{bjd} = \frac{1000V\ (V \text{ in kips})}{bjd}$

Set $j = 7/8$ (sufficiently accurate for determination of shearing stress), and $G = \frac{7bd}{8000}$

Then
$$v = \frac{1000V}{b \times 7/8 \times d} = \frac{V(\text{kips})}{\frac{7bd}{8000}} = \frac{V}{G}$$ *See Table 14*

*Bond Stress*

(29)
$$\Sigma o = \frac{8000V}{7du}$$

Unit bond stress, $u = \frac{V(\text{lb.})}{\Sigma ojd} = \frac{1000V\ (V \text{ in kips})}{\Sigma ojd}$

Set $j = 7/8$

Then
$$u = \frac{1000V}{\Sigma o 7/8 d} = \frac{8000V}{7\Sigma od} \quad \text{or} \quad \Sigma o = \frac{8000V}{7du}$$

## D. Stirrups

*Reciprocal Value of Stirrup Spacing* (s)

(30)
$$\frac{1}{s} = \frac{v'b}{A_v f_v}$$

The fundamental equation for stirrups is $A_v = \frac{V's}{f_v jd}$ in which:

$A_v$ = total cross-sectional area of a vertical stirrup
$V' = v'bjd$ = total shear to be carried by stirrups

Therefore,
$$A_v = \frac{v'bs}{f_v} \quad \text{or} \quad \frac{1}{s} = \frac{v'b}{A_v f_v}$$

The minimum spacing of stirrups occurs where $v'$ is maximum, therefore:

At point of min. $s$: max. $\frac{1}{s} = \frac{(\text{max. } v')b}{A_v f_v}$

At point of max. $s$: min. $\frac{1}{s} = \frac{(\text{min. } v')b}{A_v f_v}$

*Number of Stirrups*

(31) Triangular shear diagram: $N = 6S\left(\text{max. } \frac{1}{s}\right)$

(32) Trapezoidal shear diagram: $N = 6S\left(\text{max. } \frac{1}{s} + \text{min. } \frac{1}{s}\right)$

For triangular diagram, total shear to be taken by $N$ stirrups:

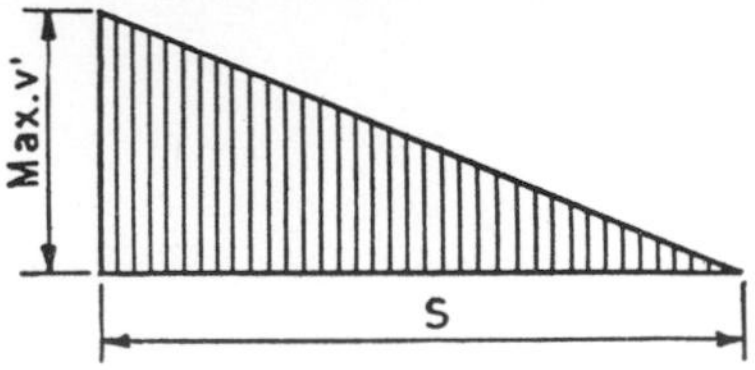


$$\frac{12S\,(\text{max. } v')b}{2}$$

Capacity of each stirrup $= A_v f_v$, therefore:

$$N = \frac{6S(\text{max. } v')b}{A_v f_v}$$

From derivation of Equation 30: $\text{max. } v' = \dfrac{\left(\text{max. } \frac{1}{s}\right) A_v f_v}{b}$, therefore

$$N = \frac{6S\left(\text{max. } \frac{1}{s}\right) A_v f_v b}{A_v f_v b} = 6S\left(\text{max. } \frac{1}{s}\right)$$

For trapezoidal diagram, total shear to be taken by $N$ stirrups:

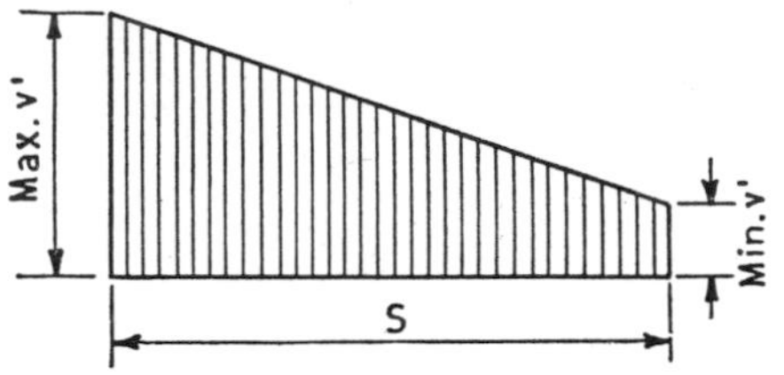


$$\frac{12S}{2}(\text{max. } v' + \text{min. } v')b$$

Capacity of each stirrup $= A_v f_v$, therefore:

$$N = \frac{6S}{A_v f_v}(\text{max. } v' + \text{min. } v')b$$

From derivation of Equation 30:

$$\text{max. } v' + \text{min. } v' = \frac{A_v f_v}{b}\left(\text{max. } \frac{1}{s} + \text{min. } \frac{1}{s}\right), \text{ therefore,}$$

$$N = 6S\left(\text{max. } \frac{1}{s} + \text{min. } \frac{1}{s}\right)$$

### *Minimum Beam Depth for Embedment of Vertical Stirrups:*

$$\left.\begin{array}{ll} \text{Deformed bars: } & d = (f_v - 10{,}000)\dfrac{10c}{f'_c} + 7c + 2 \\ \text{Plain bars: } & d = (f_v - 10{,}000)\dfrac{12.5c}{f'_c} + 7c + 2 \end{array}\right\} \textit{See Table 15}$$

Code requirements for stirrup embedment:

A stirrup shall have sufficient embedment to develop a stress of $f_v$ at mid-point of effective depth, $d$.

A standard hook provides embedment equal to a tensile stress of 10,000 psi. at the beginning of the hooked end.

For the hook dimensions in the sketch of Table 15 it is seen that the straight length between hook and mid-point of effective depth equals $\left(\frac{d}{2} - \frac{7c}{2} - 1\right)$. This length must develop by bond a tensile stress of $(f_v - 10{,}000)$ psi.

Deformed bars ($u = 0.05f'_c$): $(f_v - 10{,}000) \times \dfrac{\pi c^2}{4} = \left(\dfrac{d}{2} - \dfrac{7c}{2} - 1\right) \times \pi c \times 0.05f'_c$

$$d = (f_v - 10{,}000)\,\frac{10c}{f'_c} + 7c + 2$$

Plain bars ($u = 0.04f'_c$): $(f_v - 10{,}000) \times \dfrac{\pi c^2}{4} = \left(\dfrac{d}{2} - \dfrac{7c}{2} - 1\right) \times \pi c \times 0.04f'_c$

$$d = (f_v - 10{,}000)\frac{12.5c}{f'_c} + 7c + 2$$

## E1. Columns*—Concentric Load, Design

### *Tied Columns*

Joint Committee Code 1940: $P = 0.80\,(0.225f'_cA_g + A_sf_s)$

$= 0.18f'_cA_g + 0.8A_sf_s$

American Concrete Institute Code 1936: $P = 0.70A_g(0.22f'_c + f_sp_g)$

$= 0.154f'_cA_g + 0.7f_sA_g \times \frac{A_s}{A_g}$

$= 0.154f'_cA_g + 0.7f_sA_s$

American Concrete Institute Code 1928: $P = 0.225f'_cA_g[1 + (n - 1)p_g]$

Insert $n = \frac{30{,}000}{f'_c}$ which gives:

$$P = 0.225f'_cA_g + 0.225f'_cA_g \times \frac{A_s}{A_g} \times \frac{30{,}000}{f'_c} - 0.225f'_cA_g \times \frac{A_s}{A_g}$$

$$= 0.225f'_cA_g + (6750 - 0.225f'_c)A_s$$

New York Code 1938: $P = f_cA_g(1 + np_g)$ in which $\begin{cases} f_c = 0.25f'_c \\ n = \frac{30{,}000}{f'_c} \end{cases}$

$$P = 0.25f'_cA_g + 0.25f'_cA_g \times \frac{30{,}000}{f'_c} \times \frac{A_s}{A_g}$$

$$= 0.25f'_cA_g + 7500A_s$$

Chicago Code 1937: $P = A_g(0.20f'_c + 0.9f_rp_g)$

$= 0.20f'_cA_g + 0.9f_rA_s$

### *Spiral Columns*

Joint Committee Code 1940: $P = 0.225f'_cA_g + A_sf_s$

American Concrete Institute Code 1936: $P = A_g(0.22f'_c + f_sp_g)$

$= 0.22f'_cA_g + f_sA_g \times \frac{A_s}{A_g}$

$= 0.22f'_cA_g + f_sA_s$

American Concrete Institute Code 1928:

$$P = A_c[1 + (n - 1)p]f_c, \text{ in which } f_c = [300 + (0.10 + 4p)f'_c]$$

$$= A_c[1 + (n - 1)p] \times [300 + (0.10 + 4p)f'_c]$$

New York Code 1938: $P = A_cf_c(1 + 15p + 50p')$

$= f_c(A_c + 15A_c \times \frac{A_s}{A_c} + 50p'A_c)$

$= f_c(A_c + 15A_s + 50p'A_c)$

Chicago Code 1937: $P = A_c(0.225f'_c + f_rp + 2f_rp')$

$= 0.225f'_cA_c + f_rA_c \times \frac{A_s}{A_c} + 2f_rp'A_c$

$= 0.225f'_cA_c + f_rA_s + 2f_rp'A_c$

*In each group of equations in this section, the equation given first is as it is written in the code and the equation given last as it is used in the tables, except that the tables give loads in kips instead of lb.

## E2. Columns—Eccentric Load, Investigation

### *Compression on Entire Area of any Symmetrical Column Section*

(33) $$f_c = \frac{1000N}{A_g} \frac{1}{1 + (n-1)p}\left(1 \pm D\frac{e'}{t}\right) \begin{Bmatrix} + \text{ for max. } f_c \\ - \text{ for min. } f_c \end{Bmatrix}$$ *See Table 33*

in which:

$N$ : eccentric load (kips) on symmetrical column section
$e'$ : distance from $N$ to centroid of section
$A_g$: gross area of concrete section
$p$ : ratio of longitudinal reinforcement ($A_s = pA_g$)
$t$ : over-all depth of concrete section

Extreme fiber stresses may be determined as the sum of

(a) stresses due to concentric load $N$:

$$\frac{1000N}{A_g} \frac{1}{1 + (n-1)p}$$

(b) stresses due to bending moment $Ne'$:

$$\pm \frac{1000Ne'}{I} \times \frac{t}{2}$$

in which $I$ is moment of inertia of transformed section:

$$I = R^2 A_g[1 + (n-1)p] \quad (R\text{: radius of gyration})$$

Sum of stresses in (a) and (b) equals:

$$f_c = \frac{1000N}{A_g} \frac{1}{1 + (n-1)p}\left(1 \pm \frac{e't}{2R^2}\right)$$

which may be written as:

$$f_c = \frac{1000N}{A_g} \frac{1}{1 + (n-1)p}\left(1 \pm \frac{t^2}{2R^2} \times \frac{e'}{t}\right)$$

This is Equation 33 when $\frac{t^2}{2R^2}$ is denoted as $D$.

Values of $\frac{t^2}{2R^2}$ are given in Table 33 for three types of symmetrical column sections.

Equations for $\frac{t^2}{2R^2}$ may be derived as follows (using the definition of $R^2 = \frac{I}{A}$):

(a) Rectangular section with symmetrical reinforcement at faces with max.$f_c$ and min.$f_c$:

$$\frac{t^2}{2} \times \frac{1}{R^2} = \frac{t^2}{2} \times \frac{A}{I} = \frac{t^2}{2} \frac{bt + (n-1)pbt}{\frac{1}{12}bt^3 + (n-1)pbt\left(\frac{gt}{2}\right)^2}$$

$gt$: distance between bars at opposite faces

Divide numerator and denominator by $bt^3$ and set $\frac{t^2}{2R^2} = D$:

$$D = \frac{1 + (n-1)p}{1/6 + 1/2(n-1)pg^2}$$

(b) Square section with reinforcement equidistantly spaced within a spiral:

$$\frac{t^2}{2} \times \frac{1}{R^2} = \frac{t^2}{2} \times \frac{A}{I} = \frac{t^2}{2} \frac{t^2 + (n-1)pt^2}{\frac{1}{12}t^4 + 1/2(n-1)pt^2\left(\frac{gt}{2}\right)^2}$$

$gt$: diameter of circle through bar centers

Divide numerator and denominator by $t^4$ and set $\frac{t^2}{2R^2} = D$:

$$D = \frac{1 + (n-1)p}{\frac{1}{6} + \frac{1}{4}(n-1)pg^2}$$

(c) Round section with reinforcement equidistantly spaced within a spiral:

$$\frac{t^2}{2} \times \frac{1}{R^2} = \frac{t^2}{2} \times \frac{A}{I} = \frac{t^2}{2} \cdot \frac{\frac{\pi}{4}t^2 + (n-1)p\frac{\pi}{4}t^2}{\frac{\pi}{64}t^4 + \frac{1}{2}(n-1)p\frac{\pi}{4}t^2\left(\frac{gt}{2}\right)^2}$$

$gt$: diameter of circle through bar centers

Divide numerator and denominator by $\frac{\pi}{4}t^4$ and set $\frac{t^2}{2R^2} = D$:

$$D = \frac{1 + (n-1)p}{\frac{1}{8} + \frac{1}{4}(n-1)pg^2}$$

## *Compression on Entire Area or Tension on Part of Area of Symmetrical Column Sections*

The equations that follow will not be derived here. Some of them are available in several textbooks* and others require mathematical operations of considerable length.**

(a) *Rectangular Column with Ties*

$k \geq 1$†: Entire section in compression,

$$Q = \frac{1}{1 + np} + \frac{2\frac{e'}{t}}{\frac{1}{3} + g^2np}$$

$k < 1$: Part of section in tension,

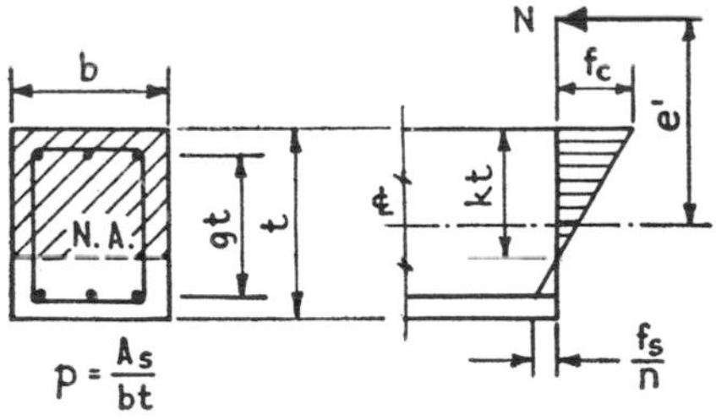


$$\frac{e'}{t} = \frac{k^2(1 - \frac{2}{3}k) + g^2np}{2k^2 + 2np(2k-1)}$$

$$Q = \frac{2k}{k^2 + np(2k-1)}$$

For any value of $k$:

$$f_c = \frac{1000N}{bt} \times Q \qquad f_s = nf_c\left(\frac{1+g}{2k} - 1\right)††$$

Values of $Q$ and $k$ to be selected from Diagram 30.

*See *Structural Members and Connections*, Hool and Kinne. McGraw-Hill (First Edition) 1923, page 534.

**See Thesis for the Degree of Master of Science, by T. A. Olson, University of Illinois, 1937, reported in part in "The Resistance of Reinforced Concrete Columns to Eccentric Loads," by Richart and Olson, *Journal of American Concrete Institute*, March-April, 1938. Similar equations may be found in *Reinforced Concrete Structures* by Dean Peabody, Jr. John Wiley and Sons, 1936, page 249.

†In this section, the distance from extreme fiber to axis of zero stress is denoted as $kt$, $t$ being over-all depth of concrete section.

††Negative $f_s$-value denotes compression in the bars on the "tensile" side of the section.

(b) *Square Column with Spiral*

$k \geqq 1$: Entire section in compression, $Q = \dfrac{1}{1 + np} + \dfrac{2\dfrac{e'}{t}}{\frac{1}{3} + \frac{1}{2}g^2np}$

$k < 1$: Part of section in tension,

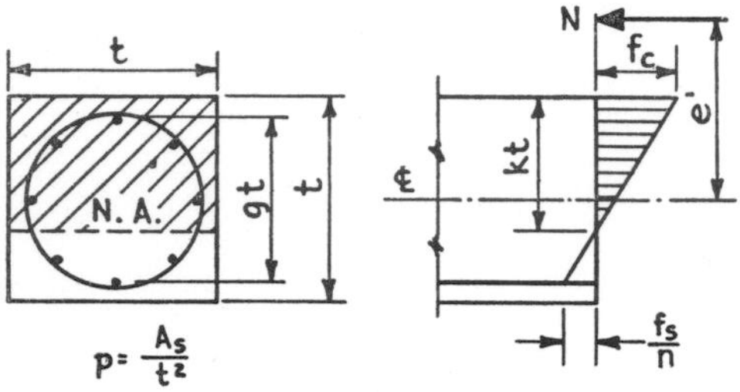


$$\frac{e'}{t} = \frac{k^2(1 - \frac{2}{3}k) + \frac{1}{2}g^2np}{2k^2 + 2np(2k - 1)}$$

$$Q = \frac{2k}{k^2 + np(2k - 1)}$$

For any value of $k$:

$$f_c = \frac{1000N}{t^2} \times Q \qquad f_s = nf_c\left(\frac{1 + g}{2k} - 1\right)$$

Values of $Q$ and $k$ to be selected from Diagram 31. The equations are identical with those for rectangular sections, with the exception that $\frac{1}{2}g^2$ is substituted for $g^2$ and $t^2$ for $bt$.

(c) *Round Column with Spiral*

$k \geqq 1$: Entire section in compression, $Q = \dfrac{1}{1 + np} + \dfrac{2\dfrac{e'}{t}}{\frac{1}{4} + \frac{1}{2}g^2np}$

$k < 1$: Part of section in tension,

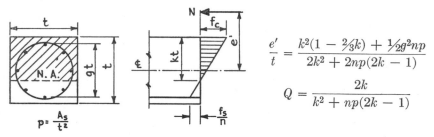

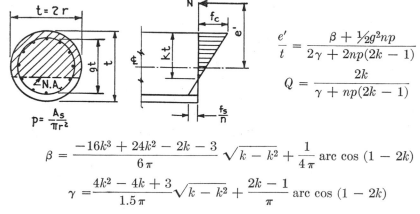

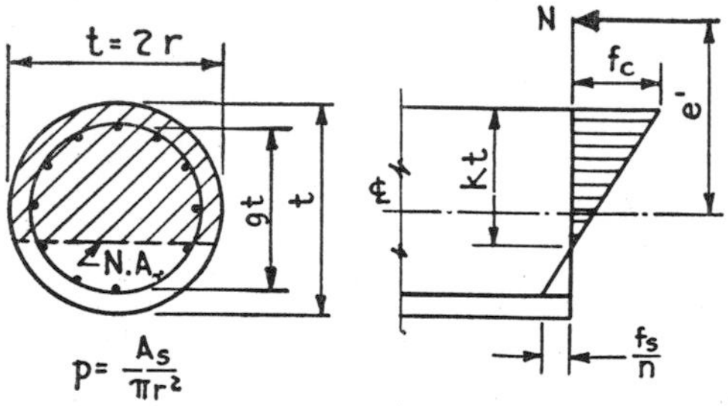


$$\frac{e'}{t} = \frac{\beta + \frac{1}{2}g^2np}{2\gamma + 2np(2k - 1)}$$

$$Q = \frac{2k}{\gamma + np(2k - 1)}$$

$$\beta = \frac{-16k^3 + 24k^2 - 2k - 3}{6\pi}\sqrt{k - k^2} + \frac{1}{4\pi}\text{ arc cos }(1 - 2k)$$

$$\gamma = \frac{4k^2 - 4k + 3}{1.5\pi}\sqrt{k - k^2} + \frac{2k - 1}{\pi}\text{ arc cos }(1 - 2k)$$

For any value of $k$:

$$f_c = \frac{1000N}{\pi r^2} \times Q \qquad f_s = nf_c\left(\frac{1 + g}{2k} - 1\right)$$

Values of $Q$ and $k$ to be selected from Diagram 32.

## E3. Columns—Eccentric Load, Design

### *Reinforcement*

When the concrete section and the allowable stress $f_p$ are known or estimated compute

$$(34)\qquad Q = \frac{\text{gross area of concrete}}{1000N} f_p$$

Depending upon the type of section, enter Diagrams 30, 31 or 32. Select value of $np$ required and determine

$$(35)\qquad A_s = \frac{np}{n} \times (\text{gross area of concrete})$$

For equations used in connection with the diagrams, see "Columns—Eccentric Load, Investigation".

### *Allowable Stresses*

Allowable stresses $f_p$ in extreme concrete fibers of eccentrically loaded column sections differ from allowable stresses in concentrically loaded columns. Equations for $f_p$ are summarized below for the five codes for which design tables are presented in Tables 18 to 29.

(a) *Joint Committee Code 1940—All Types of Reinforcement:*

$$(36)\qquad f_p = f_a \frac{1 + D\frac{e'}{t}}{1 + \frac{f_a}{0.45f'_c} \times D\frac{e'}{t}} \qquad \textit{See Table 34}$$

in which $D = \frac{t^2}{2R^2}$ and $f_a = \frac{\text{concentric load capacity}}{A_g + (n-1)A_s}$

The equation for $f_p$ is presented in the Joint Committee Code 1940 in substantially the following form:

$$f_p = f_a \frac{1 + \frac{e'c}{R^2}}{1 + \frac{f_a}{0.45f'_c} \times \frac{e'c}{R^2}} \quad \text{in which } f_a = \frac{\text{concentric load capacity}}{A_g + (n-1)A_s}$$

In the fraction $\frac{e'c}{R^2}$ set $c = \frac{t}{2}$ and multiply numerator and denominator by $t$:

$$\frac{e'c}{R^2} = \frac{e'\frac{t}{2}}{R^2} = \frac{e't}{2R^2} \times \frac{t}{t} = \frac{e'}{t} \times \frac{t^2}{2R^2} = \frac{e'}{t} \times D$$

Values of $D = \frac{t^2}{2R^2}$ are given in Table 33.

Substitute in the Joint Committee equation: $\frac{e'c}{R^2} = \frac{e'}{t} \times D$, which gives Equation 36.

For calculation of tabular values in Table 34, divide Equation 36 by $f'_c$:

$$\frac{f_p}{f'_c} = \frac{f_a}{f'_c} \frac{1 + D\frac{e'}{t}}{1 + \frac{f_a}{f'_c} \times \frac{1}{0.45} \times D\frac{e'}{t}}$$

and solve for $D\frac{e'}{t}$:

$$D\frac{e'}{t} = \frac{\frac{fp}{f'c}\,\frac{f'c}{fa} - 1}{1 - \frac{fp}{f'c} \times \frac{1}{0.45}}$$

The table value, $D\frac{e'}{t}$, is here expressed in terms of two variables, $\frac{fp}{f'c}$ and $\frac{f'c}{fa}$, and the Joint Committee equation is thus transformed so as to make its form convenient for tabulation.

(b) *American Concrete Institute Code 1936—All Types of Reinforcement*

$$f_p = f_a \frac{1 + D\frac{e'}{t}}{1 + 0.8D\frac{e'}{t}} \qquad (37)$$

in which $D = \frac{t^2}{2R^2}$ and $f_a = \frac{\text{concentric load capacity}}{A_g + (n-1)A_s}$

The equations in Joint Committee Code 1940 and American Concrete Institute Code 1936 are identical with the one exception that the factor 0.8 in Equation 37 is replaced by $\frac{f_a}{0.45f'_c}$ in Equation 36. Determine $f_p$ from Equation 37 as follows:

Compute $f_a$ and $D\frac{e'}{t}$

$f_p$ equals $f_a$ multiplied by $\left(\frac{f_p}{f_a}\right) = \frac{1 + D\frac{e'}{t}}{1 + 0.8D\frac{e'}{t}}$ the value of which may be taken from table below.

| $D\frac{e'}{t}$ | 0.0 | 0.5 | 1.0 | 1.5 | 2.0 | 2.5 | 3.0 | 3.5 | 4.0 | 4.5 | 5.0 | 5.5 | 6.0 | 6.5 | 7.0 | 7.5 | 8.0 | 8.5 | 9.0 | 9.5 |
|---|---|---|---|---|---|---|---|---|---|---|---|---|---|---|---|---|---|---|---|---|
| $\frac{f_p}{f_a}$ | 1.00 | 1.07 | 1.11 | 1.14 | 1.15 | 1.17 | 1.18 | 1.18 | 1.19 | 1.20 | 1.20 | 1.20 | 1.21 | 1.21 | 1.21 | 1.21 | 1.22 | 1.22 | 1.22 | 1.22 |

(c) *American Concrete Institute Code 1928*

**(38)** Columns with spirals: $f_p = f_a + 0.15f'_c$

in which $f_a = \frac{\text{concentric load capacity}}{A_c + (n-1)A_s}$

**(39)** Columns with ties: $f_p = 0.3f'_c$

(d) *New York Code 1938*

**(40)** Columns with spirals: $f_p = \frac{\text{concentric load capacity}}{A_g}$

$f_p$ to be not more than $0.50f'_c$.

**(41)** Columns with ties: $f_p = 0.45f'_c$ at floor line; $0.40f'_c$ elsewhere.

(e) *Chicago Code 1937*

**(42)** Columns with spirals: $f_p = 0.36f'_c$

**(43)** Columns with ties: $f_p = 0.32f'_c$

# Table 1. Coefficients ($K, k, j, p$) for Rectangular Sections

| $f'_c$ and $n$ | $f_c$ | $K$ | $k$ | $j$ | $p$ | $K$ | $k$ | $j$ | $p$ |
|---|---|---|---|---|---|---|---|---|---|
| | | $f_s$ = 8,000 | | $a$ = 0.53 | | $f_s$ = 10,000 | | $a$ = 0.68 | |
| | 650 | 146 | 0.549 | 0.817 | 0.0223 | 134 | 0.494 | 0.835 | 0.0161 |
| | 700 | 161 | 0.568 | 0.811 | 0.0249 | 149 | 0.512 | 0.830 | 0.0179 |
| 2000 | 750 | 177 | 0.584 | 0.806 | 0.0274 | 163 | 0.529 | 0.824 | 0.0198 |
| | 800 | 192 | 0.600 | 0.800 | 0.0300 | 179 | 0.546 | 0.818 | 0.0218 |
| | 900 | 224 | 0.628 | 0.791 | 0.0353 | 209 | 0.574 | 0.809 | 0.0258 |
| 15 | 1000 | 255 | 0.652 | 0.783 | 0.0408 | 240 | 0.600 | 0.800 | 0.0300 |
| | 1200 | 320 | 0.693 | 0.769 | 0.0520 | 303 | 0.643 | 0.786 | 0.0386 |
| | 1350 | 368 | 0.717 | 0.761 | 0.0605 | 351 | 0.669 | 0.777 | 0.0452 |
| | 800 | 179 | 0.546 | 0.818 | 0.0273 | 164 | 0.490 | 0.837 | 0.0196 |
| | 875 | 202 | 0.568 | 0.811 | 0.0311 | 186 | 0.512 | 0.830 | 0.0224 |
| 2500 | 950 | 225 | 0.588 | 0.804 | 0.0349 | 208 | 0.533 | 0.823 | 0.0253 |
| | 1000 | 240 | 0.600 | 0.800 | 0.0375 | 223 | 0.546 | 0.818 | 0.0273 |
| | 1125 | 280 | 0.628 | 0.791 | 0.0442 | 261 | 0.574 | 0.809 | 0.0323 |
| 12 | 1250 | 319 | 0.652 | 0.783 | 0.0509 | 300 | 0.600 | 0.800 | 0.0375 |
| | 1500 | 400 | 0.693 | 0.769 | 0.0650 | 379 | 0.643 | 0.786 | 0.0482 |
| | 1700 | 464 | 0.718 | 0.761 | 0.0763 | 443 | 0.671 | 0.777 | 0.0570 |
| | 975 | 219 | 0.549 | 0.817 | 0.0335 | 201 | 0.494 | 0.835 | 0.0241 |
| | 1050 | 242 | 0.568 | 0.811 | 0.0373 | 223 | 0.512 | 0.830 | 0.0269 |
| 3000 | 1125 | 265 | 0.584 | 0.806 | 0.0411 | 245 | 0.529 | 0.824 | 0.0298 |
| | 1200 | 288 | 0.600 | 0.800 | 0.0450 | 268 | 0.546 | 0.818 | 0.0328 |
| | 1350 | 335 | 0.628 | 0.791 | 0.0530 | 313 | 0.574 | 0.809 | 0.0387 |
| 10 | 1500 | 383 | 0.652 | 0.783 | 0.0611 | 360 | 0.600 | 0.800 | 0.0450 |
| | 1800 | 480 | 0.693 | 0.769 | 0.0780 | 455 | 0.643 | 0.786 | 0.0579 |
| | 2025 | 553 | 0.717 | 0.761 | 0.0907 | 527 | 0.669 | 0.777 | 0.0677 |
| | 1200 | 268 | 0.546 | 0.818 | 0.0410 | 246 | 0.490 | 0.837 | 0.0294 |
| | 1300 | 298 | 0.565 | 0.812 | 0.0459 | 275 | 0.510 | 0.830 | 0.0332 |
| 3750 | 1400 | 329 | 0.583 | 0.806 | 0.0510 | 305 | 0.528 | 0.824 | 0.0370 |
| | 1500 | 360 | 0.600 | 0.800 | 0.0563 | 335 | 0.546 | 0.818 | 0.0410 |
| | 1700 | 423 | 0.630 | 0.790 | 0.0669 | 396 | 0.576 | 0.808 | 0.0490 |
| 8 | 1875 | 479 | 0.652 | 0.783 | 0.0764 | 450 | 0.600 | 0.800 | 0.0563 |
| | 2250 | 600 | 0.693 | 0.769 | 0.0975 | 568 | 0.643 | 0.786 | 0.0723 |
| | 2525 | 689 | 0.716 | 0.762 | 0.1130 | 657 | 0.669 | 0.777 | 0.0845 |

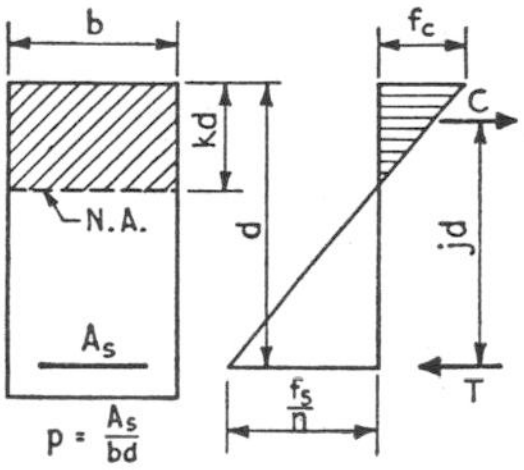


$$k = \frac{1}{1 + f_s/nf_c}$$

$$j = 1 - \frac{1}{3}k$$

$$p^* = \frac{f_c}{2f_s} \times k$$

$$K = \frac{f_c}{2} kj$$

$$a = \frac{f_s}{12{,}000} \times \text{(average } j\text{-value)}$$

for use in $A_s = \frac{M}{ad}$ or $A_s = \frac{NE}{adi}$

| $f'_c$ and $n$ | $f_c$ | $K$ | $k$ | $j$ | $p$ | $K$ | $k$ | $j$ | $p$ | $K$ | $k$ | $j$ | $p$ |
|---|---|---|---|---|---|---|---|---|---|---|---|---|---|
| | | $f_s$ = 12,000 | | $a$ = 0.83 | | $f_s$ = 14,000 | | $a$ = 0.98 | | $f_s$ = 16,000 | | $a$ = 1.13 | |
| | 650 | 124 | 0.448 | 0.851 | 0.0121 | 115 | 0.411 | 0.863 | 0.0095 | 108 | 0.379 | 0.874 | 0.0077 |
| | 700 | 138 | 0.467 | 0.844 | 0.0136 | 129 | 0.429 | 0.857 | 0.0107 | 120 | 0.396 | 0.868 | 0.0087 |
| 2000 | 750 | 152 | 0.484 | 0.839 | 0.0151 | 142 | 0.446 | 0.851 | 0.0119 | 133 | 0.413 | 0.862 | 0.0097 |
| | 800 | 167 | 0.500 | 0.833 | 0.0167 | 156 | 0.462 | 0.846 | 0.0132 | 147 | 0.429 | 0.857 | 0.0107 |
| | 900 | 196 | 0.529 | 0.824 | 0.0198 | 185 | 0.491 | 0.836 | 0.0158 | 175 | 0.458 | 0.847 | 0.0129 |
| 15 | 1000 | 227 | 0.556 | 0.815 | 0.0232 | 214 | 0.517 | 0.828 | 0.0185 | 203 | 0.484 | 0.839 | 0.0151 |
| | 1200 | 288 | 0.600 | 0.800 | 0.0300 | 274 | 0.563 | 0.812 | 0.0241 | 262 | 0.529 | 0.824 | 0.0198 |
| | 1350 | 335 | 0.628 | 0.791 | 0.0353 | 320 | 0.591 | 0.803 | 0.0285 | 307 | 0.559 | 0.814 | 0.0236 |
| | 800 | 151 | 0.444 | 0.852 | 0.0148 | 141 | 0.407 | 0.864 | 0.0116 | 131 | 0.375 | 0.875 | 0.0094 |
| | 875 | 173 | 0.467 | 0.844 | 0.0170 | 161 | 0.429 | 0.857 | 0.0134 | 150 | 0.396 | 0.868 | 0.0108 |
| 2500 | 950 | 194 | 0.487 | 0.838 | 0.0193 | 181 | 0.449 | 0.850 | 0.0152 | 170 | 0.416 | 0.861 | 0.0124 |
| | 1000 | 208 | 0.500 | 0.833 | 0.0208 | 195 | 0.462 | 0.846 | 0.0165 | 184 | 0.429 | 0.857 | 0.0134 |
| | 1125 | 246 | 0.529 | 0.825 | 0.0248 | 231 | 0.491 | 0.836 | 0.0197 | 218 | 0.458 | 0.847 | 0.0161 |
| 12 | 1250 | 283 | 0.556 | 0.815 | 0.0290 | 268 | 0.517 | 0.828 | 0.0231 | 254 | 0.484 | 0.839 | 0.0189 |
| | 1500 | 360 | 0.600 | 0.800 | 0.0375 | 343 | 0.563 | 0.812 | 0.0302 | 327 | 0.529 | 0.824 | 0.0248 |
| | 1700 | 423 | 0.630 | 0.790 | 0.0447 | 404 | 0.593 | 0.802 | 0.0360 | 387 | 0.560 | 0.813 | 0.0298 |
| | 975 | 186 | 0.448 | 0.851 | 0.0182 | 173 | 0.411 | 0.863 | 0.0143 | 161 | 0.379 | 0.874 | 0.0115 |
| | 1050 | 207 | 0.467 | 0.844 | 0.0204 | 193 | 0.429 | 0.857 | 0.0161 | 180 | 0.396 | 0.868 | 0.0130 |
| 3000 | 1125 | 229 | 0.484 | 0.839 | 0.0227 | 213 | 0.446 | 0.851 | 0.0179 | 200 | 0.413 | 0.862 | 0.0145 |
| | 1200 | 250 | 0.500 | 0.833 | 0.0250 | 235 | 0.462 | 0.846 | 0.0198 | 221 | 0.429 | 0.857 | 0.0161 |
| | 1350 | 294 | 0.529 | 0.824 | 0.0298 | 277 | 0.491 | 0.836 | 0.0237 | 262 | 0.458 | 0.847 | 0.0193 |
| 10 | 1500 | 340 | 0.556 | 0.815 | 0.0348 | 321 | 0.517 | 0.828 | 0.0277 | 305 | 0.484 | 0.839 | 0.0227 |
| | 1800 | 432 | 0.600 | 0.800 | 0.0450 | 411 | 0.563 | 0.812 | 0.0362 | 392 | 0.529 | 0.824 | 0.0298 |
| | 2025 | 503 | 0.628 | 0.791 | 0.0530 | 480 | 0.591 | 0.803 | 0.0427 | 461 | 0.559 | 0.814 | 0.0354 |
| | 1200 | 227 | 0.444 | 0.852 | 0.0222 | 211 | 0.407 | 0.864 | 0.0174 | 197 | 0.375 | 0.875 | 0.0141 |
| | 1300 | 255 | 0.464 | 0.845 | 0.0251 | 238 | 0.426 | 0.858 | 0.0198 | 223 | 0.394 | 0.869 | 0.0160 |
| 3750 | 1400 | 284 | 0.483 | 0.839 | 0.0282 | 265 | 0.444 | 0.852 | 0.0222 | 249 | 0.412 | 0.863 | 0.0180 |
| | 1500 | 312 | 0.500 | 0.833 | 0.0313 | 293 | 0.461 | 0.846 | 0.0247 | 276 | 0.429 | 0.857 | 0.0201 |
| | 1700 | 371 | 0.531 | 0.823 | 0.0376 | 350 | 0.493 | 0.836 | 0.0299 | 331 | 0.460 | 0.847 | 0.0244 |
| 8 | 1875 | 425 | 0.556 | 0.815 | 0.0434 | 401 | 0.517 | 0.828 | 0.0346 | 381 | 0.484 | 0.839 | 0.0284 |
| | 2250 | 540 | 0.600 | 0.800 | 0.0563 | 514 | 0.562 | 0.813 | 0.0452 | 490 | 0.529 | 0.824 | 0.0372 |
| | 2525 | 626 | 0.627 | 0.791 | 0.0660 | 599 | 0.591 | 0.803 | 0.0533 | 574 | 0.558 | 0.814 | 0.0440 |

*"Balanced steel ratio" applies to problems involving bending only.

# Table 1. (*continued*)

| $f'_c$ and $n$ | $f_c$ | $K$ | $k$ | $j$ | $p$ | $K$ | $k$ | $j$ | $p$ | $K$ | $k$ | $j$ | $p$ |
|---|---|---|---|---|---|---|---|---|---|---|---|---|---|
| | | $f_s$ = 18,000 | | $a$ = 1.29 | | $f_s$ = 20,000 | | $a$ = 1.44 | | $f_s$ = 22,000 | | $a$ = 1.60 | |
| | 650 | 101 | 0.351 | 0.883 | 0.0063 | 95 | 0.328 | 0.891 | 0.0053 | 90 | 0.307 | 0.898 | 0.0045 |
| | 700 | 113 | 0.368 | 0.877 | 0.0072 | 107 | 0.344 | 0.885 | 0.0060 | 101 | 0.323 | 0.892 | 0.0051 |
| 2000 | 750 | 126 | 0.385 | 0.872 | 0.0080 | 119 | 0.360 | 0.880 | 0.0068 | 112 | 0.338 | 0.887 | 0.0058 |
| | 800 | 139 | 0.400 | 0.867 | 0.0089 | 131 | 0.375 | 0.875 | 0.0075 | 125 | 0.353 | 0.882 | 0.0064 |
| | 900 | 165 | 0.429 | 0.857 | 0.0107 | 157 | 0.403 | 0.866 | 0.0091 | 149 | 0.380 | 0.873 | 0.0078 |
| 15 | 1000 | 193 | 0.455 | 0.848 | 0.0126 | 184 | 0.429 | 0.857 | 0.0107 | 175 | 0.405 | 0.865 | 0.0092 |
| | 1200 | 250 | 0.500 | 0.833 | 0.0167 | 239 | 0.474 | 0.842 | 0.0142 | 230 | 0.450 | 0.850 | 0.0123 |
| | 1350 | 294 | 0.529 | 0.824 | 0.0198 | 282 | 0.503 | 0.832 | 0.0170 | 272 | 0.479 | 0.840 | 0.0147 |
| | 800 | 123 | 0.348 | 0.884 | 0.0077 | 116 | 0.324 | 0.892 | 0.0065 | 109 | 0.304 | 0.899 | 0.0055 |
| | 875 | 141 | 0.368 | 0.877 | 0.0089 | 133 | 0.344 | 0.885 | 0.0075 | 126 | 0.323 | 0.892 | 0.0064 |
| 2500 | 950 | 161 | 0.388 | 0.871 | 0.0102 | 152 | 0.363 | 0.879 | 0.0086 | 144 | 0.341 | 0.886 | 0.0074 |
| | 1000 | 173 | 0.400 | 0.867 | 0.0111 | 164 | 0.375 | 0.875 | 0.0094 | 156 | 0.353 | 0.882 | 0.0080 |
| | 1125 | 207 | 0.429 | 0.857 | 0.0134 | 196 | 0.403 | 0.866 | 0.0113 | 187 | 0.380 | 0.873 | 0.0097 |
| 12 | 1250 | 241 | 0.455 | 0.848 | 0.0158 | 230 | 0.429 | 0.857 | 0.0134 | 219 | 0.405 | 0.865 | 0.0115 |
| | 1500 | 312 | 0.500 | 0.833 | 0.0208 | 299 | 0.474 | 0.842 | 0.0178 | 287 | 0.450 | 0.850 | 0.0153 |
| | 1700 | 371 | 0.531 | 0.823 | 0.0251 | 357 | 0.505 | 0.832 | 0.0215 | 343 | 0.481 | 0.840 | 0.0186 |
| | 975 | 151 | 0.351 | 0.883 | 0.0095 | 142 | 0.328 | 0.891 | 0.0080 | 134 | 0.307 | 0.898 | 0.0068 |
| | 1050 | 169 | 0.368 | 0.877 | 0.0107 | 160 | 0.344 | 0.885 | 0.0090 | 151 | 0.323 | 0.892 | 0.0077 |
| 3000 | 1125 | 189 | 0.385 | 0.872 | 0.0120 | 178 | 0.360 | 0.880 | 0.0101 | 169 | 0.338 | 0.887 | 0.0086 |
| | 1200 | 208 | 0.400 | 0.867 | 0.0133 | 197 | 0.375 | 0.875 | 0.0113 | 187 | 0.353 | 0.882 | 0.0096 |
| | 1350 | 248 | 0.429 | 0.857 | 0.0161 | 236 | 0.403 | 0.866 | 0.0136 | 224 | 0.380 | 0.873 | 0.0117 |
| 10 | 1500 | 289 | 0.455 | 0.848 | 0.0190 | 276 | 0.429 | 0.857 | 0.0161 | 263 | 0.405 | 0.865 | 0.0138 |
| | 1800 | 375 | 0.500 | 0.833 | 0.0250 | 359 | 0.474 | 0.842 | 0.0213 | 344 | 0.450 | 0.850 | 0.0184 |
| | 2025 | 441 | 0.529 | 0.824 | 0.0298 | 424 | 0.503 | 0.832 | 0.0255 | 407 | 0.479 | 0.840 | 0.0221 |
| | 1200 | 185 | 0.348 | 0.884 | 0.0116 | 173 | 0.324 | 0.892 | 0.0097 | 164 | 0.304 | 0.899 | 0.0083 |
| | 1300 | 209 | 0.366 | 0.878 | 0.0132 | 197 | 0.342 | 0.886 | 0.0111 | 186 | 0.321 | 0.893 | 0.0095 |
| 3750 | 1400 | 234 | 0.384 | 0.872 | 0.0149 | 221 | 0.359 | 0.880 | 0.0126 | 209 | 0.337 | 0.888 | 0.0107 |
| | 1500 | 260 | 0.400 | 0.867 | 0.0167 | 246 | 0.375 | 0.875 | 0.0141 | 234 | 0.353 | 0.882 | 0.0120 |
| | 1700 | 313 | 0.430 | 0.857 | 0.0203 | 298 | 0.405 | 0.865 | 0.0172 | 283 | 0.382 | 0.873 | 0.0148 |
| 8 | 1875 | 362 | 0.455 | 0.848 | 0.0237 | 345 | 0.429 | 0.857 | 0.0201 | 328 | 0.405 | 0.865 | 0.0173 |
| | 2250 | 469 | 0.500 | 0.833 | 0.0313 | 449 | 0.474 | 0.842 | 0.0267 | 430 | 0.450 | 0.850 | 0.0230 |
| | 2525 | 550 | 0.529 | 0.824 | 0.0371 | 528 | 0.503 | 0.832 | 0.0318 | 508 | 0.479 | 0.840 | 0.0275 |
| | | $f_s$ = 24,000 | | $a$ = 1.76 | | $f_s$ = 27,000 | | $a$ = 2.00 | | $f_s$ = 30,000 | | $a$ = 2.24 | |
| | 650 | 85 | 0.289 | 0.904 | 0.0039 | 79 | 0.265 | 0.912 | 0.0032 | 73 | 0.245 | 0.918 | 0.0027 |
| | 700 | 96 | 0.304 | 0.899 | 0.0044 | 89 | 0.280 | 0.907 | 0.0036 | 83 | 0.259 | 0.914 | 0.0030 |
| 2000 | 750 | 107 | 0.319 | 0.894 | 0.0050 | 99 | 0.294 | 0.902 | 0.0041 | 93 | 0.273 | 0.909 | 0.0034 |
| | 800 | 118 | 0.333 | 0.889 | 0.0055 | 111 | 0.308 | 0.897 | 0.0046 | 104 | 0.286 | 0.905 | 0.0038 |
| | 900 | 143 | 0.360 | 0.880 | 0.0067 | 133 | 0.333 | 0.889 | 0.0055 | 125 | 0.310 | 0.897 | 0.0047 |
| 15 | 1000 | 168 | 0.385 | 0.872 | 0.0080 | 157 | 0.357 | 0.881 | 0.0066 | 148 | 0.333 | 0.889 | 0.0055 |
| | 1200 | 220 | 0.429 | 0.857 | 0.0107 | 208 | 0.400 | 0.867 | 0.0089 | 197 | 0.375 | 0.875 | 0.0075 |
| | 1350 | 262 | 0.458 | 0.847 | 0.0129 | 248 | 0.429 | 0.857 | 0.0107 | 236 | 0.403 | 0.866 | 0.0091 |
| | 800 | 104 | 0.286 | 0.905 | 0.0048 | 96 | 0.262 | 0.913 | 0.0039 | 89 | 0.242 | 0.919 | 0.0032 |
| | 875 | 120 | 0.304 | 0.899 | 0.0055 | 111 | 0.280 | 0.907 | 0.0045 | 104 | 0.259 | 0.914 | 0.0038 |
| 2500 | 950 | 137 | 0.322 | 0.893 | 0.0064 | 127 | 0.297 | 0.901 | 0.0052 | 119 | 0.275 | 0.908 | 0.0044 |
| | 1000 | 148 | 0.333 | 0.889 | 0.0069 | 138 | 0.308 | 0.897 | 0.0057 | 129 | 0.286 | 0.905 | 0.0048 |
| | 1125 | 178 | 0.360 | 0.880 | 0.0084 | 167 | 0.333 | 0.889 | 0.0069 | 156 | 0.310 | 0.897 | 0.0058 |
| 12 | 1250 | 210 | 0.385 | 0.872 | 0.0100 | 197 | 0.357 | 0.881 | 0.0083 | 185 | 0.333 | 0.889 | 0.0069 |
| | 1500 | 276 | 0.429 | 0.857 | 0.0134 | 260 | 0.400 | 0.867 | 0.0111 | 246 | 0.375 | 0.875 | 0.0094 |
| | 1700 | 331 | 0.460 | 0.847 | 0.0163 | 313 | 0.430 | 0.857 | 0.0135 | 298 | 0.405 | 0.865 | 0.0115 |
| | 975 | 127 | 0.289 | 0.904 | 0.0059 | 118 | 0.265 | 0.912 | 0.0048 | 110 | 0.245 | 0.918 | 0.0040 |
| | 1050 | 143 | 0.304 | 0.899 | 0.0067 | 133 | 0.280 | 0.907 | 0.0054 | 124 | 0.259 | 0.914 | 0.0045 |
| 3000 | 1125 | 160 | 0.319 | 0.894 | 0.0075 | 149 | 0.294 | 0.902 | 0.0061 | 140 | 0.273 | 0.909 | 0.0051 |
| | 1200 | 178 | 0.333 | 0.889 | 0.0083 | 166 | 0.308 | 0.897 | 0.0068 | 155 | 0.286 | 0.905 | 0.0057 |
| | 1350 | 214 | 0.360 | 0.880 | 0.0101 | 200 | 0.333 | 0.889 | 0.0083 | 188 | 0.310 | 0.897 | 0.0070 |
| 10 | 1500 | 252 | 0.385 | 0.872 | 0.0120 | 236 | 0.357 | 0.881 | 0.0099 | 222 | 0.333 | 0.889 | 0.0083 |
| | 1800 | 331 | 0.429 | 0.857 | 0.0161 | 312 | 0.400 | 0.867 | 0.0133 | 295 | 0.375 | 0.875 | 0.0113 |
| | 2025 | 393 | 0.458 | 0.847 | 0.0193 | 372 | 0.429 | 0.857 | 0.0161 | 353 | 0.403 | 0.866 | 0.0136 |
| | 1200 | 155 | 0.286 | 0.905 | 0.0071 | 144 | 0.262 | 0.913 | 0.0058 | 133 | 0.242 | 0.919 | 0.0048 |
| | 1300 | 176 | 0.302 | 0.899 | 0.0082 | 164 | 0.278 | 0.907 | 0.0067 | 153 | 0.257 | 0.914 | 0.0056 |
| 3750 | 1400 | 199 | 0.318 | 0.894 | 0.0093 | 185 | 0.293 | 0.902 | 0.0076 | 173 | 0.272 | 0.909 | 0.0063 |
| | 1500 | 222 | 0.333 | 0.889 | 0.0104 | 207 | 0.308 | 0.897 | 0.0086 | 194 | 0.286 | 0.905 | 0.0071 |
| | 1700 | 270 | 0.362 | 0.879 | 0.0128 | 253 | 0.335 | 0.888 | 0.0106 | 238 | 0.312 | 0.896 | 0.0088 |
| 8 | 1875 | 315 | 0.385 | 0.872 | 0.0150 | 295 | 0.357 | 0.881 | 0.0124 | 278 | 0.333 | 0.889 | 0.0104 |
| | 2250 | 414 | 0.429 | 0.857 | 0.0201 | 390 | 0.400 | 0.867 | 0.0166 | 369 | 0.375 | 0.875 | 0.0141 |
| | 2525 | 489 | 0.457 | 0.848 | 0.0240 | 463 | 0.428 | 0.857 | 0.0200 | 440 | 0.402 | 0.866 | 0.0169 |

# Table 2. Resisting Moments of Rectangular Sections One Foot Wide (Slabs)

**Values of $\frac{Kd^2}{1000}$**

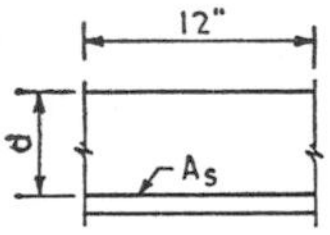


Enter table with known $M$ or $NE$ (ft.kips)
Select effective depth ($d$: in.)

| $f_s$ | $f'_c$ and $n$ | $f_c$ | $d$: Effective depth | | | | | | | | | | | | | | | | | |
|---|---|---|---|---|---|---|---|---|---|---|---|---|---|---|---|---|---|---|---|---|
| | | | 2 | 2½ | 3 | 3½ | 4 | 4½ | 5 | 5½ | 6 | 6½ | 7 | 7½ | 8 | 8½ | 9 | 10 | 11 | 12 |
| | | 650 | 0.43 | 0.68 | 0.97 | 1.32 | 1.73 | 2.2 | 2.7 | 3.3 | 3.9 | 4.6 | 5.3 | 6.1 | 6.9 | 7.8 | 8.7 | 10.8 | 13.1 | 15.6 |
| | | 700 | 0.48 | 0.75 | 1.08 | 1.47 | 1.92 | 2.4 | 3.0 | 3.6 | 4.3 | 5.1 | 5.9 | 6.8 | 7.7 | 8.7 | 9.7 | 12.0 | 14.5 | 17.3 |
| | 2000 | 750 | 0.53 | 0.83 | 1.20 | 1.63 | 2.13 | 2.7 | 3.3 | 4.0 | 4.8 | 5.6 | 6.5 | 7.5 | 8.5 | 9.6 | 10.8 | 13.3 | 16.1 | 19.2 |
| | | 800 | 0.59 | 0.92 | 1.32 | 1.80 | 2.35 | 3.0 | 3.7 | 4.4 | 5.3 | 6.2 | 7.2 | 8.3 | 9.4 | 10.6 | 11.9 | 14.7 | 17.8 | 21.2 |
| | | 900 | 0.70 | 1.09 | 1.58 | 2.14 | 2.80 | 3.5 | 4.4 | 5.3 | 6.3 | 7.4 | 8.6 | 9.8 | 11.2 | 12.6 | 14.2 | 17.5 | 21.2 | 25.2 |
| | 15 | 1000 | 0.81 | 1.27 | 1.83 | 2.49 | 3.25 | 4.1 | 5.1 | 6.1 | 7.3 | 8.6 | 9.9 | 11.4 | 13.0 | 14.7 | 16.4 | 20.3 | 24.6 | 29.2 |
| | | 1200 | 1.05 | 1.64 | 2.36 | 3.21 | 4.19 | 5.3 | 6.6 | 7.9 | 9.4 | 11.1 | 12.8 | 14.7 | 16.8 | 18.9 | 21.2 | 26.2 | 31.7 | 37.7 |
| | | 1350 | 1.23 | 1.92 | 2.76 | 3.76 | 4.91 | 6.2 | 7.7 | 9.3 | 11.1 | 13.0 | 15.0 | 17.3 | 19.6 | 22.2 | 24.9 | 30.7 | 37.2 | 44.2 |
| | | 800 | 0.52 | 0.82 | 1.18 | 1.60 | 2.10 | 2.7 | 3.3 | 4.0 | 4.7 | 5.5 | 6.4 | 7.4 | 8.4 | 9.5 | 10.6 | 13.1 | 15.9 | 18.9 |
| | | 875 | 0.60 | 0.94 | 1.35 | 1.84 | 2.40 | 3.0 | 3.8 | 4.5 | 5.4 | 6.3 | 7.4 | 8.4 | 9.6 | 10.8 | 12.2 | 15.0 | 18.2 | 21.6 |
| | 2500 | 950 | 0.68 | 1.06 | 1.53 | 2.08 | 2.72 | 3.4 | 4.3 | 5.1 | 6.1 | 7.2 | 8.3 | 9.6 | 10.9 | 12.3 | 13.8 | 17.0 | 20.6 | 24.5 |
| 16,000 | | 1000 | 0.74 | 1.15 | 1.66 | 2.25 | 2.94 | 3.7 | 4.6 | 5.6 | 6.6 | 7.8 | 9.0 | 10.4 | 11.8 | 13.3 | 14.9 | 18.4 | 22.3 | 26.5 |
| | | 1125 | 0.87 | 1.36 | 1.96 | 2.67 | 3.49 | 4.4 | 5.5 | 6.6 | 7.8 | 9.2 | 10.7 | 12.3 | 14.0 | 15.8 | 17.7 | 21.8 | 26.4 | 31.4 |
| | 12 | 1250 | 1.02 | 1.59 | 2.29 | 3.11 | 4.06 | 5.1 | 6.3 | 7.7 | 9.1 | 10.7 | 12.4 | 14.3 | 16.3 | 18.4 | 20.6 | 25.4 | 30.7 | 36.6 |
| | | 1500 | 1.31 | 2.04 | 2.94 | 4.01 | 5.23 | 6.6 | 8.2 | 9.9 | 11.8 | 13.8 | 16.0 | 18.4 | 20.9 | 23.6 | 26.5 | 32.7 | 39.6 | 47.1 |
| | | 1700 | 1.55 | 2.42 | 3.48 | 4.74 | 6.19 | 7.8 | 9.7 | 11.7 | 13.9 | 16.4 | 19.0 | 21.8 | 24.8 | 28.0 | 31.3 | 38.7 | 46.8 | 55.7 |
| | | 975 | 0.64 | 1.01 | 1.45 | 1.97 | 2.58 | 3.3 | 4.0 | 4.9 | 5.8 | 6.8 | 7.9 | 9.1 | 10.3 | 11.6 | 13.0 | 16.1 | 19.5 | 23.2 |
| | | 1050 | 0.72 | 1.13 | 1.62 | 2.21 | 2.88 | 3.6 | 4.5 | 5.4 | 6.5 | 7.6 | 8.8 | 10.1 | 11.5 | 13.0 | 14.6 | 18.0 | 21.8 | 25.9 |
| | 3000 | 1125 | 0.80 | 1.25 | 1.80 | 2.45 | 3.20 | 4.1 | 5.0 | 6.1 | 7.2 | 8.5 | 9.8 | 11.3 | 12.8 | 14.5 | 16.2 | 20.0 | 24.2 | 28.8 |
| | | 1200 | 0.88 | 1.38 | 1.99 | 2.71 | 3.54 | 4.5 | 5.5 | 6.7 | 8.0 | 9.3 | 10.8 | 12.4 | 14.1 | 16.0 | 17.9 | 22.1 | 26.7 | 31.8 |
| | | 1350 | 1.05 | 1.64 | 2.36 | 3.21 | 4.19 | 5.3 | 6.6 | 7.9 | 9.4 | 11.1 | 12.8 | 14.7 | 16.8 | 18.9 | 21.2 | 26.2 | 31.7 | 37.7 |
| | 10 | 1500 | 1.22 | 1.91 | 2.75 | 3.74 | 4.88 | 6.2 | 7.6 | 9.2 | 11.0 | 12.9 | 14.9 | 17.2 | 19.5 | 22.0 | 24.7 | 30.5 | 36.9 | 43.9 |
| | | 1800 | 1.67 | 2.46 | 3.63 | 4.80 | 6.27 | 7.9 | 9.8 | 11.9 | 14.1 | 16.6 | 19.2 | 22.1 | 25.1 | 28.3 | 31.8 | 39.2 | 47.4 | 50.4 |
| | | 2025 | 1.84 | 2.88 | 4.15 | 5.65 | 7.38 | 9.3 | 11.5 | 13.9 | 16.6 | 19.5 | 22.6 | 25.9 | 29.5 | 33.3 | 37.3 | 46.1 | 55.8 | 66.4 |
| | | 650 | 0.40 | 0.63 | 0.91 | 1.24 | 1.62 | 2.0 | 2.5 | 3.1 | 3.6 | 4.3 | 4.9 | 5.7 | 6.5 | 7.3 | 8.2 | 10.1 | 12.2 | 14.5 |
| | | 700 | 0.45 | 0.71 | 1.02 | 1.38 | 1.81 | 2.3 | 2.8 | 3.4 | 4.1 | 4.8 | 5.5 | 6.4 | 7.2 | 8.2 | 9.2 | 11.3 | 13.7 | 16.3 |
| | 2000 | 750 | 0.50 | 0.79 | 1.13 | 1.54 | 2.02 | 2.6 | 3.2 | 3.8 | 4.5 | 5.3 | 6.2 | 7.1 | 8.1 | 9.1 | 10.2 | 12.6 | 15.2 | 18.1 |
| | | 800 | 0.56 | 0.87 | 1.25 | 1.70 | 2.22 | 2.8 | 3.5 | 4.2 | 5.0 | 5.9 | 6.8 | 7.8 | 8.9 | 10.0 | 11.3 | 13.9 | 16.8 | 20.0 |
| | | 900 | 0.66 | 1.03 | 1.49 | 2.02 | 2.64 | 3.3 | 4.1 | 5.0 | 5.9 | 7.0 | 8.1 | 9.3 | 10.6 | 11.9 | 13.4 | 16.5 | 20.0 | 23.8 |
| | 15 | 1000 | 0.77 | 1.21 | 1.74 | 2.36 | 3.09 | 3.9 | 4.8 | 5.8 | 6.9 | 8.2 | 9.5 | 10.9 | 12.4 | 13.9 | 15.6 | 19.3 | 23.4 | 27.8 |
| | | 1200 | 1.00 | 1.56 | 2.25 | 3.06 | 4.00 | 5.1 | 6.3 | 7.6 | 9.0 | 10.6 | 12.3 | 14.1 | 16.0 | 18.1 | 20.3 | 25.0 | 30.3 | 36.0 |
| | | 1350 | 1.18 | 1.84 | 2.65 | 3.60 | 4.70 | 6.0 | 7.4 | 8.9 | 10.6 | 12.4 | 14.4 | 16.5 | 18.8 | 21.2 | 23.8 | 29.4 | 35.6 | 42.3 |
| | | 800 | 0.49 | 0.77 | 1.11 | 1.51 | 1.97 | 2.5 | 3.1 | 3.7 | 4.4 | 5.2 | 6.0 | 6.9 | 7.9 | 8.9 | 10.0 | 12.3 | 14.9 | 17.7 |
| | | 875 | 0.56 | 0.88 | 1.27 | 1.73 | 2.26 | 2.9 | 3.5 | 4.3 | 5.1 | 6.0 | 6.9 | 7.9 | 9.0 | 10.2 | 11.4 | 14.1 | 17.1 | 20.3 |
| | 2500 | 950 | 0.64 | 1.01 | 1.45 | 1.97 | 2.58 | 3.3 | 4.0 | 4.9 | 5.8 | 6.8 | 7.9 | 9.1 | 10.3 | 11.6 | 13.0 | 16.1 | 19.5 | 23.2 |
| | | 1000 | 0.69 | 1.08 | 1.56 | 2.12 | 2.77 | 3.5 | 4.3 | 5.2 | 6.2 | 7.3 | 8.5 | 9.7 | 11.1 | 12.5 | 14.0 | 17.3 | 20.9 | 24.9 |
| | | 1125 | 0.83 | 1.29 | 1.86 | 2.54 | 3.31 | 4.2 | 5.2 | 6.3 | 7.5 | 8.7 | 10.1 | 11.6 | 13.2 | 15.0 | 16.8 | 20.7 | 25.0 | 29.8 |
| | 12 | 1250 | 0.96 | 1.51 | 2.17 | 2.95 | 3.86 | 4.9 | 6.0 | 7.3 | 8.7 | 10.2 | 11.8 | 13.6 | 15.4 | 17.4 | 19.5 | 24.1 | 29.2 | 34.7 |
| | | 1500 | 1.25 | 1.95 | 2.81 | 3.82 | 4.99 | 6.3 | 7.8 | 9.4 | 11.2 | 13.2 | 15.3 | 17.6 | 20.0 | 22.5 | 25.3 | 31.2 | 37.8 | 44.9 |
| | | 1700 | 1.48 | 2.32 | 3.34 | 4.55 | 5.94 | 7.5 | 9.3 | 11.2 | 13.4 | 15.7 | 18.2 | 20.9 | 23.7 | 26.8 | 30.1 | 37.1 | 44.9 | 53.4 |
| 18,000 | | 975 | 0.60 | 0.94 | 1.36 | 1.85 | 2.42 | 3.1 | 3.8 | 4.6 | 5.4 | 6.4 | 7.4 | 8.5 | 9.7 | 10.9 | 12.2 | 15.1 | 18.3 | 21.7 |
| | | 1050 | 0.68 | 1.06 | 1.52 | 2.07 | 2.70 | 3.4 | 4.2 | 5.1 | 6.1 | 7.1 | 8.3 | 9.5 | 10.8 | 12.2 | 13.7 | 16.9 | 20.4 | 24.3 |
| | 3000 | 1125 | 0.76 | 1.18 | 1.70 | 2.32 | 3.02 | 3.8 | 4.7 | 5.7 | 6.8 | 8.0 | 9.3 | 10.6 | 12.1 | 13.7 | 15.3 | 18.9 | 22.9 | 27.2 |
| | | 1200 | 0.83 | 1.30 | 1.87 | 2.55 | 3.33 | 4.2 | 5.2 | 6.3 | 7.5 | 8.8 | 10.2 | 11.7 | 13.3 | 15.0 | 16.8 | 20.8 | 25.2 | 30.0 |
| | | 1350 | 0.99 | 1.55 | 2.23 | 3.04 | 3.97 | 5.0 | 6.2 | 7.5 | 8.9 | 10.5 | 12.2 | 14.0 | 15.9 | 17.9 | 20.1 | 24.8 | 30.0 | 35.7 |
| | 10 | 1500 | 1.16 | 1.81 | 2.60 | 3.54 | 4.62 | 5.9 | 7.2 | 8.7 | 10.4 | 12.2 | 14.2 | 16.3 | 18.5 | 20.9 | 23.4 | 28.9 | 35.0 | 41.6 |
| | | 1800 | 1.50 | 2.34 | 3.38 | 4.59 | 6.00 | 7.6 | 9.4 | 11.3 | 13.5 | 15.8 | 18.4 | 21.1 | 24.0 | 27.1 | 30.4 | 37.5 | 45.4 | 54.0 |
| | | 2025 | 1.76 | 2.76 | 3.97 | 5.40 | 7.06 | 8.9 | 11.0 | 13.3 | 15.9 | 18.6 | 21.6 | 24.8 | 28.2 | 31.9 | 35.7 | 44.1 | 53.4 | 63.5 |
| | | 1200 | 0.74 | 1.16 | 1.67 | 2.27 | 2.96 | 3.7 | 4.6 | 5.6 | 6.7 | 7.8 | 9.1 | 10.4 | 11.8 | 13.4 | 15.0 | 18.5 | 22.4 | 26.6 |
| | | 1300 | 0.84 | 1.31 | 1.88 | 2.56 | 3.34 | 4.2 | 5.2 | 6.3 | 7.5 | 8.8 | 10.2 | 11.8 | 13.4 | 15.1 | 16.9 | 20.9 | 25.3 | 30.1 |
| | 3750 | 1400 | 0.94 | 1.46 | 2.11 | 2.87 | 3.74 | 4.7 | 5.9 | 7.1 | 8.4 | 9.9 | 11.5 | 13.2 | 15.0 | 16.9 | 19.0 | 23.4 | 28.3 | 33.7 |
| | | 1500 | 1.04 | 1.63 | 2.34 | 3.19 | 4.16 | 5.3 | 6.5 | 7.9 | 9.4 | 11.0 | 12.7 | 14.6 | 16.6 | 18.8 | 21.1 | 26.0 | 31.5 | 37.4 |
| | | 1700 | 1.25 | 1.96 | 2.82 | 3.83 | 5.01 | 6.3 | 7.8 | 9.5 | 11.3 | 13.2 | 15.3 | 17.6 | 20.0 | 22.6 | 25.4 | 31.3 | 37.9 | 45.1 |
| | 8 | 1875 | 1.45 | 2.26 | 3.26 | 4.43 | 5.79 | 7.3 | 9.1 | 11.0 | 13.0 | 15.3 | 17.7 | 20.4 | 23.2 | 26.2 | 29.3 | 36.2 | 43.8 | 52.1 |
| | | 2250 | 1.88 | 2.93 | 4.22 | 5.75 | 7.50 | 9.5 | 11.7 | 14.2 | 16.9 | 19.8 | 23.0 | 26.4 | 30.0 | 33.9 | 38.0 | 46.9 | 56.8 | 67.6 |
| | | 2525 | 2.20 | 3.44 | 4.95 | 6.74 | 8.80 | 11.1 | 13.8 | 16.6 | 19.8 | 23.2 | 27.0 | 30.9 | 35.2 | 39.7 | 44.6 | 55.0 | 66.6 | 79.2 |

# Table 2. (*continued*)

| $f_s$ | $f'_c$ and $n$ | $f_c$ | *d*: Effective depth 2 | 2½ | 3 | 3½ | 4 | 4½ | 5 | 5½ | 6 | 6½ | 7 | 7½ | 8 | 8½ | 9 | 10 | 11 | 12 |
|---|---|---|---|---|---|---|---|---|---|---|---|---|---|---|---|---|---|---|---|---|
| 20,000 | | 650 | 0.38 | 0.59 | 0.86 | 1.16 | 1.52 | 1.9 | 2.4 | 2.9 | 3.4 | 4.0 | 4.7 | 5.3 | 6.1 | 6.9 | 7.7 | 9.5 | 11.5 | 13.7 |
| | | 700 | 0.43 | 0.67 | 0.96 | 1.31 | 1.71 | 2.2 | 2.7 | 3.2 | 3.9 | 4.5 | 5.2 | 6.0 | 6.8 | 7.7 | 8.7 | 10.7 | 12.9 | 15.4 |
| | 2000 | 750 | 0.48 | 0.74 | 1.07 | 1.46 | 1.90 | 2.4 | 3.0 | 3.6 | 4.3 | 5.0 | 5.8 | 6.7 | 7.6 | 8.6 | 9.6 | 11.9 | 14.4 | 17.1 |
| | | 800 | 0.52 | 0.82 | 1.18 | 1.60 | 2.10 | 2.7 | 3.3 | 4.0 | 4.7 | 5.5 | 6.4 | 7.4 | 8.4 | 9.5 | 10.6 | 13.1 | 15.9 | 18.9 |
| | | 900 | 0.63 | 0.98 | 1.41 | 1.92 | 2.51 | 3.2 | 3.9 | 4.7 | 5.7 | 6.6 | 7.7 | 8.8 | 10.0 | 11.3 | 12.7 | 15.7 | 19.0 | 22.6 |
| | 15 | 1000 | 0.74 | 1.15 | 1.66 | 2.25 | 2.94 | 3.7 | 4.6 | 5.6 | 6.6 | 7.8 | 9.0 | 10.4 | 11.8 | 13.3 | 14.9 | 18.4 | 22.3 | 26.5 |
| | | 1200 | 0.96 | 1.49 | 2.15 | 2.93 | 3.82 | 4.8 | 6.0 | 7.2 | 8.6 | 10.1 | 11.7 | 13.4 | 15.3 | 17.3 | 19.4 | 23.9 | 28.9 | 34.4 |
| | | 1350 | 1.13 | 1.76 | 2.54 | 3.45 | 4.51 | 5.7 | 7.1 | 8.5 | 10.2 | 11.9 | 13.8 | 15.9 | 18.1 | 20.4 | 22.8 | 28.2 | 34.1 | 40.6 |
| | | 800 | 0.46 | 0.73 | 1.04 | 1.42 | 1.86 | 2.3 | 2.9 | 3.5 | 4.2 | 4.9 | 5.7 | 6.5 | 7.4 | 8.4 | 9.4 | 11.6 | 14.0 | 16.7 |
| | | 875 | 0.53 | 0.83 | 1.20 | 1.63 | 2.13 | 2.7 | 3.3 | 4.0 | 4.8 | 5.6 | 6.5 | 7.5 | 8.5 | 9.6 | 10.8 | 13.3 | 16.1 | 19.2 |
| | 2500 | 950 | 0.61 | 0.95 | 1.37 | 1.86 | 2.43 | 3.1 | 3.8 | 4.6 | 5.5 | 6.4 | 7.4 | 8.6 | 9.7 | 11.0 | 12.3 | 15.2 | 18.4 | 21.9 |
| | | 1000 | 0.66 | 1.03 | 1.48 | 2.01 | 2.62 | 3.3 | 4.1 | 5.0 | 5.9 | 6.9 | 8.0 | 9.2 | 10.5 | 11.8 | 13.3 | 16.4 | 19.8 | 23.6 |
| | | 1125 | 0.78 | 1.23 | 1.76 | 2.40 | 3.14 | 4.0 | 4.9 | 5.9 | 7.1 | 8.3 | 9.6 | 11.0 | 12.5 | 14.2 | 15.9 | 19.6 | 23.7 | 28.2 |
| | 12 | 1250 | 0.92 | 1.44 | 2.07 | 2.82 | 3.68 | 4.7 | 5.8 | 7.0 | 8.3 | 9.7 | 11.3 | 12.9 | 14.7 | 16.6 | 18.6 | 23.0 | 27.8 | 33.1 |
| | | 1500 | 1.20 | 1.87 | 2.69 | 3.66 | 4.78 | 6.1 | 7.5 | 9.0 | 10.8 | 12.6 | 14.7 | 16.8 | 19.1 | 21.6 | 24.2 | 29.9 | 36.2 | 43.1 |
| | | 1700 | 1.43 | 2.23 | 3.21 | 4.37 | 5.71 | 7.2 | 8.9 | 10.8 | 12.9 | 15.1 | 17.5 | 20.1 | 22.8 | 25.8 | 28.9 | 35.7 | 43.2 | 51.4 |
| | | 975 | 0.57 | 0.89 | 1.28 | 1.74 | 2.27 | 2.9 | 3.6 | 4.3 | 5.1 | 6.0 | 7.0 | 8.0 | 9.1 | 10.3 | 11.5 | 14.2 | 17.2 | 20.4 |
| | | 1050 | 0.64 | 1.00 | 1.44 | 1.96 | 2.56 | 3.2 | 4.0 | 4.8 | 5.8 | 6.8 | 7.8 | 9.0 | 10.2 | 11.6 | 13.0 | 16.0 | 19.4 | 23.0 |
| | 3000 | 1125 | 0.71 | 1.11 | 1.60 | 2.18 | 2.85 | 3.6 | 4.5 | 5.4 | 6.4 | 7.5 | 8.7 | 10.0 | 11.4 | 12.9 | 14.4 | 17.8 | 21.5 | 25.6 |
| | | 1200 | 0.79 | 1.23 | 1.77 | 2.41 | 3.15 | 4.0 | 4.9 | 6.0 | 7.1 | 8.3 | 9.7 | 11.1 | 12.6 | 14.2 | 16.0 | 19.7 | 23.8 | 28.4 |
| | | 1350 | 0.94 | 1.48 | 2.12 | 2.89 | 3.78 | 4.8 | 5.9 | 7.1 | 8.5 | 10.0 | 11.6 | 13.3 | 15.1 | 17.1 | 19.1 | 23.6 | 28.6 | 34.0 |
| | 10 | 1500 | 1.10 | 1.73 | 2.48 | 3.38 | 4.42 | 5.6 | 6.9 | 8.3 | 9.9 | 11.7 | 13.5 | 15.5 | 17.7 | 19.9 | 22.4 | 27.6 | 33.4 | 39.7 |
| | | 1800 | 1.44 | 2.24 | 3.23 | 4.40 | 5.74 | 7.3 | 9.0 | 10.9 | 12.9 | 15.2 | 17.6 | 20.2 | 23.0 | 25.9 | 29.1 | 35.9 | 43.4 | 51.7 |
| | | 2025 | 1.70 | 2.65 | 3.82 | 5.19 | 6.78 | 8.6 | 10.6 | 12.8 | 15.3 | 17.9 | 20.8 | 23.9 | 27.1 | 30.6 | 34.3 | 42.4 | 51.3 | 61.1 |
| | | 1200 | 0.69 | 1.08 | 1.56 | 2.12 | 2.77 | 3.5 | 4.3 | 5.2 | 6.2 | 7.3 | 8.5 | 9.7 | 11.1 | 12.5 | 14.0 | 17.3 | 20.9 | 24.9 |
| | | 1300 | 0.79 | 1.23 | 1.77 | 2.41 | 3.15 | 4.0 | 4.9 | 6.0 | 7.1 | 8.3 | 9.7 | 11.1 | 12.6 | 14.2 | 16.0 | 19.7 | 23.8 | 28.4 |
| | 3750 | 1400 | 0.88 | 1.38 | 1.99 | 2.71 | 3.54 | 4.5 | 5.5 | 6.7 | 8.0 | 9.3 | 10.8 | 12.4 | 14.1 | 16.0 | 17.9 | 22.1 | 26.7 | 31.8 |
| | | 1500 | 0.98 | 1.54 | 2.21 | 3.01 | 3.94 | 5.0 | 6.2 | 7.4 | 8.9 | 10.4 | 12.1 | 13.8 | 15.7 | 17.8 | 19.9 | 24.6 | 29.8 | 35.4 |
| | | 1700 | 1.19 | 1.86 | 2.68 | 3.65 | 4.77 | 6.0 | 7.5 | 9.0 | 10.7 | 12.6 | 14.6 | 16.8 | 19.1 | 21.5 | 24.1 | 29.8 | 36.1 | 42.9 |
| | 8 | 1875 | 1.38 | 2.16 | 3.11 | 4.23 | 5.52 | 7.0 | 8.6 | 10.4 | 12.4 | 14.6 | 16.9 | 19.4 | 22.1 | 24.9 | 27.9 | 34.5 | 41.7 | 49.7 |
| | | 2250 | 1.80 | 2.81 | 4.04 | 5.50 | 7.18 | 9.1 | 11.2 | 13.6 | 16.2 | 19.0 | 22.0 | 25.3 | 28.7 | 32.4 | 36.4 | 44.9 | 54.3 | 64.7 |
| | | 2525 | 2.11 | 3.30 | 4.75 | 6.47 | 8.45 | 10.7 | 13.2 | 16.0 | 19.0 | 22.3 | 25.9 | 29.7 | 33.8 | 38.1 | 42.8 | 52.8 | 63.9 | 76.0 |
| 22,000 | | 650 | 0.36 | 0.56 | 0.81 | 1.10 | 1.44 | 1.8 | 2.3 | 2.7 | 3.2 | 3.8 | 4.4 | 5.1 | 5.8 | 6.5 | 7.3 | 9.0 | 10.9 | 13.0 |
| | | 700 | 0.40 | 0.63 | 0.91 | 1.24 | 1.62 | 2.0 | 2.5 | 3.1 | 3.6 | 4.2 | 4.9 | 5.7 | 6.5 | 7.3 | 8.2 | 10.1 | 12.2 | 14.5 |
| | 2000 | 750 | 0.45 | 0.70 | 1.01 | 1.37 | 1.79 | 2.3 | 2.8 | 3.4 | 4.0 | 4.7 | 5.5 | 6.3 | 7.2 | 8.1 | 9.1 | 11.2 | 13.6 | 16.1 |
| | | 800 | 0.50 | 0.78 | 1.13 | 1.53 | 2.00 | 2.5 | 3.1 | 3.8 | 4.5 | 5.3 | 6.1 | 7.0 | 8.0 | 9.0 | 10.1 | 12.5 | 15.1 | 18.0 |
| | | 900 | 0.60 | 0.93 | 1.34 | 1.83 | 2.38 | 3.0 | 3.7 | 4.5 | 5.4 | 6.3 | 7.3 | 8.4 | 9.5 | 10.8 | 12.1 | 14.9 | 18.0 | 21.5 |
| | 15 | 1000 | 0.70 | 1.09 | 1.58 | 2.14 | 2.80 | 3.5 | 4.4 | 5.3 | 6.3 | 7.4 | 8.6 | 9.8 | 11.2 | 12.6 | 14.2 | 17.5 | 21.2 | 25.2 |
| | | 1200 | 0.92 | 1.44 | 2.07 | 2.82 | 3.68 | 4.7 | 5.8 | 7.0 | 8.3 | 9.7 | 11.3 | 12.9 | 14.7 | 16.6 | 18.6 | 23.0 | 27.8 | 33.1 |
| | | 1350 | 1.09 | 1.70 | 2.45 | 3.33 | 4.35 | 5.5 | 6.8 | 8.2 | 9.8 | 11.4 | 13.3 | 15.3 | 17.4 | 19.7 | 22.0 | 27.2 | 32.9 | 39.2 |
| | | 800 | 0.44 | 0.68 | 0.98 | 1.34 | 1.74 | 2.2 | 2.7 | 3.3 | 3.9 | 4.6 | 5.3 | 6.1 | 7.0 | 7.9 | 8.8 | 10.9 | 13.2 | 15.7 |
| | | 875 | 0.50 | 0.79 | 1.13 | 1.54 | 2.02 | 2.6 | 3.2 | 3.8 | 4.5 | 5.3 | 6.2 | 7.1 | 8.1 | 9.1 | 10.2 | 12.6 | 15.2 | 18.1 |
| | 2500 | 950 | 0.58 | 0.90 | 1.30 | 1.76 | 2.30 | 2.9 | 3.6 | 4.4 | 5.2 | 6.1 | 7.1 | 8.1 | 9.2 | 10.4 | 11.7 | 14.4 | 17.4 | 20.7 |
| | | 1000 | 0.62 | 0.98 | 1.40 | 1.91 | 2.50 | 3.2 | 3.9 | 4.7 | 5.6 | 6.6 | 7.6 | 8.8 | 10.0 | 11.3 | 12.6 | 15.6 | 18.9 | 22.5 |
| | | 1125 | 0.75 | 1.17 | 1.68 | 2.29 | 2.99 | 3.8 | 4.7 | 5.7 | 6.7 | 7.9 | 9.2 | 10.5 | 12.0 | 13.5 | 15.1 | 18.7 | 22.6 | 26.9 |
| | 12 | 1250 | 0.88 | 1.37 | 1.97 | 2.68 | 3.50 | 4.4 | 5.5 | 6.6 | 7.9 | 9.2 | 10.7 | 12.3 | 14.0 | 15.8 | 17.7 | 21.9 | 26.5 | 31.5 |
| | | 1500 | 1.15 | 1.79 | 2.58 | 3.52 | 4.59 | 5.8 | 7.2 | 8.7 | 10.3 | 12.1 | 14.1 | 16.1 | 18.4 | 20.7 | 23.2 | 28.7 | 34.7 | 41.3 |
| | | 1700 | 1.37 | 2.14 | 3.09 | 4.20 | 5.49 | 6.9 | 8.6 | 10.4 | 12.3 | 14.4 | 16.8 | 19.3 | 22.0 | 24.8 | 27.8 | 34.3 | 41.5 | 49.4 |
| | | 975 | 0.54 | 0.84 | 1.21 | 1.64 | 2.14 | 2.7 | 3.4 | 4.1 | 4.8 | 5.6 | 6.6 | 7.5 | 8.6 | 9.7 | 10.9 | 13.4 | 16.2 | 19.3 |
| | | 1050 | 0.60 | 0.94 | 1.36 | 1.85 | 2.42 | 3.1 | 3.8 | 4.6 | 5.4 | 6.4 | 7.4 | 8.5 | 9.7 | 10.9 | 12.2 | 15.1 | 18.3 | 21.7 |
| | 3000 | 1125 | 0.68 | 1.06 | 1.52 | 2.07 | 2.70 | 3.4 | 4.2 | 5.1 | 6.1 | 7.1 | 8.3 | 9.5 | 10.8 | 12.2 | 13.7 | 16.9 | 20.4 | 24.3 |
| | | 1200 | 0.75 | 1.17 | 1.68 | 2.29 | 2.99 | 3.8 | 4.7 | 5.7 | 6.7 | 7.9 | 9.2 | 10.5 | 12.0 | 13.5 | 15.1 | 18.7 | 22.6 | 26.9 |
| | | 1350 | 0.90 | 1.40 | 2.02 | 2.74 | 3.58 | 4.5 | 5.6 | 6.8 | 8.1 | 9.5 | 11.0 | 12.6 | 14.3 | 16.2 | 18.1 | 22.4 | 27.1 | 32.3 |
| | 10 | 1500 | 1.05 | 1.64 | 2.37 | 3.22 | 4.21 | 5.3 | 6.6 | 8.0 | 9.5 | 11.1 | 12.9 | 14.8 | 16.8 | 19.0 | 21.3 | 26.3 | 31.8 | 37.9 |
| | | 1800 | 1.38 | 2.15 | 3.10 | 4.21 | 5.50 | 7.0 | 8.6 | 10.4 | 12.4 | 14.5 | 16.9 | 19.4 | 22.0 | 24.9 | 27.9 | 34.4 | 41.6 | 49.5 |
| | | 2025 | 1.63 | 2.54 | 3.66 | 4.99 | 6.51 | 8.2 | 10.2 | 12.3 | 14.7 | 17.2 | 19.9 | 22.9 | 26.0 | 29.4 | 33.0 | 40.7 | 49.2 | 58.6 |
| | | 1200 | 0.66 | 1.03 | 1.48 | 2.01 | 2.62 | 3.3 | 4.1 | 5.0 | 5.9 | 6.9 | 8.0 | 9.2 | 10.5 | 11.8 | 13.3 | 16.4 | 19.8 | 23.6 |
| | | 1300 | 0.74 | 1.16 | 1.67 | 2.28 | 2.98 | 3.8 | 4.7 | 5.6 | 6.7 | 7.9 | 9.1 | 10.5 | 11.9 | 13.4 | 15.1 | 18.6 | 22.5 | 26.8 |
| | 3750 | 1400 | 0.84 | 1.31 | 1.88 | 2.56 | 3.34 | 4.2 | 5.2 | 6.3 | 7.5 | 8.8 | 10.2 | 11.8 | 13.4 | 15.1 | 16.9 | 20.9 | 25.3 | 30.1 |
| | | 1500 | 0.94 | 1.46 | 2.11 | 2.87 | 3.74 | 4.7 | 5.9 | 7.1 | 8.4 | 9.9 | 11.5 | 13.2 | 15.0 | 16.9 | 19.0 | 23.4 | 28.3 | 33.7 |
| | | 1700 | 1.13 | 1.77 | 2.55 | 3.47 | 4.53 | 5.7 | 7.1 | 8.6 | 10.2 | 12.0 | 13.9 | 15.9 | 18.1 | 20.4 | 22.9 | 28.3 | 34.2 | 40.8 |
| | 8 | 1875 | 1.31 | 2.05 | 2.95 | 4.02 | 5.25 | 6.6 | 8.2 | 9.9 | 11.8 | 13.9 | 16.1 | 18.5 | 21.0 | 23.7 | 26.6 | 32.8 | 39.7 | 47.2 |
| | | 2250 | 1.72 | 2.69 | 3.87 | 5.27 | 6.88 | 8.7 | 10.8 | 13.0 | 15.5 | 18.2 | 21.1 | 24.2 | 27.5 | 31.1 | 34.8 | 43.0 | 52.0 | 61.9 |
| | | 2525 | 2.03 | 3.18 | 4.57 | 6.22 | 8.13 | 10.3 | 12.7 | 15.4 | 18.3 | 21.5 | 24.9 | 28.6 | 32.5 | 36.7 | 41.1 | 50.8 | 61.5 | 73.2 |

## Table 2. *(continued)*

| $f_s$ | $f'_c$ and $n$ | $f_c$ | d: Effective depth 2 | 2½ | 3 | 3½ | 4 | 4½ | 5 | 5½ | 6 | 6½ | 7 | 7½ | 8 | 8½ | 9 | 10 | 11 | 12 |
|---|---|---|---|---|---|---|---|---|---|---|---|---|---|---|---|---|---|---|---|---|
| 24,000 | 2000 | 650 | 0.34 | 0.53 | 0.77 | 1.04 | 1.36 | 1.7 | 2.1 | 2.6 | 3.1 | 3.6 | 4.2 | 4.8 | 5.4 | 6.1 | 6.9 | 8.5 | 10.3 | 12.2 |
| | | 700 | 0.38 | 0.60 | 0.86 | 1.18 | 1.54 | 1.9 | 2.4 | 2.9 | 3.5 | 4.1 | 4.7 | 5.4 | 6.1 | 6.9 | 7.8 | 9.6 | 11.6 | 13.8 |
| | | 750 | 0.43 | 0.67 | 0.96 | 1.31 | 1.71 | 2.2 | 2.7 | 3.2 | 3.9 | 4.5 | 5.2 | 6.0 | 6.8 | 7.7 | 8.7 | 10.7 | 12.9 | 15.4 |
| | | 800 | 0.47 | 0.74 | 1.06 | 1.45 | 1.89 | 2.4 | 3.0 | 3.6 | 4.2 | 5.0 | 5.8 | 6.6 | 7.6 | 8.5 | 9.6 | 11.8 | 14.3 | 17.0 |
| | | 900 | 0.57 | 0.89 | 1.29 | 1.75 | 2.29 | 2.9 | 3.6 | 4.3 | 5.1 | 6.0 | 7.0 | 8.0 | 9.2 | 10.3 | 11.6 | 14.3 | 17.3 | 20.6 |
| | 15 | 1000 | 0.67 | 1.05 | 1.51 | 2.06 | 2.69 | 3.4 | 4.2 | 5.1 | 6.0 | 7.1 | 8.2 | 9.5 | 10.8 | 12.1 | 13.6 | 16.8 | 20.3 | 24.2 |
| | | 1200 | 0.88 | 1.38 | 1.98 | 2.70 | 3.52 | 4.5 | 5.5 | 6.7 | 7.9 | 9.3 | 10.8 | 12.4 | 14.1 | 15.9 | 17.8 | 22.0 | 26.6 | 31.7 |
| | | 1350 | 1.05 | 1.64 | 2.36 | 3.21 | 4.19 | 5.3 | 6.6 | 7.9 | 9.4 | 11.1 | 12.8 | 14.7 | 16.8 | 18.9 | 21.2 | 26.2 | 31.7 | 37.7 |
| | 2500 | 800 | 0.42 | 0.65 | 0.94 | 1.27 | 1.66 | 2.1 | 2.6 | 3.1 | 3.7 | 4.4 | 5.1 | 5.9 | 6.7 | 7.5 | 8.4 | 10.4 | 12.6 | 15.0 |
| | | 875 | 0.48 | 0.75 | 1.08 | 1.47 | 1.92 | 2.4 | 3.0 | 3.6 | 4.3 | 5.1 | 5.9 | 6.8 | 7.7 | 8.7 | 9.7 | 12.0 | 14.5 | 17.3 |
| | | 950 | 0.55 | 0.86 | 1.23 | 1.68 | 2.19 | 2.8 | 3.4 | 4.1 | 4.9 | 5.8 | 6.7 | 7.7 | 8.8 | 9.9 | 11.1 | 13.7 | 16.6 | 19.7 |
| | | 1000 | 0.59 | 0.93 | 1.33 | 1.81 | 2.37 | 3.0 | 3.7 | 4.5 | 5.3 | 6.3 | 7.3 | 8.3 | 9.5 | 10.7 | 12.0 | 14.8 | 17.9 | 21.3 |
| | | 1125 | 0.71 | 1.11 | 1.60 | 2.18 | 2.85 | 3.6 | 4.5 | 5.4 | 6.4 | 7.5 | 8.7 | 10.0 | 11.4 | 12.9 | 14.4 | 17.8 | 21.5 | 25.6 |
| | 12 | 1250 | 0.84 | 1.31 | 1.89 | 2.57 | 3.36 | 4.3 | 5.3 | 6.4 | 7.6 | 8.9 | 10.3 | 11.8 | 13.4 | 15.2 | 17.0 | 21.0 | 25.4 | 30.2 |
| | | 1500 | 1.10 | 1.73 | 2.48 | 3.38 | 4.42 | 5.6 | 6.9 | 8.3 | 9.9 | 11.7 | 13.5 | 15.5 | 17.7 | 19.9 | 22.4 | 27.6 | 33.4 | 39.7 |
| | | 1700 | 1.32 | 2.07 | 2.98 | 4.05 | 5.30 | 6.7 | 8.3 | 10.0 | 11.9 | 14.0 | 16.2 | 18.6 | 21.2 | 23.9 | 26.8 | 33.1 | 40.1 | 47.7 |
| | 3000 | 975 | 0.51 | 0.79 | 1.14 | 1.56 | 2.03 | 2.6 | 3.2 | 3.8 | 4.6 | 5.4 | 6.2 | 7.1 | 8.1 | 9.2 | 10.3 | 12.7 | 15.4 | 18.3 |
| | | 1050 | 0.57 | 0.89 | 1.29 | 1.75 | 2.29 | 2.9 | 3.6 | 4.3 | 5.1 | 6.0 | 7.0 | 8.0 | 9.2 | 10.3 | 11.6 | 14.3 | 17.3 | 20.6 |
| | | 1125 | 0.64 | 1.00 | 1.44 | 1.96 | 2.56 | 3.2 | 4.0 | 4.8 | 5.8 | 6.8 | 7.8 | 9.0 | 10.2 | 11.6 | 13.0 | 16.0 | 19.4 | 23.0 |
| | | 1200 | 0.71 | 1.11 | 1.60 | 2.18 | 2.85 | 3.6 | 4.5 | 5.4 | 6.4 | 7.5 | 8.7 | 10.0 | 11.4 | 12.9 | 14.4 | 17.8 | 21.5 | 25.6 |
| | | 1350 | 0.86 | 1.34 | 1.93 | 2.62 | 3.42 | 4.3 | 5.4 | 6.5 | 7.7 | 9.0 | 10.5 | 12.0 | 13.7 | 15.5 | 17.3 | 21.4 | 25.9 | 30.8 |
| | 10 | 1500 | 1.01 | 1.58 | 2.27 | 3.09 | 4.03 | 5.1 | 6.3 | 7.6 | 9.1 | 10.6 | 12.3 | 14.2 | 16.1 | 18.2 | 20.4 | 25.2 | 30.5 | 36.3 |
| | | 1800 | 1.32 | 2.07 | 2.98 | 4.05 | 5.30 | 6.7 | 8.3 | 10.0 | 11.9 | 14.0 | 16.2 | 18.6 | 21.2 | 23.9 | 26.8 | 33.1 | 40.1 | 47.7 |
| | | 2025 | 1.57 | 2.46 | 3.54 | 4.81 | 6.29 | 8.0 | 9.8 | 11.9 | 14.1 | 16.6 | 19.3 | 22.1 | 25.2 | 28.4 | 31.8 | 39.3 | 47.6 | 56.6 |
| | 3750 | 1200 | 0.62 | 0.97 | 1.40 | 1.90 | 2.48 | 3.1 | 3.9 | 4.7 | 5.6 | 6.5 | 7.6 | 8.7 | 9.9 | 11.2 | 12.6 | 15.5 | 18.8 | 22.3 |
| | | 1300 | 0.70 | 1.10 | 1.58 | 2.16 | 2.82 | 3.6 | 4.4 | 5.3 | 6.3 | 7.4 | 8.6 | 9.9 | 11.3 | 12.7 | 14.3 | 17.6 | 21.3 | 25.3 |
| | | 1400 | 0.80 | 1.24 | 1.79 | 2.44 | 3.18 | 4.0 | 5.0 | 6.0 | 7.2 | 8.4 | 9.8 | 11.2 | 12.7 | 14.4 | 16.1 | 19.9 | 24.1 | 28.7 |
| | | 1500 | 0.89 | 1.39 | 2.00 | 2.72 | 3.55 | 4.5 | 5.6 | 6.7 | 8.0 | 9.4 | 10.9 | 12.5 | 14.2 | 16.0 | 18.0 | 22.2 | 26.9 | 32.0 |
| | | 1700 | 1.08 | 1.69 | 2.43 | 3.31 | 4.32 | 5.5 | 6.8 | 8.2 | 9.7 | 11.4 | 13.2 | 15.2 | 17.3 | 19.5 | 21.9 | 27.0 | 32.7 | 38.9 |
| | 8 | 1875 | 1.26 | 1.97 | 2.84 | 3.86 | 5.04 | 6.4 | 7.9 | 9.5 | 11.3 | 13.3 | 15.4 | 17.7 | 20.2 | 22.0 | 25.5 | 31.5 | 38.1 | 45.1 |
| | | 2250 | 1.66 | 2.59 | 3.73 | 5.07 | 6.62 | 8.4 | 10.4 | 12.5 | 14.9 | 17.5 | 20.3 | 23.3 | 26.5 | 29.9 | 33.5 | 41.4 | 50.1 | 59.6 |
| | | 2525 | 1.90 | 3.00 | 4.40 | 5.99 | 7.82 | 9.9 | 12.2 | 14.8 | 17.0 | 20.7 | 24.0 | 27.5 | [illegible] | [illegible] | [illegible] | [illegible] | [illegible] | 70.1 |
| 27,000 | 2000 | 650 | 0.32 | 0.50 | 0.71 | 0.97 | 1.26 | 1.6 | 2.0 | 2.4 | 2.8 | 3.3 | 3.8 | 4.4 | 5.1 | 5.7 | 6.4 | 7.9 | 9.6 | 11.4 |
| | | 700 | 0.36 | 0.56 | 0.80 | 1.09 | 1.42 | 1.8 | 2.2 | 2.7 | 3.2 | 3.8 | 4.4 | 5.0 | 5.7 | 6.4 | 7.2 | 8.9 | 10.8 | 12.8 |
| | | 750 | 0.40 | 0.62 | 0.89 | 1.21 | 1.58 | 2.0 | 2.5 | 3.0 | 3.6 | 4.2 | 4.9 | 5.6 | 6.3 | 7.2 | 8.0 | 9.9 | 12.0 | 14.3 |
| | | 800 | 0.44 | 0.69 | 1.00 | 1.36 | 1.78 | 2.2 | 2.8 | 3.4 | 4.0 | 4.7 | 5.4 | 6.2 | 7.1 | 8.0 | 9.0 | 11.1 | 13.4 | 16.0 |
| | | 900 | 0.53 | 0.83 | 1.20 | 1.63 | 2.13 | 2.7 | 3.3 | 4.0 | 4.8 | 5.6 | 6.5 | 7.5 | 8.5 | 9.6 | 10.8 | 13.3 | 16.1 | 19.2 |
| | 15 | 1000 | 0.63 | 0.98 | 1.41 | 1.92 | 2.51 | 3.2 | 3.9 | 4.7 | 5.7 | 6.6 | 7.7 | 8.8 | 10.0 | 11.3 | 12.7 | 15.7 | 19.0 | 22.6 |
| | | 1200 | 0.83 | 1.30 | 1.87 | 2.55 | 3.33 | 4.2 | 5.2 | 6.3 | 7.5 | 8.8 | 10.2 | 11.7 | 13.3 | 15.0 | 16.8 | 20.8 | 25.2 | 30.0 |
| | | 1350 | 0.99 | 1.55 | 2.23 | 3.04 | 3.97 | 5.0 | 6.2 | 7.5 | 8.9 | 10.5 | 12.2 | 14.0 | 15.9 | 17.9 | 20.1 | 24.8 | 30.0 | 35.7 |
| | 2500 | 800 | 0.38 | 0.60 | 0.86 | 1.18 | 1.54 | 1.9 | 2.4 | 2.9 | 3.5 | 4.1 | 4.7 | 5.4 | 6.1 | 6.9 | 7.8 | 9.6 | 11.6 | 13.8 |
| | | 875 | 0.44 | 0.69 | 1.00 | 1.36 | 1.78 | 2.2 | 2.8 | 3.4 | 4.0 | 4.7 | 5.4 | 6.2 | 7.1 | 8.0 | 9.0 | 11.1 | 13.4 | 16.0 |
| | | 950 | 0.51 | 0.79 | 1.14 | 1.56 | 2.03 | 2.6 | 3.2 | 3.8 | 4.6 | 5.4 | 6.2 | 7.1 | 8.1 | 9.2 | 10.3 | 12.7 | 15.4 | 18.3 |
| | | 1000 | 0.55 | 0.86 | 1.24 | 1.69 | 2.21 | 2.8 | 3.5 | 4.2 | 5.0 | 5.8 | 6.8 | 7.8 | 8.8 | 10.0 | 11.2 | 13.8 | 16.7 | 19.9 |
| | | 1125 | 0.67 | 1.04 | 1.50 | 2.05 | 2.67 | 3.4 | 4.2 | 5.1 | 6.0 | 7.1 | 8.2 | 9.4 | 10.7 | 12.1 | 13.5 | 16.7 | 20.2 | 24.0 |
| | 12 | 1250 | 0.79 | 1.23 | 1.77 | 2.41 | 3.15 | 4.0 | 4.9 | 6.0 | 7.1 | 8.3 | 9.7 | 11.1 | 12.6 | 14.2 | 16.0 | 19.7 | 23.8 | 28.4 |
| | | 1500 | 1.04 | 1.63 | 2.34 | 3.19 | 4.16 | 5.3 | 6.5 | 7.9 | 9.4 | 11.0 | 12.7 | 14.6 | 16.6 | 18.8 | 21.1 | 26.0 | 31.5 | 37.4 |
| | | 1700 | 1.25 | 1.96 | 2.82 | 3.83 | 5.01 | 6.3 | 7.8 | 9.5 | 11.3 | 13.2 | 15.3 | 17.6 | 20.0 | 22.6 | 25.4 | 31.3 | 37.9 | 45.1 |
| | 3000 | 975 | 0.47 | 0.74 | 1.06 | 1.45 | 1.89 | 2.4 | 3.0 | 3.6 | 4.2 | 5.0 | 5.8 | 6.6 | 7.6 | 8.5 | 9.6 | 11.8 | 14.3 | 17.0 |
| | | 1050 | 0.53 | 0.83 | 1.20 | 1.63 | 2.13 | 2.7 | 3.3 | 4.0 | 4.8 | 5.6 | 6.5 | 7.5 | 8.5 | 9.6 | 10.8 | 13.3 | 16.1 | 19.2 |
| | | 1125 | 0.60 | 0.93 | 1.34 | 1.83 | 2.38 | 3.0 | 3.7 | 4.5 | 5.4 | 6.3 | 7.3 | 8.4 | 9.5 | 10.8 | 12.1 | 14.9 | 18.0 | 21.5 |
| | | 1200 | 0.66 | 1.04 | 1.49 | 2.03 | 2.66 | 3.4 | 4.2 | 5.0 | 6.0 | 7.0 | 8.1 | 9.3 | 10.6 | 12.0 | 13.4 | 16.6 | 20.1 | 23.9 |
| | | 1350 | 0.80 | 1.25 | 1.80 | 2.45 | 3.20 | 4.1 | 5.0 | 6.1 | 7.2 | 8.5 | 9.8 | 11.3 | 12.8 | 14.5 | 16.2 | 20.0 | 24.2 | 28.8 |
| | 10 | 1500 | 0.94 | 1.48 | 2.12 | 2.89 | 3.78 | 4.8 | 5.9 | 7.1 | 8.5 | 10.0 | 11.6 | 13.3 | 15.1 | 17.1 | 19.1 | 23.6 | 28.6 | 34.0 |
| | | 1800 | 1.25 | 1.95 | 2.81 | 3.82 | 4.99 | 6.3 | 7.8 | 9.4 | 11.2 | 13.2 | 15.3 | 17.6 | 20.0 | 22.5 | 25.3 | 31.2 | 37.8 | 44.9 |
| | | 2025 | 1.49 | 2.33 | 3.35 | 4.56 | 5.95 | 7.5 | 9.3 | 11.3 | 13.4 | 15.7 | 18.2 | 20.9 | 23.8 | 26.9 | 30.1 | 37.2 | 45.0 | 53.6 |
| | 3750 | 1200 | 0.58 | 0.90 | 1.30 | 1.76 | 2.30 | 2.9 | 3.6 | 4.4 | 5.2 | 6.1 | 7.1 | 8.1 | 9.2 | 10.4 | 11.7 | 14.4 | 17.4 | 20.7 |
| | | 1300 | 0.66 | 1.03 | 1.48 | 2.01 | 2.62 | 3.3 | 4.1 | 5.0 | 5.9 | 6.9 | 8.0 | 9.2 | 10.5 | 11.8 | 13.3 | 16.4 | 19.8 | 23.6 |
| | | 1400 | 0.74 | 1.16 | 1.67 | 2.27 | 2.96 | 3.7 | 4.6 | 5.6 | 6.7 | 7.8 | 9.1 | 10.4 | 11.8 | 13.4 | 15.0 | 18.5 | 22.4 | 26.6 |
| | | 1500 | 0.83 | 1.29 | 1.86 | 2.54 | 3.31 | 4.2 | 5.2 | 6.3 | 7.5 | 8.7 | 10.1 | 11.6 | 13.2 | 15.0 | 16.8 | 20.7 | 25.0 | 29.8 |
| | | 1700 | 1.01 | 1.58 | 2.28 | 3.10 | 4.05 | 5.1 | 6.3 | 7.7 | 9.1 | 10.7 | 12.4 | 14.2 | 16.2 | 18.3 | 20.5 | 25.3 | 30.6 | 36.4 |
| | 8 | 1875 | 1.18 | 1.84 | 2.66 | 3.61 | 4.72 | 6.0 | 7.4 | 8.9 | 10.6 | 12.5 | 14.5 | 16.6 | 18.9 | 21.3 | 23.9 | 29.5 | 35.7 | 42.5 |
| | | 2250 | 1.56 | 2.44 | 3.51 | 4.78 | 6.24 | 7.9 | 9.8 | 11.8 | 14.0 | 16.5 | 19.1 | 21.9 | 25.0 | 28.2 | 31.6 | 39.0 | 47.2 | 56.2 |
| | | 2525 | 1.85 | 2.89 | 4.17 | 5.67 | 7.41 | 9.4 | 11.6 | 14.0 | 16.3 | 19.6 | 22.7 | 26.0 | 29.6 | 33.5 | 37.5 | 46.3 | 56.0 | 66.7 |

# Table 3. Areas and Perimeters of Bars in Sections One Foot Wide (Slabs)

**Areas $A_s$ (or $A'_s$)** given in bold type (top) in sq.in.
**Perimeters $\Sigma o$,** given in light type (bottom) in in.

Enter table with values of $A_s$ (or $A'_s$) and $\Sigma o = \dfrac{V}{\frac{7}{8} du}$ ($V$ : lb.; $d$ : in.; $u$ : psi.)

Coefficients $a$ inserted in table are for use in $A_s = \dfrac{M}{ad}$ or $A_s = \dfrac{NE}{adi}$

| Spacing | $\frac{1}{4}\phi$ | $\frac{3}{8}\phi$ | $\frac{1}{2}\phi$ | $\frac{1}{2}\square$ | $\frac{5}{8}\phi$ | $\frac{3}{4}\phi$ | $\frac{7}{8}\phi$ | $1\phi$ | $1\square$ | $1\frac{1}{8}\square$ | $1\frac{1}{4}\square$ | Spacing |
|---|---|---|---|---|---|---|---|---|---|---|---|---|
| 2 | **0.30**<br>2.9 | **0.66**<br>7.1 | **1.20**<br>9.4 | **1.50**<br>12.0 | **1.86**<br>11.8 | **2.64**<br>14.2 | | | | | | 2 |
| 2¼ | **0.27**<br>2.6 | **0.59**<br>6.3 | **1.07**<br>8.4 | **1.33**<br>10.7 | **1.65**<br>10.5 | **2.35**<br>12.6 | **3.20**<br>14.7 | | | | | 2¼ |
| 2½ | **0.24**<br>2.4 | **0.53**<br>5.7 | **0.96**<br>7.5 | **1.20**<br>9.6 | **1.49**<br>9.4 | **2.11**<br>11.3 | **2.88**<br>13.2 | **3.79**<br>15.1 | | | | 2½ |
| 2¾ | **0.22**<br>2.1 | **0.48**<br>5.1 | **0.87**<br>6.9 | **1.09**<br>8.7 | **1.35**<br>8.6 | **1.92**<br>10.3 | **2.62**<br>12.0 | **3.45**<br>13.7 | | | | 2¾ |
| 3 | **0.20**<br>2.0 | **0.44**<br>4.7 | **0.80**<br>6.3 | **1.00**<br>8.0 | **1.24**<br>7.8 | **1.76**<br>9.4 | **2.40**<br>11.0 | **3.16**<br>12.6 | **4.00**<br>16.0 | | | 3 |
| 3¼ | **0.18**<br>1.8 | **0.41**<br>4.4 | **0.74**<br>5.8 | **0.92**<br>7.4 | **1.14**<br>7.2 | **1.62**<br>8.7 | **2.22**<br>10.2 | **2.92**<br>11.6 | **3.69**<br>14.8 | | | 3¼ |
| 3½ | **0.17**<br>1.7 | **0.38**<br>4.0 | **0.69**<br>5.4 | **0.86**<br>6.9 | **1.06**<br>6.7 | **1.51**<br>8.1 | **2.06**<br>9.4 | **2.71**<br>10.8 | **3.43**<br>13.7 | **4.36**<br>15.4 | | 3½ |
| 3¾ | **0.16**<br>1.6 | **0.35**<br>3.8 | **0.64**<br>5.0 | **0.80**<br>6.4 | **0.99**<br>6.3 | **1.41**<br>7.5 | **1.92**<br>8.8 | **2.53**<br>10.0 | **3.20**<br>12.8 | **4.06**<br>14.4 | **4.99**<br>16.0 | 3¾ |
| 4 | **0.15**<br>1.5 | **0.33**<br>3.5 | **0.60**<br>4.7 | **0.75**<br>6.0 | **0.93**<br>5.9 | **1.32**<br>7.1 | **1.80**<br>8.3 | **2.37**<br>9.4 | **3.00**<br>12.0 | **3.81**<br>13.5 | **4.68**<br>15.0 | 4 |
| 4¼ | **0.14**<br>1.4 | **0.31**<br>3.3 | **0.56**<br>4.4 | **0.71**<br>5.6 | **0.88**<br>5.5 | **1.24**<br>6.7 | **1.69**<br>7.8 | **2.23**<br>8.9 | **2.82**<br>11.3 | **3.59**<br>12.7 | **4.40**<br>14.1 | 4¼ |
| 4½ | **0.13**<br>1.3 | **0.29**<br>3.1 | **0.53**<br>4.2 | **0.67**<br>5.3 | **0.83**<br>5.2 | **1.17**<br>6.3 | **1.60**<br>7.3 | **2.11**<br>8.4 | **2.67**<br>10.7 | **3.39**<br>12.0 | **4.16**<br>13.3 | 4½ |
| 4¾ | **0.13**<br>1.2 | **0.28**<br>3.0 | **0.51**<br>4.0 | **0.63**<br>5.1 | **0.78**<br>5.0 | **1.11**<br>6.0 | **1.52**<br>6.9 | **2.00**<br>7.9 | **2.53**<br>10.1 | **3.21**<br>11.4 | **3.94**<br>12.6 | 4¾ |
| 5 | **0.12**<br>1.2 | **0.26**<br>2.8 | **0.48**<br>3.8 | **0.60**<br>4.8 | **0.74**<br>4.7 | **1.06**<br>5.7 | **1.44**<br>6.6 | **1.90**<br>7.5 | **2.40**<br>9.6 | **3.05**<br>10.8 | **3.74**<br>12.0 | 5 |
| 5¼ | **0.11**<br>1.1 | **0.25**<br>2.7 | **0.46**<br>3.6 | **0.57**<br>4.6 | **0.71**<br>4.5 | **1.01**<br>5.4 | **1.37**<br>6.3 | **1.81**<br>7.2 | **2.29**<br>9.1 | **2.90**<br>10.3 | **3.57**<br>11.4 | 5¼ |
| 5½ | **0.11**<br>1.1 | **0.24**<br>2.6 | **0.44**<br>3.4 | **0.55**<br>4.4 | **0.68**<br>4.3 | **0.96**<br>5.1 | **1.31**<br>6.0 | **1.72**<br>6.9 | **2.18**<br>8.7 | **2.77**<br>9.8 | **3.40**<br>10.9 | 5½ |
| 5¾ | **0.10**<br>1.0 | **0.23**<br>2.5 | **0.42**<br>3.3 | **0.52**<br>4.2 | **0.65**<br>4.1 | **0.92**<br>4.9 | **1.25**<br>5.7 | **1.65**<br>6.6 | **2.09**<br>8.3 | **2.65**<br>9.4 | **3.26**<br>10.4 | 5¾ |
| 6 | **0.10**<br>1.0 | **0.22**<br>2.4 | **0.40**<br>3.1 | **0.50**<br>4.0 | **0.62**<br>3.9 | **0.88**<br>4.7 | **1.20**<br>5.5 | **1.58**<br>6.3 | **2.00**<br>8.0 | **2.54**<br>9.0 | **3.12**<br>10.0 | 6 |
| 6½ | **0.09**<br>0.9 | **0.20**<br>2.2 | **0.37**<br>2.9 | **0.46**<br>3.7 | **0.57**<br>3.6 | **0.81**<br>4.4 | **1.11**<br>5.1 | **1.46**<br>5.8 | **1.85**<br>7.4 | **2.35**<br>8.3 | **2.88**<br>9.2 | 6½ |
| 7 | **0.09**<br>0.8 | **0.19**<br>2.0 | **0.34**<br>2.7 | **0.43**<br>3.4 | **0.53**<br>3.4 | **0.75**<br>4.0 | **1.03**<br>4.7 | **1.35**<br>5.4 | **1.71**<br>6.9 | **2.18**<br>7.7 | **2.67**<br>8.6 | 7 |
| 7½ | **0.08**<br>0.8 | **0.18**<br>1.9 | **0.32**<br>2.5 | **0.40**<br>3.2 | **0.50**<br>3.1 | **0.70**<br>3.8 | **0.96**<br>4.4 | **1.26**<br>5.0 | **1.60**<br>6.4 | **2.03**<br>7.2 | **2.50**<br>8.0 | 7½ |
| 8 | **0.08**<br>0.7 | **0.17**<br>1.8 | **0.30**<br>2.4 | **0.38**<br>3.0 | **0.47**<br>2.9 | **0.66**<br>3.5 | **0.90**<br>4.1 | **1.19**<br>4.7 | **1.50**<br>6.0 | **1.91**<br>6.8 | **2.34**<br>7.5 | 8 |
| 8½ | **0.07**<br>0.7 | **0.16**<br>1.7 | **0.28**<br>2.2 | **0.35**<br>2.8 | **0.44**<br>2.8 | **0.62**<br>3.3 | **0.85**<br>3.9 | **1.12**<br>4.4 | **1.41**<br>5.6 | **1.79**<br>6.4 | **2.20**<br>7.1 | 8½ |
| 9 | **0.07**<br>0.7 | **0.15**<br>1.6 | **0.27**<br>2.1 | **0.33**<br>2.7 | **0.41**<br>2.6 | **0.59**<br>3.1 | **0.80**<br>3.7 | **1.05**<br>4.2 | **1.33**<br>5.3 | **1.69**<br>6.0 | **2.08**<br>6.7 | 9 |
| 9½ | **0.06**<br>0.6 | **0.14**<br>1.5 | **0.25**<br>2.0 | **0.32**<br>2.5 | **0.39**<br>2.5 | **0.56**<br>3.0 | **0.76**<br>3.5 | **1.00**<br>4.0 | **1.26**<br>5.1 | **1.60**<br>5.7 | **1.97**<br>6.3 | 9½ |
| 10 | **0.06**<br>0.6 | **0.13**<br>1.4 | **0.24**<br>1.9 | **0.30**<br>2.4 | **0.37**<br>2.4 | **0.53**<br>2.8 | **0.72**<br>3.3 | **0.95**<br>3.8 | **1.20**<br>4.8 | **1.52**<br>5.4 | **1.87**<br>6.0 | 10 |
| 10½ | **0.06**<br>0.6 | **0.13**<br>1.3 | **0.23**<br>1.8 | **0.29**<br>2.3 | **0.35**<br>2.2 | **0.50**<br>2.7 | **0.69**<br>3.1 | **0.90**<br>3.6 | **1.14**<br>4.6 | **1.45**<br>5.1 | **1.78**<br>5.7 | 10½ |
| 11 | **0.05**<br>0.5 | **0.12**<br>1.3 | **0.22**<br>1.7 | **0.27**<br>2.2 | **0.34**<br>2.2 | **0.48**<br>2.6 | **0.65**<br>3.0 | **0.86**<br>3.4 | **1.09**<br>4.4 | **1.39**<br>4.9 | **1.70**<br>5.5 | 11 |
| 11½ | | | **0.21**<br>1.6 | **0.26**<br>2.1 | **0.32**<br>2.0 | **0.46**<br>2.5 | **0.63**<br>2.9 | **0.82**<br>3.3 | **1.04**<br>4.2 | **1.33**<br>4.7 | **1.63**<br>5.2 | 11½ |
| 12 | | | **0.20**<br>1.6 | **0.25**<br>2.0 | **0.31**<br>2.0 | **0.44**<br>2.4 | **0.60**<br>2.8 | **0.79**<br>3.1 | **1.00**<br>4.0 | **1.27**<br>4.5 | **1.56**<br>5.0 | 12 |
| 13 | | | **0.18**<br>1.4 | **0.23**<br>1.8 | **0.29**<br>1.8 | **0.41**<br>2.2 | **0.55**<br>2.5 | **0.73**<br>2.9 | **0.92**<br>3.7 | **1.17**<br>4.2 | **1.44**<br>4.6 | 13 |
| 14 | | | **0.17**<br>1.3 | **0.21**<br>1.7 | **0.27**<br>1.7 | **0.38**<br>2.0 | **0.51**<br>2.4 | **0.68**<br>2.7 | **0.86**<br>3.4 | **1.09**<br>3.9 | **1.34**<br>4.3 | 14 |
| 15 | | | **0.16**<br>1.3 | **0.20**<br>1.6 | **0.25**<br>1.6 | **0.35**<br>1.9 | **0.48**<br>2.2 | **0.63**<br>2.5 | **0.80**<br>3.2 | **1.02**<br>3.6 | **1.25**<br>4.0 | 15 |
| 16 | | | **0.15**<br>1.2 | **0.19**<br>1.5 | **0.23**<br>1.5 | **0.33**<br>1.8 | **0.45**<br>2.1 | **0.59**<br>2.4 | **0.75**<br>3.0 | **0.95**<br>3.4 | **1.17**<br>3.8 | 16 |
| 17 | | | **0.14**<br>1.1 | **0.18**<br>1.4 | **0.22**<br>1.4 | **0.31**<br>1.7 | **0.42**<br>1.9 | **0.56**<br>2.2 | **0.71**<br>2.8 | **0.90**<br>3.2 | **1.10**<br>3.5 | 17 |
| 18 | | | **0.13**<br>1.0 | **0.17**<br>1.3 | **0.21**<br>1.3 | **0.29**<br>1.6 | **0.40**<br>1.8 | **0.53**<br>2.1 | **0.67**<br>2.7 | **0.85**<br>3.0 | **1.04**<br>3.3 | 18 |

$$a = \frac{f_s}{12{,}000} \times j$$

| $f_s$ | $a$ |
|---|---|
| 8,000 | 0.53 |
| 10,000 | 0.68 |
| 12,000 | 0.83 |
| 14,000 | 0.98 |
| 16,000 | 1.13 |
| 18,000 | 1.29 |
| 20,000 | 1.44 |
| 22,000 | 1.60 |
| 24,000 | 1.76 |
| 27,000 | 2.00 |
| 30,000 | 2.24 |

# Table 4. Coefficients ($F$) for Resisting Moments of Rectangular and T-Sections

**Values of** $F = \dfrac{bd^2}{12{,}000}$

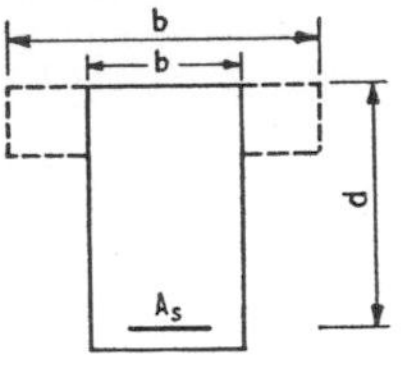


(a) Enter table with known value of $F = \dfrac{M}{K}$ or $\dfrac{NE}{K}$ ($M$ or $NE$ in ft.kips; $K$ from Tables 1 or 8); select $b$ and $d$ (in.)

(b) Enter table with known value of $b$ and $d$; compute resisting moment in concrete: $K \times F$ (ft.kips)

| $d$ | $b$: Width of compressive area | | | | | | | | | | | | | | | | | | | | | |
|---|---|---|---|---|---|---|---|---|---|---|---|---|---|---|---|---|---|---|---|---|---|---|
| | 4 | 5 | 6 | 7 | 7½ | 8 | 9 | 9½ | 10 | 11½ | 12 | 13 | 15 | 17 | 19 | 21 | 23 | 25 | 30 | 36 | 42 | 48 |
| 5 | .008 | .010 | .013 | .015 | .016 | .017 | .019 | .020 | .021 | .024 | .025 | .027 | .031 | .035 | .040 | .044 | .048 | .052 | .063 | .075 | .088 | .100 |
| 5½ | .010 | .013 | .015 | .018 | .019 | .020 | .023 | .024 | .025 | .029 | .030 | .033 | .038 | .043 | .048 | .053 | .058 | .063 | .076 | .091 | .106 | .121 |
| 6 | .012 | .015 | .018 | .021 | .023 | .024 | .027 | .029 | .030 | .035 | .036 | .039 | .045 | .051 | .057 | .063 | .069 | .075 | .090 | .108 | .126 | .144 |
| 6½ | .014 | .018 | .021 | .025 | .026 | .028 | .032 | .033 | .035 | .040 | .042 | .046 | .053 | .060 | .067 | .074 | .081 | .088 | .106 | .127 | .148 | .169 |
| 7 | .016 | .020 | .025 | .029 | .031 | .033 | .037 | .039 | .041 | .047 | .049 | .053 | .061 | .069 | .078 | .086 | .094 | .102 | .123 | .147 | .172 | .196 |
| 7½ | .019 | .023 | .028 | .033 | .035 | .038 | .042 | .045 | .047 | .054 | .056 | .061 | .070 | .080 | .089 | .098 | .108 | .117 | .141 | .169 | .197 | .225 |
| 8 | .021 | .027 | .032 | .037 | .040 | .043 | .048 | .051 | .053 | .061 | .064 | .069 | .080 | .091 | .101 | .112 | .123 | .133 | .160 | .192 | .224 | .256 |
| 8½ | .024 | .030 | .036 | .042 | .045 | .048 | .054 | .057 | .060 | .069 | .072 | .078 | .090 | .102 | .114 | .126 | .138 | .151 | .181 | .217 | .253 | .289 |
| 9 | .027 | .034 | .041 | .047 | .051 | .054 | .061 | .064 | .068 | .078 | .081 | .088 | .101 | .115 | .128 | .142 | .155 | .169 | .203 | .243 | .284 | .324 |
| 9½ | .030 | .038 | .045 | .053 | .056 | .060 | .068 | .071 | .075 | .087 | .090 | .098 | .113 | .128 | .143 | .158 | .173 | .188 | .226 | .271 | .316 | .361 |
| 10 | .033 | .042 | .050 | .058 | .063 | .067 | .075 | .079 | .083 | .096 | .100 | .108 | .125 | .142 | .158 | .175 | .192 | .208 | .250 | .300 | .350 | .400 |
| 10½ | .037 | .046 | .055 | .064 | .069 | .074 | .083 | .087 | .092 | .106 | .110 | .119 | .138 | .156 | .175 | .193 | .211 | .230 | .276 | .331 | .386 | .441 |
| 11 | .040 | .050 | .061 | .071 | .076 | .081 | .091 | .096 | .101 | .116 | .121 | .131 | .151 | .171 | .192 | .212 | .232 | .252 | .303 | .363 | .424 | .484 |
| 11½ | .044 | .055 | .066 | .077 | .083 | .088 | .099 | .105 | .110 | .127 | .132 | .143 | .165 | .187 | .209 | .231 | .253 | .276 | .331 | .397 | .463 | .529 |
| 12 | .048 | .060 | .072 | .084 | .090 | .096 | .108 | .114 | .120 | .138 | .144 | .156 | .180 | .204 | .228 | .252 | .276 | .300 | .360 | .432 | .504 | .576 |
| 12½ | .052 | .065 | .078 | .091 | .098 | .104 | .117 | .124 | .130 | .150 | .156 | .169 | .195 | .221 | .247 | .273 | .299 | .326 | .391 | .469 | .547 | .625 |
| 13 | .056 | .070 | .085 | .099 | .106 | .113 | .126 | .134 | .141 | .162 | .169 | .183 | .211 | .239 | .268 | .296 | .324 | .352 | .422 | .507 | .592 | .676 |
| 13½ | .061 | .076 | .091 | .106 | .114 | .122 | .137 | .144 | .152 | .175 | .182 | .197 | .228 | .258 | .289 | .319 | .349 | .380 | .456 | .547 | .638 | .729 |
| 14 | .065 | .082 | .098 | .114 | .122 | .131 | .147 | .155 | .163 | .188 | .196 | .212 | .245 | .278 | .310 | .343 | .376 | .408 | .490 | .588 | .686 | .784 |
| 14½ | .070 | .088 | .105 | .123 | .131 | .140 | .158 | .166 | .175 | .201 | .210 | .228 | .263 | .298 | .333 | .368 | .403 | .438 | .526 | .631 | .736 | .841 |
| 15 | .075 | .094 | .113 | .131 | .141 | .150 | .169 | .178 | .188 | .216 | .225 | .244 | .281 | .319 | .356 | .394 | .431 | .469 | .563 | .675 | .788 | 0.90 |
| 15½ | .080 | .100 | .120 | .140 | .150 | .160 | .180 | .190 | .200 | .230 | .240 | .260 | .300 | .340 | .380 | .421 | .461 | .500 | .601 | .721 | .842 | 0.96 |
| 16 | .085 | .107 | .128 | .149 | .160 | .171 | .192 | .203 | .213 | .245 | .256 | .277 | .320 | .363 | .405 | .448 | .491 | .533 | .640 | .768 | .896 | 1.02 |
| 16½ | .091 | .113 | .136 | .159 | .170 | .182 | .204 | .216 | .227 | .261 | .272 | .295 | .340 | .386 | .431 | .476 | .522 | .568 | .681 | .817 | .953 | 1.09 |
| 17 | | .120 | .145 | .169 | .181 | .193 | .217 | .229 | .241 | .277 | .289 | .313 | .361 | .409 | .458 | .506 | .554 | .602 | .723 | 0.87 | 1.01 | 1.16 |
| 17½ | | .128 | .153 | .179 | .191 | .204 | .230 | .242 | .255 | .294 | .306 | .332 | .383 | .434 | .485 | .536 | .587 | .638 | .766 | 0.92 | 1.07 | 1.23 |
| 18 | | .135 | .162 | .189 | .203 | .216 | .243 | .257 | .270 | .311 | .324 | .351 | .405 | .459 | .513 | .567 | .621 | .675 | .810 | 0.97 | 1.13 | 1.30 |
| 18½ | | .143 | .171 | .200 | .214 | .228 | .257 | .271 | .285 | .328 | .342 | .371 | .428 | .485 | .542 | .599 | .656 | .713 | .856 | 1.03 | 1.20 | 1.37 |
| 19 | | | .180 | .211 | .226 | .241 | .271 | .286 | .301 | .346 | .361 | .391 | .451 | .511 | .572 | .632 | .692 | 0.75 | 0.90 | 1.08 | 1.26 | 1.44 |
| 20 | | | .200 | .233 | .250 | .267 | .300 | .317 | .333 | .383 | .400 | .433 | .500 | .567 | .633 | .700 | .767 | 0.83 | 1.00 | 1.20 | 1.40 | 1.60 |
| 21 | | | .221 | .257 | .276 | .294 | .331 | .349 | .368 | .423 | .441 | .478 | .551 | .625 | .698 | .772 | .845 | 0.92 | 1.10 | 1.32 | 1.54 | 1.76 |
| 22 | | | .242 | .282 | .302 | .323 | .363 | .383 | .403 | .464 | .484 | .524 | .605 | .686 | .766 | .847 | .928 | 1.01 | 1.21 | 1.45 | 1.69 | 1.94 |
| 23 | | | | .309 | .331 | .353 | .397 | .419 | .441 | .507 | .529 | .573 | .661 | .749 | 0.84 | 0.93 | 1.01 | 1.10 | 1.32 | 1.59 | 1.85 | 2.12 |
| 24 | | | | .336 | .360 | .384 | .432 | .456 | .480 | .552 | .576 | .624 | .720 | .816 | 0.91 | 1.01 | 1.10 | 1.20 | 1.44 | 1.73 | 2.02 | 2.30 |
| 25 | | | | .365 | .391 | .417 | .469 | .495 | .521 | .599 | .625 | .677 | .781 | .885 | 0.99 | 1.09 | 1.20 | 1.30 | 1.56 | 1.87 | 2.19 | 2.50 |
| 26 | | | | .394 | .422 | .451 | .507 | .535 | .563 | .648 | .676 | .732 | .845 | .958 | 1.07 | 1.18 | 1.30 | 1.41 | 1.69 | 2.03 | 2.37 | 2.70 |
| 27 | | | | | .456 | .486 | .547 | .577 | .608 | .699 | .729 | .790 | 0.91 | 1.03 | 1.15 | 1.28 | 1.40 | 1.52 | 1.82 | 2.19 | 2.55 | 2.92 |
| 28 | | | | | .490 | .523 | .588 | .621 | .653 | .751 | .784 | .849 | 0.98 | 1.11 | 1.24 | 1.37 | 1.50 | 1.63 | 1.96 | 2.35 | 2.74 | 3.14 |
| 29 | | | | | .526 | .561 | .631 | .666 | .701 | .806 | .841 | .911 | 1.05 | 1.19 | 1.33 | 1.47 | 1.61 | 1.75 | 2.10 | 2.52 | 2.94 | 3.36 |
| 30 | | | | | .562 | .600 | .675 | .712 | .750 | .862 | .900 | .975 | 1.13 | 1.28 | 1.43 | 1.58 | 1.73 | 1.88 | 2.25 | 2.70 | 3.15 | 3.60 |
| 31 | | | | | | .641 | .721 | .761 | .801 | 0.92 | 0.96 | 1.04 | 1.20 | 1.36 | 1.52 | 1.68 | 1.84 | 2.00 | 2.40 | 2.88 | 3.36 | 3.85 |
| 32 | | | | | | .683 | .768 | .811 | .853 | 0.98 | 1.02 | 1.11 | 1.28 | 1.45 | 1.62 | 1.79 | 1.96 | 2.13 | 2.56 | 3.07 | 3.58 | 4.10 |
| 33 | | | | | | .726 | .817 | .862 | .908 | 1.04 | 1.09 | 1.18 | 1.36 | 1.54 | 1.72 | 1.91 | 2.09 | 2.27 | 2.72 | 3.27 | 3.81 | 4.36 |
| 34 | | | | | | .771 | .867 | .915 | .963 | 1.11 | 1.16 | 1.25 | 1.45 | 1.64 | 1.83 | 2.02 | 2.22 | 2.41 | 2.89 | 3.47 | 4.05 | 4.62 |
| 36 | | | | | | | 0.97 | 1.03 | 1.08 | 1.24 | 1.30 | 1.40 | 1.62 | 1.84 | 2.05 | 2.27 | 2.48 | 2.70 | 3.24 | 3.89 | 4.54 | 5.18 |
| 38 | | | | | | | 1.08 | 1.14 | 1.20 | 1.38 | 1.44 | 1.56 | 1.81 | 2.05 | 2.29 | 2.53 | 2.77 | 3.01 | 3.61 | 4.33 | 5.05 | 5.78 |
| 40 | | | | | | | 1.20 | 1.27 | 1.33 | 1.53 | 1.60 | 1.73 | 2.00 | 2.27 | 2.53 | 2.80 | 3.07 | 3.33 | 4.00 | 4.80 | 5.60 | 6.40 |
| 42 | | | | | | | 1.32 | 1.40 | 1.47 | 1.69 | 1.76 | 1.91 | 2.21 | 2.50 | 2.79 | 3.09 | 3.38 | 3.68 | 4.41 | 5.29 | 6.17 | 7.06 |
| 44 | | | | | | | | 1.53 | 1.61 | 1.86 | 1.94 | 2.10 | 2.42 | 2.74 | 3.07 | 3.39 | 3.71 | 4.03 | 4.84 | 5.81 | 6.78 | 7.74 |
| 46 | | | | | | | | 1.67 | 1.76 | 2.03 | 2.12 | 2.29 | 2.64 | 3.00 | 3.35 | 3.70 | 4.06 | 4.41 | 5.29 | 6.35 | 7.40 | 8.46 |
| 48 | | | | | | | | 1.82 | 1.92 | 2.21 | 2.30 | 2.50 | 2.88 | 3.26 | 3.65 | 4.03 | 4.42 | 4.80 | 5.76 | 6.91 | 8.06 | 9.22 |
| 50 | | | | | | | | 1.98 | 2.08 | 2.40 | 2.50 | 2.71 | 3.13 | 3.54 | 3.96 | 4.38 | 4.79 | 5.21 | 6.25 | 7.50 | 8.75 | 10.0 |
| 52 | | | | | | | | | 2.25 | 2.59 | 2.70 | 2.93 | 3.38 | 3.83 | 4.28 | 4.73 | 5.18 | 5.63 | 6.76 | 8.11 | 9.46 | 10.8 |
| 54 | | | | | | | | | 2.43 | 2.79 | 2.92 | 3.16 | 3.65 | 4.16 | 4.62 | 5.11 | 5.59 | 6.08 | 7.29 | 8.75 | 10.2 | 11.7 |
| 56 | | | | | | | | | 2.61 | 3.01 | 3.17 | 3.40 | 3.92 | 4.44 | 4.97 | 5.49 | 6.01 | 6.54 | 7.84 | 9.41 | 11.0 | 12.5 |
| 58 | | | | | | | | | 2.80 | 3.23 | 3.39 | 3.64 | 4.21 | 4.77 | 5.33 | 5.89 | 6.45 | 7.01 | 8.41 | 10.1 | 11.8 | 13.5 |
| 60 | | | | | | | | | | 3.45 | 3.60 | 3.90 | 4.50 | 5.10 | 5.70 | 6.30 | 6.90 | 7.50 | 9.00 | 10.8 | 12.6 | 14.4 |
| 64 | | | | | | | | | | 3.92 | 4.09 | 4.43 | 5.12 | 5.80 | 6.48 | 7.17 | 7.85 | 8.53 | 10.2 | 12.3 | 14.3 | 16.4 |
| 68 | | | | | | | | | | 4.43 | 4.62 | 5.01 | 5.78 | 6.55 | 7.32 | 8.09 | 8.86 | 9.63 | 11.6 | 13.9 | 16.2 | 18.5 |
| 72 | | | | | | | | | | 4.97 | 5.18 | 5.61 | 6.48 | 7.34 | 8.21 | 9.07 | 9.93 | 10.8 | 13.0 | 15.5 | 18.1 | 20.7 |

# Table 5. Areas and Perimeters of Various Combinations of Bars

Areas, $A_s$ (or $A'_s$) given in bold type (top) sq. in.
Perimeters, $\Sigma o$, in light type (bottom) in.
For use of table, see Example 2.

Columns headed [0 | 5] contain data for bars of *one* size in groups of one to ten.

Columns headed [1 | 2 | 3 | 4 | 5] contain data for bars of *two* sizes with from one to five of each size.

| | | | 0 | 5 | | 1 | 2 | 3 | 4 | 5 | | 1 | 2 | 3 | 4 | 5 | | 1 | 2 | 3 | 4 | 5 |
|---|---|---|---|---|---|---|---|---|---|---|---|---|---|---|---|---|---|---|---|---|---|---|
| | 1 | | **0.20** | **1.20** | | **0.31** | **0.42** | **0.53** | **0.64** | **0.75** | | | | | | | | | | | | |
| | | | 1.6 | 9.4 | | 2.7 | 3.9 | 5.1 | 6.3 | 7.5 | | | | | | | | | | | | |
| | 2 | | **0.40** | **1.40** | | **0.51** | **0.62** | **0.73** | **0.84** | **0.95** | | | | | | | | | | | | |
| | | | 3.1 | 11.0 | | 4.3 | 5.5 | 6.7 | 7.9 | 9.0 | | | | | | | | | | | | |
| ½φ | 3 | ½φ | **0.60** | **1.60** | ⅜φ | **0.71** | **0.82** | **0.93** | **1.04** | **1.15** | | | | | | | | | | | | |
| | | | 4.7 | 12.6 | | 5.9 | 7.1 | 8.2 | 9.4 | 10.6 | | | | | | | | | | | | |
| | 4 | | **0.80** | **1.80** | | **0.91** | **1.02** | **1.13** | **1.24** | **1.35** | | | | | | | | | | | | |
| | | | 6.3 | 14.1 | | 7.5 | 8.6 | 9.8 | 11.0 | 12.2 | | | | | | | | | | | | |
| | 5 | | **1.00** | **2.00** | | **1.11** | **1.22** | **1.33** | **1.44** | **1.55** | | | | | | | | | | | | |
| | | | 7.9 | 15.7 | | 9.0 | 10.2 | 11.4 | 12.6 | 13.7 | | | | | | | | | | | | |
| | 1 | | **0.25** | **1.50** | | **0.45** | **0.65** | **0.85** | **1.05** | **1.25** | | **0.36** | **0.47** | **0.58** | **0.69** | **0.80** | | | | | | |
| | | | 2.0 | 12.0 | | 3.6 | 5.1 | 6.7 | 8.3 | 9.9 | | 3.2 | 4.4 | 5.5 | 6.7 | 7.9 | | | | | | |
| | 2 | | **0.50** | **1.75** | | **0.70** | **0.90** | **1.10** | **1.30** | **1.50** | | **0.61** | **0.72** | **0.83** | **0.94** | **1.05** | | | | | | |
| | | | 4.0 | 14.0 | | 5.6 | 7.1 | 8.7 | 10.3 | 11.9 | | 5.2 | 6.4 | 7.5 | 8.7 | 9.9 | | | | | | |
| ½□ | 3 | ½□ | **0.75** | **2.00** | ½φ | **0.95** | **1.15** | **1.35** | **1.55** | **1.75** | ⅜φ | **0.86** | **0.97** | **1.08** | **1.19** | **1.30** | | | | | | |
| | | | 6.0 | 16.0 | | 7.6 | 9.1 | 10.7 | 12.3 | 13.9 | | 7.2 | 8.4 | 9.5 | 10.7 | 11.9 | | | | | | |
| | 4 | | **1.00** | **2.25** | | **1.20** | **1.40** | **1.60** | **1.80** | **2.00** | | **1.11** | **1.22** | **1.33** | **1.44** | **1.55** | | | | | | |
| | | | 8.0 | 18.0 | | 9.6 | 11.1 | 12.7 | 14.3 | 15.9 | | 9.2 | 10.4 | 11.5 | 12.7 | 13.9 | | | | | | |
| | 5 | | **1.25** | **2.50** | | **1.45** | **1.65** | **1.85** | **2.05** | **2.25** | | **1.36** | **1.47** | **1.58** | **1.69** | **1.80** | | | | | | |
| | | | 10.0 | 20.0 | | 11.6 | 13.1 | 14.7 | 16.3 | 17.9 | | 11.2 | 12.4 | 13.5 | 14.7 | 15.9 | | | | | | |
| | 1 | | **0.31** | **1.86** | | **0.56** | **0.81** | **1.06** | **1.31** | **1.56** | | **0.51** | **0.71** | **0.91** | **1.11** | **1.31** | | **0.42** | **0.53** | **0.64** | **0.75** | **0.86** |
| | | | 2.0 | 11.8 | | 4.0 | 6.0 | 8.0 | 10.0 | 12.0 | | 3.5 | 5.1 | 6.7 | 8.2 | 9.8 | | 3.1 | 4.3 | 5.5 | 6.7 | 7.9 |
| | 2 | | **0.62** | **2.17** | | **0.87** | **1.12** | **1.37** | **1.62** | **1.87** | | **0.82** | **1.02** | **1.22** | **1.42** | **1.62** | | **0.73** | **0.84** | **0.95** | **1.06** | **1.17** |
| | | | 3.9 | 13.7 | | 5.9 | 7.9 | 9.9 | 11.9 | 13.9 | | 5.5 | 7.1 | 8.6 | 10.2 | 11.8 | | 5.1 | 6.3 | 7.5 | 8.6 | 9.8 |
| ⅝φ | 3 | ⅝φ | **0.93** | **2.48** | ½□ | **1.18** | **1.43** | **1.68** | **1.93** | **2.18** | ½φ | **1.13** | **1.33** | **1.53** | **1.73** | **1.93** | ⅜φ | **1.04** | **1.15** | **1.26** | **1.37** | **1.48** |
| | | | 5.9 | 15.7 | | 7.9 | 9.9 | 11.9 | 13.9 | 15.9 | | 7.5 | 9.0 | 10.6 | 12.2 | 13.7 | | 7.1 | 8.2 | 9.4 | 10.6 | 11.8 |
| | 4 | | **1.24** | **2.79** | | **1.49** | **1.74** | **1.99** | **2.24** | **2.49** | | **1.44** | **1.64** | **1.84** | **2.04** | **2.24** | | **1.35** | **1.46** | **1.57** | **1.68** | **1.79** |
| | | | 7.9 | 17.6 | | 9.8 | 11.8 | 13.8 | 15.8 | 17.8 | | 9.4 | 11.0 | 12.6 | 14.1 | 15.7 | | 9.0 | 10.2 | 11.4 | 12.6 | 13.8 |
| | 5 | | **1.55** | **3.10** | | **1.80** | **2.05** | **2.30** | **2.55** | **2.80** | | **1.75** | **1.95** | **2.15** | **2.35** | **2.55** | | **1.66** | **1.77** | **1.88** | **1.99** | **2.10** |
| | | | 9.8 | 19.6 | | 11.8 | 13.8 | 15.8 | 17.8 | 19.8 | | 11.4 | 13.0 | 14.5 | 16.1 | 17.7 | | 11.0 | 12.2 | 13.3 | 14.5 | 15.7 |
| | 1 | | **0.44** | **2.64** | | **0.75** | **1.06** | **1.37** | **1.68** | **1.99** | | **0.69** | **0.94** | **1.19** | **1.44** | **1.69** | | **0.64** | **0.84** | **1.04** | **1.24** | **1.44** |
| | | | 2.4 | 14.1 | | 4.3 | 6.3 | 8.2 | 10.2 | 12.2 | | 4.4 | 6.4 | 8.4 | 10.4 | 12.4 | | 3.9 | 5.5 | 7.1 | 8.6 | 10.2 |
| | 2 | | **0.88** | **3.08** | | **1.19** | **1.50** | **1.81** | **2.12** | **2.43** | | **1.13** | **1.38** | **1.63** | **1.88** | **2.13** | | **1.08** | **1.28** | **1.48** | **1.68** | **1.88** |
| | | | 4.7 | 16.5 | | 6.7 | 8.6 | 10.6 | 12.6 | 14.5 | | 6.7 | 8.7 | 10.7 | 12.7 | 14.7 | | 6.3 | 7.9 | 9.4 | 11.0 | 12.6 |
| ¾φ | 3 | ¾φ | **1.32** | **3.52** | ⅝φ | **1.63** | **1.94** | **2.25** | **2.56** | **2.87** | ½□ | **1.57** | **1.82** | **2.07** | **2.32** | **2.57** | ½φ | **1.52** | **1.72** | **1.92** | **2.12** | **2.32** |
| | | | 7.1 | 18.8 | | 9.0 | 11.0 | 13.0 | 14.9 | 16.9 | | 9.1 | 11.1 | 13.1 | 15.1 | 17.1 | | 8.6 | 10.2 | 11.8 | 13.4 | 14.9 |
| | 4 | | **1.76** | **3.96** | | **2.07** | **2.38** | **2.69** | **3.00** | **3.31** | | **2.01** | **2.26** | **2.51** | **2.76** | **3.01** | | **1.96** | **2.16** | **2.36** | **2.56** | **2.76** |
| | | | 9.4 | 21.2 | | 11.4 | 13.4 | 15.3 | 17.3 | 19.2 | | 11.4 | 13.4 | 15.4 | 17.4 | 19.4 | | 11.0 | 12.6 | 14.1 | 15.7 | 17.3 |
| | 5 | | **2.20** | **4.40** | | **2.51** | **2.82** | **3.13** | **3.44** | **3.75** | | **2.45** | **2.70** | **2.95** | **3.20** | **3.45** | | **2.40** | **2.60** | **2.80** | **3.00** | **3.20** |
| | | | 11.8 | 23.6 | | 13.7 | 15.7 | 17.7 | 19.6 | 21.6 | | 13.8 | 15.8 | 17.8 | 19.8 | 21.8 | | 13.4 | 14.9 | 16.5 | 18.1 | 19.6 |
| | 1 | | **0.60** | **3.60** | | **1.04** | **1.48** | **1.92** | **2.36** | **2.80** | | **0.91** | **1.22** | **1.53** | **1.84** | **2.15** | | **0.85** | **1.10** | **1.35** | **1.60** | **1.85** |
| | | | 2.7 | 16.5 | | 5.1 | 7.5 | 9.8 | 12.2 | 14.5 | | 4.7 | 6.7 | 8.6 | 10.6 | 12.6 | | 4.7 | 6.7 | 8.7 | 10.7 | 12.7 |
| | 2 | | **1.20** | **4.20** | | **1.64** | **2.08** | **2.52** | **2.96** | **3.40** | | **1.51** | **1.82** | **2.13** | **2.44** | **2.75** | | **1.45** | **1.70** | **1.95** | **2.20** | **2.45** |
| | | | 5.5 | 19.2 | | 7.9 | 10.2 | 12.6 | 14.9 | 17.3 | | 7.5 | 9.4 | 11.4 | 13.3 | 15.3 | | 7.5 | 9.5 | 11.5 | 13.5 | 15.5 |
| ⅞φ | 3 | ⅞φ | **1.80** | **4.80** | ¾φ | **2.24** | **2.68** | **3.12** | **3.56** | **4.00** | ⅝φ | **2.11** | **2.42** | **2.73** | **3.04** | **3.35** | ½□ | **2.05** | **2.30** | **2.55** | **2.80** | **3.05** |
| | | | 8.2 | 22.0 | | 10.6 | 13.0 | 15.3 | 17.7 | 20.0 | | 10.2 | 12.2 | 14.1 | 16.1 | 18.1 | | 10.2 | 12.2 | 14.2 | 16.2 | 18.2 |
| | 4 | | **2.40** | **5.40** | | **2.84** | **3.28** | **3.72** | **4.16** | **4.60** | | **2.71** | **3.02** | **3.33** | **3.64** | **3.95** | | **2.65** | **2.90** | **3.15** | **3.40** | **3.65** |
| | | | 11.0 | 24.7 | | 13.4 | 15.7 | 18.1 | 20.4 | 22.8 | | 13.0 | 14.9 | 16.9 | 18.8 | 20.8 | | 13.0 | 15.0 | 17.0 | 19.0 | 21.0 |
| | 5 | | **3.00** | **6.00** | | **3.44** | **3.88** | **4.32** | **4.76** | **5.20** | | **3.31** | **3.62** | **3.93** | **4.24** | **4.55** | | **3.25** | **3.50** | **3.75** | **4.00** | **4.25** |
| | | | 13.7 | 27.5 | | 16.1 | 18.5 | 20.8 | 23.2 | 25.5 | | 15.7 | 17.7 | 19.6 | 21.6 | 23.6 | | 15.7 | 17.7 | 19.7 | 21.7 | 23.7 |
| | 1 | | **0.79** | **4.74** | | **1.39** | **1.99** | **2.59** | **3.19** | **3.79** | | **1.23** | **1.67** | **2.11** | **2.55** | **2.99** | | **1.10** | **1.41** | **1.72** | **2.03** | **2.34** |
| | | | 3.1 | 18.8 | | 5.9 | 8.6 | 11.4 | 14.1 | 16.9 | | 5.5 | 7.9 | 10.2 | 12.6 | 14.9 | | 5.1 | 7.1 | 9.0 | 11.0 | 13.0 |
| | 2 | | **1.58** | **5.53** | | **2.18** | **2.78** | **3.38** | **3.98** | **4.58** | | **2.02** | **2.46** | **2.90** | **3.34** | **3.78** | | **1.89** | **2.20** | **2.51** | **2.82** | **3.13** |
| | | | 6.3 | 22.0 | | 9.0 | 11.8 | 14.5 | 17.3 | 20.0 | | 8.6 | 11.0 | 13.4 | 15.7 | 18.1 | | 8.2 | 10.2 | 12.2 | 14.1 | 16.1 |
| 1φ | 3 | 1φ | **2.37** | **6.32** | ⅞φ | **2.97** | **3.57** | **4.17** | **4.77** | **5.37** | ¾φ | **2.81** | **3.25** | **3.69** | **4.13** | **4.57** | ⅝φ | **2.68** | **2.99** | **3.30** | **3.61** | **3.92** |
| | | | 9.4 | 25.1 | | 12.2 | 14.9 | 17.7 | 20.4 | 23.2 | | 11.8 | 14.1 | 16.5 | 18.9 | 21.2 | | 11.4 | 13.3 | 15.3 | 17.3 | 19.2 |
| | 4 | | **3.16** | **7.11** | | **3.76** | **4.36** | **4.96** | **5.56** | **6.16** | | **3.60** | **4.04** | **4.48** | **4.92** | **5.36** | | **3.47** | **3.78** | **4.09** | **4.40** | **4.71** |
| | | | 12.6 | 28.3 | | 15.3 | 18.1 | 20.8 | 23.6 | 26.3 | | 14.9 | 17.3 | 19.6 | 22.0 | 24.3 | | 14.5 | 16.5 | 18.5 | 20.4 | 22.4 |
| | 5 | | **3.95** | **7.90** | | **4.55** | **5.15** | **5.75** | **6.35** | **6.95** | | **4.39** | **4.83** | **5.27** | **5.71** | **6.15** | | **4.26** | **4.57** | **4.88** | **5.19** | **5.50** |
| | | | 15.7 | 31.4 | | 18.5 | 21.2 | 24.0 | 26.7 | 29.5 | | 18.1 | 20.4 | 22.8 | 25.1 | 27.5 | | 17.7 | 19.6 | 21.6 | 23.6 | 25.5 |
| | 1 | | **1.00** | **6.00** | | **1.79** | **2.58** | **3.37** | **4.16** | **4.95** | | **1.60** | **2.20** | **2.80** | **3.40** | **4.00** | | **1.44** | **1.88** | **2.32** | **2.76** | **3.20** |
| | | | 4.0 | 24.0 | | 7.1 | 10.3 | 13.4 | 16.6 | 19.7 | | 6.7 | 9.5 | 12.2 | 15.0 | 17.7 | | 6.4 | 8.7 | 11.1 | 13.4 | 15.8 |
| | 2 | | **2.00** | **7.00** | | **2.79** | **3.58** | **4.37** | **5.16** | **5.95** | | **2.60** | **3.20** | **3.80** | **4.40** | **5.00** | | **2.44** | **2.88** | **3.32** | **3.76** | **4.20** |
| | | | 8.0 | 28.0 | | 11.1 | 14.3 | 17.4 | 20.6 | 23.7 | | 10.7 | 13.5 | 16.2 | 19.0 | 21.7 | | 10.4 | 12.7 | 15.1 | 17.4 | 19.8 |
| 1□ | 3 | 1□ | **3.00** | **8.00** | 1φ | **3.79** | **4.58** | **5.37** | **6.16** | **6.95** | ⅞φ | **3.60** | **4.20** | **4.80** | **5.40** | **6.00** | ¾φ | **3.44** | **3.88** | **4.32** | **4.76** | **5.20** |
| | | | 12.0 | 32.0 | | 15.1 | 18.3 | 21.4 | 24.6 | 27.7 | | 14.7 | 17.5 | 20.2 | 23.0 | 25.7 | | 14.4 | 16.7 | 19.1 | 21.4 | 23.8 |
| | 4 | | **4.00** | **9.00** | | **4.79** | **5.58** | **6.37** | **7.16** | **7.95** | | **4.60** | **5.20** | **5.80** | **6.40** | **7.00** | | **4.44** | **4.88** | **5.32** | **5.76** | **6.20** |
| | | | 16.0 | 36.0 | | 19.1 | 22.3 | 25.4 | 28.6 | 31.7 | | 18.7 | 21.5 | 24.2 | 27.0 | 29.7 | | 18.4 | 20.7 | 23.1 | 25.4 | 27.8 |
| | 5 | | **5.00** | **10.00** | | **5.79** | **6.58** | **7.37** | **8.16** | **8.95** | | **5.60** | **6.20** | **6.80** | **7.40** | **8.00** | | **5.44** | **5.88** | **6.32** | **6.76** | **7.20** |
| | | | 20.0 | 40.0 | | 23.1 | 26.3 | 29.4 | 32.6 | 35.7 | | 22.7 | 25.5 | 28.2 | 31.0 | 33.7 | | 22.4 | 24.7 | 27.1 | 29.4 | 31.8 |
| | 1 | | **1.27** | **7.62** | | **2.27** | **3.27** | **4.27** | **5.27** | **6.27** | | **2.06** | **2.85** | **3.64** | **4.43** | **5.22** | | **1.87** | **2.47** | **3.07** | **3.67** | **4.27** |
| | | | 4.5 | 27.0 | | 8.5 | 12.5 | 16.5 | 20.5 | 24.5 | | 7.6 | 10.8 | 13.9 | 17.1 | 20.2 | | 7.2 | 10.0 | 12.7 | 15.5 | 18.2 |
| | 2 | | **2.54** | **8.89** | | **3.54** | **4.54** | **5.54** | **6.54** | **7.54** | | **3.33** | **4.12** | **4.91** | **5.70** | **6.49** | | **3.14** | **3.74** | **4.34** | **4.94** | **5.54** |
| | | | 9.0 | 31.5 | | 13.0 | 17.0 | 21.0 | 25.0 | 29.0 | | 12.1 | 15.3 | 18.4 | 21.6 | 24.7 | | 11.7 | 14.5 | 17.2 | 20.0 | 22.7 |
| 1⅛□ | 3 | 1⅛□ | **3.81** | **10.16** | 1□ | **4.81** | **5.81** | **6.81** | **7.81** | **8.81** | 1φ | **4.60** | **5.39** | **6.18** | **6.97** | **7.76** | ⅞φ | **4.41** | **5.01** | **5.61** | **6.21** | **6.81** |
| | | | 13.5 | 36.0 | | 17.5 | 21.5 | 25.5 | 29.5 | 33.5 | | 16.6 | 19.8 | 22.9 | 26.1 | 29.2 | | 16.2 | 19.0 | 21.7 | 24.5 | 27.2 |
| | 4 | | **5.08** | **11.43** | | **6.08** | **7.08** | **8.08** | **9.08** | **10.08** | | **5.87** | **6.66** | **7.45** | **8.24** | **9.03** | | **5.68** | **6.28** | **6.88** | **7.48** | **8.08** |
| | | | 18.0 | 40.5 | | 22.0 | 26.0 | 30.0 | 34.0 | 38.0 | | 21.1 | 24.3 | 27.4 | 30.6 | 33.7 | | 20.7 | 23.5 | 26.2 | 29.0 | 31.7 |
| | 5 | | **6.35** | **12.70** | | **7.35** | **8.35** | **9.35** | **10.35** | **11.35** | | **7.14** | **7.93** | **8.72** | **9.51** | **10.30** | | **6.95** | **7.55** | **8.15** | **8.75** | **9.35** |
| | | | 22.5 | 45.0 | | 26.5 | 30.5 | 34.5 | 38.5 | 42.5 | | 25.6 | 28.8 | 31.9 | 35.1 | 38.2 | | 25.2 | 28.0 | 30.7 | 33.5 | 36.2 |
| | 1 | | **1.56** | **9.36** | | **2.83** | **4.10** | **5.37** | **6.64** | **7.91** | | **2.56** | **3.56** | **4.56** | **5.56** | **6.56** | | **2.35** | **3.14** | **3.93** | **4.72** | **5.51** |
| | | | 5.0 | 30.0 | | 9.5 | 14.0 | 18.5 | 23.0 | 27.5 | | 9.0 | 13.0 | 17.0 | 21.0 | 25.0 | | 8.1 | 11.3 | 14.4 | 17.6 | 20.7 |
| | 2 | | **3.12** | **10.92** | | **4.39** | **5.66** | **6.93** | **8.20** | **9.47** | | **4.12** | **5.12** | **6.12** | **7.12** | **8.12** | | **3.91** | **4.70** | **5.49** | **6.28** | **7.07** |
| | | | 10.0 | 35.0 | | 14.5 | 19.0 | 23.5 | 28.0 | 32.5 | | 14.0 | 18.0 | 22.0 | 26.0 | 30.0 | | 13.1 | 16.3 | 19.4 | 22.6 | 25.7 |
| 1¼□ | 3 | 1¼□ | **4.68** | **12.48** | 1⅛□ | **5.95** | **7.22** | **8.49** | **9.76** | **11.03** | 1□ | **5.68** | **6.68** | **7.68** | **8.68** | **9.68** | 1φ | **5.47** | **6.26** | **7.05** | **7.84** | **8.63** |
| | | | 15.0 | 40.0 | | 19.5 | 24.0 | 28.5 | 33.0 | 37.5 | | 19.0 | 23.0 | 27.0 | 31.0 | 35.0 | | 18.1 | 21.3 | 24.4 | 27.6 | 30.7 |
| | 4 | | **6.24** | **14.04** | | **7.51** | **8.78** | **10.05** | **11.32** | **12.59** | | **7.24** | **8.24** | **9.24** | **10.24** | **11.24** | | **7.03** | **7.82** | **8.61** | **9.40** | **10.19** |
| | | | 20.0 | 45.0 | | 24.5 | 29.0 | 33.5 | 38.0 | 42.5 | | 24.0 | 28.0 | 32.0 | 36.0 | 40.0 | | 23.1 | 26.3 | 29.4 | 32.6 | 35.7 |
| | 5 | | **7.80** | **15.60** | | **9.07** | **10.34** | **11.61** | **12.88** | **14.15** | | **8.80** | **9.80** | **10.80** | **11.80** | **12.80** | | **8.59** | **9.38** | **10.17** | **10.96** | **11.75** |
| | | | 25.0 | 50.0 | | 29.5 | 34.0 | 38.5 | 43.0 | 47.5 | | 29.0 | 33.0 | 37.0 | 41.0 | 45.0 | | 28.1 | 31.3 | 34.4 | 37.6 | 40.7 |

# Table 6. Minimum Web Widths for Various Combinations of Bars

Bold type (top): width of beam webs with bars not specially anchored.
Light type (bottom): width of beam webs with bars specially anchored.
Widths required for joist webs: 2 in. less than table values. All units in inches.
For use of table, see Example 2.

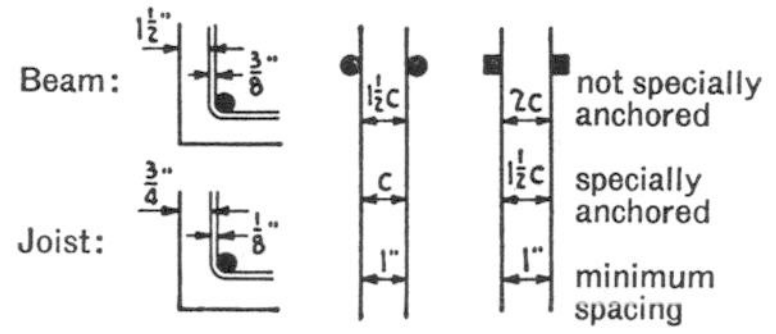


Columns headed | 0 | 5 | contain data for bars of *one* size in groups of one to ten.
Columns headed | 1 | 2 | 3 | 4 | 5 | contain data for bars of *two* sizes with from one to five of each size. Data are in accordance with A. C. I. Code 1936.

| | | 0 | 5 |
|---|---|---|---|
| | 1 | **—**<br>— | **12.0**<br>12.0 |
| | 2 | **6.0**<br>6.0 | **13.5**<br>13.5 |
| 3/8φ or 1/2φ | 3 | **7.5**<br>7.5 | **15.0**<br>15.0 |
| | 4 | **9.0**<br>9.0 | **16.5**<br>16.5 |
| | 5 | **10.5**<br>10.5 | **18.0**<br>18.0 |
| | 1 | **—**<br>— | **13.5**<br>13.5 |
| | 2 | **6.5**<br>6.5 | **15.0**<br>15.0 |
| 1/2□ | 3 | **8.0**<br>8.0 | **17.0**<br>17.0 |
| | 4 | **10.0**<br>10.0 | **18.5**<br>18.5 |
| | 5 | **11.5**<br>11.5 | **20.5**<br>20.5 |
| | 1 | **—**<br>— | **12.5**<br>12.5 |
| | 2 | **6.0**<br>6.0 | **14.5**<br>14.5 |
| 5/8φ | 3 | **8.0**<br>8.0 | **16.0**<br>16.0 |
| | 4 | **9.5**<br>9.5 | **17.5**<br>17.5 |
| | 5 | **11.0**<br>11.0 | **19.0**<br>19.0 |
| | 1 | **—**<br>— | **14.0**<br>13.5 |
| | 2 | **6.5**<br>6.5 | **16.0**<br>15.0 |
| 3/4φ | 3 | **8.5**<br>8.0 | **18.0**<br>17.0 |
| | 4 | **10.5**<br>10.0 | **19.5**<br>18.5 |
| | 5 | **12.0**<br>11.5 | **21.5**<br>20.5 |
| | 1 | <br>— | **16.0**<br>14.0 |
| | 2 | **7.0**<br>6.5 | **18.0**<br>16.0 |
| 7/8φ | 3 | **9.0**<br>8.5 | **20.0**<br>18.0 |
| | 4 | **11.5**<br>10.5 | **22.5**<br>20.0 |
| | 5 | **13.5**<br>12.5 | **24.5**<br>21.5 |
| | 1 | **—**<br>— | **17.5**<br>15.0 |
| | 2 | **7.5**<br>7.0 | **20.0**<br>17.0 |
| 1φ | 3 | **10.0**<br>9.0 | **22.5**<br>19.0 |
| | 4 | **12.5**<br>11.0 | **25.0**<br>21.0 |
| | 5 | **15.0**<br>13.0 | **27.5**<br>23.0 |
| | 1 | **—**<br>— | **20.0**<br>17.5 |
| | 2 | **8.0**<br>7.5 | **23.0**<br>20.0 |
| 1□ | 3 | **11.0**<br>10.0 | **26.0**<br>22.5 |
| | 4 | **14.0**<br>12.5 | **29.0**<br>25.0 |
| | 5 | **17.0**<br>15.0 | **32.0**<br>27.5 |
| | 1 | **—**<br>— | **22.0**<br>19.0 |
| | 2 | **8.5**<br>8.0 | **25.5**<br>22.0 |
| 1 1/8□ | 3 | **12.0**<br>10.5 | **28.5**<br>25.0 |
| | 4 | **15.0**<br>13.5 | **32.0**<br>27.5 |
| | 5 | **18.5**<br>16.5 | **35.5**<br>30.5 |
| | 1 | **—**<br>— | **24.0**<br>21.0 |
| | 2 | **9.0**<br>8.5 | **27.5**<br>24.0 |
| 1 1/4□ | 3 | **12.5**<br>11.5 | **31.5**<br>27.0 |
| | 4 | **16.5**<br>14.5 | **35.0**<br>30.0 |
| | 5 | **20.0**<br>17.5 | **39.0**<br>33.5 |

| | | | 1 | 2 | 3 | 4 | 5 |
|---|---|---|---|---|---|---|---|
| | 1 | | **6.0**<br>6.0 | **7.5**<br>7.5 | **9.0**<br>9.0 | **10.5**<br>10.5 | **12.0**<br>12.0 |
| | 2 | | **8.0**<br>8.0 | **9.5**<br>9.5 | **11.0**<br>11.0 | **12.5**<br>12.5 | **14.0**<br>14.0 |
| 1/2□ | 3 | 3/8φ or 1/2φ | **9.5**<br>9.5 | **11.0**<br>11.0 | **12.5**<br>12.5 | **14.0**<br>14.0 | **15.5**<br>15.5 |
| | 4 | | **11.5**<br>11.5 | **13.0**<br>13.0 | **14.5**<br>14.5 | **16.0**<br>16.0 | **17.5**<br>17.5 |
| | 5 | | **13.0**<br>13.0 | **14.5**<br>14.5 | **16.0**<br>16.0 | **17.5**<br>17.5 | **19.0**<br>19.0 |
| | 1 | | **6.5**<br>6.5 | **8.0**<br>8.0 | **10.0**<br>10.0 | **11.5**<br>11.5 | **13.5**<br>13.5 |
| | 2 | | **8.0**<br>8.0 | **9.5**<br>9.5 | **11.5**<br>11.5 | **13.0**<br>13.0 | **15.0**<br>15.0 |
| 5/8φ | 3 | 1/2□ | **9.5**<br>9.5 | **11.5**<br>11.5 | **13.0**<br>13.0 | **15.0**<br>15.0 | **16.5**<br>16.5 |
| | 4 | | **11.0**<br>11.0 | **13.0**<br>13.0 | **14.5**<br>14.5 | **16.5**<br>16.5 | **18.0**<br>18.0 |
| | 5 | | **13.0**<br>13.0 | **14.5**<br>14.5 | **16.5**<br>16.5 | **18.0**<br>18.0 | **20.0**<br>20.0 |
| | 1 | | **6.5**<br>6.5 | **8.0**<br>8.0 | **9.5**<br>9.5 | **11.0**<br>11.0 | **13.0**<br>13.0 |
| | 2 | | **8.0**<br>8.0 | **10.0**<br>9.5 | **11.5**<br>11.5 | **13.0**<br>13.0 | **14.5**<br>14.5 |
| 3/4φ | 3 | 5/8φ | **10.0**<br>10.0 | **11.5**<br>11.5 | **13.5**<br>13.0 | **15.0**<br>14.5 | **16.5**<br>16.5 |
| | 4 | | **12.0**<br>11.5 | **13.5**<br>13.0 | **15.0**<br>15.0 | **17.0**<br>16.5 | **18.5**<br>18.0 |
| | 5 | | **14.0**<br>13.5 | **15.5**<br>15.0 | **17.0**<br>16.5 | **18.5**<br>18.0 | **20.5**<br>20.0 |
| | 1 | | **6.5**<br>6.5 | **8.5**<br>8.5 | **10.5**<br>10.0 | **12.5**<br>12.0 | **14.0**<br>13.5 |
| | 2 | | **9.0**<br>8.5 | **11.0**<br>10.0 | **12.5**<br>12.0 | **14.5**<br>13.5 | **16.5**<br>15.5 |
| 7/8φ | 3 | 3/4φ | **11.0**<br>10.5 | **13.0**<br>12.0 | **15.0**<br>14.0 | **16.5**<br>15.5 | **18.5**<br>17.5 |
| | 4 | | **13.5**<br>12.0 | **15.0**<br>14.0 | **17.0**<br>15.5 | **19.0**<br>17.5 | **21.0**<br>19.0 |
| | 5 | | **15.5**<br>14.0 | **17.5**<br>16.0 | **19.0**<br>17.5 | **21.0**<br>19.5 | **23.0**<br>21.0 |
| | 1 | | **7.0**<br>7.0 | **9.5**<br>8.5 | **11.5**<br>10.5 | **13.5**<br>12.5 | **16.0**<br>14.5 |
| | 2 | | **9.5**<br>9.0 | **12.0**<br>10.5 | **14.0**<br>12.5 | **16.0**<br>14.5 | **18.5**<br>16.5 |
| 1φ | 3 | 7/8φ | **12.0**<br>11.0 | **14.5**<br>12.5 | **16.5**<br>14.5 | **18.5**<br>16.5 | **21.0**<br>18.5 |
| | 4 | | **14.5**<br>13.0 | **17.0**<br>14.5 | **19.0**<br>16.5 | **21.0**<br>18.5 | **23.5**<br>20.5 |
| | 5 | | **17.0**<br>15.0 | **19.5**<br>16.5 | **21.5**<br>18.5 | **23.5**<br>20.5 | **26.0**<br>22.5 |
| | 1 | | **7.5**<br>7.0 | **10.0**<br>9.0 | **12.5**<br>11.0 | **15.0**<br>13.0 | **17.5**<br>15.0 |
| | 2 | | **10.5**<br>9.5 | **13.0**<br>11.5 | **15.5**<br>13.5 | **18.0**<br>15.5 | **20.5**<br>17.5 |
| 1□ | 3 | 1φ | **13.5**<br>12.0 | **16.0**<br>14.0 | **18.5**<br>16.0 | **21.0**<br>18.0 | **23.5**<br>20.0 |
| | 4 | | **16.5**<br>14.5 | **19.0**<br>16.5 | **21.5**<br>18.5 | **24.0**<br>20.5 | **26.5**<br>22.5 |
| | 5 | | **19.5**<br>17.0 | **22.0**<br>19.0 | **24.5**<br>21.0 | **27.0**<br>23.0 | **29.5**<br>25.0 |
| | 1 | | **8.0**<br>7.5 | **11.0**<br>10.0 | **14.0**<br>12.5 | **17.0**<br>15.0 | **20.0**<br>17.5 |
| | 2 | | **11.5**<br>10.5 | **14.5**<br>13.0 | **17.5**<br>15.5 | **20.5**<br>18.0 | **23.5**<br>20.5 |
| 1 1/8□ | 3 | 1□ | **15.0**<br>13.0 | **18.0**<br>15.5 | **21.0**<br>18.0 | **24.0**<br>20.5 | **27.0**<br>23.0 |
| | 4 | | **18.0**<br>16.0 | **21.0**<br>18.5 | **24.0**<br>21.0 | **27.0**<br>23.5 | **30.0**<br>26.0 |
| | 5 | | **21.5**<br>19.0 | **24.5**<br>21.5 | **27.5**<br>24.0 | **30.5**<br>26.5 | **33.5**<br>29.0 |
| | 1 | | **8.5**<br>8.0 | **12.0**<br>11.0 | **15.5**<br>13.5 | **18.5**<br>16.5 | **22.0**<br>19.5 |
| | 2 | | **12.5**<br>11.0 | **15.5**<br>14.0 | **19.0**<br>17.0 | **22.5**<br>19.5 | **26.0**<br>22.5 |
| 1 1/4□ | 3 | 1 1/8□ | **16.0**<br>14.5 | **19.5**<br>17.0 | **23.0**<br>20.0 | **26.0**<br>22.5 | **29.5**<br>25.5 |
| | 4 | | **20.0**<br>17.5 | **23.0**<br>20.0 | **26.5**<br>23.0 | **30.0**<br>26.0 | **33.5**<br>28.5 |
| | 5 | | **23.5**<br>20.5 | **27.0**<br>23.5 | **30.5**<br>26.0 | **33.5**<br>29.0 | **37.0**<br>32.0 |

| | | | 1 | 2 | 3 | 4 | 5 |
|---|---|---|---|---|---|---|---|
| | 1 | | **6.0**<br>6.0 | **7.5**<br>7.5 | **9.0**<br>9.0 | **10.5**<br>10.5 | **12.0**<br>12.0 |
| | 2 | | **7.5**<br>7.5 | **9.0**<br>9.0 | **10.5**<br>10.5 | **12.0**<br>12.0 | **13.5**<br>13.5 |
| 5/8φ | 3 | 3/8φ or 1/2φ | **9.5**<br>9.5 | **11.0**<br>11.0 | **12.5**<br>12.5 | **14.0**<br>14.0 | **15.5**<br>15.5 |
| | 4 | | **11.0**<br>11.0 | **12.5**<br>12.5 | **14.0**<br>14.0 | **15.5**<br>15.5 | **17.0**<br>17.0 |
| | 5 | | **12.5**<br>12.5 | **14.0**<br>14.0 | **15.5**<br>15.5 | **17.0**<br>17.0 | **18.5**<br>18.5 |
| | 1 | | **6.5**<br>6.5 | **8.0**<br>8.0 | **10.0**<br>10.0 | **11.5**<br>11.5 | **13.5**<br>13.5 |
| | 2 | | **8.5**<br>8.0 | **10.0**<br>10.0 | **12.0**<br>11.5 | **13.5**<br>13.5 | **15.5**<br>15.0 |
| 3/4φ | 3 | 1/2□ | **10.0**<br>10.0 | **12.0**<br>11.5 | **13.5**<br>13.5 | **15.5**<br>15.0 | **17.0**<br>17.0 |
| | 4 | | **12.0**<br>11.5 | **14.0**<br>13.5 | **15.5**<br>15.0 | **17.5**<br>17.0 | **19.0**<br>18.5 |
| | 5 | | **14.0**<br>13.5 | **15.5**<br>15.0 | **17.5**<br>17.0 | **19.0**<br>18.5 | **21.0**<br>20.5 |
| | 1 | | **6.5**<br>6.5 | **8.0**<br>8.0 | **9.5**<br>9.5 | **11.5**<br>11.5 | **13.0**<br>13.0 |
| | 2 | | **8.5**<br>8.5 | **10.0**<br>10.0 | **12.0**<br>11.5 | **13.5**<br>13.0 | **15.0**<br>15.0 |
| 7/8φ | 3 | 5/8φ | **11.0**<br>10.0 | **12.5**<br>12.0 | **14.0**<br>13.5 | **15.5**<br>15.0 | **17.5**<br>16.5 |
| | 4 | | **13.0**<br>12.0 | **14.5**<br>13.5 | **16.5**<br>15.5 | **18.0**<br>17.0 | **19.5**<br>18.5 |
| | 5 | | **15.0**<br>14.0 | **17.0**<br>15.5 | **18.5**<br>17.0 | **20.0**<br>19.0 | **21.5**<br>20.5 |
| | 1 | | **7.0**<br>6.5 | **8.5**<br>8.5 | **10.5**<br>10.0 | **12.5**<br>12.0 | **14.5**<br>13.5 |
| | 2 | | **9.5**<br>8.5 | **11.0**<br>10.5 | **13.0**<br>12.0 | **15.0**<br>14.0 | **17.0**<br>15.5 |
| 1φ | 3 | 3/4φ | **12.0**<br>10.5 | **13.5**<br>12.5 | **15.5**<br>14.0 | **17.5**<br>16.0 | **19.5**<br>17.5 |
| | 4 | | **14.5**<br>12.5 | **16.0**<br>14.5 | **18.0**<br>16.0 | **20.0**<br>18.0 | **22.0**<br>19.5 |
| | 5 | | **17.0**<br>14.5 | **18.5**<br>16.5 | **20.5**<br>18.0 | **22.5**<br>20.0 | **24.5**<br>21.5 |
| | 1 | | **7.0**<br>7.0 | **9.5**<br>8.5 | **11.5**<br>10.5 | **13.5**<br>12.5 | **16.0**<br>14.5 |
| | 2 | | **10.0**<br>9.5 | **12.5**<br>11.0 | **14.5**<br>13.0 | **16.5**<br>15.0 | **19.0**<br>17.0 |
| 1□ | 3 | 7/8φ | **13.0**<br>12.0 | **15.5**<br>13.5 | **17.5**<br>15.5 | **19.5**<br>17.5 | **22.0**<br>19.5 |
| | 4 | | **16.0**<br>14.5 | **18.5**<br>16.0 | **20.5**<br>18.0 | **22.5**<br>20.0 | **25.0**<br>22.0 |
| | 5 | | **19.0**<br>17.0 | **21.5**<br>18.5 | **23.5**<br>20.5 | **25.5**<br>22.5 | **28.0**<br>24.5 |
| | 1 | | **7.5**<br>7.0 | **10.0**<br>9.0 | **12.5**<br>11.0 | **15.0**<br>13.0 | **17.5**<br>15.0 |
| | 2 | | **11.0**<br>10.0 | **13.5**<br>12.0 | **16.0**<br>14.0 | **18.5**<br>16.0 | **21.0**<br>18.0 |
| 1 1/8□ | 3 | 1φ | **14.5**<br>12.5 | **17.0**<br>14.5 | **19.5**<br>16.5 | **22.0**<br>18.5 | **24.5**<br>20.5 |
| | 4 | | **17.5**<br>15.5 | **20.0**<br>17.5 | **22.5**<br>19.5 | **25.0**<br>21.5 | **27.5**<br>23.5 |
| | 5 | | **21.0**<br>18.5 | **23.5**<br>20.5 | **26.0**<br>22.5 | **28.5**<br>24.5 | **31.0**<br>26.5 |
| | 1 | | **8.0**<br>7.5 | **11.0**<br>10.0 | **14.0**<br>12.5 | **17.0**<br>15.0 | **20.0**<br>17.5 |
| | 2 | | **12.0**<br>11.0 | **15.0**<br>13.5 | **18.0**<br>16.0 | **21.0**<br>18.5 | **24.0**<br>21.0 |
| 1 1/4□ | 3 | 1□ | **15.5**<br>14.0 | **18.5**<br>16.5 | **21.5**<br>19.0 | **24.5**<br>21.5 | **27.5**<br>24.0 |
| | 4 | | **19.5**<br>17.0 | **22.5**<br>19.5 | **25.5**<br>22.0 | **28.5**<br>24.5 | **31.5**<br>27.0 |
| | 5 | | **23.0**<br>20.0 | **26.0**<br>22.5 | **29.0**<br>25.0 | **32.0**<br>27.5 | **35.0**<br>30.0 |

| | | | 1 | 2 | 3 | 4 | 5 |
|---|---|---|---|---|---|---|---|
| | 1 | | **6.0**<br>6.0 | **7.5**<br>7.5 | **9.0**<br>9.0 | **10.5**<br>10.5 | **12.0**<br>12.0 |
| | 2 | | **8.0**<br>8.0 | **9.5**<br>9.5 | **11.0**<br>11.0 | **12.5**<br>12.5 | **14.0**<br>14.0 |
| 3/4φ | 3 | 3/8φ or 1/2φ | **10.0**<br>9.5 | **11.5**<br>11.0 | **13.0**<br>12.5 | **14.5**<br>14.0 | **16.0**<br>15.5 |
| | 4 | | **11.5**<br>11.5 | **13.5**<br>13.0 | **14.5**<br>14.5 | **16.5**<br>16.0 | **17.5**<br>17.5 |
| | 5 | | **13.5**<br>13.0 | **15.0**<br>14.5 | **16.5**<br>16.0 | **18.0**<br>17.5 | **19.5**<br>19.0 |
| | 1 | | **6.5**<br>6.5 | **8.5**<br>8.5 | **10.0**<br>10.0 | **11.5**<br>11.5 | **13.5**<br>13.5 |
| | 2 | | **8.5**<br>8.5 | **10.5**<br>10.0 | **12.5**<br>12.0 | **14.0**<br>13.5 | **15.5**<br>15.5 |
| 7/8φ | 3 | 1/2□ | **11.0**<br>10.5 | **12.5**<br>12.0 | **14.5**<br>13.5 | **16.0**<br>15.5 | **18.0**<br>17.5 |
| | 4 | | **13.0**<br>12.0 | **15.0**<br>14.0 | **16.5**<br>15.5 | **18.5**<br>17.5 | **20.0**<br>19.0 |
| | 5 | | **15.5**<br>14.0 | **17.0**<br>15.5 | **18.5**<br>17.5 | **20.5**<br>19.5 | **21.5**<br>21.0 |
| | 1 | | **6.5**<br>6.5 | **8.0**<br>8.0 | **9.5**<br>9.5 | **11.5**<br>11.5 | **13.0**<br>13.0 |
| | 2 | | **9.0**<br>8.5 | **10.5**<br>10.0 | **12.5**<br>11.5 | **14.0**<br>13.5 | **15.5**<br>15.0 |
| 1φ | 3 | 5/8φ | **11.5**<br>10.5 | **13.0**<br>12.0 | **14.5**<br>13.5 | **16.5**<br>15.5 | **18.0**<br>17.0 |
| | 4 | | **14.0**<br>12.5 | **15.5**<br>14.0 | **17.5**<br>15.5 | **19.0**<br>17.5 | **20.5**<br>19.0 |
| | 5 | | **16.5**<br>14.5 | **18.0**<br>16.0 | **19.5**<br>17.5 | **21.5**<br>19.5 | **23.0**<br>21.0 |
| | 1 | | **6.5**<br>6.5 | **8.5**<br>8.5 | **10.5**<br>10.0 | **12.5**<br>12.0 | **14.5**<br>13.5 |
| | 2 | | **9.5**<br>9.0 | **11.5**<br>11.0 | **13.5**<br>12.5 | **15.5**<br>14.5 | **17.5**<br>16.0 |
| 1□ | 3 | 3/4φ | **12.5**<br>11.5 | **14.5**<br>13.5 | **16.5**<br>15.0 | **18.5**<br>17.0 | **20.5**<br>18.5 |
| | 4 | | **15.5**<br>14.0 | **17.5**<br>16.0 | **19.5**<br>17.5 | **21.5**<br>19.5 | **23.5**<br>21.0 |
| | 5 | | **18.5**<br>16.5 | **20.5**<br>18.5 | **22.5**<br>20.0 | **24.5**<br>22.0 | **26.5**<br>23.5 |
| | 1 | | **7.5**<br>7.0 | **9.5**<br>8.5 | **11.5**<br>10.5 | **13.5**<br>12.5 | **16.0**<br>14.5 |
| | 2 | | **10.5**<br>9.5 | **12.5**<br>11.5 | **15.0**<br>13.5 | **17.0**<br>15.5 | **19.5**<br>17.5 |
| 1 1/8□ | 3 | 7/8φ | **14.0**<br>12.5 | **16.0**<br>14.5 | **18.5**<br>16.5 | **20.5**<br>18.0 | **22.5**<br>20.0 |
| | 4 | | **17.5**<br>15.5 | **19.5**<br>17.5 | **21.5**<br>19.0 | **24.0**<br>21.0 | **26.0**<br>23.0 |
| | 5 | | **20.5**<br>18.0 | **23.0**<br>20.0 | **25.0**<br>22.0 | **27.5**<br>23.5 | **29.5**<br>25.5 |
| | 1 | | **7.5**<br>7.0 | **10.0**<br>9.0 | **12.5**<br>11.0 | **15.0**<br>13.0 | **17.5**<br>15.0 |
| | 2 | | **11.5**<br>10.5 | **14.0**<br>12.5 | **16.5**<br>14.5 | **19.0**<br>16.5 | **21.5**<br>18.5 |
| 1 1/4□ | 3 | 1φ | **15.0**<br>13.5 | **17.5**<br>15.5 | **20.0**<br>17.5 | **22.5**<br>19.5 | **25.0**<br>21.5 |
| | 4 | | **19.0**<br>16.5 | **21.5**<br>18.5 | **24.0**<br>20.5 | **26.5**<br>22.5 | **29.0**<br>24.5 |
| | 5 | | **22.5**<br>19.5 | **25.0**<br>21.5 | **27.5**<br>23.5 | **30.0**<br>25.5 | **32.5**<br>27.5 |

# Table 7. Coefficients ($c$) for Compressive Reinforcement for Rectangular and T-Sections

$f_s = 8{,}000$

| $f'_c$ and $n$ | $f_c$ | $\frac{d'}{d}$ = 0.02 | 0.04 | 0.06 | 0.08 | 0.10 | 0.12 | 0.14 | 0.16 | 0.18 | 0.20 |
|---|---|---|---|---|---|---|---|---|---|---|---|
| | 650 | 0.72 | 0.67 | 0.63 | 0.60 | 0.56 | 0.52 | 0.49 | 0.45 | 0.42 | 0.39 |
| | 700 | 0.77 | 0.73 | 0.69 | 0.65 | 0.61 | 0.57 | 0.53 | 0.49 | 0.46 | 0.42 |
| 2000 | 750 | 0.83 | 0.78 | 0.74 | 0.69 | 0.65 | 0.61 | 0.57 | 0.53 | 0.50 | 0.46 |
| | 800 | 0.88 | 0.84 | 0.79 | 0.74 | 0.70 | 0.66 | 0.62 | 0.57 | 0.54 | 0.50 |
| | 900 | 1.00 | 0.94 | 0.89 | 0.84 | 0.79 | 0.75 | 0.70 | 0.66 | 0.61 | 0.57 |
| 15 | 1000 | 1.11 | 1.05 | 0.99 | 0.94 | 0.89 | 0.84 | 0.79 | 0.74 | 0.69 | 0.65 |
| | 1200 | 1.34 | 1.27 | 1.21 | 1.14 | 1.08 | 1.02 | 0.96 | 0.91 | 0.85 | 0.80 |
| | 1350 | 1.50 | 1.43 | 1.36 | 1.29 | 1.22 | 1.15 | 1.09 | 1.03 | 0.97 | 0.91 |
| | 800 | 0.69 | 0.65 | 0.61 | 0.58 | 0.54 | 0.50 | 0.47 | 0.44 | 0.40 | 0.37 |
| | 875 | 0.76 | 0.72 | 0.68 | 0.64 | 0.60 | 0.56 | 0.52 | 0.48 | 0.45 | 0.42 |
| 2500 | 950 | 0.83 | 0.78 | 0.74 | 0.69 | 0.65 | 0.61 | 0.57 | 0.53 | 0.50 | 0.46 |
| | 1000 | 0.87 | 0.82 | 0.78 | 0.73 | 0.69 | 0.64 | 0.60 | 0.56 | 0.53 | 0.49 |
| | 1125 | 0.98 | 0.93 | 0.88 | 0.83 | 0.78 | 0.73 | 0.69 | 0.65 | 0.60 | 0.56 |
| 12 | 1250 | 1.09 | 1.03 | 0.98 | 0.92 | 0.87 | 0.82 | 0.77 | 0.73 | 0.68 | 0.63 |
| | 1500 | 1.31 | 1.25 | 1.18 | 1.12 | 1.06 | 1.00 | 0.95 | 0.89 | 0.84 | 0.78 |
| | 1700 | 1.48 | 1.41 | 1.34 | 1.27 | 1.21 | 1.14 | 1.08 | 1.02 | 0.96 | 0.90 |
| | 975 | 0.69 | 0.65 | 0.61 | 0.57 | 0.54 | 0.50 | 0.47 | 0.43 | 0.40 | 0.37 |
| | 1050 | 0.75 | 0.70 | 0.66 | 0.62 | 0.58 | 0.55 | 0.51 | 0.48 | 0.44 | 0.41 |
| 3000 | 1125 | 0.80 | 0.75 | 0.71 | 0.67 | 0.63 | 0.59 | 0.55 | 0.51 | 0.48 | 0.44 |
| | 1200 | 0.85 | 0.81 | 0.76 | 0.72 | 0.68 | 0.63 | 0.59 | 0.55 | 0.52 | 0.48 |
| | 1350 | 0.96 | 0.91 | 0.86 | 0.81 | 0.77 | 0.72 | 0.68 | 0.63 | 0.59 | 0.55 |
| 10 | 1500 | 1.07 | 1.01 | 0.96 | 0.91 | 0.86 | 0.81 | 0.76 | 0.71 | 0.67 | 0.62 |
| | 1800 | 1.29 | 1.22 | 1.16 | 1.10 | 1.04 | 0.99 | 0.93 | 0.87 | 0.82 | 0.77 |
| | 2025 | 1.45 | 1.38 | 1.31 | 1.24 | 1.18 | 1.11 | 1.05 | 0.99 | 0.93 | 0.88 |
| | 1200 | 0.66 | 0.62 | 0.59 | 0.55 | 0.52 | 0.48 | 0.45 | 0.42 | 0.39 | 0.36 |
| | 1300 | 0.72 | 0.68 | 0.64 | 0.60 | 0.56 | 0.52 | 0.49 | 0.46 | 0.42 | 0.39 |
| 3750 | 1400 | 0.77 | 0.73 | 0.69 | 0.65 | 0.61 | 0.57 | 0.53 | 0.50 | 0.46 | 0.43 |
| | 1500 | 0.83 | 0.78 | 0.74 | 0.70 | 0.66 | 0.62 | 0.58 | 0.54 | 0.50 | 0.47 |
| | 1700 | 0.94 | 0.89 | 0.84 | 0.80 | 0.75 | 0.71 | 0.66 | 0.62 | 0.58 | 0.54 |
| 8 | 1875 | 1.04 | 0.98 | 0.93 | 0.88 | 0.83 | 0.78 | 0.74 | 0.69 | 0.65 | 0.61 |
| | 2250 | 1.25 | 1.19 | 1.13 | 1.07 | 1.01 | 0.96 | 0.90 | 0.85 | 0.80 | 0.75 |
| | 2525 | 1.40 | 1.33 | 1.27 | 1.20 | 1.14 | 1.08 | 1.02 | 0.96 | 0.90 | 0.85 |

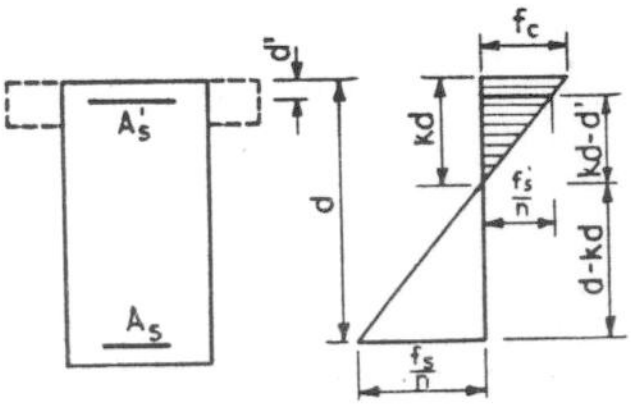


$$c = \frac{f_s(n-1)\left(1-\frac{d'}{d}\right)\left(k-\frac{d'}{d}\right)}{12{,}000\,n(1-k)}$$

Enter table with known values of $\frac{d'}{d}$, $f_s$, $n$ and $f_c$; select value of $c$

Compute $A'_s = \frac{M - KF}{cd}$ or $\frac{NE - KF}{cd}$.

$K$ from Tables 1 or 8, $F$ from Table 4

$f_s = 10{,}000$

| $f'_c$ and $n$ | $f_c$ | $\frac{d'}{d}$ = 0.02 | 0.04 | 0.06 | 0.08 | 0.10 | 0.12 | 0.14 | 0.16 | 0.18 | 0.20 |
|---|---|---|---|---|---|---|---|---|---|---|---|
| | 650 | 0.71 | 0.67 | 0.63 | 0.59 | 0.54 | 0.51 | 0.47 | 0.43 | 0.40 | 0.36 |
| | 700 | 0.77 | 0.72 | 0.68 | 0.63 | 0.59 | 0.55 | 0.51 | 0.47 | 0.43 | 0.40 |
| 2000 | 750 | 0.82 | 0.78 | 0.73 | 0.68 | 0.64 | 0.59 | 0.55 | 0.51 | 0.47 | 0.43 |
| | 800 | 0.88 | 0.83 | 0.78 | 0.73 | 0.69 | 0.64 | 0.60 | 0.56 | 0.51 | 0.47 |
| | 900 | 0.99 | 0.94 | 0.88 | 0.83 | 0.78 | 0.73 | 0.68 | 0.63 | 0.59 | 0.55 |
| 15 | 1000 | 1.10 | 1.04 | 0.99 | 0.93 | 0.87 | 0.82 | 0.77 | 0.72 | 0.67 | 0.62 |
| | 1200 | 1.33 | 1.26 | 1.19 | 1.13 | 1.06 | 1.00 | 0.94 | 0.88 | 0.83 | 0.77 |
| | 1350 | 1.49 | 1.42 | 1.34 | 1.27 | 1.20 | 1.13 | 1.07 | 1.00 | 0.94 | 0.88 |
| | 800 | 0.69 | 0.65 | 0.61 | 0.56 | 0.53 | 0.49 | 0.45 | 0.41 | 0.38 | 0.35 |
| | 875 | 0.75 | 0.71 | 0.66 | 0.62 | 0.58 | 0.54 | 0.50 | 0.46 | 0.43 | 0.39 |
| 2500 | 950 | 0.82 | 0.77 | 0.73 | 0.68 | 0.64 | 0.59 | 0.55 | 0.51 | 0.47 | 0.44 |
| | 1000 | 0.87 | 0.82 | 0.77 | 0.72 | 0.67 | 0.63 | 0.59 | 0.55 | 0.50 | 0.47 |
| | 1125 | 0.97 | 0.92 | 0.87 | 0.81 | 0.76 | 0.72 | 0.67 | 0.62 | 0.58 | 0.54 |
| 12 | 1250 | 1.08 | 1.03 | 0.97 | 0.91 | 0.86 | 0.81 | 0.75 | 0.71 | 0.66 | 0.61 |
| | 1500 | 1.31 | 1.24 | 1.17 | 1.11 | 1.05 | 0.98 | 0.93 | 0.87 | 0.81 | 0.76 |
| | 1700 | 1.48 | 1.41 | 1.33 | 1.26 | 1.19 | 1.12 | 1.06 | 1.00 | 0.93 | 0.87 |
| | 975 | 0.69 | 0.65 | 0.60 | 0.56 | 0.53 | 0.49 | 0.45 | 0.42 | 0.38 | 0.35 |
| | 1050 | 0.74 | 0.70 | 0.65 | 0.61 | 0.57 | 0.53 | 0.49 | 0.45 | 0.42 | 0.38 |
| 3000 | 1125 | 0.79 | 0.75 | 0.70 | 0.66 | 0.61 | 0.57 | 0.53 | 0.49 | 0.46 | 0.42 |
| | 1200 | 0.85 | 0.80 | 0.75 | 0.71 | 0.66 | 0.62 | 0.58 | 0.54 | 0.50 | 0.46 |
| | 1350 | 0.96 | 0.90 | 0.85 | 0.80 | 0.75 | 0.70 | 0.66 | 0.61 | 0.57 | 0.53 |
| 10 | 1500 | 1.07 | 1.01 | 0.95 | 0.90 | 0.84 | 0.79 | 0.74 | 0.69 | 0.65 | 0.60 |
| | 1800 | 1.28 | 1.22 | 1.15 | 1.09 | 1.03 | 0.97 | 0.91 | 0.85 | 0.80 | 0.74 |
| | 2025 | 1.44 | 1.37 | 1.30 | 1.23 | 1.16 | 1.09 | 1.03 | 0.97 | 0.91 | 0.85 |
| | 1200 | 0.66 | 0.62 | 0.58 | 0.54 | 0.50 | 0.46 | 0.43 | 0.40 | 0.36 | 0.33 |
| | 1300 | 0.71 | 0.67 | 0.63 | 0.59 | 0.55 | 0.51 | 0.47 | 0.44 | 0.40 | 0.37 |
| 3750 | 1400 | 0.77 | 0.72 | 0.68 | 0.64 | 0.59 | 0.55 | 0.52 | 0.48 | 0.44 | 0.40 |
| | 1500 | 0.83 | 0.78 | 0.73 | 0.69 | 0.64 | 0.60 | 0.56 | 0.52 | 0.48 | 0.44 |
| | 1700 | 0.94 | 0.88 | 0.83 | 0.78 | 0.74 | 0.69 | 0.64 | 0.60 | 0.56 | 0.52 |
| 8 | 1875 | 1.03 | 0.98 | 0.92 | 0.87 | 0.82 | 0.77 | 0.72 | 0.67 | 0.63 | 0.58 |
| | 2250 | 1.25 | 1.18 | 1.12 | 1.06 | 1.00 | 0.94 | 0.88 | 0.83 | 0.78 | 0.72 |
| | 2525 | 1.40 | 1.33 | 1.26 | 1.19 | 1.13 | 1.06 | 1.00 | 0.94 | 0.88 | 0.83 |

$f_s = 12{,}000$

| $f'_c$ and $n$ | $f_c$ | $\frac{d'}{d}$ = 0.02 | 0.04 | 0.06 | 0.08 | 0.10 | 0.12 | 0.14 | 0.16 | 0.18 | 0.20 |
|---|---|---|---|---|---|---|---|---|---|---|---|
| | 650 | 0.71 | 0.66 | 0.62 | 0.57 | 0.53 | 0.49 | 0.45 | 0.41 | 0.37 | 0.34 |
| | 700 | 0.77 | 0.72 | 0.67 | 0.62 | 0.58 | 0.53 | 0.49 | 0.45 | 0.41 | 0.37 |
| 2000 | 750 | 0.82 | 0.77 | 0.72 | 0.67 | 0.62 | 0.58 | 0.53 | 0.49 | 0.45 | 0.41 |
| | 800 | 0.88 | 0.82 | 0.77 | 0.72 | 0.67 | 0.62 | 0.58 | 0.53 | 0.49 | 0.45 |
| | 900 | 0.99 | 0.93 | 0.87 | 0.82 | 0.76 | 0.71 | 0.66 | 0.61 | 0.57 | 0.52 |
| 15 | 1000 | 1.10 | 1.04 | 0.98 | 0.92 | 0.86 | 0.81 | 0.75 | 0.70 | 0.65 | 0.60 |
| | 1200 | 1.32 | 1.25 | 1.18 | 1.11 | 1.05 | 0.98 | 0.92 | 0.86 | 0.80 | 0.75 |
| | 1350 | 1.49 | 1.41 | 1.34 | 1.26 | 1.19 | 1.12 | 1.05 | 0.99 | 0.92 | 0.86 |
| | 800 | 0.68 | 0.64 | 0.60 | 0.55 | 0.51 | 0.47 | 0.43 | 0.39 | 0.36 | 0.32 |
| | 875 | 0.75 | 0.70 | 0.66 | 0.61 | 0.57 | 0.52 | 0.48 | 0.44 | 0.40 | 0.37 |
| 2500 | 950 | 0.82 | 0.77 | 0.72 | 0.67 | 0.62 | 0.58 | 0.53 | 0.49 | 0.45 | 0.41 |
| | 1000 | 0.86 | 0.81 | 0.76 | 0.71 | 0.66 | 0.61 | 0.57 | 0.52 | 0.48 | 0.44 |
| | 1125 | 0.96 | 0.91 | 0.85 | 0.80 | 0.75 | 0.69 | 0.65 | 0.60 | 0.55 | 0.51 |
| 12 | 1250 | 1.08 | 1.02 | 0.96 | 0.90 | 0.85 | 0.79 | 0.74 | 0.69 | 0.64 | 0.59 |
| | 1500 | 1.30 | 1.23 | 1.16 | 1.10 | 1.03 | 0.97 | 0.91 | 0.85 | 0.79 | 0.73 |
| | 1700 | 1.48 | 1.40 | 1.33 | 1.25 | 1.18 | 1.11 | 1.04 | 0.98 | 0.91 | 0.85 |
| | 975 | 0.68 | 0.64 | 0.59 | 0.55 | 0.51 | 0.47 | 0.43 | 0.39 | 0.36 | 0.32 |
| | 1050 | 0.74 | 0.69 | 0.65 | 0.60 | 0.56 | 0.52 | 0.47 | 0.44 | 0.40 | 0.36 |
| 3000 | 1125 | 0.79 | 0.74 | 0.70 | 0.65 | 0.60 | 0.56 | 0.52 | 0.47 | 0.43 | 0.40 |
| | 1200 | 0.85 | 0.79 | 0.74 | 0.70 | 0.65 | 0.60 | 0.56 | 0.51 | 0.47 | 0.43 |
| | 1350 | 0.95 | 0.90 | 0.84 | 0.79 | 0.74 | 0.69 | 0.69 | 0.59 | 0.55 | 0.50 |
| 10 | 1500 | 1.06 | 1.00 | 0.94 | 0.89 | 0.83 | 0.78 | 0.73 | 0.67 | 0.62 | 0.58 |
| | 1800 | 1.28 | 1.21 | 1.14 | 1.08 | 1.01 | 0.95 | 0.89 | 0.83 | 0.77 | 0.72 |
| | 2025 | 1.44 | 1.36 | 1.29 | 1.22 | 1.15 | 1.08 | 1.01 | 0.95 | 0.89 | 0.83 |
| | 1200 | 0.65 | 0.61 | 0.57 | 0.53 | 0.49 | 0.45 | 0.41 | 0.38 | 0.34 | 0.31 |
| | 1300 | 0.71 | 0.66 | 0.62 | 0.58 | 0.53 | 0.49 | 0.45 | 0.42 | 0.38 | 0.34 |
| 3750 | 1400 | 0.77 | 0.72 | 0.67 | 0.63 | 0.58 | 0.54 | 0.50 | 0.46 | 0.42 | 0.38 |
| | 1500 | 0.82 | 0.77 | 0.72 | 0.68 | 0.63 | 0.59 | 0.54 | 0.50 | 0.46 | 0.42 |
| | 1700 | 0.93 | 0.88 | 0.83 | 0.77 | 0.72 | 0.67 | 0.63 | 0.58 | 0.54 | 0.49 |
| 8 | 1875 | 1.03 | 0.98 | 0.92 | 0.86 | 0.81 | 0.76 | 0.70 | 0.66 | 0.61 | 0.56 |
| | 2250 | 1.24 | 1.18 | 1.11 | 1.05 | 0.98 | 0.92 | 0.87 | 0.81 | 0.75 | 0.70 |
| | 2525 | 1.39 | 1.32 | 1.25 | 1.18 | 1.11 | 1.05 | 0.98 | 0.92 | 0.86 | 0.80 |

## Table 7. *(continued)*

| $f'_c$ and $n$ | $f_c$ | $f_s = 14,000$ $\frac{d'}{d}$ 0.02 | 0.04 | 0.06 | 0.08 | 0.10 | 0.12 | 0.14 | 0.16 | 0.18 | 0.20 | $f_s = 16,000$ $\frac{d'}{d}$ 0.02 | 0.04 | 0.06 | 0.08 | 0.10 | 0.12 | 0.14 | 0.16 | 0.18 | 0.20 |
|---|---|---|---|---|---|---|---|---|---|---|---|---|---|---|---|---|---|---|---|---|---|
| | 650 | 0.71 | 0.66 | 0.61 | 0.56 | 0.52 | 0.47 | 0.43 | 0.39 | 0.35 | 0.31 | 0.71 | 0.65 | 0.60 | 0.55 | 0.50 | 0.46 | 0.41 | 0.37 | 0.33 | 0.29 |
| | 700 | 0.76 | 0.71 | 0.66 | 0.61 | 0.56 | 0.52 | 0.47 | 0.43 | 0.39 | 0.35 | 0.76 | 0.70 | 0.65 | 0.60 | 0.55 | 0.50 | 0.45 | 0.41 | 0.36 | 0.32 |
| 2000 | 750 | 0.82 | 0.77 | 0.71 | 0.66 | 0.61 | 0.56 | 0.52 | 0.47 | 0.43 | 0.39 | 0.81 | 0.76 | 0.70 | 0.65 | 0.60 | 0.55 | 0.50 | 0.45 | 0.41 | 0.36 |
| | 800 | 0.88 | 0.82 | 0.76 | 0.71 | 0.66 | 0.61 | 0.56 | 0.51 | 0.47 | 0.42 | 0.87 | 0.81 | 0.76 | 0.70 | 0.65 | 0.59 | 0.54 | 0.49 | 0.44 | 0.40 |
| | 900 | 0.99 | 0.93 | 0.87 | 0.81 | 0.75 | 0.70 | 0.65 | 0.60 | 0.55 | 0.50 | 0.98 | 0.92 | 0.86 | 0.80 | 0.74 | 0.68 | 0.63 | 0.57 | 0.52 | 0.47 |
| 15 | 1000 | 1.10 | 1.03 | 0.97 | 0.91 | 0.85 | 0.79 | 0.73 | 0.68 | 0.62 | 0.57 | 1.10 | 1.03 | 0.96 | 0.90 | 0.83 | 0.77 | 0.71 | 0.66 | 0.60 | 0.55 |
| | 1200 | 1.33 | 1.25 | 1.18 | 1.11 | 1.04 | 0.97 | 0.91 | 0.84 | 0.78 | 0.72 | 1.32 | 1.24 | 1.16 | 1.09 | 1.02 | 0.95 | 0.88 | 0.82 | 0.76 | 0.70 |
| | 1350 | 1.49 | 1.41 | 1.33 | 1.25 | 1.18 | 1.10 | 1.03 | 0.96 | 0.90 | 0.83 | 1.49 | 1.41 | 1.32 | 1.24 | 1.17 | 1.09 | 1.02 | 0.95 | 0.88 | 0.81 |
| | 800 | 0.68 | 0.63 | 0.59 | 0.54 | 0.50 | 0.45 | 0.41 | 0.37 | 0.34 | 0.30 | 0.68 | 0.63 | 0.58 | 0.53 | 0.48 | 0.44 | 0.40 | 0.35 | 0.31 | 0.27 |
| | 875 | 0.75 | 0.70 | 0.65 | 0.60 | 0.55 | 0.51 | 0.46 | 0.42 | 0.38 | 0.34 | 0.75 | 0.69 | 0.64 | 0.59 | 0.54 | 0.49 | 0.45 | 0.40 | 0.36 | 0.32 |
| 2500 | 950 | 0.82 | 0.76 | 0.71 | 0.66 | 0.61 | 0.56 | 0.52 | 0.47 | 0.43 | 0.39 | 0.81 | 0.76 | 0.70 | 0.65 | 0.59 | 0.54 | 0.50 | 0.45 | 0.41 | 0.36 |
| | 1000 | 0.86 | 0.80 | 0.75 | 0.70 | 0.65 | 0.60 | 0.55 | 0.50 | 0.46 | 0.42 | 0.86 | 0.80 | 0.74 | 0.69 | 0.63 | 0.58 | 0.53 | 0.48 | 0.44 | 0.39 |
| | 1125 | 0.97 | 0.91 | 0.85 | 0.79 | 0.74 | 0.69 | 0.63 | 0.58 | 0.54 | 0.49 | 0.97 | 0.90 | 0.84 | 0.78 | 0.73 | 0.67 | 0.62 | 0.56 | 0.51 | 0.47 |
| 12 | 1250 | 1.08 | 1.01 | 0.95 | 0.89 | 0.83 | 0.77 | 0.72 | 0.66 | 0.61 | 0.56 | 1.08 | 1.01 | 0.94 | 0.88 | 0.82 | 0.76 | 0.70 | 0.64 | 0.59 | 0.54 |
| | 1500 | 1.30 | 1.23 | 1.16 | 1.09 | 1.02 | 0.95 | 0.89 | 0.83 | 0.77 | 0.71 | 1.29 | 1.22 | 1.14 | 1.07 | 1.00 | 0.93 | 0.87 | 0.80 | 0.74 | 0.68 |
| | 1700 | 1.47 | 1.39 | 1.32 | 1.24 | 1.17 | 1.09 | 1.02 | 0.96 | 0.89 | 0.83 | 1.47 | 1.39 | 1.31 | 1.23 | 1.15 | 1.08 | 1.00 | 0.93 | 0.87 | 0.80 |
| | 975 | 0.68 | 0.63 | 0.59 | 0.54 | 0.50 | 0.46 | 0.42 | 0.38 | 0.34 | 0.30 | 0.68 | 0.63 | 0.58 | 0.53 | 0.49 | 0.44 | 0.40 | 0.36 | 0.32 | 0.28 |
| | 1050 | 0.74 | 0.69 | 0.64 | 0.59 | 0.54 | 0.50 | 0.46 | 0.42 | 0.38 | 0.34 | 0.73 | 0.68 | 0.63 | 0.58 | 0.53 | 0.48 | 0.44 | 0.39 | 0.35 | 0.31 |
| 3000 | 1125 | 0.79 | 0.74 | 0.69 | 0.64 | 0.59 | 0.54 | 0.50 | 0.46 | 0.41 | 0.37 | 0.78 | 0.73 | 0.68 | 0.63 | 0.58 | 0.53 | 0.48 | 0.43 | 0.39 | 0.35 |
| | 1200 | 0.85 | 0.79 | 0.74 | 0.69 | 0.64 | 0.59 | 0.54 | 0.49 | 0.45 | 0.41 | 0.84 | 0.78 | 0.73 | 0.67 | 0.62 | 0.57 | 0.52 | 0.48 | 0.43 | 0.39 |
| | 1350 | 0.95 | 0.89 | 0.84 | 0.78 | 0.73 | 0.67 | 0.62 | 0.57 | 0.53 | 0.48 | 0.95 | 0.89 | 0.83 | 0.77 | 0.71 | 0.66 | 0.61 | 0.55 | 0.50 | 0.46 |
| 10 | 1500 | 1.06 | 1.00 | 0.93 | 0.87 | 0.82 | 0.76 | 0.70 | 0.65 | 0.60 | 0.55 | 1.06 | 0.99 | 0.93 | 0.86 | 0.80 | 0.74 | 0.69 | 0.63 | 0.58 | 0.53 |
| | 1800 | 1.28 | 1.21 | 1.14 | 1.07 | 1.00 | 0.94 | 0.87 | 0.81 | 0.75 | 0.70 | 1.27 | 1.20 | 1.12 | 1.05 | 0.98 | 0.92 | 0.85 | 0.79 | 0.73 | 0.67 |
| | 2025 | 1.44 | 1.36 | 1.28 | 1.21 | 1.13 | 1.06 | 1.00 | 0.93 | 0.87 | 0.80 | 1.44 | 1.36 | 1.28 | 1.20 | 1.12 | 1.05 | 0.98 | 0.91 | 0.85 | 0.78 |
| | 1200 | 0.65 | 0.61 | 0.56 | 0.52 | 0.48 | 0.43 | 0.40 | 0.36 | 0.32 | 0.29 | 0.65 | 0.60 | 0.55 | 0.51 | 0.46 | 0.42 | 0.38 | 0.34 | 0.30 | 0.26 |
| | 1300 | 0.71 | 0.66 | 0.61 | 0.57 | 0.52 | 0.48 | 0.44 | 0.40 | 0.36 | 0.32 | 0.71 | 0.65 | 0.60 | 0.56 | 0.51 | 0.46 | 0.42 | 0.38 | 0.34 | 0.30 |
| 3750 | 1400 | 0.76 | 0.71 | 0.66 | 0.61 | 0.57 | 0.52 | 0.48 | 0.44 | 0.40 | 0.36 | 0.76 | 0.71 | 0.66 | 0.61 | 0.56 | 0.51 | 0.46 | [illegible] | 0.38 | 0.34 |
| | 1500 | 0.82 | 0.77 | 0.71 | 0.66 | 0.62 | 0.57 | 0.52 | 0.48 | 0.44 | 0.40 | 0.82 | 0.76 | 0.71 | 0.66 | 0.60 | 0.56 | 0.51 | 0.46 | 0.42 | 0.37 |
| | 1700 | 0.93 | 0.87 | 0.82 | 0.76 | 0.71 | 0.66 | 0.61 | 0.56 | 0.52 | 0.47 | 0.93 | 0.87 | 0.81 | 0.76 | 0.70 | 0.65 | 0.59 | 0.54 | 0.50 | 0.45 |
| 8 | 1875 | 1.03 | 0.97 | 0.91 | 0.85 | 0.79 | 0.74 | 0.68 | 0.63 | 0.58 | 0.54 | 1.03 | 0.96 | 0.90 | 0.84 | 0.78 | 0.72 | 0.67 | 0.62 | 0.56 | 0.51 |
| | 2250 | 1.24 | 1.17 | 1.10 | 1.03 | 0.97 | 0.91 | 0.85 | 0.79 | 0.73 | 0.68 | 1.24 | 1.16 | 1.09 | 1.02 | 0.96 | 0.89 | 0.83 | 0.77 | 0.71 | 0.65 |
| | 2525 | 1.40 | 1.32 | 1.25 | 1.17 | 1.10 | 1.03 | 0.97 | 0.90 | 0.84 | 0.78 | 1.39 | 1.31 | 1.24 | 1.16 | 1.09 | 1.02 | 0.95 | 0.88 | 0.82 | 0.76 |

| $f'_c$ and $n$ | $f_c$ | $f_s = 18,000$ $\frac{d'}{d}$ 0.02 | 0.04 | 0.06 | 0.08 | 0.10 | 0.12 | 0.14 | 0.16 | 0.18 | 0.20 | $f_s = 20,000$ $\frac{d'}{d}$ 0.02 | 0.04 | 0.06 | 0.08 | 0.10 | 0.12 | 0.14 | 0.16 | 0.18 | 0.20 |
|---|---|---|---|---|---|---|---|---|---|---|---|---|---|---|---|---|---|---|---|---|---|
| | 650 | 0.70 | 0.64 | 0.59 | 0.54 | 0.49 | 0.44 | 0.39 | 0.35 | 0.30 | 0.26 | 0.70 | 0.64 | 0.58 | 0.53 | 0.47 | 0.42 | 0.38 | 0.33 | 0.28 | 0.24 |
| | 700 | 0.76 | 0.70 | 0.64 | 0.59 | 0.53 | 0.48 | 0.43 | 0.39 | 0.34 | 0.30 | 0.76 | 0.69 | 0.63 | 0.58 | 0.52 | 0.47 | 0.42 | 0.37 | 0.32 | 0.27 |
| 2000 | 750 | 0.81 | 0.75 | 0.69 | 0.64 | 0.58 | 0.53 | 0.48 | 0.43 | 0.38 | 0.34 | 0.81 | 0.75 | 0.69 | 0.63 | 0.57 | 0.51 | 0.46 | 0.41 | 0.36 | 0.31 |
| | 800 | 0.87 | 0.81 | 0.75 | 0.69 | 0.63 | 0.58 | 0.52 | 0.47 | 0.42 | 0.37 | 0.87 | 0.80 | 0.74 | 0.68 | 0.62 | 0.56 | 0.50 | 0.45 | 0.40 | 0.35 |
| | 900 | 0.98 | 0.92 | 0.85 | 0.79 | 0.73 | 0.67 | 0.61 | 0.55 | 0.50 | 0.45 | 0.98 | 0.91 | 0.84 | 0.78 | 0.71 | 0.65 | 0.59 | 0.53 | 0.48 | 0.42 |
| 15 | 1000 | 1.09 | 1.02 | 0.95 | 0.89 | 0.82 | 0.76 | 0.70 | 0.64 | 0.58 | 0.52 | 1.09 | 1.02 | 0.95 | 0.88 | 0.81 | 0.74 | 0.68 | 0.62 | 0.56 | 0.50 |
| | 1200 | 1.32 | 1.24 | 1.16 | 1.08 | 1.01 | 0.94 | 0.87 | 0.80 | 0.74 | 0.67 | 1.32 | 1.23 | 1.15 | 1.07 | 1.00 | 0.92 | 0.85 | 0.78 | 0.71 | 0.65 |
| | 1350 | 1.48 | 1.40 | 1.31 | 1.23 | 1.15 | 1.07 | 0.99 | 0.92 | 0.85 | 0.78 | 1.48 | 1.39 | 1.30 | 1.22 | 1.14 | 1.06 | 0.98 | 0.90 | 0.83 | 0.76 |
| | 800 | 0.68 | 0.62 | 0.57 | 0.52 | 0.47 | 0.42 | 0.38 | 0.33 | 0.29 | 0.25 | 0.67 | 0.62 | 0.56 | 0.51 | 0.46 | 0.41 | 0.36 | 0.31 | 0.27 | 0.22 |
| | 875 | 0.74 | 0.68 | 0.63 | 0.58 | 0.53 | 0.47 | 0.43 | 0.38 | 0.34 | 0.29 | 0.74 | 0.68 | 0.62 | 0.56 | 0.51 | 0.46 | 0.41 | 0.36 | 0.31 | 0.27 |
| 2500 | 950 | 0.81 | 0.75 | 0.69 | 0.64 | 0.58 | 0.53 | 0.48 | 0.43 | 0.38 | 0.34 | 0.81 | 0.74 | 0.68 | 0.63 | 0.57 | 0.51 | 0.46 | 0.41 | 0.36 | 0.31 |
| | 1000 | 0.85 | 0.79 | 0.73 | 0.68 | 0.62 | 0.56 | 0.51 | 0.46 | 0.41 | 0.37 | 0.85 | 0.78 | 0.72 | 0.66 | 0.60 | 0.55 | 0.49 | 0.44 | 0.39 | 0.34 |
| | 1125 | 0.96 | 0.90 | 0.84 | 0.77 | 0.71 | 0.65 | 0.60 | 0.54 | 0.49 | 0.44 | 0.96 | 0.89 | 0.83 | 0.76 | 0.70 | 0.64 | 0.58 | 0.52 | 0.47 | 0.42 |
| 12 | 1250 | 1.08 | 1.01 | 0.94 | 0.87 | 0.81 | 0.74 | 0.68 | 0.63 | 0.57 | 0.52 | 1.07 | 1.00 | 0.93 | 0.86 | 0.79 | 0.73 | 0.66 | 0.60 | 0.55 | 0.49 |
| | 1500 | 1.29 | 1.22 | 1.14 | 1.06 | 0.99 | 0.92 | 0.85 | 0.78 | 0.72 | 0.66 | 1.29 | 1.21 | 1.13 | 1.05 | 0.98 | 0.90 | 0.83 | 0.77 | 0.70 | 0.64 |
| | 1700 | 1.47 | 1.38 | 1.30 | 1.22 | 1.14 | 1.06 | 0.98 | 0.91 | 0.84 | 0.78 | 1.47 | 1.38 | 1.29 | 1.21 | 1.13 | 1.05 | 0.97 | 0.89 | 0.82 | 0.75 |
| | 975 | 0.67 | 0.62 | 0.57 | 0.52 | 0.47 | 0.42 | 0.38 | 0.33 | 0.29 | 0.25 | 0.67 | 0.62 | 0.56 | 0.51 | 0.46 | 0.41 | 0.36 | 0.32 | 0.27 | 0.23 |
| | 1050 | 0.73 | 0.67 | 0.62 | 0.57 | 0.52 | 0.47 | 0.42 | 0.37 | 0.33 | 0.29 | 0.73 | 0.67 | 0.61 | 0.55 | 0.50 | 0.45 | 0.40 | 0.35 | 0.31 | 0.26 |
| 3000 | 1125 | 0.78 | 0.73 | 0.67 | 0.62 | 0.56 | 0.51 | 0.46 | 0.41 | 0.37 | 0.33 | 0.78 | 0.72 | 0.66 | 0.60 | 0.55 | 0.50 | 0.44 | 0.39 | 0.35 | 0.30 |
| | 1200 | 0.84 | 0.78 | 0.72 | 0.66 | 0.61 | 0.55 | 0.50 | 0.45 | 0.41 | 0.36 | 0.84 | 0.77 | 0.71 | 0.65 | 0.59 | 0.54 | 0.48 | 0.43 | 0.38 | 0.33 |
| | 1350 | 0.95 | 0.88 | 0.82 | 0.76 | 0.70 | 0.64 | 0.59 | 0.53 | 0.48 | 0.43 | 0.94 | 0.88 | 0.81 | 0.75 | 0.69 | 0.63 | 0.57 | 0.51 | 0.46 | 0.41 |
| 10 | 1500 | 1.06 | 0.99 | 0.92 | 0.85 | 0.79 | 0.73 | 0.67 | 0.61 | 0.56 | 0.50 | 1.05 | 0.98 | 0.91 | 0.84 | 0.78 | 0.71 | 0.65 | 0.59 | 0.54 | 0.48 |
| | 1800 | 1.27 | 1.19 | 1.12 | 1.04 | 0.97 | 0.90 | 0.83 | 0.77 | 0.71 | 0.65 | 1.27 | 1.19 | 1.11 | 1.03 | 0.96 | 0.89 | 0.82 | 0.75 | 0.69 | 0.63 |
| | 2025 | 1.43 | 1.35 | 1.26 | 1.18 | 1.11 | 1.03 | 0.96 | 0.89 | 0.82 | 0.75 | 1.43 | 1.34 | 1.26 | 1.17 | 1.09 | 1.02 | 0.94 | 0.87 | 0.80 | 0.73 |
| | 1200 | 0.65 | 0.59 | 0.54 | 0.50 | 0.45 | 0.40 | 0.36 | 0.32 | 0.28 | 0.24 | 0.64 | 0.59 | 0.54 | 0.48 | 0.43 | 0.39 | 0.34 | 0.30 | 0.26 | 0.21 |
| | 1300 | 0.70 | 0.65 | 0.59 | 0.54 | 0.49 | 0.45 | 0.40 | 0.36 | 0.32 | 0.27 | 0.70 | 0.64 | 0.59 | 0.53 | 0.48 | 0.43 | 0.38 | 0.34 | 0.29 | 0.25 |
| 3750 | 1400 | 0.76 | 0.70 | 0.65 | 0.60 | 0.54 | 0.49 | 0.45 | 0.40 | 0.36 | 0.31 | 0.76 | 0.70 | 0.64 | 0.58 | 0.53 | 0.48 | 0.43 | 0.38 | 0.33 | 0.28 |
| | 1500 | 0.82 | 0.76 | 0.70 | 0.64 | 0.59 | 0.54 | 0.49 | 0.44 | 0.40 | 0.35 | 0.81 | 0.75 | 0.69 | 0.63 | 0.58 | 0.52 | 0.47 | 0.42 | 0.37 | 0.33 |
| | 1700 | 0.93 | 0.86 | 0.80 | 0.74 | 0.68 | 0.63 | 0.57 | 0.52 | 0.47 | 0.42 | 0.92 | 0.86 | 0.79 | 0.73 | 0.67 | 0.61 | 0.56 | 0.50 | 0.45 | 0.40 |
| 8 | 1875 | 1.03 | 0.96 | 0.89 | 0.83 | 0.77 | 0.71 | 0.65 | 0.60 | 0.54 | 0.49 | 1.02 | 0.95 | 0.89 | 0.82 | 0.76 | 0.69 | 0.63 | 0.58 | 0.52 | 0.47 |
| | 2250 | 1.23 | 1.16 | 1.09 | 1.01 | 0.95 | 0.88 | 0.81 | 0.75 | 0.69 | 0.63 | 1.23 | 1.16 | 1.08 | 1.00 | 0.93 | 0.86 | 0.80 | 0.73 | 0.67 | 0.61 |
| | 2525 | 1.39 | 1.31 | 1.23 | 1.15 | 1.08 | 1.01 | 0.93 | 0.86 | 0.80 | 0.73 | 1.39 | 1.30 | 1.22 | 1.14 | 1.06 | 0.99 | 0.92 | 0.85 | 0.78 | 0.71 |

# Table 7. (*continued*)

| $f'_c$ and $n$ | $f_c$ | $f_s = 22{,}000$, $\frac{d'}{d}$ = 0.02 | 0.04 | 0.06 | 0.08 | 0.10 | 0.12 | 0.14 | 0.16 | 0.18 | 0.20 |
|---|---|---|---|---|---|---|---|---|---|---|---|
| | 650 | 0.69 | 0.63 | 0.57 | 0.52 | 0.46 | 0.41 | 0.36 | 0.30 | 0.26 | 0.21 |
| | 700 | 0.75 | 0.69 | 0.62 | 0.56 | 0.51 | 0.45 | 0.40 | 0.35 | 0.30 | 0.25 |
| 2000 | 750 | 0.81 | 0.74 | 0.68 | 0.61 | 0.55 | 0.50 | 0.44 | 0.39 | 0.34 | 0.29 |
| | 800 | 0.86 | 0.80 | 0.73 | 0.66 | 0.60 | 0.54 | 0.48 | 0.43 | 0.38 | 0.32 |
| | 900 | 0.97 | 0.90 | 0.83 | 0.76 | 0.70 | 0.63 | 0.57 | 0.51 | 0.45 | 0.40 |
| 15 | 1000 | 1.09 | 1.01 | 0.93 | 0.86 | 0.79 | 0.72 | 0.66 | 0.59 | 0.53 | 0.47 |
| | 1200 | 1.31 | 1.23 | 1.14 | 1.06 | 0.98 | 0.90 | 0.83 | 0.76 | 0.69 | 0.62 |
| | 1350 | 1.48 | 1.38 | 1.29 | 1.21 | 1.12 | 1.04 | 0.96 | 0.88 | 0.81 | 0.73 |
| | 800 | 0.67 | 0.61 | 0.55 | 0.50 | 0.44 | 0.39 | 0.34 | 0.29 | 0.25 | 0.20 |
| | 875 | 0.74 | 0.67 | 0.61 | 0.55 | 0.50 | 0.44 | 0.39 | 0.34 | 0.29 | 0.24 |
| 2500 | 950 | 0.80 | 0.74 | 0.67 | 0.61 | 0.55 | 0.50 | 0.44 | 0.39 | 0.34 | 0.29 |
| | 1000 | 0.85 | 0.78 | 0.72 | 0.65 | 0.59 | 0.53 | 0.48 | 0.42 | 0.37 | 0.32 |
| | 1125 | 0.96 | 0.89 | 0.82 | 0.75 | 0.68 | 0.62 | 0.56 | 0.50 | 0.44 | 0.39 |
| 12 | 1250 | 1.07 | 0.99 | 0.92 | 0.84 | 0.77 | 0.71 | 0.64 | 0.58 | 0.52 | 0.46 |
| | 1500 | 1.29 | 1.20 | 1.12 | 1.04 | 0.96 | 0.89 | 0.82 | 0.75 | 0.68 | 0.61 |
| | 1700 | 1.46 | 1.37 | 1.28 | 1.19 | 1.11 | 1.03 | 0.95 | 0.87 | 0.80 | 0.73 |
| | 975 | 0.67 | 0.61 | 0.55 | 0.50 | 0.44 | 0.39 | 0.34 | 0.29 | 0.25 | 0.20 |
| | 1050 | 0.72 | 0.66 | 0.60 | 0.54 | 0.49 | 0.44 | 0.38 | 0.33 | 0.29 | 0.24 |
| 3000 | 1125 | 0.78 | 0.71 | 0.65 | 0.59 | 0.53 | 0.48 | 0.42 | 0.37 | 0.32 | 0.28 |
| | 1200 | 0.83 | 0.77 | 0.70 | 0.64 | 0.58 | 0.52 | 0.47 | 0.41 | 0.36 | 0.31 |
| | 1350 | 0.94 | 0.87 | 0.80 | 0.73 | 0.67 | 0.61 | 0.55 | 0.49 | 0.44 | 0.38 |
| 10 | 1500 | 1.05 | 0.97 | 0.90 | 0.83 | 0.76 | 0.69 | 0.63 | 0.57 | 0.51 | 0.45 |
| | 1800 | 1.26 | 1.18 | 1.10 | 1.02 | 0.94 | 0.87 | 0.80 | 0.73 | 0.67 | 0.60 |
| | 2025 | 1.43 | 1.34 | 1.25 | 1.17 | 1.08 | 1.00 | 0.92 | 0.85 | 0.78 | 0.71 |
| | 1200 | 0.64 | 0.58 | 0.53 | 0.47 | 0.42 | 0.37 | 0.33 | 0.28 | 0.23 | 0.19 |
| | 1300 | 0.70 | 0.64 | 0.58 | 0.52 | 0.47 | 0.42 | 0.37 | 0.32 | 0.27 | 0.23 |
| 3750 | 1400 | 0.75 | 0.69 | 0.63 | 0.57 | 0.52 | 0.46 | 0.41 | 0.36 | 0.31 | 0.27 |
| | 1500 | 0.81 | 0.75 | 0.68 | 0.62 | 0.56 | 0.51 | 0.45 | 0.40 | 0.35 | 0.30 |
| | 1700 | 0.92 | 0.85 | 0.79 | 0.72 | 0.66 | 0.60 | 0.54 | 0.48 | 0.43 | 0.38 |
| 8 | 1875 | 1.02 | 0.95 | 0.87 | 0.81 | 0.74 | 0.68 | 0.61 | 0.55 | 0.50 | 0.44 |
| | 2250 | 1.23 | 1.15 | 1.07 | 0.99 | 0.92 | 0.85 | 0.78 | 0.71 | 0.65 | 0.58 |
| | 2525 | 1.39 | 1.30 | 1.21 | 1.13 | 1.05 | 0.97 | 0.90 | 0.83 | 0.76 | 0.69 |

| $f'_c$ and $n$ | $f_c$ | $f_s = 24{,}000$, $\frac{d'}{d}$ = 0.02 | 0.04 | 0.06 | 0.08 | 0.10 | 0.12 | 0.14 | 0.16 | 0.18 | 0.20 |
|---|---|---|---|---|---|---|---|---|---|---|---|
| | 650 | 0.69 | 0.63 | 0.57 | 0.51 | 0.45 | 0.39 | 0.34 | 0.28 | 0.23 | 0.19 |
| | 700 | 0.75 | 0.68 | 0.62 | 0.55 | 0.49 | 0.43 | 0.38 | 0.32 | 0.27 | 0.22 |
| 2000 | 750 | 0.80 | 0.74 | 0.67 | 0.60 | 0.54 | 0.48 | 0.42 | 0.37 | 0.31 | 0.26 |
| | 800 | 0.86 | 0.79 | 0.72 | 0.65 | 0.59 | 0.53 | 0.47 | 0.41 | 0.35 | 0.30 |
| | 900 | 0.97 | 0.90 | 0.82 | 0.75 | 0.68 | 0.62 | 0.55 | 0.49 | 0.43 | 0.37 |
| 15 | 1000 | 1.09 | 1.01 | 0.93 | 0.85 | 0.78 | 0.71 | 0.64 | 0.57 | 0.51 | 0.45 |
| | 1200 | 1.31 | 1.22 | 1.13 | 1.05 | 0.97 | 0.89 | 0.81 | 0.74 | 0.67 | 0.60 |
| | 1350 | 1.48 | 1.38 | 1.29 | 1.20 | 1.11 | 1.02 | 0.94 | 0.86 | 0.79 | 0.71 |
| | 800 | 0.67 | 0.61 | 0.55 | 0.49 | 0.43 | 0.37 | 0.32 | 0.27 | 0.22 | 0.18 |
| | 875 | 0.73 | 0.67 | 0.61 | 0.54 | 0.48 | 0.43 | 0.37 | 0.32 | 0.27 | 0.22 |
| 2500 | 950 | 0.80 | 0.73 | 0.67 | 0.60 | 0.54 | 0.48 | 0.42 | 0.37 | 0.31 | 0.26 |
| | 1000 | 0.84 | 0.77 | 0.70 | 0.64 | 0.58 | 0.52 | 0.46 | 0.40 | 0.34 | 0.29 |
| | 1125 | 0.96 | 0.88 | 0.81 | 0.74 | 0.67 | 0.61 | 0.54 | 0.48 | 0.42 | 0.37 |
| 12 | 1250 | 1.07 | 0.99 | 0.91 | 0.84 | 0.76 | 0.69 | 0.63 | 0.56 | 0.50 | 0.44 |
| | 1500 | 1.29 | 1.20 | 1.11 | 1.03 | 0.95 | 0.87 | 0.80 | 0.73 | 0.66 | 0.59 |
| | 1700 | 1.46 | 1.37 | 1.28 | 1.19 | 1.10 | 1.02 | 0.93 | 0.85 | 0.78 | 0.71 |
| | 975 | 0.67 | 0.60 | 0.54 | 0.49 | 0.43 | 0.38 | 0.32 | 0.27 | 0.23 | 0.18 |
| | 1050 | 0.72 | 0.66 | 0.59 | 0.53 | 0.48 | 0.42 | 0.36 | 0.31 | 0.26 | 0.22 |
| 3000 | 1125 | 0.77 | 0.71 | 0.64 | 0.58 | 0.52 | 0.46 | 0.41 | 0.35 | 0.30 | 0.25 |
| | 1200 | 0.83 | 0.76 | 0.69 | 0.63 | 0.57 | 0.51 | 0.45 | 0.39 | 0.34 | 0.29 |
| | 1350 | 0.94 | 0.86 | 0.79 | 0.73 | 0.66 | 0.59 | 0.53 | 0.47 | 0.42 | 0.36 |
| 10 | 1500 | 1.05 | 0.97 | 0.89 | 0.82 | 0.75 | 0.68 | 0.62 | 0.55 | 0.49 | 0.43 |
| | 1800 | 1.26 | 1.18 | 1.09 | 1.01 | 0.93 | 0.86 | 0.78 | 0.71 | 0.64 | 0.58 |
| | 2025 | 1.43 | 1.33 | 1.24 | 1.16 | 1.07 | 0.99 | 0.91 | 0.83 | 0.76 | 0.69 |
| | 1200 | 0.64 | 0.58 | 0.52 | 0.46 | 0.41 | 0.36 | 0.31 | 0.26 | 0.21 | 0.17 |
| | 1300 | 0.69 | 0.63 | 0.57 | 0.51 | 0.46 | 0.40 | 0.35 | 0.30 | 0.25 | 0.20 |
| 3750 | 1400 | 0.75 | 0.69 | 0.62 | 0.56 | 0.50 | 0.45 | 0.39 | 0.34 | 0.29 | 0.24 |
| | 1500 | 0.81 | 0.74 | 0.67 | 0.61 | 0.55 | 0.49 | 0.44 | 0.38 | 0.33 | 0.28 |
| | 1700 | 0.92 | 0.85 | 0.78 | 0.71 | 0.65 | 0.58 | 0.52 | 0.47 | 0.41 | 0.36 |
| 8 | 1875 | 1.02 | 0.94 | 0.87 | 0.80 | 0.73 | 0.66 | 0.60 | 0.54 | 0.48 | 0.42 |
| | 2250 | 1.23 | 1.14 | 1.06 | 0.98 | 0.91 | 0.83 | 0.76 | 0.69 | 0.63 | 0.56 |
| | 2525 | 1.38 | 1.29 | 1.20 | 1.12 | 1.04 | 0.96 | 0.88 | 0.80 | 0.73 | 0.66 |

| $f'_c$ and $n$ | $f_c$ | $f_s = 27{,}000$, $\frac{d'}{d}$ = 0.02 | 0.04 | 0.06 | 0.08 | 0.10 | 0.12 | 0.14 | 0.16 | 0.18 | 0.20 |
|---|---|---|---|---|---|---|---|---|---|---|---|
| | 650 | 0.69 | 0.62 | 0.55 | 0.49 | 0.42 | 0.36 | 0.31 | 0.25 | 0.20 | 0.15 |
| | 700 | 0.74 | 0.67 | 0.60 | 0.54 | 0.47 | 0.41 | 0.35 | 0.29 | 0.24 | 0.19 |
| 2000 | 750 | 0.80 | 0.73 | 0.66 | 0.59 | 0.52 | 0.46 | 0.39 | 0.33 | 0.28 | 0.22 |
| | 800 | 0.86 | 0.78 | 0.71 | 0.64 | 0.57 | 0.50 | 0.44 | 0.38 | 0.32 | 0.26 |
| | 900 | 0.97 | 0.89 | 0.81 | 0.73 | 0.66 | 0.59 | 0.52 | 0.46 | 0.40 | 0.34 |
| 15 | 1000 | 1.08 | 0.99 | 0.91 | 0.83 | 0.76 | 0.68 | 0.61 | 0.54 | 0.47 | 0.41 |
| | 1200 | 1.30 | 1.21 | 1.12 | 1.03 | 0.95 | 0.86 | 0.78 | 0.71 | 0.63 | 0.56 |
| | 1350 | 1.47 | 1.37 | 1.28 | 1.18 | 1.09 | 1.00 | 0.91 | 0.83 | 0.75 | 0.67 |
| | 800 | 0.66 | 0.60 | 0.53 | 0.47 | 0.41 | 0.35 | 0.29 | 0.24 | 0.19 | 0.14 |
| | 875 | 0.73 | 0.66 | 0.59 | 0.53 | 0.46 | 0.40 | 0.34 | 0.29 | 0.23 | 0.18 |
| 2500 | 950 | 0.80 | 0.72 | 0.65 | 0.59 | 0.52 | 0.46 | 0.40 | 0.34 | 0.28 | 0.23 |
| | 1000 | 0.84 | 0.77 | 0.70 | 0.63 | 0.56 | 0.49 | 0.43 | 0.37 | 0.31 | 0.26 |
| | 1125 | 0.95 | 0.87 | 0.79 | 0.72 | 0.65 | 0.58 | 0.51 | 0.45 | 0.39 | 0.33 |
| 12 | 1250 | 1.06 | 0.98 | 0.90 | 0.82 | 0.74 | 0.67 | 0.60 | 0.53 | 0.47 | 0.40 |
| | 1500 | 1.28 | 1.19 | 1.10 | 1.01 | 0.93 | 0.85 | 0.77 | 0.69 | 0.62 | 0.55 |
| | 1700 | 1.45 | 1.36 | 1.26 | 1.16 | 1.07 | 0.99 | 0.90 | 0.82 | 0.74 | 0.67 |
| | 975 | 0.66 | 0.59 | 0.53 | 0.47 | 0.41 | 0.35 | 0.29 | 0.24 | 0.19 | 0.14 |
| | 1050 | 0.72 | 0.65 | 0.58 | 0.52 | 0.46 | 0.40 | 0.34 | 0.28 | 0.23 | 0.18 |
| 3000 | 1125 | 0.77 | 0.70 | 0.63 | 0.57 | 0.50 | 0.44 | 0.38 | 0.32 | 0.27 | 0.22 |
| | 1200 | 0.83 | 0.75 | 0.68 | 0.61 | 0.55 | 0.48 | 0.42 | 0.36 | 0.31 | 0.25 |
| | 1350 | 0.93 | 0.85 | 0.78 | 0.71 | 0.64 | 0.57 | 0.50 | 0.44 | 0.38 | 0.32 |
| 10 | 1500 | 1.04 | 0.96 | 0.88 | 0.80 | 0.73 | 0.66 | 0.59 | 0.52 | 0.46 | 0.40 |
| | 1800 | 1.26 | 1.17 | 1.08 | 0.99 | 0.91 | 0.83 | 0.76 | 0.68 | 0.61 | 0.54 |
| | 2025 | 1.42 | 1.32 | 1.23 | 1.14 | 1.05 | 0.96 | 0.88 | 0.80 | 0.72 | 0.65 |
| | 1200 | 0.63 | 0.57 | 0.51 | 0.45 | 0.39 | 0.33 | 0.28 | 0.23 | 0.18 | 0.13 |
| | 1300 | 0.69 | 0.62 | 0.56 | 0.50 | 0.44 | 0.38 | 0.32 | 0.27 | 0.22 | 0.17 |
| 3750 | 1400 | 0.74 | 0.68 | 0.61 | 0.55 | 0.48 | 0.42 | 0.37 | 0.31 | 0.26 | 0.21 |
| | 1500 | 0.80 | 0.73 | 0.66 | 0.60 | 0.53 | 0.47 | 0.41 | 0.35 | 0.30 | 0.25 |
| | 1700 | 0.91 | 0.84 | 0.77 | 0.70 | 0.63 | 0.56 | 0.50 | 0.44 | 0.38 | 0.32 |
| 8 | 1875 | 1.01 | 0.93 | 0.85 | 0.78 | 0.71 | 0.64 | 0.57 | 0.51 | 0.44 | 0.38 |
| | 2250 | 1.22 | 1.13 | 1.05 | 0.97 | 0.89 | 0.81 | 0.73 | 0.66 | 0.59 | 0.52 |
| | 2525 | 1.38 | 1.28 | 1.19 | 1.10 | 1.02 | 0.93 | 0.85 | 0.78 | 0.70 | 0.63 |

| $f'_c$ and $n$ | $f_c$ | $f_s = 30{,}000$, $\frac{d'}{d}$ = 0.02 | 0.04 | 0.06 | 0.08 | 0.10 | 0.12 | 0.14 | 0.16 | 0.18 | 0.20 |
|---|---|---|---|---|---|---|---|---|---|---|---|
| | 650 | 0.68 | 0.61 | 0.54 | 0.47 | 0.40 | 0.34 | 0.28 | 0.22 | 0.16 | 0.11 |
| | 700 | 0.74 | 0.66 | 0.59 | 0.52 | 0.45 | 0.39 | 0.32 | 0.26 | 0.20 | 0.15 |
| 2000 | 750 | 0.80 | 0.72 | 0.64 | 0.57 | 0.50 | 0.43 | 0.37 | 0.31 | 0.25 | 0.19 |
| | 800 | 0.85 | 0.77 | 0.70 | 0.62 | 0.55 | 0.48 | 0.41 | 0.35 | 0.28 | 0.23 |
| | 900 | 0.96 | 0.87 | 0.79 | 0.71 | 0.64 | 0.57 | 0.49 | 0.43 | 0.36 | 0.30 |
| 15 | 1000 | 1.07 | 0.98 | 0.90 | 0.81 | 0.73 | 0.66 | 0.58 | 0.51 | 0.44 | 0.37 |
| | 1200 | 1.30 | 1.20 | 1.11 | 1.01 | 0.92 | 0.84 | 0.75 | 0.67 | 0.60 | 0.52 |
| | 1350 | 1.47 | 1.36 | 1.26 | 1.16 | 1.07 | 0.97 | 0.88 | 0.80 | 0.71 | 0.63 |
| | 800 | 0.66 | 0.59 | 0.52 | 0.45 | 0.39 | 0.33 | 0.27 | 0.21 | 0.15 | 0.10 |
| | 875 | 0.72 | 0.65 | 0.58 | 0.51 | 0.44 | 0.38 | 0.32 | 0.26 | 0.20 | 0.15 |
| 2500 | 950 | 0.79 | 0.71 | 0.64 | 0.57 | 0.50 | 0.43 | 0.37 | 0.31 | 0.25 | 0.19 |
| | 1000 | 0.84 | 0.76 | 0.68 | 0.61 | 0.54 | 0.47 | 0.40 | 0.34 | 0.28 | 0.22 |
| | 1125 | 0.94 | 0.86 | 0.78 | 0.70 | 0.63 | 0.56 | 0.49 | 0.42 | 0.35 | 0.29 |
| 12 | 1250 | 1.05 | 0.97 | 0.88 | 0.80 | 0.72 | 0.64 | 0.57 | 0.50 | 0.43 | 0.37 |
| | 1500 | 1.27 | 1.18 | 1.09 | 1.00 | 0.91 | 0.82 | 0.74 | 0.66 | 0.59 | 0.51 |
| | 1700 | 1.45 | 1.35 | 1.25 | 1.15 | 1.06 | 0.97 | 0.88 | 0.79 | 0.71 | 0.63 |
| | 975 | 0.66 | 0.59 | 0.52 | 0.45 | 0.39 | 0.33 | 0.27 | 0.21 | 0.16 | 0.11 |
| | 1050 | 0.71 | 0.64 | 0.57 | 0.50 | 0.43 | 0.37 | 0.31 | 0.25 | 0.20 | 0.14 |
| 3000 | 1125 | 0.77 | 0.69 | 0.62 | 0.55 | 0.48 | 0.42 | 0.35 | 0.29 | 0.24 | 0.18 |
| | 1200 | 0.82 | 0.74 | 0.67 | 0.60 | 0.53 | 0.46 | 0.40 | 0.33 | 0.27 | 0.22 |
| | 1350 | 0.93 | 0.85 | 0.77 | 0.69 | 0.62 | 0.55 | 0.48 | 0.41 | 0.35 | 0.29 |
| 10 | 1500 | 1.04 | 0.95 | 0.86 | 0.79 | 0.71 | 0.63 | 0.56 | 0.49 | 0.42 | 0.36 |
| | 1800 | 1.25 | 1.16 | 1.07 | 0.98 | 0.89 | 0.81 | 0.73 | 0.65 | 0.58 | 0.50 |
| | 2025 | 1.42 | 1.32 | 1.22 | 1.12 | 1.03 | 0.94 | 0.85 | 0.77 | 0.69 | 0.61 |
| | 1200 | 0.63 | 0.56 | 0.49 | 0.43 | 0.37 | 0.31 | 0.25 | 0.20 | 0.15 | 0.10 |
| | 1300 | 0.68 | 0.61 | 0.55 | 0.48 | 0.42 | 0.36 | 0.30 | 0.24 | 0.19 | 0.13 |
| 3750 | 1400 | 0.74 | 0.67 | 0.60 | 0.53 | 0.46 | 0.40 | 0.34 | 0.28 | 0.23 | 0.17 |
| | 1500 | 0.80 | 0.72 | 0.65 | 0.58 | 0.51 | 0.45 | 0.38 | 0.32 | 0.27 | 0.21 |
| | 1700 | 0.91 | 0.83 | 0.75 | 0.68 | 0.61 | 0.54 | 0.47 | 0.41 | 0.34 | 0.28 |
| 8 | 1875 | 1.01 | 0.92 | 0.84 | 0.76 | 0.69 | 0.61 | 0.54 | 0.48 | 0.41 | 0.35 |
| | 2250 | 1.22 | 1.13 | 1.04 | 0.95 | 0.87 | 0.79 | 0.71 | 0.63 | 0.56 | 0.49 |
| | 2525 | 1.37 | 1.27 | 1.18 | 1.08 | 0.99 | 0.91 | 0.82 | 0.74 | 0.67 | 0.59 |

# Table 8. Coefficients ($a$ and $K$) for T-Sections

$f_s = 16{,}000$

| $f'_c$ and $n$ | $f_c$ | $t/d$ = 0.06 | 0.08 | 0.10 | 0.12 | 0.14 | 0.16 | 0.18 | 0.20 | 0.24 | 0.28 | 0.32 | 0.36 | 0.40 |
|---|---|---|---|---|---|---|---|---|---|---|---|---|---|---|
| | $a$ | 1.29 | 1.28 | 1.27 | 1.26 | 1.25 | 1.24 | 1.23 | 1.22 | 1.20 | 1.18 | 1.16 | 1.14 | 1.13 |
| | | $K$ | | | | | | | | | | | | |
| | 650 | 35 | 45 | 54 | 62 | 69 | 76 | 82 | 87 | 96 | 102 | 106 | 107 | 108 |
| | 700 | 38 | 48 | 58 | 67 | 75 | 83 | 90 | 95 | 105 | 112 | 117 | 120 | 120 |
| 2000 | 750 | 41 | 52 | 63 | 73 | 82 | 90 | 97 | 104 | 114 | 123 | 128 | 132 | 133 |
| | 800 | 43 | 56 | 67 | 78 | 88 | 96 | 104 | 112 | 124 | 133 | 140 | 144 | 147 |
| | 900 | 49 | 63 | 76 | 89 | 100 | 110 | 119 | 128 | 143 | 154 | 163 | 169 | 173 |
| 15 | 1000 | 55 | 71 | 85 | 99 | 112 | 124 | 134 | 144 | 161 | 175 | 186 | 194 | 199 |
| | 1200 | 66 | 85 | 103 | 120 | 136 | 151 | 164 | 177 | 199 | 217 | 231 | 243 | 251 |
| | 1350 | 74 | 96 | 117 | 136 | 154 | 171 | 187 | 201 | 227 | 248 | 266 | 280 | 290 |
| | 800 | 43 | 55 | 66 | 76 | 85 | 93 | 101 | 107 | 117 | 125 | 129 | 131 | 131 |
| | 875 | 47 | 60 | 73 | 84 | 93 | 103 | 112 | 118 | 131 | 140 | 146 | 149 | 150 |
| 2500 | 950 | 51 | 66 | 80 | 92 | 103 | 114 | 123 | 131 | 145 | 156 | 163 | 168 | 170 |
| | 1000 | 54 | 70 | 84 | 97 | 110 | 121 | 131 | 140 | 155 | 166 | 175 | 180 | 183 |
| | 1125 | 61 | 79 | 95 | 111 | 125 | 137 | 149 | 160 | 178 | 193 | 203 | 211 | 216 |
| 12 | 1250 | 68 | 88 | 107 | 124 | 140 | 154 | 168 | 180 | 202 | 219 | 232 | 242 | 249 |
| | 1500 | 82 | 107 | 129 | 150 | 170 | 188 | 205 | 221 | 248 | 271 | 289 | 303 | 314 |
| | 1700 | 94 | 121 | 147 | 172 | 194 | 215 | 235 | 253 | 286 | 313 | 335 | 352 | 366 |
| | 975 | 53 | 67 | 81 | 93 | 104 | 114 | 123 | 131 | 144 | 153 | 158 | 161 | 161 |
| | 1050 | 57 | 73 | 87 | 101 | 113 | 124 | 134 | 143 | 158 | 168 | 175 | 179 | 180 |
| 3000 | 1125 | 61 | 78 | 94 | 109 | 122 | 134 | 145 | 155 | 172 | 184 | 193 | 198 | 200 |
| | 1200 | 65 | 84 | 101 | 117 | 131 | 145 | 157 | 168 | 186 | 200 | 210 | 216 | 220 |
| | 1350 | 74 | 95 | 114 | 133 | 150 | 165 | 179 | 192 | 214 | 231 | 244 | 253 | 259 |
| 10 | 1500 | 82 | 106 | 128 | 149 | 168 | 185 | 202 | 216 | 242 | 262 | 278 | 290 | 298 |
| | 1800 | 99 | 128 | 155 | 180 | 204 | 226 | 246 | 265 | 298 | 325 | 347 | 364 | 376 |
| | 2025 | 111 | 145 | 176 | 205 | 231 | 257 | 280 | 302 | 340 | 372 | 398 | 419 | 435 |
| | 1200 | 64 | 83 | 100 | 115 | 129 | 142 | 154 | 165 | 183 | 199 | 211 | 222 | 230 |
| | 1300 | 70 | 90 | 109 | 126 | 141 | 156 | 170 | 181 | 202 | 220 | 234 | 247 | 258 |
| 3750 | 1400 | 76 | 98 | 118 | 136 | 154 | 169 | 184 | 198 | 221 | 241 | 258 | 272 | 285 |
| | 1500 | 81 | 105 | 127 | 147 | 166 | 183 | 199 | 214 | 240 | 263 | 281 | 298 | 312 |
| | 1700 | 93 | 120 | 145 | 168 | 190 | 210 | 229 | 245 | 278 | 305 | 328 | 348 | 366 |
| 8 | 1875 | 102 | 133 | 161 | 187 | 211 | 234 | 256 | 276 | 311 | 342 | 369 | 393 | 414 |
| | 2250 | 124 | 160 | 195 | 227 | 257 | 285 | 312 | 337 | 382 | 422 | 457 | 489 | 516 |
| | 2525 | 141 | 181 | 219 | 256 | 291 | 323 | 354 | 382 | 434 | 481 | 521 | 558 | 591 |

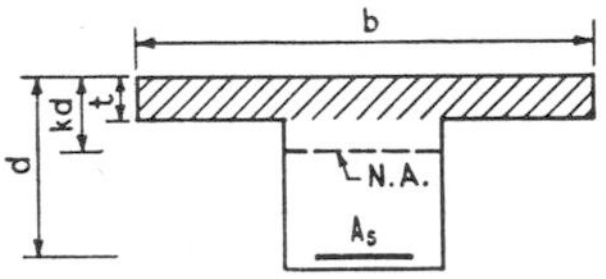


$$K = \frac{f_c}{2} \times \frac{t}{d} \times \left(2 - \frac{t}{d} - \frac{t}{kd} + \frac{2t^2}{3kd^2}\right)$$

$$a = \frac{f_s}{12{,}000} \times (\text{average value of } j)$$

Average values of $j$ are taken from Table 9;

$a$ and $K$ are used in:

$$A_s = \frac{M}{ad} \text{ or } A_s = \frac{NE}{adi}$$

$$A'_s = \frac{M - KF}{cd} \text{ or } A'_s = \frac{NE - KF}{cd}$$

$f_s = 18{,}000$

| $f'_c$ and $n$ | $f_c$ | $t/d$ = 0.06 | 0.08 | 0.10 | 0.12 | 0.14 | 0.16 | 0.18 | 0.20 | 0.24 | 0.28 | 0.32 | 0.36 | 0.40 |
|---|---|---|---|---|---|---|---|---|---|---|---|---|---|---|
| | $a$ | 1.46 | 1.44 | 1.43 | 1.41 | 1.40 | 1.39 | 1.38 | 1.37 | 1.35 | 1.33 | 1.31 | 1.29 | 1.27 |
| | | $K$ | | | | | | | | | | | | |
| | 650 | 35 | 44 | 53 | 61 | 68 | 74 | 80 | 85 | 93 | 97 | 100 | 101 | 101 |
| | 700 | 38 | 48 | 58 | 66 | 74 | 81 | 88 | 93 | 102 | 108 | 111 | 113 | 113 |
| 2000 | 750 | 40 | 51 | 62 | 71 | 80 | 88 | 95 | 101 | 111 | 118 | 123 | 125 | 126 |
| | 800 | 43 | 55 | 67 | 77 | 86 | 95 | 103 | 109 | 121 | 129 | 134 | 138 | 139 |
| | 900 | 49 | 63 | 76 | 88 | 99 | 108 | 118 | 126 | 139 | 150 | 157 | 162 | 165 |
| 15 | 1000 | 54 | 70 | 85 | 98 | 111 | 122 | 133 | 142 | 158 | 171 | 180 | 187 | 191 |
| | 1200 | 66 | 85 | 103 | 120 | 135 | 149 | 162 | 174 | 195 | 213 | 226 | 236 | 243 |
| | 1350 | 74 | 96 | 116 | 135 | 153 | 169 | 185 | 199 | 224 | 244 | 260 | 273 | 282 |
| | 800 | 43 | 54 | 65 | 75 | 84 | 92 | 98 | 104 | 113 | 119 | 122 | 123 | 123 |
| | 875 | 47 | 60 | 72 | 83 | 93 | 102 | 109 | 116 | 127 | 135 | 139 | 141 | 141 |
| 2500 | 950 | 51 | 66 | 79 | 91 | 102 | 112 | 121 | 129 | 141 | 151 | 157 | 160 | 161 |
| | 1000 | 54 | 69 | 83 | 96 | 108 | 119 | 128 | 137 | 151 | 161 | 168 | 172 | 173 |
| | 1125 | 61 | 79 | 95 | 110 | 123 | 136 | 147 | 157 | 174 | 187 | 197 | 203 | 206 |
| 12 | 1250 | 68 | 88 | 106 | 123 | 138 | 153 | 166 | 177 | 198 | 213 | 225 | 234 | 239 |
| | 1500 | 82 | 106 | 129 | 149 | 169 | 186 | 203 | 218 | 244 | 266 | 282 | 295 | 304 |
| | 1700 | 93 | 121 | 147 | 171 | 193 | 214 | 233 | 251 | 282 | 307 | 328 | 344 | 356 |
| | 975 | 52 | 67 | 80 | 92 | 102 | 112 | 120 | 127 | 139 | 146 | 150 | 151 | 151 |
| | 1050 | 56 | 72 | 86 | 100 | 111 | 122 | 131 | 140 | 153 | 162 | 167 | 169 | 169 |
| 3000 | 1125 | 61 | 78 | 93 | 108 | 121 | 132 | 143 | 152 | 167 | 178 | 185 | 188 | 189 |
| | 1200 | 65 | 83 | 100 | 115 | 130 | 142 | 154 | 164 | 181 | 193 | 202 | 206 | 208 |
| | 1350 | 73 | 94 | 114 | 131 | 147 | 163 | 176 | 188 | 209 | 225 | 236 | 243 | 247 |
| 10 | 1500 | 82 | 105 | 127 | 147 | 166 | 182 | 199 | 213 | 237 | 256 | 270 | 280 | 287 |
| | 1800 | 98 | 127 | 154 | 179 | 203 | 224 | 244 | 261 | 293 | 319 | 339 | 354 | 365 |
| | 2025 | 111 | 144 | 175 | 203 | 230 | 254 | 277 | 298 | 335 | 365 | 390 | 409 | 423 |
| | 1200 | 64 | 82 | 98 | 113 | 126 | 137 | 147 | 156 | 170 | 179 | 184 | 185 | 185 |
| | 1300 | 70 | 89 | 107 | 123 | 138 | 151 | 163 | 172 | 189 | 200 | 206 | 209 | 209 |
| 3750 | 1400 | 76 | 97 | 116 | 134 | 150 | 164 | 177 | 189 | 207 | 221 | 229 | 234 | 234 |
| | 1500 | 81 | 104 | 125 | 144 | 162 | 178 | 192 | 205 | 226 | 242 | 252 | 258 | 260 |
| | 1700 | 92 | 119 | 143 | 166 | 186 | 205 | 222 | 237 | 263 | 283 | 298 | 307 | 312 |
| 8 | 1875 | 102 | 131 | 159 | 184 | 207 | 228 | 248 | 266 | 296 | 320 | 338 | 351 | 358 |
| | 2250 | 123 | 159 | 193 | 224 | 253 | 280 | 305 | 327 | 366 | 399 | 424 | 443 | 456 |
| | 2525 | 139 | 179 | 218 | 254 | 287 | 317 | 346 | 372 | 418 | 456 | 487 | 510 | 528 |

$f_s = 20{,}000$

| $f'_c$ and $n$ | $f_c$ | $t/d$ = 0.06 | 0.08 | 0.10 | 0.12 | 0.14 | 0.16 | 0.18 | 0.20 | 0.24 | 0.28 | 0.32 | 0.36 | 0.40 |
|---|---|---|---|---|---|---|---|---|---|---|---|---|---|---|
| | $a$ | 1.62 | 1.60 | 1.59 | 1.57 | 1.56 | 1.55 | 1.53 | 1.52 | 1.50 | 1.48 | 1.45 | 1.43 | 1.41 |
| | | $K$ | | | | | | | | | | | | |
| | 650 | 35 | 44 | 53 | 60 | 67 | 73 | 78 | 83 | 89 | 93 | 95 | 95 | 95 |
| | 700 | 37 | 48 | 57 | 66 | 73 | 80 | 86 | 91 | 99 | 104 | 106 | 107 | 107 |
| 2000 | 750 | 40 | 51 | 62 | 71 | 79 | 87 | 93 | 99 | 108 | 114 | 118 | 119 | 119 |
| | 800 | 43 | 55 | 66 | 76 | 85 | 93 | 101 | 107 | 117 | 125 | 129 | 131 | 131 |
| | 900 | 49 | 62 | 75 | 87 | 97 | 107 | 116 | 123 | 136 | 145 | 152 | 156 | 157 |
| 15 | 1000 | 54 | 70 | 84 | 97 | 110 | 121 | 131 | 140 | 155 | 166 | 175 | 180 | 183 |
| | 1200 | 65 | 84 | 102 | 119 | 134 | 148 | 160 | 172 | 192 | 208 | 221 | 229 | 235 |
| | 1350 | 74 | 96 | 116 | 134 | 152 | 168 | 183 | 196 | 220 | 240 | 255 | 266 | 275 |
| | 800 | 43 | 54 | 65 | 74 | 82 | 90 | 96 | 101 | 109 | 114 | 116 | 116 | 116 |
| | 875 | 47 | 60 | 71 | 82 | 91 | 100 | 107 | 113 | 123 | 130 | 133 | 133 | 133 |
| 2500 | 950 | 51 | 65 | 78 | 90 | 100 | 110 | 118 | 126 | 137 | 145 | 150 | 152 | 152 |
| | 1000 | 54 | 69 | 83 | 95 | 107 | 117 | 126 | 134 | 147 | 156 | 161 | 164 | 164 |
| | 1125 | 61 | 78 | 94 | 108 | 122 | 134 | 145 | 154 | 170 | 181 | 190 | 195 | 196 |
| 12 | 1250 | 68 | 87 | 105 | 122 | 137 | 151 | 163 | 174 | 193 | 208 | 219 | 225 | 229 |
| | 1500 | 82 | 106 | 128 | 148 | 167 | 185 | 201 | 215 | 240 | 260 | 276 | 287 | 294 |
| | 1700 | 93 | 120 | 146 | 169 | 191 | 212 | 231 | 247 | 278 | 302 | 321 | 336 | 346 |
| | 975 | 52 | 66 | 79 | 90 | 101 | 109 | 117 | 124 | 134 | 140 | 142 | 142 | 142 |
| | 1050 | 56 | 71 | 86 | 98 | 110 | 120 | 128 | 136 | 148 | 156 | 159 | 160 | 160 |
| 3000 | 1125 | 60 | 77 | 92 | 106 | 119 | 130 | 140 | 148 | 162 | 171 | 176 | 178 | 178 |
| | 1200 | 65 | 83 | 99 | 114 | 128 | 140 | 151 | 161 | 176 | 187 | 194 | 197 | 197 |
| | 1350 | 73 | 94 | 113 | 130 | 146 | 160 | 173 | 185 | 204 | 218 | 228 | 234 | 236 |
| 10 | 1500 | 81 | 105 | 126 | 146 | 164 | 181 | 196 | 209 | 232 | 250 | 262 | 271 | 275 |
| | 1800 | 98 | 126 | 153 | 178 | 201 | 222 | 241 | 258 | 288 | 312 | 331 | 344 | 353 |
| | 2025 | 111 | 143 | 174 | 202 | 228 | 252 | 274 | 295 | 330 | 359 | 382 | 399 | 411 |
| | 1200 | 64 | 81 | 97 | 111 | 123 | 134 | 144 | 152 | 164 | 171 | 173 | 173 | 173 |
| | 1300 | 69 | 88 | 106 | 121 | 136 | 148 | 159 | 168 | 183 | 192 | 196 | 197 | 197 |
| 3750 | 1400 | 75 | 96 | 115 | 132 | 148 | 162 | 174 | 184 | 201 | 213 | 219 | 221 | 221 |
| | 1500 | 81 | 103 | 124 | 143 | 160 | 175 | 189 | 201 | 220 | 234 | 242 | 246 | 246 |
| | 1700 | 92 | 118 | 142 | 164 | 184 | 202 | 219 | 233 | 257 | 276 | 288 | 295 | 298 |
| 8 | 1875 | 102 | 131 | 158 | 183 | 205 | 226 | 245 | 262 | 290 | 312 | 328 | 338 | 344 |
| | 2250 | 123 | 158 | 191 | 222 | 251 | 277 | 301 | 323 | 359 | 390 | 414 | 431 | 441 |
| | 2525 | 138 | 179 | 216 | 252 | 284 | 314 | 342 | 367 | 412 | 448 | 477 | 498 | 514 |

## Table 8. (*continued*)

$f_s = 22{,}000$

| $f'_c$ and $n$ | $f_c$ | $\frac{t}{d}$ = 0.06 | 0.08 | 0.10 | 0.12 | 0.14 | 0.16 | 0.18 | 0.20 | 0.24 | 0.28 | 0.32 | 0.36 | 0.40 |
|---|---|---|---|---|---|---|---|---|---|---|---|---|---|---|
| | $a$ | 1.78 | 1.76 | 1.75 | 1.73 | 1.72 | 1.70 | 1.69 | 1.67 | 1.65 | 1.62 | 1.60 | 1.57 | 1.55 |
| | | $K$ | | | | | | | | | | | | |
| | 650 | 34 | 43 | 52 | 59 | 66 | 72 | 76 | 80 | 86 | 89 | 90 | 90 | 90 |
| | 700 | 37 | 47 | 56 | 65 | 72 | 78 | 84 | 88 | 95 | 99 | 101 | 101 | 101 |
| 2000 | 750 | 40 | 51 | 61 | 70 | 78 | 85 | 91 | 96 | 105 | 110 | 112 | 112 | 112 |
| | 800 | 43 | 55 | 65 | 75 | 84 | 92 | 99 | 105 | 114 | 120 | 124 | 125 | 125 |
| | 900 | 48 | 62 | 74 | 86 | 96 | 105 | 114 | 121 | 133 | 141 | 146 | 149 | 149 |
| 15 | 1000 | 54 | 69 | 84 | 96 | 108 | 119 | 129 | 137 | 152 | 162 | 169 | 174 | 175 |
| | 1200 | 65 | 84 | 102 | 118 | 133 | 146 | 159 | 170 | 189 | 204 | 215 | 223 | 227 |
| | 1350 | 74 | 95 | 115 | 134 | 151 | 166 | 181 | 193 | 216 | 235 | 249 | 260 | 267 |
| | 800 | 42 | 53 | 64 | 73 | 81 | 88 | 94 | 98 | 105 | 109 | 109 | 109 | 109 |
| | 875 | 46 | 59 | 70 | 81 | 90 | 98 | 105 | 110 | 119 | 124 | 126 | 126 | 126 |
| 2500 | 950 | 50 | 65 | 77 | 89 | 99 | 108 | 116 | 123 | 133 | 140 | 143 | 144 | 144 |
| | 1000 | 53 | 68 | 82 | 94 | 105 | 115 | 123 | 131 | 143 | 150 | 155 | 156 | 156 |
| | 1125 | 60 | 77 | 93 | 107 | 120 | 132 | 142 | 151 | 166 | 177 | 183 | 186 | 187 |
| 12 | 1250 | 67 | 87 | 104 | 120 | 135 | 149 | 161 | 171 | 189 | 202 | 211 | 217 | 219 |
| | 1500 | 82 | 105 | 127 | 147 | 166 | 183 | 198 | 212 | 236 | 255 | 269 | 279 | 284 |
| | 1700 | 93 | 120 | 145 | 168 | 190 | 210 | 228 | 245 | 273 | 297 | 315 | 328 | 337 |
| | 975 | 51 | 65 | 78 | 89 | 99 | 107 | 114 | 120 | 129 | 134 | 134 | 134 | 134 |
| | 1050 | 56 | 71 | 85 | 97 | 108 | 117 | 126 | 133 | 143 | 149 | 151 | 151 | 151 |
| 3000 | 1125 | 60 | 76 | 91 | 105 | 117 | 128 | 137 | 145 | 157 | 165 | 168 | 169 | 169 |
| | 1200 | 64 | 82 | 98 | 113 | 126 | 138 | 148 | 157 | 171 | 181 | 186 | 187 | 187 |
| | 1350 | 72 | 93 | 112 | 129 | 144 | 158 | 171 | 181 | 199 | 212 | 220 | 224 | 224 |
| 10 | 1500 | 81 | 104 | 125 | 145 | 162 | 178 | 193 | 206 | 227 | 243 | 254 | 260 | 263 |
| | 1800 | 98 | 126 | 152 | 177 | 199 | 219 | 238 | 255 | 283 | 306 | 323 | 334 | 341 |
| | 2025 | 110 | 143 | 173 | 200 | 226 | 250 | 271 | 291 | 325 | 353 | 374 | 390 | 400 |
| | 1200 | 63 | 80 | 95 | 109 | 121 | 131 | 140 | 148 | 158 | 163 | 164 | 164 | 164 |
| | 1300 | 69 | 88 | 105 | 120 | 133 | 145 | 155 | 164 | 177 | 184 | 186 | 186 | 186 |
| 3750 | 1400 | 74 | 95 | 114 | 130 | 145 | 159 | 170 | 180 | 195 | 205 | 209 | 209 | 209 |
| | 1500 | 80 | 102 | 123 | 141 | 157 | 172 | 185 | 196 | 214 | 226 | 232 | 234 | 234 |
| | 1700 | 91 | 117 | 141 | 162 | 182 | 199 | 215 | 229 | 251 | 267 | 278 | 283 | 283 |
| 8 | 1875 | 101 | 130 | 157 | 181 | 203 | 223 | 241 | 257 | 284 | 304 | 317 | 325 | 328 |
| | 2250 | 122 | 158 | 190 | 221 | 249 | 274 | 297 | 318 | 354 | 382 | 403 | 418 | 427 |
| | 2525 | 138 | 178 | 215 | 250 | 282 | 311 | 338 | 363 | 406 | 440 | 466 | 486 | 499 |

$f_s = 24{,}000$

| $f'_c$ and $n$ | $f_c$ | $\frac{t}{d}$ = 0.06 | 0.08 | 0.10 | 0.12 | 0.14 | 0.16 | 0.18 | 0.20 | 0.24 | 0.28 | 0.32 | 0.36 | 0.40 |
|---|---|---|---|---|---|---|---|---|---|---|---|---|---|---|
| | $a$ | 1.94 | 1.92 | 1.90 | 1.89 | 1.87 | 1.86 | 1.84 | 1.82 | 1.80 | 1.77 | 1.74 | 1.72 | 1.70 |
| | | $K$ | | | | | | | | | | | | |
| | 650 | 34 | 43 | 51 | 58 | 65 | 70 | 74 | 78 | 83 | 85 | 85 | 85 | 85 |
| | 700 | 37 | 47 | 56 | 64 | 71 | 77 | 82 | 86 | 92 | 95 | 96 | 96 | 96 |
| 2000 | 750 | 40 | 50 | 60 | 69 | 77 | 84 | 89 | 94 | 102 | 106 | 107 | 107 | 107 |
| | 800 | 42 | 54 | 65 | 74 | 83 | 90 | 97 | 102 | 111 | 116 | 118 | 118 | 118 |
| | 900 | 48 | 62 | 74 | 85 | 95 | 104 | 112 | 119 | 130 | 137 | 141 | 143 | 143 |
| 15 | 1000 | 54 | 69 | 83 | 96 | 107 | 118 | 127 | 135 | 148 | 158 | 164 | 167 | 168 |
| | 1200 | 65 | 84 | 101 | 117 | 131 | 145 | 157 | 167 | 186 | 200 | 210 | 216 | 219 |
| | 1350 | 73 | 95 | 114 | 133 | 150 | 165 | 179 | 192 | 214 | 231 | 244 | 253 | 259 |
| | 800 | 42 | 53 | 63 | 72 | 79 | 86 | 91 | 96 | 101 | 104 | 104 | 104 | 104 |
| | 875 | 46 | 58 | 70 | 80 | 88 | 96 | 102 | 108 | 115 | 119 | 120 | 120 | 120 |
| 2500 | 950 | 50 | 64 | 76 | 88 | 97 | 106 | 114 | 120 | 129 | 135 | 137 | 137 | 137 |
| | 1000 | 53 | 68 | 81 | 93 | 104 | 113 | 121 | 128 | 139 | 145 | 148 | 148 | 148 |
| | 1125 | 60 | 77 | 92 | 106 | 119 | 130 | 140 | 148 | 162 | 171 | 177 | 178 | 178 |
| 12 | 1250 | 67 | 86 | 104 | 120 | 134 | 147 | 159 | 169 | 186 | 198 | 205 | 209 | 210 |
| | 1500 | 81 | 105 | 126 | 146 | 164 | 181 | 196 | 209 | 232 | 250 | 262 | 271 | 275 |
| | 1700 | 92 | 119 | 144 | 167 | 189 | 208 | 226 | 242 | 270 | 292 | 308 | 320 | 327 |
| | 975 | 51 | 65 | 77 | 88 | 97 | 105 | 112 | 117 | 124 | 127 | 127 | 127 | 127 |
| | 1050 | 55 | 70 | 84 | 96 | 106 | 115 | 123 | 129 | 138 | 143 | 143 | 143 | 143 |
| 3000 | 1125 | 59 | 75 | 90 | 104 | 115 | 125 | 134 | 141 | 152 | 158 | 160 | 160 | 160 |
| | 1200 | 64 | 81 | 97 | 111 | 124 | 135 | 145 | 153 | 166 | 174 | 177 | 178 | 178 |
| | 1350 | 72 | 92 | 111 | 127 | 142 | 156 | 168 | 178 | 194 | 205 | 212 | 214 | 214 |
| 10 | 1500 | 81 | 103 | 124 | 143 | 161 | 176 | 190 | 203 | 223 | 237 | 246 | 251 | 252 |
| | 1800 | 98 | 125 | 151 | 175 | 197 | 217 | 235 | 251 | 279 | 300 | 315 | 325 | 330 |
| | 2025 | 110 | 142 | 172 | 199 | 224 | 247 | 269 | 288 | 321 | 347 | 366 | 380 | 389 |
| | 1200 | 62 | 79 | 94 | 108 | 119 | 129 | 137 | 143 | 152 | 155 | 155 | 155 | 155 |
| | 1300 | 68 | 87 | 103 | 118 | 131 | 142 | 152 | 159 | 170 | 176 | 176 | 176 | 176 |
| 3750 | 1400 | 74 | 94 | 112 | 129 | 143 | 156 | 167 | 176 | 189 | 197 | 199 | 199 | 199 |
| | 1500 | 80 | 102 | 122 | 139 | 155 | 169 | 182 | 192 | 208 | 218 | 222 | 222 | 222 |
| | 1700 | 90 | 116 | 140 | 161 | 180 | 197 | 211 | 225 | 245 | 260 | 268 | 270 | 270 |
| 8 | 1875 | 101 | 129 | 155 | 179 | 201 | 220 | 238 | 253 | 278 | 296 | 308 | 314 | 315 |
| | 2250 | 122 | 157 | 189 | 219 | 246 | 271 | 294 | 314 | 348 | 375 | 394 | 406 | 412 |
| | 2525 | 137 | 177 | 214 | 248 | 280 | 309 | 335 | 359 | 400 | 432 | 456 | 473 | 484 |

$f_s = 27{,}000$

| $f'_c$ and $n$ | $f_c$ | $\frac{t}{d}$ = 0.06 | 0.08 | 0.10 | 0.12 | 0.14 | 0.16 | 0.18 | 0.20 | 0.24 | 0.28 | 0.32 | 0.36 | 0.40 |
|---|---|---|---|---|---|---|---|---|---|---|---|---|---|---|
| | $a$ | 2.18 | 2.16 | 2.14 | 2.12 | 2.11 | 2.09 | 2.07 | 2.05 | 2.02 | 1.99 | 1.96 | 1.93 | 1.91 |
| | | $K$ | | | | | | | | | | | | |
| | 650 | 34 | 43 | 50 | 57 | 63 | 68 | 72 | 74 | 78 | 79 | 79 | 79 | 79 |
| | 700 | 36 | 46 | 55 | 62 | 69 | 74 | 79 | 83 | 87 | 89 | 89 | 89 | 89 |
| 2000 | 750 | 39 | 50 | 59 | 67 | 75 | 81 | 86 | 91 | 97 | 99 | 99 | 99 | 99 |
| | 800 | 42 | 54 | 64 | 73 | 81 | 88 | 94 | 99 | 106 | 110 | 111 | 111 | 111 |
| | 900 | 48 | 61 | 74 | 84 | 93 | 102 | 109 | 115 | 125 | 131 | 133 | 133 | 133 |
| 15 | 1000 | 53 | 68 | 82 | 94 | 105 | 115 | 124 | 131 | 144 | 151 | 156 | 157 | 157 |
| | 1200 | 65 | 83 | 100 | 115 | 130 | 142 | 154 | 164 | 181 | 193 | 202 | 207 | 208 |
| | 1350 | 73 | 94 | 113 | 131 | 148 | 163 | 176 | 188 | 209 | 225 | 236 | 244 | 247 |
| | 800 | 41 | 52 | 62 | 70 | 77 | 83 | 88 | 91 | 95 | 96 | 96 | 96 | 96 |
| | 875 | 46 | 58 | 69 | 78 | 86 | 93 | 99 | 103 | 109 | 111 | 111 | 111 | 111 |
| 2500 | 950 | 50 | 63 | 75 | 86 | 95 | 103 | 110 | 116 | 123 | 127 | 127 | 127 | 127 |
| | 1000 | 53 | 67 | 80 | 91 | 101 | 110 | 118 | 124 | 133 | 137 | 138 | 138 | 138 |
| | 1125 | 60 | 76 | 91 | 105 | 116 | 127 | 136 | 144 | 156 | 163 | 166 | 167 | 167 |
| 12 | 1250 | 67 | 85 | 102 | 118 | 132 | 144 | 155 | 164 | 179 | 189 | 195 | 197 | 197 |
| | 1500 | 81 | 104 | 125 | 144 | 162 | 178 | 192 | 205 | 226 | 242 | 252 | 258 | 260 |
| | 1700 | 92 | 119 | 143 | 166 | 186 | 205 | 222 | 237 | 264 | 283 | 298 | 307 | 312 |
| | 975 | 50 | 64 | 75 | 86 | 94 | 101 | 107 | 112 | 117 | 118 | 118 | 118 | 118 |
| | 1050 | 55 | 69 | 82 | 94 | 104 | 112 | 119 | 124 | 131 | 133 | 133 | 133 | 133 |
| 3000 | 1125 | 59 | 75 | 89 | 102 | 113 | 122 | 130 | 136 | 145 | 149 | 149 | 149 | 149 |
| | 1200 | 63 | 80 | 96 | 110 | 122 | 132 | 141 | 148 | 159 | 165 | 166 | 166 | 166 |
| | 1350 | 72 | 91 | 110 | 125 | 140 | 152 | 163 | 173 | 187 | 196 | 200 | 200 | 200 |
| 10 | 1500 | 80 | 102 | 123 | 141 | 158 | 172 | 186 | 197 | 215 | 227 | 234 | 236 | 236 |
| | 1800 | 97 | 125 | 150 | 173 | 194 | 213 | 231 | 246 | 271 | 290 | 303 | 310 | 312 |
| | 2025 | 110 | 141 | 170 | 197 | 222 | 244 | 264 | 283 | 313 | 337 | 354 | 365 | 371 |
| | 1200 | 62 | 78 | 93 | 105 | 116 | 124 | 131 | 137 | 143 | 144 | 144 | 144 | 144 |
| | 1300 | 68 | 86 | 102 | 116 | 128 | 138 | 146 | 153 | 161 | 164 | 164 | 164 | 164 |
| 3750 | 1400 | 73 | 93 | 111 | 126 | 140 | 151 | 161 | 169 | 180 | 185 | 185 | 185 | 185 |
| | 1500 | 79 | 100 | 120 | 137 | 152 | 165 | 176 | 186 | 199 | 206 | 207 | 207 | 207 |
| | 1700 | 90 | 115 | 138 | 158 | 176 | 192 | 206 | 218 | 236 | 248 | 253 | 253 | 253 |
| 8 | 1875 | 100 | 128 | 154 | 177 | 197 | 215 | 232 | 247 | 269 | 284 | 293 | 295 | 295 |
| | 2250 | 121 | 156 | 187 | 216 | 243 | 267 | 288 | 308 | 339 | 362 | 378 | 387 | 390 |
| | 2525 | 137 | 176 | 212 | 246 | 276 | 304 | 329 | 352 | 391 | 420 | 441 | 455 | 462 |

$f_s = 30{,}000$

| $f'_c$ and $n$ | $f_c$ | $\frac{t}{d}$ = 0.06 | 0.08 | 0.10 | 0.12 | 0.14 | 0.16 | 0.18 | 0.20 | 0.24 | 0.28 | 0.32 | 0.36 | 0.40 |
|---|---|---|---|---|---|---|---|---|---|---|---|---|---|---|
| | $a$ | 2.43 | 2.40 | 2.38 | 2.36 | 2.34 | 2.32 | 2.30 | 2.28 | 2.24 | 2.21 | 2.17 | 2.14 | 2.11 |
| | | $K$ | | | | | | | | | | | | |
| | 650 | 33 | 42 | 49 | 56 | 61 | 65 | 69 | 71 | 73 | 73 | 73 | 73 | 73 |
| | 700 | 36 | 46 | 54 | 61 | 67 | 72 | 76 | 79 | 82 | 83 | 83 | 83 | 83 |
| 2000 | 750 | 39 | 49 | 59 | 67 | 73 | 79 | 84 | 88 | 92 | 93 | 93 | 93 | 93 |
| | 800 | 42 | 53 | 63 | 72 | 79 | 86 | 91 | 96 | 101 | 103 | 104 | 104 | 104 |
| | 900 | 47 | 60 | 73 | 82 | 91 | 99 | 106 | 112 | 119 | 124 | 125 | 125 | 125 |
| 15 | 1000 | 53 | 68 | 81 | 93 | 104 | 113 | 121 | 128 | 139 | 145 | 148 | 148 | 148 |
| | 1200 | 64 | 82 | 99 | 114 | 128 | 140 | 151 | 161 | 176 | 187 | 194 | 197 | 197 |
| | 1350 | 73 | 94 | 113 | 130 | 146 | 160 | 173 | 185 | 204 | 218 | 228 | 234 | 236 |
| | 800 | 41 | 51 | 61 | 68 | 75 | 80 | 84 | 87 | 89 | 89 | 89 | 89 | 89 |
| | 875 | 45 | 57 | 67 | 76 | 84 | 90 | 95 | 99 | 103 | 104 | 104 | 104 | 104 |
| 2500 | 950 | 49 | 63 | 74 | 84 | 93 | 100 | 106 | 111 | 117 | 119 | 119 | 119 | 119 |
| | 1000 | 52 | 66 | 79 | 90 | 99 | 107 | 114 | 119 | 127 | 129 | 129 | 129 | 129 |
| | 1125 | 59 | 75 | 90 | 103 | 114 | 124 | 133 | 140 | 150 | 155 | 156 | 156 | 156 |
| 12 | 1250 | 66 | 85 | 102 | 116 | 129 | 141 | 151 | 160 | 173 | 181 | 185 | 185 | 185 |
| | 1500 | 80 | 103 | 124 | 143 | 160 | 175 | 189 | 201 | 220 | 234 | 242 | 246 | 246 |
| | 1700 | 92 | 118 | 142 | 164 | 184 | 202 | 219 | 233 | 258 | 276 | 288 | 295 | 298 |
| | 975 | 50 | 63 | 74 | 84 | 92 | 98 | 103 | 107 | 110 | 110 | 110 | 110 | 110 |
| | 1050 | 54 | 68 | 81 | 92 | 101 | 108 | 114 | 119 | 124 | 124 | 124 | 124 | 124 |
| 3000 | 1125 | 58 | 74 | 88 | 100 | 110 | 119 | 126 | 131 | 138 | 140 | 140 | 140 | 140 |
| | 1200 | 63 | 79 | 94 | 108 | 119 | 129 | 137 | 143 | 152 | 155 | 155 | 155 | 155 |
| | 1350 | 71 | 90 | 108 | 123 | 137 | 149 | 159 | 168 | 180 | 186 | 188 | 188 | 188 |
| 10 | 1500 | 80 | 102 | 122 | 139 | 155 | 169 | 182 | 192 | 208 | 218 | 222 | 222 | 222 |
| | 1800 | 96 | 124 | 149 | 171 | 192 | 210 | 226 | 241 | 264 | 280 | 291 | 295 | 295 |
| | 2025 | 109 | 140 | 169 | 195 | 219 | 241 | 260 | 277 | 306 | 327 | 342 | 350 | 353 |
| | 1200 | 61 | 77 | 91 | 102 | 112 | 120 | 126 | 130 | 133 | 133 | 133 | 133 | 133 |
| | 1300 | 67 | 85 | 100 | 113 | 124 | 134 | 141 | 146 | 152 | 153 | 153 | 153 | 153 |
| 3750 | 1400 | 73 | 92 | 109 | 124 | 137 | 147 | 156 | 163 | 171 | 173 | 173 | 173 | 173 |
| | 1500 | 78 | 99 | 118 | 134 | 149 | 161 | 171 | 179 | 190 | 194 | 194 | 194 | 194 |
| | 1700 | 90 | 114 | 136 | 156 | 173 | 188 | 201 | 211 | 227 | 236 | 238 | 238 | 238 |
| 8 | 1875 | 99 | 127 | 153 | 174 | 194 | 212 | 227 | 240 | 260 | 272 | 277 | 278 | 278 |
| | 2250 | 121 | 155 | 186 | 214 | 240 | 263 | 283 | 301 | 330 | 351 | 363 | 369 | 369 |
| | 2525 | 136 | 175 | 211 | 243 | 273 | 300 | 324 | 346 | 381 | 408 | 426 | 436 | 440 |

# Table 9. Coefficients ($j$ *and* $y$) for T-Sections

Values of $j = 1 - \dfrac{k - \dfrac{2t}{3d}}{2k - \dfrac{t}{d}} \times \dfrac{t}{d}$ and $y = \dfrac{1 - \dfrac{2t}{3kd}}{2 - \dfrac{t}{kd}}$

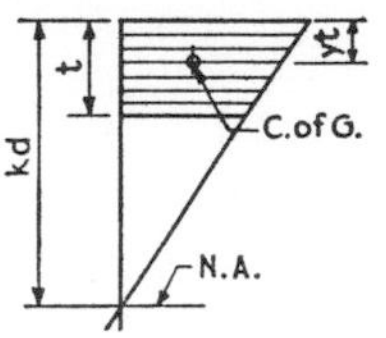


(a) Enter table with known value of $\frac{t}{d}$ and $k$; select $j$

(b) Enter table with known value of $\frac{t}{kd}$; select $y$; compute $j = 1 - y\frac{t}{d}$

| $k$ | $j$, $\frac{t}{d}$ = 0.06 | 0.08 | 0.10 | 0.12 | 0.14 | 0.16 | 0.18 | 0.20 | 0.22 | 0.24 | 0.26 | 0.28 | 0.30 | 0.32 | 0.34 | 0.36 | 0.38 | 0.40 |
|---|---|---|---|---|---|---|---|---|---|---|---|---|---|---|---|---|---|---|
| 0.20 | 0.97 | 0.96 | 0.96 | 0.95 | 0.94 | 0.94 | 0.93 | 0.93 | | | | | | | | | | |
| 0.25 | 0.97 | 0.96 | 0.95 | 0.95 | 0.94 | 0.93 | 0.93 | 0.92 | 0.92 | 0.92 | | | | | | | | |
| 0.30 | 0.97 | 0.96 | 0.95 | 0.94 | 0.94 | 0.93 | 0.92 | 0.92 | 0.91 | 0.91 | 0.90 | 0.90 | 0.90 | | | | | |
| 0.35 | 0.97 | 0.96 | 0.95 | 0.94 | 0.94 | 0.93 | 0.92 | 0.91 | 0.91 | 0.90 | 0.90 | 0.89 | 0.89 | 0.89 | 0.88 | | | |
| 0.40 | 0.97 | 0.96 | 0.95 | 0.94 | 0.93 | 0.93 | 0.92 | 0.91 | 0.90 | 0.90 | 0.89 | 0.89 | 0.88 | 0.88 | 0.87 | 0.87 | 0.87 | 0.87 |
| 0.45 | 0.97 | 0.96 | 0.95 | 0.94 | 0.93 | 0.93 | 0.92 | 0.91 | 0.90 | 0.89 | 0.89 | 0.88 | 0.88 | 0.87 | 0.87 | 0.86 | 0.86 | 0.85 |
| 0.50 | 0.97 | 0.96 | 0.95 | 0.94 | 0.93 | 0.93 | 0.92 | 0.91 | 0.90 | 0.89 | 0.89 | 0.88 | 0.87 | 0.87 | 0.86 | 0.85 | 0.85 | 0.84 |
| 0.55 | 0.97 | 0.96 | 0.95 | 0.94 | 0.93 | 0.92 | 0.92 | 0.91 | 0.90 | 0.89 | 0.88 | 0.88 | 0.87 | 0.86 | 0.85 | 0.85 | 0.84 | 0.84 |
| 0.60 | 0.97 | 0.96 | 0.95 | 0.94 | 0.93 | 0.92 | 0.92 | 0.91 | 0.90 | 0.89 | 0.88 | 0.87 | 0.87 | 0.86 | 0.85 | 0.85 | 0.84 | 0.83 |

| $\frac{t}{kd}$ | 0.15 | 0.20 | 0.25 | 0.30 | 0.35 | 0.40 | 0.45 | 0.50 | 0.55 | 0.60 | 0.65 | 0.70 | 0.75 | 0.80 | 0.85 | 0.90 | 0.95 | 1.00 |
|---|---|---|---|---|---|---|---|---|---|---|---|---|---|---|---|---|---|---|
| $y$ | 0.49 | 0.48 | 0.48 | 0.47 | 0.46 | 0.46 | 0.45 | 0.44 | 0.44 | 0.43 | 0.42 | 0.41 | 0.40 | 0.39 | 0.38 | 0.36 | 0.35 | 0.33 |

# Table 10. Coefficients ($i$) for Sections Subject to Bending and Axial Load

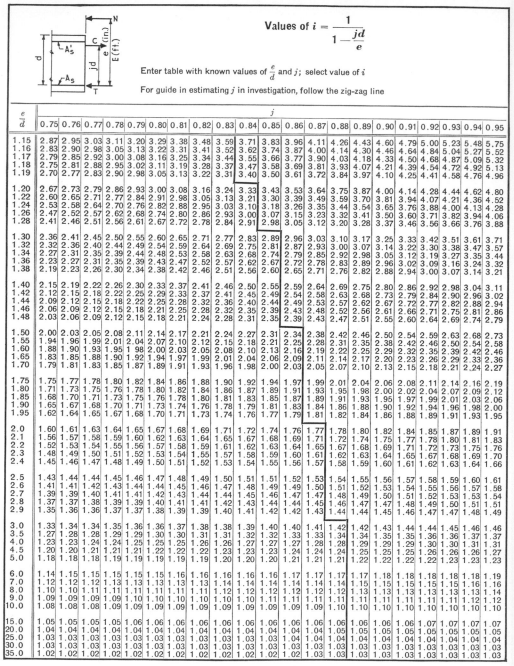

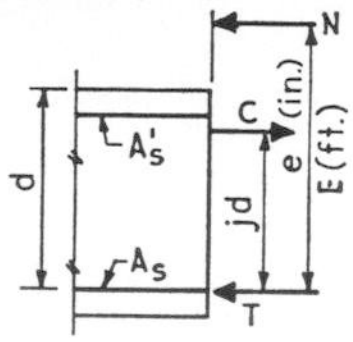


Values of $i = \dfrac{1}{1 - \dfrac{jd}{e}}$

Enter table with known values of $\frac{e}{d}$ and $j$; select value of $i$

For guide in estimating $j$ in investigation, follow the zig-zag line

| $\frac{e}{d}$ | j = 0.75 | 0.76 | 0.77 | 0.78 | 0.79 | 0.80 | 0.81 | 0.82 | 0.83 | 0.84 | 0.85 | 0.86 | 0.87 | 0.88 | 0.89 | 0.90 | 0.91 | 0.92 | 0.93 | 0.94 | 0.95 |
|---|---|---|---|---|---|---|---|---|---|---|---|---|---|---|---|---|---|---|---|---|---|
| 1.15 | 2.87 | 2.95 | 3.03 | 3.11 | 3.20 | 3.29 | 3.38 | 3.48 | 3.59 | 3.71 | 3.83 | 3.96 | 4.11 | 4.26 | 4.43 | 4.60 | 4.79 | 5.00 | 5.23 | 5.48 | 5.75 |
| 1.16 | 2.83 | 2.90 | 2.98 | 3.05 | 3.13 | 3.22 | 3.31 | 3.41 | 3.52 | 3.62 | 3.74 | 3.87 | 4.00 | 4.14 | 4.30 | 4.46 | 4.64 | 4.84 | 5.04 | 5.27 | 5.52 |
| 1.17 | 2.79 | 2.85 | 2.92 | 3.00 | 3.08 | 3.16 | 3.25 | 3.34 | 3.44 | 3.55 | 3.66 | 3.77 | 3.90 | 4.03 | 4.18 | 4.33 | 4.50 | 4.68 | 4.87 | 5.09 | 5.32 |
| 1.18 | 2.75 | 2.81 | 2.88 | 2.95 | 3.02 | 3.11 | 3.19 | 3.28 | 3.37 | 3.47 | 3.58 | 3.69 | 3.81 | 3.93 | 4.07 | 4.21 | 4.39 | 4.54 | 4.72 | 4.92 | 5.13 |
| 1.19 | 2.70 | 2.77 | 2.83 | 2.90 | 2.98 | 3.05 | 3.13 | 3.22 | 3.31 | 3.40 | 3.50 | 3.61 | 3.72 | 3.84 | 3.97 | 4.10 | 4.25 | 4.41 | 4.58 | 4.76 | 4.96 |
| 1.20 | 2.67 | 2.73 | 2.79 | 2.86 | 2.93 | 3.00 | 3.08 | 3.16 | 3.24 | 3.33 | 3.43 | 3.53 | 3.64 | 3.75 | 3.87 | 4.00 | 4.14 | 4.28 | 4.44 | 4.62 | 4.80 |
| 1.22 | 2.60 | 2.65 | 2.71 | 2.77 | 2.84 | 2.91 | 2.98 | 3.05 | 3.13 | 3.21 | 3.30 | 3.39 | 3.49 | 3.59 | 3.70 | 3.81 | 3.94 | 4.07 | 4.21 | 4.36 | 4.52 |
| 1.24 | 2.53 | 2.58 | 2.64 | 2.70 | 2.76 | 2.82 | 2.88 | 2.95 | 3.03 | 3.10 | 3.18 | 3.26 | 3.35 | 3.44 | 3.54 | 3.65 | 3.76 | 3.88 | 4.00 | 4.13 | 4.28 |
| 1.26 | 2.47 | 2.52 | 2.57 | 2.62 | 2.68 | 2.74 | 2.80 | 2.86 | 2.93 | 3.00 | 3.07 | 3.15 | 3.23 | 3.32 | 3.41 | 3.50 | 3.60 | 3.71 | 3.82 | 3.94 | 4.06 |
| 1.28 | 2.41 | 2.46 | 2.51 | 2.56 | 2.61 | 2.67 | 2.72 | 2.78 | 2.84 | 2.91 | 2.98 | 3.05 | 3.12 | 3.20 | 3.28 | 3.37 | 3.46 | 3.56 | 3.66 | 3.76 | 3.88 |
| 1.30 | 2.36 | 2.41 | 2.45 | 2.50 | 2.55 | 2.60 | 2.65 | 2.71 | 2.77 | 2.83 | 2.89 | 2.96 | 3.03 | 3.10 | 3.17 | 3.25 | 3.33 | 3.42 | 3.51 | 3.61 | 3.71 |
| 1.32 | 2.32 | 2.36 | 2.40 | 2.44 | 2.49 | 2.54 | 2.59 | 2.64 | 2.69 | 2.75 | 2.81 | 2.87 | 2.93 | 3.00 | 3.07 | 3.14 | 3.22 | 3.30 | 3.38 | 3.47 | 3.57 |
| 1.34 | 2.27 | 2.31 | 2.35 | 2.39 | 2.44 | 2.48 | 2.53 | 2.58 | 2.63 | 2.68 | 2.74 | 2.79 | 2.85 | 2.92 | 2.98 | 3.05 | 3.12 | 3.19 | 3.27 | 3.35 | 3.44 |
| 1.36 | 2.23 | 2.27 | 2.31 | 2.35 | 2.39 | 2.43 | 2.47 | 2.52 | 2.57 | 2.62 | 2.67 | 2.72 | 2.78 | 2.83 | 2.89 | 2.96 | 3.02 | 3.09 | 3.16 | 3.24 | 3.32 |
| 1.38 | 2.19 | 2.23 | 2.26 | 2.30 | 2.34 | 2.38 | 2.42 | 2.46 | 2.51 | 2.56 | 2.60 | 2.65 | 2.71 | 2.76 | 2.82 | 2.88 | 2.94 | 3.00 | 3.07 | 3.14 | 3.21 |
| 1.40 | 2.15 | 2.19 | 2.22 | 2.26 | 2.30 | 2.33 | 2.37 | 2.41 | 2.46 | 2.50 | 2.55 | 2.59 | 2.64 | 2.69 | 2.75 | 2.80 | 2.86 | 2.92 | 2.98 | 3.04 | 3.11 |
| 1.42 | 2.12 | 2.15 | 2.18 | 2.22 | 2.25 | 2.29 | 2.33 | 2.37 | 2.41 | 2.45 | 2.49 | 2.54 | 2.58 | 2.63 | 2.68 | 2.73 | 2.79 | 2.84 | 2.90 | 2.96 | 3.02 |
| 1.44 | 2.09 | 2.12 | 2.15 | 2.18 | 2.22 | 2.25 | 2.28 | 2.32 | 2.36 | 2.40 | 2.44 | 2.49 | 2.53 | 2.57 | 2.62 | 2.67 | 2.72 | 2.77 | 2.82 | 2.88 | 2.94 |
| 1.46 | 2.06 | 2.09 | 2.12 | 2.15 | 2.18 | 2.21 | 2.25 | 2.28 | 2.32 | 2.35 | 2.39 | 2.43 | 2.48 | 2.52 | 2.56 | 2.61 | 2.66 | 2.71 | 2.75 | 2.81 | 2.86 |
| 1.48 | 2.03 | 2.06 | 2.09 | 2.12 | 2.15 | 2.18 | 2.21 | 2.24 | 2.28 | 2.31 | 2.35 | 2.39 | 2.43 | 2.47 | 2.51 | 2.55 | 2.60 | 2.64 | 2.69 | 2.74 | 2.79 |
| 1.50 | 2.00 | 2.03 | 2.05 | 2.08 | 2.11 | 2.14 | 2.17 | 2.21 | 2.24 | 2.27 | 2.31 | 2.34 | 2.38 | 2.42 | 2.46 | 2.50 | 2.54 | 2.59 | 2.63 | 2.68 | 2.73 |
| 1.55 | 1.94 | 1.96 | 1.99 | 2.01 | 2.04 | 2.07 | 2.10 | 2.12 | 2.15 | 2.18 | 2.21 | 2.25 | 2.28 | 2.31 | 2.35 | 2.38 | 2.42 | 2.46 | 2.50 | 2.54 | 2.58 |
| 1.60 | 1.88 | 1.90 | 1.93 | 1.95 | 1 98 | 2.00 | 2.03 | 2.05 | 2.08 | 2.10 | 2.13 | 2.16 | 2.19 | 2.22 | 2.25 | 2.29 | 2.32 | 2.35 | 2.39 | 2.42 | 2.46 |
| 1.65 | 1.83 | 1.85 | 1.88 | 1.90 | 1.92 | 1.94 | 1.97 | 1.99 | 2.01 | 2.04 | 2.06 | 2.09 | 2.11 | 2.14 | 2.17 | 2.20 | 2.23 | 2.26 | 2.29 | 2.33 | 2.36 |
| 1.70 | 1.79 | 1.81 | 1.83 | 1.85 | 1.87 | 1.89 | 1.91 | 1.93 | 1.96 | 1.98 | 2.00 | 2.03 | 2.05 | 2.07 | 2.10 | 2.13 | 2.15 | 2.18 | 2.21 | 2.24 | 2.27 |
| 1.75 | 1.75 | 1.77 | 1.78 | 1.80 | 1.82 | 1.84 | 1.86 | 1.88 | 1.90 | 1.92 | 1.94 | 1.97 | 1.99 | 2.01 | 2.04 | 2.06 | 2.08 | 2.11 | 2.14 | 2.16 | 2.19 |
| 1.80 | 1.71 | 1.73 | 1.75 | 1.76 | 1.78 | 1.80 | 1.82 | 1.84 | 1.86 | 1.87 | 1.89 | 1.91 | 1.93 | 1.95 | 1.98 | 2.00 | 2.02 | 2.04 | 2.07 | 2.09 | 2.12 |
| 1.85 | 1.68 | 1.70 | 1.71 | 1.73 | 1.75 | 1.76 | 1.78 | 1.80 | 1.81 | 1.83 | 1.85 | 1.87 | 1.89 | 1.91 | 1.93 | 1.95 | 1.97 | 1.99 | 2.01 | 2.03 | 2.06 |
| 1.90 | 1.65 | 1.67 | 1.68 | 1.70 | 1.71 | 1.73 | 1.74 | 1.76 | 1.78 | 1.79 | 1.81 | 1.83 | 1.84 | 1.86 | 1.88 | 1.90 | 1.92 | 1.94 | 1.96 | 1.98 | 2.00 |
| 1.95 | 1.62 | 1.64 | 1.65 | 1.67 | 1.68 | 1.70 | 1.71 | 1.73 | 1.74 | 1.76 | 1.77 | 1.79 | 1.81 | 1.82 | 1.84 | 1.86 | 1.88 | 1.89 | 1.91 | 1.93 | 1.95 |
| 2.0 | 1.60 | 1.61 | 1.63 | 1.64 | 1.65 | 1.67 | 1.68 | 1.69 | 1.71 | 1.72 | 1.74 | 1.76 | 1.77 | 1.78 | 1.80 | 1.82 | 1.84 | 1.85 | 1.87 | 1.89 | 1.91 |
| 2.1 | 1.56 | 1.57 | 1.58 | 1.59 | 1.60 | 1.62 | 1.63 | 1.64 | 1.65 | 1.67 | 1.68 | 1.69 | 1.71 | 1.72 | 1.74 | 1.75 | 1.77 | 1.78 | 1.80 | 1.81 | 1.83 |
| 2.2 | 1.52 | 1.53 | 1.54 | 1.55 | 1.56 | 1.57 | 1.58 | 1.59 | 1.61 | 1.62 | 1.63 | 1.64 | 1.65 | 1.67 | 1.68 | 1.69 | 1.71 | 1.72 | 1.73 | 1.75 | 1.76 |
| 2.3 | 1.48 | 1.49 | 1.50 | 1.51 | 1.52 | 1.53 | 1.54 | 1.55 | 1.57 | 1.58 | 1.59 | 1.60 | 1.61 | 1.62 | 1.63 | 1.64 | 1.65 | 1.67 | 1.68 | 1.69 | 1.70 |
| 2.4 | 1.45 | 1.46 | 1.47 | 1.48 | 1.49 | 1.50 | 1.51 | 1.52 | 1.53 | 1.54 | 1.55 | 1.56 | 1.57 | 1.58 | 1.59 | 1.60 | 1.61 | 1.62 | 1.63 | 1.64 | 1.66 |
| 2.5 | 1.43 | 1.44 | 1.44 | 1.45 | 1.46 | 1.47 | 1.48 | 1.49 | 1.50 | 1.51 | 1.51 | 1.52 | 1.53 | 1.54 | 1.55 | 1.56 | 1.57 | 1.58 | 1.59 | 1.60 | 1.61 |
| 2.6 | 1.41 | 1.41 | 1.42 | 1.43 | 1.44 | 1.44 | 1.45 | 1.46 | 1.47 | 1.48 | 1.49 | 1.49 | 1.50 | 1.51 | 1.52 | 1.53 | 1.54 | 1.55 | 1.56 | 1.57 | 1.58 |
| 2.7 | 1.39 | 1.39 | 1.40 | 1.41 | 1.41 | 1.42 | 1.43 | 1.44 | 1.44 | 1.45 | 1.46 | 1.47 | 1.47 | 1.48 | 1.49 | 1.50 | 1.51 | 1.52 | 1.53 | 1.53 | 1.54 |
| 2.8 | 1.37 | 1.37 | 1.38 | 1.39 | 1.39 | 1.40 | 1.41 | 1.41 | 1.42 | 1.43 | 1.44 | 1.44 | 1.45 | 1.46 | 1.47 | 1.47 | 1.48 | 1.49 | 1.50 | 1.51 | 1.51 |
| 2.9 | 1.35 | 1.36 | 1.36 | 1.37 | 1.37 | 1.38 | 1.39 | 1.39 | 1.40 | 1.41 | 1.42 | 1.42 | 1.43 | 1.44 | 1.44 | 1.45 | 1.46 | 1.47 | 1.47 | 1.48 | 1.49 |
| 3.0 | 1.33 | 1.34 | 1.34 | 1.35 | 1.36 | 1.36 | 1.37 | 1.38 | 1.38 | 1.39 | 1.40 | 1.40 | 1.41 | 1.42 | 1.42 | 1.43 | 1.44 | 1.44 | 1.45 | 1.46 | 1.46 |
| 3.5 | 1.27 | 1.28 | 1.28 | 1.29 | 1.29 | 1.30 | 1.30 | 1.31 | 1.31 | 1.32 | 1.32 | 1.33 | 1.33 | 1.34 | 1.34 | 1.35 | 1.35 | 1.36 | 1.36 | 1.37 | 1.37 |
| 4.0 | 1.23 | 1.23 | 1.24 | 1.24 | 1.25 | 1.25 | 1.25 | 1.26 | 1.26 | 1.27 | 1.27 | 1.27 | 1.28 | 1.28 | 1.29 | 1.29 | 1.29 | 1.30 | 1.30 | 1.31 | 1.31 |
| 4.5 | 1.20 | 1.20 | 1.21 | 1.21 | 1.21 | 1.22 | 1.22 | 1.22 | 1.23 | 1.23 | 1.23 | 1.24 | 1.24 | 1.24 | 1.25 | 1.25 | 1.25 | 1.26 | 1.26 | 1.26 | 1.27 |
| 5.0 | 1.18 | 1.18 | 1.18 | 1.19 | 1.19 | 1.19 | 1.19 | 1.19 | 1.20 | 1.20 | 1.20 | 1.21 | 1.21 | 1.21 | 1.22 | 1.22 | 1.22 | 1.22 | 1.23 | 1.23 | 1.23 |
| 6.0 | 1.14 | 1.15 | 1.15 | 1.15 | 1.15 | 1.15 | 1.16 | 1.16 | 1.16 | 1.16 | 1.16 | 1.17 | 1.17 | 1.17 | 1.17 | 1.18 | 1.18 | 1.18 | 1.18 | 1.18 | 1.19 |
| 7.0 | 1.12 | 1.12 | 1.12 | 1.13 | 1.13 | 1.13 | 1.13 | 1.13 | 1.14 | 1.14 | 1.14 | 1.14 | 1.14 | 1.14 | 1.15 | 1.15 | 1.15 | 1.15 | 1.15 | 1.16 | 1.16 |
| 8.0 | 1.10 | 1.10 | 1.11 | 1.11 | 1.11 | 1.11 | 1.11 | 1.11 | 1.12 | 1.12 | 1.12 | 1.12 | 1.12 | 1.12 | 1.13 | 1.13 | 1.13 | 1.13 | 1.13 | 1.13 | 1.14 |
| 9.0 | 1.09 | 1.09 | 1.09 | 1.09 | 1.10 | 1.10 | 1.10 | 1.10 | 1.10 | 1.10 | 1.11 | 1.11 | 1.11 | 1.11 | 1.11 | 1.11 | 1.11 | 1.11 | 1.11 | 1.12 | 1.12 |
| 10.0 | 1.08 | 1.08 | 1.08 | 1.09 | 1.09 | 1.09 | 1.09 | 1.09 | 1.09 | 1.09 | 1.09 | 1.09 | 1.09 | 1.10 | 1.10 | 1.10 | 1.10 | 1.10 | 1.10 | 1.10 | 1.10 |
| 15.0 | 1.05 | 1.05 | 1.05 | 1.05 | 1.06 | 1.06 | 1.06 | 1.06 | 1.06 | 1.06 | 1.06 | 1.06 | 1.06 | 1.06 | 1.06 | 1.06 | 1.06 | 1.07 | 1.07 | 1.07 | 1.07 |
| 20.0 | 1.04 | 1.04 | 1.04 | 1.04 | 1.04 | 1.04 | 1.04 | 1.04 | 1.04 | 1.04 | 1.04 | 1.04 | 1.04 | 1.05 | 1.05 | 1.05 | 1.05 | 1.05 | 1.05 | 1.05 | 1.05 |
| 25.0 | 1.03 | 1.03 | 1.03 | 1.03 | 1.03 | 1.03 | 1.03 | 1.03 | 1.03 | 1.03 | 1.03 | 1.04 | 1.04 | 1.04 | 1.04 | 1.04 | 1.04 | 1.04 | 1.04 | 1.04 | 1.04 |
| 30.0 | 1.03 | 1.03 | 1.03 | 1.03 | 1.03 | 1.03 | 1.03 | 1.03 | 1.03 | 1.03 | 1.03 | 1.03 | 1.03 | 1.03 | 1.03 | 1.03 | 1.03 | 1.03 | 1.03 | 1.03 | 1.03 |
| 35.0 | 1.02 | 1.02 | 1.02 | 1.02 | 1.02 | 1.02 | 1.02 | 1.02 | 1.02 | 1.02 | 1.02 | 1.02 | 1.03 | 1.03 | 1.03 | 1.03 | 1.03 | 1.03 | 1.03 | 1.03 | 1.03 |

# Table 11. Coefficients ($q$) for Rectangular Sections with Various Quantities of Tensile, or Tensile and Compressive Reinforcement

**Values of** $q = k\left(\frac{k}{2} + m\right)$

$$k = \sqrt{[np + (n-1)p']^2 + 2[np + (n-1)p'\frac{d'}{d}]} - [np + (n-1)p'] = \sqrt{m^2 + 2q} - m$$

in which $m = np + (n-1)p'$ and $q = np + (n-1)p'\frac{d'}{d}$

Procedure: Compute $m$ and $q$; select $k$-values from table

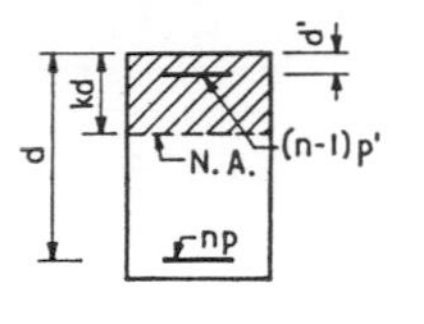


| $m$ | $k$ = 0.20 | 0.22 | 0.24 | 0.26 | 0.28 | 0.30 | 0.32 | 0.34 | 0.36 | 0.38 | 0.40 | 0.42 | 0.44 | 0.46 | 0.48 | 0.50 | 0.52 | 0.54 | 0.56 | 0.58 | 0.60 | 0.62 | 0.64 | 0.66 | 0.68 | 0.70 |
|---|---|---|---|---|---|---|---|---|---|---|---|---|---|---|---|---|---|---|---|---|---|---|---|---|---|---|
| 0.05 | .030 | .035 | .041 | .047 | .053 |
| 0.06 | .032 | .037 | .043 | .049 | .056 | .063 |
| 0.07 | .034 | .040 | .046 | .052 | .059 | .066 | .074 |
| 0.08 | .036 | .042 | .048 | .055 | .062 | .069 | .077 | .085 |
| 0.09 | .038 | .044 | .050 | .057 | .064 | .072 | .080 | .088 | .097 |
| 0.10 | .040 | .046 | .053 | .060 | .067 | .075 | .083 | .092 | .101 |
| 0.11 | .042 | .048 | .055 | .062 | .070 | .078 | .086 | .095 | .104 | .114 |
| 0.12 | .044 | .051 | .058 | .065 | .073 | .081 | .090 | .099 | .108 | .118 | .128 |
| 0.13 | .046 | .053 | .060 | .068 | .076 | .084 | .093 | .102 | .112 | .122 | .132 |
| 0.14 | .048 | .055 | .062 | .070 | .078 | .087 | .096 | .105 | .115 | .125 | .136 | .147 |
| 0.15 | .050 | .057 | .065 | .073 | .081 | .090 | .099 | .109 | .119 | .129 | .140 | .151 |
| 0.16 | .052 | .059 | .067 | .075 | .084 | .093 | .102 | .112 | .122 | .133 | .144 | .155 | .167 |
| 0.17 | .054 | .062 | .070 | .078 | .087 | .096 | .106 | .116 | .126 | .137 | .148 | .160 | .172 |
| 0.18 | .056 | .064 | .072 | .081 | .090 | .099 | .109 | .119 | .130 | .141 | .152 | .164 | .176 | .189 |
| 0.19 | .058 | .066 | .074 | .083 | .092 | .102 | .112 | .122 | .133 | .144 | .156 | .168 | .180 | .193 |
| 0.20 | .060 | .068 | .077 | .086 | .095 | .105 | .115 | .126 | .137 | .148 | .160 | .172 | .185 | .198 | .211 |
| 0.21 | .062 | .070 | .079 | .088 | .098 | .108 | .118 | .129 | .140 | .152 | .164 | .176 | .189 | .202 | .216 |
| 0.22 | .064 | .073 | .082 | .091 | .101 | .111 | .122 | .133 | .144 | .156 | .168 | .181 | .194 | .207 | .221 |
| 0.23 | .066 | .075 | .084 | .094 | .104 | .114 | .125 | .136 | .148 | .160 | .172 | .185 | .198 | .212 | .226 | .240 |
| 0.24 | .068 | .077 | .086 | .096 | .106 | .117 | .128 | .139 | .151 | .163 | .176 | .189 | .202 | .216 | .230 | .245 |
| 0.25 | .070 | .079 | .089 | .099 | .109 | .120 | .131 | .143 | .155 | .167 | .180 | .193 | .207 | .221 | .235 | .250 |
| 0.26 | .072 | .081 | .091 | .101 | .112 | .123 | .134 | .146 | .158 | .171 | .184 | .197 | .211 | .225 | .240 | .255 | .270 |
| 0.27 | .074 | .084 | .094 | .104 | .115 | .126 | .138 | .150 | .162 | .175 | .188 | .202 | .216 | .230 | .245 | .260 | .276 |
| 0.28 | .076 | .086 | .096 | .107 | .118 | .129 | .141 | .153 | .166 | .179 | .192 | .206 | .220 | .235 | .250 | .265 | .281 |
| 0.29 | .078 | .088 | .098 | .109 | .120 | .132 | .144 | .156 | .169 | .182 | .196 | .210 | .224 | .239 | .254 | .270 | .286 | .302 |
| 0.30 | .080 | .090 | .101 | .112 | .123 | .135 | .147 | .160 | .173 | .186 | .200 | .214 | .229 | .244 | .259 | .275 | .291 | .308 |
| 0.31 | .082 | .092 | .103 | .114 | .126 | .138 | .150 | .163 | .176 | .190 | .204 | .218 | .233 | .248 | .264 | .280 | .296 | .313 |
| 0.32 | .084 | .095 | .106 | .117 | .129 | .141 | .154 | .167 | .180 | .194 | .208 | .223 | .238 | .253 | .269 | .285 | .302 | .319 | .336 |
| 0.33 | .086 | .097 | .108 | .120 | .132 | .144 | .157 | .170 | .184 | .198 | .212 | .227 | .242 | .258 | .274 | .290 | .307 | .324 | .342 |
| 0.34 | .088 | .099 | .110 | .122 | .134 | .147 | .160 | .173 | .187 | .201 | .216 | .231 | .246 | .262 | .278 | .295 | .312 | .329 | .347 |
| 0.35 | .090 | .101 | .113 | .125 | .137 | .150 | .163 | .177 | .191 | .205 | .220 | .235 | .251 | .267 | .283 | .300 | .317 | .335 | .353 |
| 0.36 | .092 | .103 | .115 | .127 | .140 | .153 | .166 | .180 | .194 | .209 | .224 | .239 | .255 | .271 | .288 | .305 | .322 | .340 | .358 | .377 |
| 0.37 | .094 | .106 | .118 | .130 | .143 | .156 | .170 | .184 | .198 | .213 | .228 | .244 | .260 | .276 | .293 | .310 | .328 | .346 | .364 | .383 |
| 0.38 | .096 | .108 | .120 | .133 | .146 | .159 | .173 | .187 | .202 | .217 | .232 | .248 | .264 | .281 | .298 | .315 | .333 | .351 | .370 | .389 |
| 0.39 | .098 | .110 | .122 | .135 | .148 | .162 | .176 | .190 | .205 | .220 | .236 | .252 | .268 | .285 | .302 | .320 | .338 | .356 | .375 | .394 |
| 0.40 | .100 | .112 | .125 | .138 | .151 | .165 | .179 | .194 | .209 | .224 | .240 | .256 | .273 | .290 | .307 | .325 | .343 | .362 | .381 | .400 |
| 0.41 | .102 | .114 | .127 | .140 | .154 | .168 | .182 | .197 | .212 | .228 | .244 | .260 | .277 | .294 | .312 | .330 | .348 | .367 | .386 | .406 | .426 |
| 0.42 | .104 | .117 | .130 | .143 | .157 | .171 | .186 | .201 | .216 | .232 | .248 | .265 | .282 | .299 | .317 | .335 | .354 | .373 | .392 | .412 | .432 |
| 0.43 | .106 | .119 | .132 | .146 | .160 | .174 | .189 | .204 | .220 | .236 | .252 | .269 | .286 | .304 | .322 | .340 | .359 | .378 | .398 | .418 | .438 |
| 0.44 | .108 | .121 | .134 | .148 | .162 | .177 | .192 | .207 | .223 | .239 | .256 | .273 | .290 | .308 | .326 | .345 | .364 | .383 | .403 | .423 | .444 |
| 0.45 | .110 | .123 | .137 | .151 | .165 | .180 | .195 | .211 | .227 | .243 | .260 | .277 | .295 | .313 | .331 | .350 | .369 | .389 | .409 | .429 | .450 |
| 0.46 | .112 | .125 | .139 | .153 | .168 | .183 | .198 | .214 | .230 | .247 | .264 | .281 | .299 | .317 | .336 | .355 | .374 | .394 | .414 | .435 | .456 | .477 |
| 0.47 | .114 | .128 | .142 | .156 | .171 | .186 | .202 | .218 | .234 | .251 | .268 | .286 | .304 | .322 | .341 | .360 | .380 | .400 | .420 | .441 | .462 | .484 |
| 0.48 | .116 | .130 | .144 | .159 | .174 | .189 | .205 | .221 | .238 | .255 | .272 | .290 | .308 | .327 | .346 | .365 | .385 | .405 | .426 | .447 | .468 | .490 |
| 0.49 | .118 | .132 | .146 | .161 | .176 | .192 | .208 | .224 | .241 | .258 | .276 | .294 | .312 | .331 | .350 | .370 | .390 | .410 | .431 | .452 | .474 | .496 |
| 0.50 | .120 | .134 | .149 | .164 | .179 | .195 | .211 | .228 | .245 | .262 | .280 | .298 | .317 | .336 | .355 | .375 | .395 | .416 | .437 | .458 | .480 | .502 |
| 0.51 | .122 | .136 | .151 | .166 | .182 | .198 | .214 | .231 | .248 | .266 | .284 | .302 | .321 | .340 | .360 | .380 | .400 | .421 | .442 | .464 | .486 | .508 | .531 |
| 0.52 | .124 | .139 | .154 | .169 | .185 | .201 | .218 | .235 | .252 | .270 | .288 | .307 | .326 | .345 | .365 | .385 | .406 | .427 | .448 | .470 | .592 | .515 | .538 |
| 0.53 | .126 | .141 | .156 | .172 | .188 | .204 | .221 | .238 | .256 | .274 | .292 | .311 | .330 | .350 | .370 | .390 | .411 | .432 | .454 | .476 | .498 | .521 | .544 |
| 0.54 | .128 | .143 | .158 | .174 | .190 | .207 | .224 | .241 | .259 | .277 | .296 | .315 | .334 | .354 | .374 | .395 | .416 | .437 | .459 | .481 | .504 | .527 | .550 |
| 0.55 | .130 | .145 | .161 | .177 | .193 | .210 | .227 | .245 | .263 | .281 | .300 | .319 | .339 | .359 | .379 | .400 | .421 | .443 | .465 | .487 | .510 | .533 | .557 |
| 0.56 | .132 | .147 | .163 | .179 | .196 | .213 | .230 | .248 | .266 | .285 | .304 | .323 | .343 | .363 | .384 | .405 | .426 | .448 | .470 | .493 | .516 | .539 | .563 |
| 0.57 | .134 | .150 | .166 | .182 | .199 | .216 | .234 | .252 | .270 | .289 | .308 | .328 | .348 | .368 | .389 | .410 | .432 | .454 | .476 | .499 | .522 | .546 | .570 |
| 0.58 | .136 | .152 | .168 | .185 | .202 | .219 | .237 | .255 | .274 | .293 | .312 | .332 | .352 | .373 | .394 | .415 | .437 | .459 | .482 | .505 | .528 | .552 | .576 | .601 |
| 0.59 | .138 | .154 | .170 | .187 | .204 | .222 | .240 | .258 | .277 | .296 | .316 | .336 | .356 | .377 | .398 | .420 | .442 | .464 | .487 | .510 | .534 | .558 | .582 | .607 |
| 0.60 | .140 | .156 | .173 | .190 | .207 | .225 | .243 | .262 | .281 | .300 | .320 | .340 | .361 | .382 | .403 | .425 | .447 | .470 | .493 | .516 | .540 | .564 | .589 | .614 |
| 0.61 | .142 | .158 | .175 | .192 | .210 | .228 | .246 | .265 | .284 | .304 | .324 | .344 | .365 | .386 | .408 | .430 | .452 | .475 | .498 | .522 | .546 | .570 | .595 | .620 |
| 0.62 | .144 | .161 | .178 | .195 | .213 | .231 | .250 | .269 | .288 | .308 | .328 | .349 | .370 | .391 | .413 | .435 | .458 | .481 | .504 | .528 | .552 | .577 | .602 | .627 |
| 0.63 | .146 | .163 | .180 | .198 | .216 | .234 | .253 | .272 | .292 | .312 | .332 | .353 | .374 | .396 | .418 | .440 | .463 | .486 | .510 | .534 | .558 | .583 | .608 | .634 |
| 0.64 | .148 | .165 | .182 | .200 | .218 | .237 | .256 | .275 | .295 | .315 | .336 | .357 | .378 | .400 | .422 | .445 | .468 | .491 | .515 | .539 | .564 | .589 | .614 | .640 |
| 0.65 | .150 | .167 | .185 | .203 | .221 | .240 | .259 | .279 | .299 | .319 | .340 | .361 | .383 | .405 | .427 | .450 | .473 | .497 | .521 | .545 | .570 | .595 | .621 | .647 | .673 |
| 0.66 | .152 | .169 | .187 | .205 | .224 | .243 | .262 | .282 | .302 | .323 | .344 | .365 | .387 | .409 | .432 | .455 | .478 | .502 | .526 | .551 | .576 | .601 | .627 | .653 | .680 |
| 0.67 | .154 | .172 | .190 | .208 | .227 | .246 | .266 | .286 | .306 | .327 | .348 | .370 | .392 | .414 | .437 | .460 | .484 | .508 | .532 | .557 | .582 | .608 | .634 | .660 | .687 |
| 0.68 | .156 | .174 | .192 | .211 | .230 | .249 | .269 | .289 | .310 | .331 | .352 | .374 | .396 | .419 | .442 | .465 | .489 | .513 | .538 | .563 | .588 | .614 | .640 | .667 | .691 |
| 0.69 | .158 | .176 | .194 | .213 | .232 | .252 | .272 | .292 | .313 | .334 | .356 | .378 | .400 | .423 | .446 | .470 | .494 | .518 | .543 | .568 | .594 | .620 | .646 | .673 | .700 |
| 0.70 | .160 | .178 | .197 | .216 | .235 | .255 | .275 | .296 | .317 | .338 | .360 | .382 | .405 | .428 | .451 | .475 | .499 | .524 | .549 | .574 | .600 | .626 | .653 | .680 | .707 |
| 0.71 | .162 | .180 | .199 | .218 | .238 | .258 | .278 | .299 | .320 | .342 | .364 | .386 | .409 | .432 | .456 | .480 | .504 | .529 | .554 | .580 | .606 | .632 | .659 | .686 | .714 |
| 0.72 | .164 | .183 | .202 | .221 | .241 | .261 | .282 | .303 | .324 | .346 | .368 | .391 | .414 | .437 | .461 | .485 | .510 | .535 | .560 | .586 | .612 | .639 | .666 | .693 | .721 |
| 0.73 | .166 | .185 | .204 | .224 | .244 | .264 | .285 | .306 | .328 | .350 | .372 | .395 | .418 | .442 | .466 | .490 | .515 | .540 | .566 | .592 | .618 | .645 | .672 | .700 | .728 | .756 |
| 0.74 | .168 | .187 | .206 | .226 | .246 | .267 | .288 | .309 | .331 | .353 | .376 | .399 | .422 | .446 | .470 | .495 | .520 | .545 | .571 | .597 | .624 | .651 | .678 | .706 | .734 | .763 |

# Table 12. Coefficients ($z$) for Position of Resultant of Compressive Stresses in Rectangular Sections

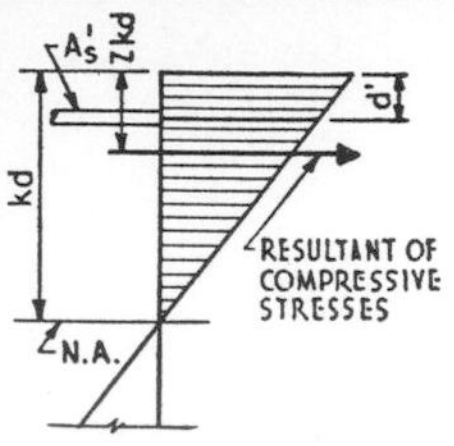


$$\text{Values of } z = \frac{\frac{1}{6} + \frac{(n-1)A'_s}{kbd} \times \frac{d'}{kd} \times \left(1 - \frac{d'}{kd}\right)}{\frac{1}{2} + \frac{(n-1)A'_s}{kbd} \times \left(1 - \frac{d'}{kd}\right)}$$

Enter table with known values of $\frac{1}{k} \times \frac{(n-1)A'_s}{bd}$ and $\frac{1}{k} \times \frac{d'}{d}$; select value of $z$

For $\frac{d'}{d} = \frac{1}{3}k$ or $A'_s = 0$: $z = \frac{1}{3}$

Compute $j = 1 - zk$ (see Table 13)

| $\frac{1}{k} \times \frac{d'}{d}$ | $\frac{1}{k} \times \frac{(n-1)A'_s}{bd}$ | | | | | | | | | | | | | | | | | | | | |
|---|---|---|---|---|---|---|---|---|---|---|---|---|---|---|---|---|---|---|---|---|---|
| | 0 | 0.05 | 0.10 | 0.15 | 0.20 | 0.25 | 0.30 | 0.35 | 0.40 | 0.45 | 0.50 | 0.55 | 0.60 | 0.65 | 0.70 | 0.75 | 0.80 | 0.85 | 0.90 | 0.95 | 1.00 |
| 0.02 | 0.33 | 0.31 | 0.28 | 0.26 | 0.24 | 0.23 | 0.22 | 0.21 | 0.20 | 0.19 | 0.18 | 0.17 | 0.16 | 0.16 | 0.15 | 0.15 | 0.14 | 0.14 | 0.13 | 0.13 | 0.13 |
| 0.04 | 0.33 | 0.31 | 0.29 | 0.27 | 0.25 | 0.24 | 0.23 | 0.22 | 0.21 | 0.20 | 0.19 | 0.18 | 0.18 | 0.17 | 0.17 | 0.16 | 0.16 | 0.15 | 0.15 | 0.14 | 0.14 |
| 0.06 | 0.33 | 0.31 | 0.29 | 0.27 | 0.26 | 0.25 | 0.24 | 0.23 | 0.22 | 0.21 | 0.20 | 0.19 | 0.19 | 0.18 | 0.18 | 0.17 | 0.17 | 0.17 | 0.16 | 0.16 | 0.16 |
| 0.08 | 0.33 | 0.31 | 0.29 | 0.28 | 0.26 | 0.25 | 0.24 | 0.23 | 0.23 | 0.22 | 0.21 | 0.21 | 0.20 | 0.20 | 0.19 | 0.19 | 0.18 | 0.18 | 0.18 | 0.17 | 0.17 |
| 0.10 | 0.33 | 0.31 | 0.30 | 0.28 | 0.27 | 0.26 | 0.25 | 0.24 | 0.24 | 0.23 | 0.22 | 0.22 | 0.21 | 0.21 | 0.20 | 0.20 | 0.20 | 0.19 | 0.19 | 0.19 | 0.18 |
| 0.12 | 0.33 | 0.32 | 0.30 | 0.29 | 0.28 | 0.27 | 0.26 | 0.25 | 0.25 | 0.24 | 0.23 | 0.23 | 0.22 | 0.22 | 0.22 | 0.21 | 0.21 | 0.21 | 0.20 | 0.20 | 0.20 |
| 0.14 | 0.33 | 0.32 | 0.31 | 0.29 | 0.28 | 0.28 | 0.27 | 0.26 | 0.25 | 0.25 | 0.24 | 0.24 | 0.24 | 0.23 | 0.23 | 0.22 | 0.22 | 0.22 | 0.22 | 0.21 | 0.21 |
| 0.16 | 0.33 | 0.32 | 0.31 | 0.30 | 0.29 | 0.28 | 0.28 | 0.27 | 0.26 | 0.26 | 0.25 | 0.25 | 0.25 | 0.24 | 0.24 | 0.24 | 0.23 | 0.23 | 0.23 | 0.23 | 0.22 |
| 0.18 | 0.33 | 0.32 | 0.31 | 0.30 | 0.30 | 0.29 | 0.28 | 0.28 | 0.27 | 0.27 | 0.26 | 0.26 | 0.26 | 0.25 | 0.25 | 0.25 | 0.25 | 0.24 | 0.24 | 0.24 | 0.24 |
| 0.20 | 0.33 | 0.32 | 0.32 | 0.31 | 0.30 | 0.30 | 0.29 | 0.29 | 0.28 | 0.28 | 0.27 | 0.27 | 0.27 | 0.27 | 0.26 | 0.26 | 0.26 | 0.26 | 0.25 | 0.25 | 0.25 |
| 0.22 | 0.33 | 0.32 | 0.32 | 0.31 | 0.31 | 0.30 | 0.30 | 0.29 | 0.29 | 0.29 | 0.28 | 0.28 | 0.28 | 0.28 | 0.27 | 0.27 | 0.27 | 0.27 | 0.27 | 0.27 | 0.26 |
| 0.24 | 0.33 | 0.33 | 0.32 | 0.32 | 0.31 | 0.31 | 0.30 | 0.30 | 0.30 | 0.30 | 0.29 | 0.29 | 0.29 | 0.29 | 0.28 | 0.28 | 0.28 | 0.28 | 0.28 | 0.28 | 0.28 |
| 0.26 | 0.33 | 0.33 | 0.32 | 0.32 | 0.32 | 0.31 | 0.31 | 0.31 | 0.31 | 0.30 | 0.30 | 0.30 | 0.30 | 0.30 | 0.30 | 0.29 | 0.29 | 0.29 | 0.29 | 0.29 | 0.29 |
| 0.28 | 0.33 | 0.33 | 0.33 | 0.32 | 0.32 | 0.32 | 0.32 | 0.32 | 0.31 | 0.31 | 0.31 | 0.31 | 0.31 | 0.31 | 0.31 | 0.31 | 0.30 | 0.30 | 0.30 | 0.30 | 0.30 |
| 0.30 | 0.33 | 0.33 | 0.33 | 0.33 | 0.33 | 0.32 | 0.32 | 0.32 | 0.32 | 0.32 | 0.32 | 0.32 | 0.32 | 0.32 | 0.32 | 0.32 | 0.32 | 0.32 | 0.32 | 0.31 | 0.31 |
| 0.32 | 0.33 | 0.33 | 0.33 | 0.33 | 0.33 | 0.33 | 0.33 | 0.33 | 0.33 | 0.33 | 0.33 | 0.33 | 0.33 | 0.33 | 0.33 | 0.33 | 0.33 | 0.33 | 0.33 | 0.33 | 0.33 |
| 0.34 | 0.33 | 0.33 | 0.33 | 0.33 | 0.34 | 0.34 | 0.34 | 0.34 | 0.34 | 0.34 | 0.34 | 0.34 | 0.34 | 0.34 | 0.34 | 0.34 | 0.34 | 0.34 | 0.34 | 0.34 | 0.34 |
| 0.36 | 0.33 | 0.33 | 0.34 | 0.34 | 0.34 | 0.34 | 0.34 | 0.34 | 0.34 | 0.34 | 0.34 | 0.34 | 0.34 | 0.35 | 0.35 | 0.35 | 0.35 | 0.35 | 0.35 | 0.35 | 0.35 |
| 0.38 | 0.33 | 0.34 | 0.34 | 0.34 | 0.34 | 0.35 | 0.35 | 0.35 | 0.35 | 0.35 | 0.35 | 0.35 | 0.35 | 0.35 | 0.36 | 0.36 | 0.36 | 0.36 | 0.36 | 0.36 | 0.36 |
| 0.40 | 0.33 | 0.34 | 0.34 | 0.34 | 0.35 | 0.35 | 0.35 | 0.35 | 0.36 | 0.36 | 0.36 | 0.36 | 0.36 | 0.36 | 0.36 | 0.37 | 0.37 | 0.37 | 0.37 | 0.37 | 0.37 |
| 0.42 | 0.33 | 0.34 | 0.34 | 0.35 | 0.35 | 0.35 | 0.36 | 0.36 | 0.36 | 0.36 | 0.37 | 0.37 | 0.37 | 0.37 | 0.37 | 0.37 | 0.38 | 0.38 | 0.38 | 0.38 | 0.38 |
| 0.44 | 0.33 | 0.34 | 0.34 | 0.35 | 0.35 | 0.36 | 0.36 | 0.36 | 0.37 | 0.37 | 0.37 | 0.37 | 0.38 | 0.38 | 0.38 | 0.38 | 0.38 | 0.39 | 0.39 | 0.39 | 0.39 |
| 0.46 | 0.33 | 0.34 | 0.35 | 0.35 | 0.36 | 0.36 | 0.36 | 0.37 | 0.37 | 0.37 | 0.38 | 0.38 | 0.38 | 0.39 | 0.39 | 0.39 | 0.39 | 0.39 | 0.40 | 0.40 | 0.40 |
| 0.48 | 0.33 | 0.34 | 0.35 | 0.35 | 0.36 | 0.36 | 0.37 | 0.37 | 0.38 | 0.38 | 0.38 | 0.39 | 0.39 | 0.39 | 0.39 | 0.40 | 0.40 | 0.40 | 0.40 | 0.41 | 0.41 |
| 0.50 | 0.33 | 0.34 | 0.35 | 0.35 | 0.36 | 0.37 | 0.37 | 0.38 | 0.38 | 0.38 | 0.39 | 0.39 | 0.40 | 0.40 | 0.40 | 0.40 | 0.41 | 0.41 | 0.41 | 0.41 | 0.42 |

# Table 13. Coefficients ($j$) for Rectangular Sections with or without Compressive Reinforcement

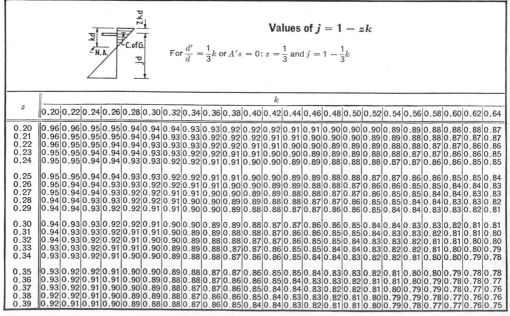

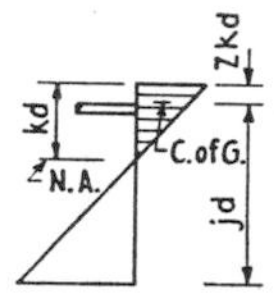


Values of $j = 1 - zk$

For $\frac{d'}{d} = \frac{1}{3}k$ or $A'_s = 0$: $z = \frac{1}{3}$ and $j = 1 - \frac{1}{3}k$

| $z$ | $k$ | | | | | | | | | | | | | | | | | | | | | | |
|---|---|---|---|---|---|---|---|---|---|---|---|---|---|---|---|---|---|---|---|---|---|---|---|
| | 0.20 | 0.22 | 0.24 | 0.26 | 0.28 | 0.30 | 0.32 | 0.34 | 0.36 | 0.38 | 0.40 | 0.42 | 0.44 | 0.46 | 0.48 | 0.50 | 0.52 | 0.54 | 0.56 | 0.58 | 0.60 | 0.62 | 0.64 |
| 0.20 | 0.96 | 0.96 | 0.95 | 0.95 | 0.94 | 0.94 | 0.94 | 0.93 | 0.93 | 0.92 | 0.92 | 0.92 | 0.91 | 0.91 | 0.90 | 0.90 | 0.90 | 0.89 | 0.89 | 0.88 | 0.88 | 0.88 | 0.87 |
| 0.21 | 0.96 | 0.95 | 0.95 | 0.95 | 0.94 | 0.94 | 0.93 | 0.93 | 0.92 | 0.92 | 0.92 | 0.91 | 0.91 | 0.90 | 0.90 | 0.90 | 0.89 | 0.89 | 0.88 | 0.88 | 0.87 | 0.87 | 0.87 |
| 0.22 | 0.96 | 0.95 | 0.95 | 0.94 | 0.94 | 0.93 | 0.93 | 0.93 | 0.92 | 0.92 | 0.91 | 0.91 | 0.90 | 0.90 | 0.89 | 0.89 | 0.89 | 0.88 | 0.88 | 0.87 | 0.87 | 0.86 | 0.86 |
| 0.23 | 0.95 | 0.95 | 0.94 | 0.94 | 0.94 | 0.93 | 0.93 | 0.92 | 0.92 | 0.91 | 0.91 | 0.90 | 0.90 | 0.89 | 0.89 | 0.89 | 0.88 | 0.88 | 0.87 | 0.87 | 0.86 | 0.86 | 0.85 |
| 0.24 | 0.95 | 0.95 | 0.94 | 0.94 | 0.93 | 0.93 | 0.92 | 0.92 | 0.91 | 0.91 | 0.90 | 0.90 | 0.89 | 0.89 | 0.88 | 0.88 | 0.88 | 0.87 | 0.87 | 0.86 | 0.86 | 0.85 | 0.85 |
| 0.25 | 0.95 | 0.95 | 0.94 | 0.94 | 0.93 | 0.93 | 0.92 | 0.92 | 0.91 | 0.91 | 0.90 | 0.90 | 0.89 | 0.89 | 0.88 | 0.88 | 0.87 | 0.87 | 0.86 | 0.86 | 0.85 | 0.85 | 0.84 |
| 0.26 | 0.95 | 0.94 | 0.94 | 0.93 | 0.93 | 0.92 | 0.92 | 0.91 | 0.91 | 0.90 | 0.90 | 0.89 | 0.89 | 0.88 | 0.88 | 0.87 | 0.86 | 0.86 | 0.85 | 0.85 | 0.84 | 0.84 | 0.83 |
| 0.27 | 0.95 | 0.94 | 0.94 | 0.93 | 0.92 | 0.92 | 0.91 | 0.91 | 0.90 | 0.90 | 0.89 | 0.89 | 0.88 | 0.88 | 0.87 | 0.87 | 0.86 | 0.85 | 0.85 | 0.84 | 0.84 | 0.83 | 0.83 |
| 0.28 | 0.94 | 0.94 | 0.93 | 0.93 | 0.92 | 0.92 | 0.91 | 0.90 | 0.90 | 0.89 | 0.89 | 0.88 | 0.88 | 0.87 | 0.87 | 0.86 | 0.85 | 0.85 | 0.84 | 0.84 | 0.83 | 0.83 | 0.82 |
| 0.29 | 0.94 | 0.94 | 0.93 | 0.92 | 0.92 | 0.91 | 0.91 | 0.90 | 0.90 | 0.89 | 0.88 | 0.88 | 0.87 | 0.87 | 0.86 | 0.86 | 0.85 | 0.84 | 0.84 | 0.83 | 0.83 | 0.82 | 0.81 |
| 0.30 | 0.94 | 0.93 | 0.93 | 0.92 | 0.92 | 0.91 | 0.90 | 0.90 | 0.89 | 0.89 | 0.88 | 0.87 | 0.87 | 0.86 | 0.86 | 0.85 | 0.84 | 0.84 | 0.83 | 0.83 | 0.82 | 0.81 | 0.81 |
| 0.31 | 0.94 | 0.93 | 0.93 | 0.92 | 0.91 | 0.91 | 0.90 | 0.89 | 0.89 | 0.88 | 0.88 | 0.87 | 0.86 | 0.86 | 0.85 | 0.85 | 0.84 | 0.83 | 0.83 | 0.82 | 0.81 | 0.81 | 0.80 |
| 0.32 | 0.94 | 0.93 | 0.92 | 0.92 | 0.91 | 0.90 | 0.90 | 0.89 | 0.88 | 0.88 | 0.87 | 0.87 | 0.86 | 0.85 | 0.85 | 0.84 | 0.83 | 0.83 | 0.82 | 0.81 | 0.81 | 0.80 | 0.80 |
| 0.33 | 0.93 | 0.93 | 0.92 | 0.91 | 0.91 | 0.90 | 0.89 | 0.89 | 0.88 | 0.87 | 0.87 | 0.86 | 0.85 | 0.85 | 0.84 | 0.84 | 0.83 | 0.82 | 0.82 | 0.81 | 0.80 | 0.80 | 0.79 |
| 0.34 | 0.93 | 0.93 | 0.92 | 0.91 | 0.90 | 0.90 | 0.89 | 0.88 | 0.88 | 0.87 | 0.86 | 0.86 | 0.85 | 0.84 | 0.84 | 0.83 | 0.82 | 0.82 | 0.81 | 0.80 | 0.80 | 0.79 | 0.78 |
| 0.35 | 0.93 | 0.92 | 0.92 | 0.91 | 0.90 | 0.90 | 0.89 | 0.88 | 0.87 | 0.87 | 0.86 | 0.85 | 0.85 | 0.84 | 0.83 | 0.83 | 0.82 | 0.81 | 0.80 | 0.80 | 0.79 | 0.78 | 0.78 |
| 0.36 | 0.93 | 0.92 | 0.91 | 0.91 | 0.90 | 0.89 | 0.88 | 0.88 | 0.87 | 0.86 | 0.86 | 0.85 | 0.84 | 0.83 | 0.83 | 0.82 | 0.81 | 0.81 | 0.80 | 0.79 | 0.78 | 0.78 | 0.77 |
| 0.37 | 0.93 | 0.92 | 0.91 | 0.90 | 0.90 | 0.89 | 0.88 | 0.87 | 0.87 | 0.86 | 0.85 | 0.84 | 0.84 | 0.83 | 0.82 | 0.82 | 0.81 | 0.80 | 0.79 | 0.79 | 0.78 | 0.77 | 0.76 |
| 0.38 | 0.92 | 0.92 | 0.91 | 0.90 | 0.89 | 0.89 | 0.88 | 0.87 | 0.86 | 0.86 | 0.85 | 0.84 | 0.83 | 0.83 | 0.82 | 0.81 | 0.80 | 0.79 | 0.79 | 0.78 | 0.77 | 0.76 | 0.76 |
| 0.39 | 0.92 | 0.91 | 0.91 | 0.90 | 0.89 | 0.88 | 0.88 | 0.87 | 0.86 | 0.85 | 0.84 | 0.84 | 0.83 | 0.82 | 0.81 | 0.81 | 0.80 | 0.79 | 0.78 | 0.77 | 0.77 | 0.76 | 0.75 |

# Table 14. Coefficients ($G$) for Calculation of Shear in Beam Web

**Values of** $G = \dfrac{7bd}{8000}$

(a) Enter table with known value of $\dfrac{V}{v}$ ($V$ in kips); select $b$ and $d$ (in.)

(b) Enter table with known values of $b$ and $d$; compute unit shear: $\dfrac{V}{G}$ (psi.)

| *d* | *b*: Width of joist or beam web | | | | | | | | | | | | | | | | |
|---|---|---|---|---|---|---|---|---|---|---|---|---|---|---|---|---|---|
| | 4 | 5 | 6 | 7 | 7½ | 8 | 9 | 9½ | 10 | 11½ | 12 | 13 | 15 | 17 | 19 | 21 | 23 |
| 5 | .018 | .022 | .026 | .031 | .033 | .035 | .039 | .042 | .044 | .050 | .053 | .057 | .066 | .074 | .083 | .092 | .101 |
| 5½ | .019 | .024 | .029 | .034 | .036 | .039 | .043 | .046 | .048 | .055 | .058 | .063 | .072 | .082 | .091 | .101 | .111 |
| 6 | .021 | .026 | .032 | .037 | .039 | .042 | .047 | .050 | .053 | .060 | .063 | .068 | .079 | .089 | .100 | .110 | .121 |
| 6½ | .023 | .028 | .034 | .040 | .043 | .046 | .051 | .054 | .057 | .065 | .068 | .074 | .085 | .097 | .108 | .119 | .131 |
| 7 | .025 | .031 | .037 | .043 | .046 | .049 | .055 | .058 | .061 | .070 | .074 | .080 | .092 | .104 | .116 | .129 | .141 |
| 7½ | .026 | .033 | .039 | .046 | .049 | .053 | .059 | .062 | .066 | .075 | .079 | .085 | .098 | .112 | .125 | .138 | .151 |
| 8 | .028 | .035 | .042 | .049 | .053 | .056 | .063 | .067 | .070 | .081 | .084 | .091 | .105 | .119 | .133 | .147 | .161 |
| 8½ | .030 | .037 | .045 | .052 | .056 | .060 | .067 | .071 | .074 | .086 | .089 | .097 | .112 | .126 | .141 | .156 | .171 |
| 9 | .032 | .039 | .047 | .055 | .059 | .063 | .071 | .075 | .079 | .091 | .095 | .102 | .118 | .134 | .150 | .165 | .181 |
| 9½ | .033 | .042 | .050 | .058 | .062 | .067 | .075 | .079 | .083 | .096 | .100 | .108 | .125 | .141 | .158 | .175 | .191 |
| 10 | .035 | .044 | .053 | .061 | .066 | .070 | .079 | .083 | .088 | .101 | .105 | .114 | .131 | .149 | .166 | .184 | .201 |
| 10½ | .037 | .046 | .055 | .064 | .069 | .074 | .083 | .087 | .092 | .106 | .110 | .119 | .138 | .156 | .175 | .193 | .211 |
| 11 | .039 | .048 | .058 | .067 | .072 | .077 | .087 | .091 | .096 | .111 | .116 | .125 | .144 | .164 | .183 | .202 | .221 |
| 11½ | .040 | .050 | .060 | .070 | .075 | .081 | .091 | .096 | .101 | .116 | .121 | .131 | .151 | .171 | .191 | .211 | .231 |
| 12 | .042 | .053 | .063 | .074 | .079 | .084 | .095 | .100 | .105 | .121 | .126 | .137 | .158 | .179 | .200 | .221 | .242 |
| 12½ | .044 | .055 | .066 | .077 | .082 | .088 | .098 | .104 | .109 | .126 | .131 | .142 | .164 | .186 | .208 | .230 | .252 |
| 13 | .046 | .057 | .068 | .080 | .085 | .091 | .102 | .108 | .114 | .131 | .137 | .148 | .171 | .193 | .216 | .239 | .262 |
| 13½ | .047 | .059 | .071 | .083 | .089 | .095 | .106 | .112 | .118 | .136 | .142 | .154 | .177 | .201 | .224 | .248 | .272 |
| 14 | .049 | .061 | .074 | .086 | .092 | .098 | .110 | .116 | .123 | .141 | .147 | .159 | .184 | .208 | .233 | .257 | .282 |
| 14½ | .051 | .063 | .076 | .089 | .095 | .102 | .114 | .121 | .127 | .146 | .152 | .165 | .190 | .216 | .241 | .266 | .292 |
| 15 | .053 | .066 | .079 | .092 | .098 | .105 | .118 | .125 | .131 | .151 | .158 | .171 | .197 | .223 | .249 | .270 | .302 |
| 15½ | .054 | .068 | .081 | .095 | .102 | .109 | .122 | .129 | .136 | .156 | .163 | .176 | .203 | .231 | .258 | .285 | .312 |
| 16 | .056 | .070 | .084 | .098 | .105 | .112 | .126 | .133 | .140 | .161 | .168 | .182 | .210 | .238 | .266 | .294 | .322 |
| 16½ | .058 | .072 | .087 | .101 | .108 | .116 | .130 | .137 | .144 | .166 | .173 | .188 | .217 | .245 | .274 | .303 | .332 |
| 17 | | .074 | .089 | .104 | .112 | .119 | .134 | .141 | .149 | .171 | .179 | .193 | .223 | .253 | .283 | .312 | .342 |
| 17½ | | .077 | .092 | .107 | .115 | .123 | .138 | .145 | .153 | .176 | .184 | .199 | .230 | .260 | .291 | .322 | .352 |
| 18 | | .079 | .095 | .110 | .118 | .126 | .142 | .150 | .158 | .181 | .189 | .205 | .236 | .268 | .299 | .331 | .362 |
| 18½ | | .081 | .097 | .113 | .121 | .130 | .146 | .154 | .162 | .186 | .194 | .210 | .243 | .275 | .308 | .340 | .372 |
| 19 | | | .100 | .116 | .125 | .133 | .150 | .158 | .166 | .191 | .200 | .218 | .249 | .283 | .310 | .349 | .382 |
| 20 | | | .105 | .123 | .131 | .140 | .158 | .166 | .175 | .201 | .210 | .228 | .263 | .298 | .333 | .368 | .403 |
| 21 | | | .110 | .129 | .138 | .147 | .165 | .175 | .184 | .211 | .221 | .239 | .276 | .312 | .349 | .386 | .423 |
| 22 | | | .116 | .135 | .144 | .154 | .173 | .183 | .193 | .221 | .231 | .250 | .289 | .327 | .366 | .404 | .443 |
| 23 | | | | .141 | .151 | .161 | .181 | .191 | .201 | .231 | .242 | .262 | .302 | .342 | .382 | .423 | .463 |
| 24 | | | | .147 | .158 | .168 | .189 | .200 | .210 | .242 | .252 | .273 | .315 | .357 | .399 | .441 | .483 |
| 25 | | | | .153 | .164 | .175 | .197 | .208 | .219 | .252 | .263 | .284 | .328 | .372 | .416 | .459 | .503 |
| 26 | | | | .159 | .171 | .182 | .205 | .216 | .228 | .262 | .273 | .296 | .341 | .387 | .432 | .478 | .523 |
| 27 | | | | | .177 | .189 | .213 | .224 | .236 | .272 | .284 | .307 | .354 | .402 | .449 | .496 | .543 |
| 28 | | | | | .184 | .196 | .221 | .233 | .245 | .282 | .294 | .318 | .368 | .417 | .466 | .515 | .564 |
| 29 | | | | | .190 | .203 | .228 | .241 | .254 | .292 | .305 | .330 | .381 | .431 | .482 | .533 | .584 |
| 30 | | | | | .197 | .210 | .236 | .249 | .263 | .302 | .315 | .341 | .394 | .446 | .499 | .551 | .604 |
| 31 | | | | | | .217 | .244 | .258 | .271 | .312 | .326 | .353 | .407 | .461 | .515 | .570 | .624 |
| 32 | | | | | | .224 | .252 | .266 | .280 | .322 | .336 | .364 | .420 | .476 | .532 | .588 | .644 |
| 33 | | | | | | .231 | .260 | .274 | .289 | .332 | .347 | .375 | .433 | .491 | .549 | .606 | .664 |
| 34 | | | | | | .238 | .268 | .283 | .298 | .342 | .357 | .387 | .446 | .506 | .565 | .625 | .684 |
| 36 | | | | | | | .284 | .299 | .315 | .362 | .378 | .410 | .473 | .536 | .599 | .662 | .725 |
| 38 | | | | | | | .299 | .316 | .333 | .382 | .399 | .432 | .499 | .565 | .632 | .698 | .765 |
| 40 | | | | | | | .315 | .333 | .350 | .403 | .420 | .455 | .525 | .595 | .665 | .735 | .805 |
| 42 | | | | | | | .331 | .349 | .368 | .423 | .441 | .478 | .551 | .625 | .698 | .772 | .845 |
| 44 | | | | | | | | .366 | .385 | .443 | .462 | .501 | .578 | .655 | .732 | .808 | 0.89 |
| 46 | | | | | | | | .383 | .403 | .463 | .483 | .523 | .604 | .684 | .765 | .845 | 0.93 |
| 48 | | | | | | | | .399 | .420 | .483 | .504 | .546 | .630 | .714 | .798 | .882 | 0.97 |
| 50 | | | | | | | | .416 | .438 | .503 | .525 | .569 | .656 | .744 | .831 | .919 | 1.01 |
| 52 | | | | | | | | | .455 | .524 | .546 | .592 | .682 | .774 | .865 | 0.96 | 1.05 |
| 54 | | | | | | | | | .473 | .544 | .567 | .614 | .709 | .804 | .898 | 0.99 | 1.09 |
| 56 | | | | | | | | | .490 | .564 | .588 | .637 | .735 | .833 | .932 | 1.03 | 1.13 |
| 58 | | | | | | | | | .508 | .584 | .609 | .660 | .762 | .863 | .965 | 1.07 | 1.17 |
| 60 | | | | | | | | | | .604 | .630 | .682 | .788 | 0.89 | 1.00 | 1.10 | 1.21 |
| 64 | | | | | | | | | | .644 | .672 | .728 | .840 | 0.95 | 1.06 | 1.18 | 1.29 |
| 68 | | | | | | | | | | .684 | .714 | .774 | .893 | 1.01 | 1.13 | 1.25 | 1.37 |
| 72 | | | | | | | | | | .725 | .756 | .819 | .945 | 1.07 | 1.20 | 1.32 | 1.45 |

## Table 15. Minimum Depths for Embedment of Vertical Hooked Stirrups

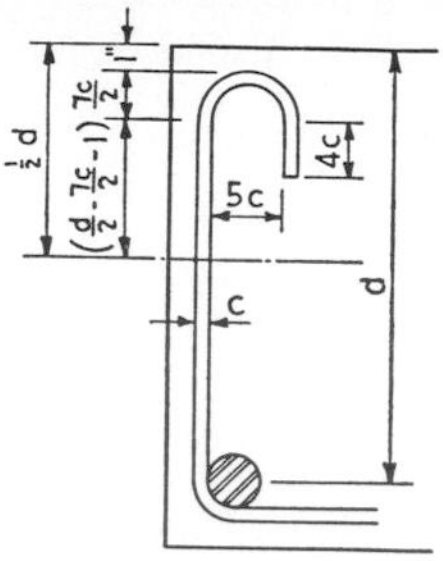


**Values of $d$**

Deformed bars: $d = (f_v - 10{,}000)\dfrac{10c}{f'_c} + 7c + 2$

Plain bars: $d = (f_v - 10{,}000)\dfrac{12.5c}{f'_c} + 7c + 2$

When web reinforcement is inclined, determine min.$d$ by multiplying values in table by $\sin x$ ($x$ = angle between tensile and web reinforcement)

| | Plain | Deformed | | | | | Plain | Deformed | | | | | Plain | Deformed | | | | |
|---|---|---|---|---|---|---|---|---|---|---|---|---|---|---|---|---|---|---|
| | ¼φ | ¼φ | ⅜φ | ½φ | ½□ | ⅝φ | ¼φ | ¼φ | ⅜φ | ½φ | ½□ | ⅝φ | ¼φ | ¼φ | ⅜φ | ½φ | ½□ | ⅝φ |
| $f'_c$ | $f_v$ = 12,000 | | | | | | $f_v$ = 14,000 | | | | | | $f_v$ = 16,000 | | | | | |
| 2000 | 6.9 | 6.3 | 8.4 | 10.5 | 10.5 | 12.6 | 10.0 | 8.8 | 12.1 | 15.5 | 15.5 | 18.9 | 13.1 | 11.3 | 15.9 | 20.5 | 20.5 | 25.1 |
| 2500 | 6.3 | 5.8 | 7.6 | 9.5 | 9.5 | 11.4 | 8.8 | 7.8 | 10.6 | 13.5 | 13.5 | 16.4 | 11.3 | 9.8 | 13.6 | 17.5 | 17.5 | 21.4 |
| 3000 | 5.8 | 5.4 | 7.1 | 8.8 | 8.8 | 10.5 | 7.9 | 7.1 | 9.6 | 12.2 | 12.2 | 14.7 | 10.0 | 8.8 | 12.1 | 15.5 | 15.5 | 18.9 |
| 3750 | 5.4 | 5.1 | 6.6 | 8.2 | 8.2 | 9.7 | 7.1 | 6.4 | 8.6 | 10.8 | 10.8 | 13.0 | 8.8 | 7.8 | 10.6 | 13.5 | 13.5 | 16.4 |
| $f'_c$ | $f_v$ = 18,000 | | | | | | $f_v$ = 20,000 | | | | | | $f_v$ = 22,000 | | | | | |
| 2000 | 16.3 | 13.8 | 19.6 | 25.5 | 25.5 | 31.4 | 19.4 | 16.3 | 23.4 | 30.5 | 30.5 | 37.6 | 22.5 | 18.8 | 27.1 | 35.5 | 35.5 | 43.9 |
| 2500 | 13.8 | 11.8 | 16.6 | 21.5 | 21.5 | 26.4 | 16.3 | 13.8 | 19.6 | 25.5 | 25.5 | 31.4 | 18.8 | 15.8 | 22.6 | 29.5 | 29.5 | 36.4 |
| 3000 | 12.1 | 10.4 | 14.6 | 18.8 | 18.8 | 23.0 | 14.2 | 12.1 | 17.1 | 22.2 | 22.2 | 27.2 | 16.3 | 13.8 | 19.6 | 25.5 | 25.5 | 31.4 |
| 3750 | 10.4 | 9.1 | 12.6 | 16.2 | 16.2 | 19.7 | 12.1 | 10.4 | 14.6 | 18.8 | 18.8 | 23.0 | 13.8 | 11.8 | 16.6 | 21.5 | 21.5 | 26.4 |
| $f'_c$ | $f_v$ = 24,000 | | | | | | $f_v$ = 27,000 | | | | | | $f_v$ = 30,000 | | | | | |
| 2000 | 25.6 | 21.3 | 30.9 | 40.5 | 40.5 | 50.1 | 30.3 | 25.0 | 36.5 | 48.0 | 48.0 | 59.5 | 35.0 | 28.8 | 42.1 | 55.5 | 55.5 | 68.9 |
| 2500 | 21.3 | 17.8 | 25.6 | 33.5 | 33.5 | 41.4 | 25.0 | 20.8 | 30.1 | 39.5 | 39.5 | 48.9 | 28.8 | 23.8 | 34.6 | 45.5 | 45.5 | 56.4 |
| 3000 | 18.3 | 15.4 | 22.1 | 28.8 | 28.8 | 35.5 | 21.5 | 17.9 | 25.9 | 33.8 | 33.8 | 41.8 | 24.6 | 20.4 | 29.6 | 38.8 | 38.8 | 48.0 |
| 3750 | 15.4 | 13.1 | 18.6 | 24.2 | 24.2 | 29.7 | 17.9 | 15.1 | 21.6 | 28.2 | 28.2 | 34.7 | 20.4 | 17.1 | 24.6 | 32.2 | 32.2 | 39.7 |

## Table 16. Coefficients for Design of Inclined Web Reinforcement

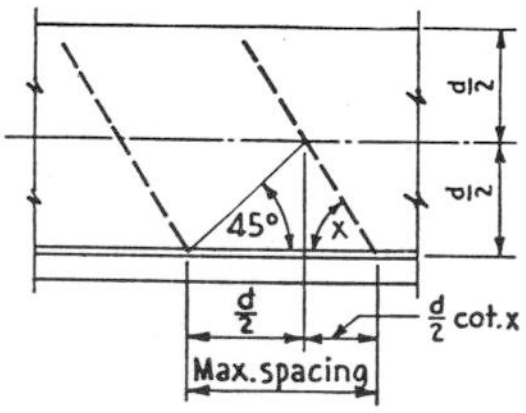


Product of $\sin x$ and values in Table 15 is minimum effective depth required

Coefficient $B$ is used in the general equation:

$$\frac{1}{s} = \frac{v'b}{BA_v f_v}$$

Maximum spacing $s$ in terms of $d$ is given for

(a) inclined stirrups with hook as in Table 15:

$$\frac{\text{max.}s}{d} = \tfrac{1}{2} + \tfrac{1}{2}\cot x$$

(b) bent bars continuous with longitudinal reinforcement:

$$\frac{\text{max.}s}{d} = \tfrac{3}{4}(\tfrac{1}{2} + \tfrac{1}{2}\cot x)$$

| $x$: Angle between tensile and web bars | 90° | 85° | 80° | 75° | 70° | 65° | 60° | 55° | 50° | 45° | 40° | 35° | 30° |
|---|---|---|---|---|---|---|---|---|---|---|---|---|---|
| $\sin x$: Beam reduction factor | 1.00 | 1.00 | 0.98 | 0.97 | 0.94 | 0.91 | 0.87 | 0.82 | 0.77 | 0.71 | 0.64 | 0.57 | 0.50 |
| $B$: $\sin x + \cos x$; used in $BA_v$ | 1.00 | 1.08 | 1.16 | 1.22 | 1.28 | 1.33 | 1.37 | 1.39 | 1.41 | 1.41 | 1.41 | 1.39 | 1.37 |
| $\frac{\text{max.}s}{d}$ Inclined stirrups | 0.50 | 0.54 | 0.59 | 0.63 | 0.68 | 0.73 | 0.79 | 0.85 | 0.92 | 1.00 | 1.10 | 1.21 | 1.37 |
| $\frac{\text{max.}s}{d}$ Bent bars | 0.38 | 0.41 | 0.44 | 0.47 | 0.51 | 0.55 | 0.59 | 0.64 | 0.69 | 0.75 | 0.82 | 0.91 | 1.02 |

# Diagram 17. Spacing of Stirrups

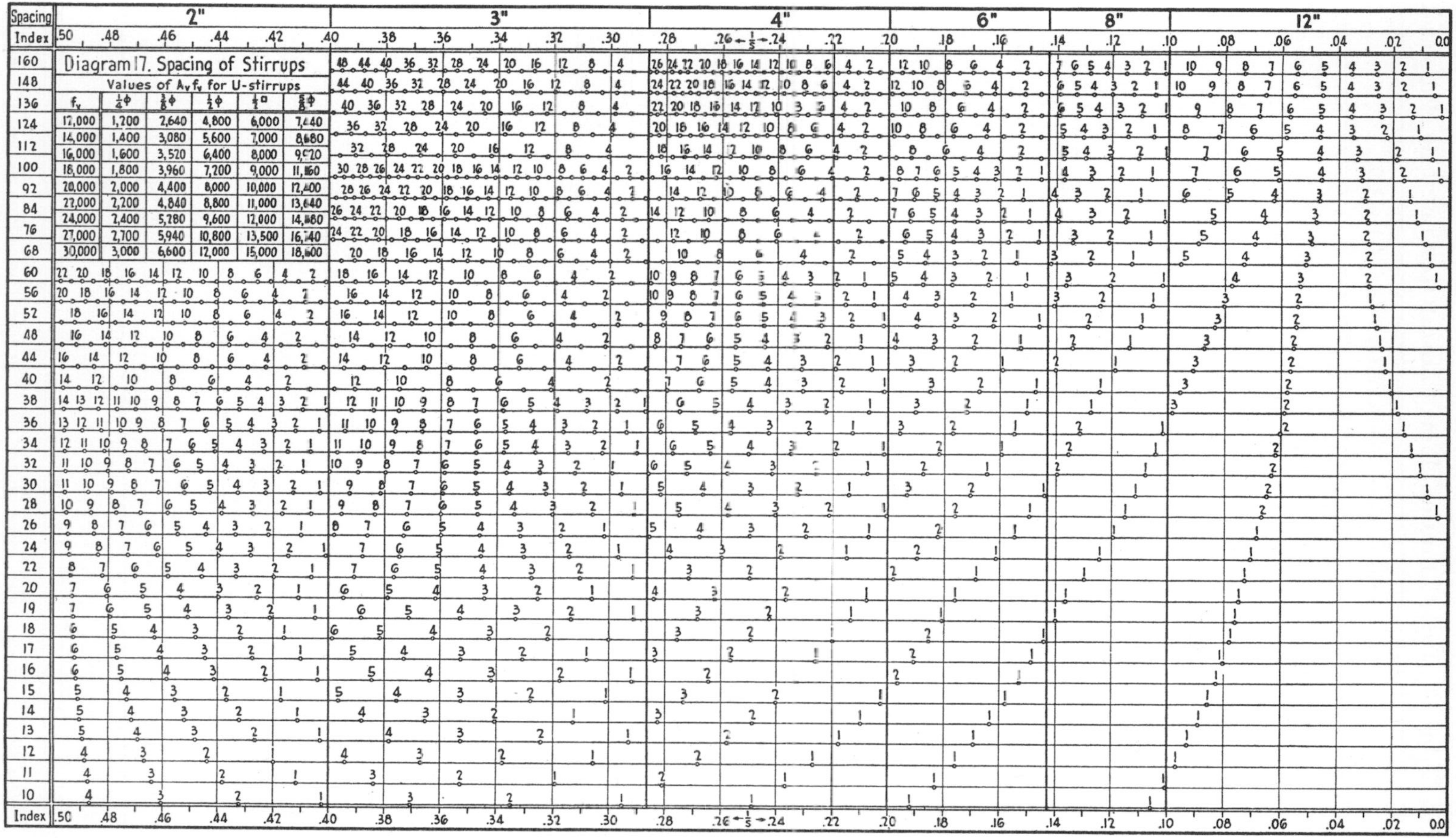
Spacing
2"
3"
4"
6"
8"
12"
Index
.50 .48 .46 .44 .42 .40 .38 .36 .34 .32 .30 .28 .26 ← 1/5 → .24 .22 .20 .18 .16 .14 .12 .10 .08 .06 .04 .02 0.0
160 148 136 124 112 100 92 84 76 68 60 56 52 48 44 40 38 36 34 32 30 28 26 24 22 20 19 18 17 16 15 14 13 12 11 10
Diagram 17. Spacing of Stirrups
Values of $A_v f_v$ for U-stirrups
$f_v$ | $\frac{1}{4}\phi$ | $\frac{3}{8}\phi$ | $\frac{1}{2}\phi$ | $\frac{1}{2}\square$ | $\frac{5}{8}\phi$
12,000 | 1,200 | 2,640 | 4,800 | 6,000 | 7,440
14,000 | 1,400 | 3,080 | 5,600 | 7,000 | 8,680
16,000 | 1,600 | 3,520 | 6,400 | 8,000 | 9,920
18,000 | 1,800 | 3,960 | 7,200 | 9,000 | 11,160
20,000 | 2,000 | 4,400 | 8,000 | 10,000 | 12,400
22,000 | 2,200 | 4,840 | 8,800 | 11,000 | 13,640
24,000 | 2,400 | 5,280 | 9,600 | 12,000 | 14,880
27,000 | 2,700 | 5,940 | 10,800 | 13,500 | 16,740
30,000 | 3,000 | 6,600 | 12,000 | 15,000 | 18,600

# Table 18. Tied Columns; Joint Committee Code 1940 (Proposed)

## Part 1. $P$ (kips) $= (0.18 f'_c A_g + 0.8 f_s A_s) \div 1000$

| Column Size | | Gross Area $A_g$ | Load on Bars, Min.: $0.008 f_s A_g \div 1000$, Max.: $0.032 f_s A_g \div 1000$; $f_s = 16{,}000$ Min. | $f_s = 16{,}000$ Max. | $f_s = 20{,}000$ Min. | $f_s = 20{,}000$ Max. | Load on Concrete $0.18 f'_c A_g \div 1000$; $f'_c$ = 2000 | 2500 | 3000 | 3750 | 5000 |
|---|---|---|---|---|---|---|---|---|---|---|---|
| 10 | 12 | 120 | 15 | 61 | 19 | 77 | 43 | 54 | 65 | 81 | 108 |
| | 14 | 140 | 18 | 72 | 22 | 90 | 50 | 63 | 76 | 95 | 126 |
| | 16 | 160 | 20 | 82 | 26 | 102 | 58 | 72 | 86 | 108 | 144 |
| | 18 | 180 | 23 | 92 | 29 | 115 | 65 | 81 | 97 | 122 | 162 |
| 12 | 12 | 144 | 18 | 74 | 23 | 92 | 52 | 65 | 78 | 97 | 130 |
| | 14 | 168 | 22 | 86 | 27 | 108 | 60 | 76 | 91 | 113 | 151 |
| | 16 | 192 | 25 | 98 | 31 | 123 | 69 | 86 | 104 | 130 | 173 |
| | 18 | 216 | 28 | 111 | 35 | 138 | 78 | 97 | 117 | 146 | 194 |
| | 20 | 240 | 31 | 123 | 38 | 154 | 86 | 108 | 130 | 162 | 216 |
| 14 | 14 | 196 | 25 | 100 | 31 | 125 | 71 | 88 | 106 | 132 | 176 |
| | 16 | 224 | 29 | 115 | 36 | 143 | 81 | 101 | 121 | 151 | 202 |
| | 18 | 252 | 32 | 129 | 40 | 161 | 91 | 113 | 136 | 170 | 227 |
| | 20 | 280 | 36 | 143 | 45 | 179 | 101 | 126 | 151 | 189 | 252 |
| | 22 | 308 | 39 | 158 | 49 | 197 | 111 | 139 | 166 | 208 | 277 |
| 16 | 16 | 256 | 33 | 131 | 41 | 164 | 92 | 115 | 138 | 173 | 230 |
| | 18 | 288 | 37 | 147 | 46 | 184 | 104 | 130 | 156 | 194 | 259 |
| | 20 | 320 | 41 | 164 | 51 | 205 | 115 | 144 | 173 | 216 | 288 |
| | 22 | 352 | 45 | 180 | 56 | 225 | 127 | 158 | 190 | 238 | 317 |
| | 24 | 384 | 49 | 197 | 61 | 246 | 138 | 173 | 207 | 259 | 346 |
| 18 | 18 | 324 | 41 | 166 | 52 | 207 | 117 | 146 | 175 | 219 | 292 |
| | 20 | 360 | 46 | 184 | 58 | 230 | 130 | 162 | 194 | 243 | 324 |
| | 22 | 396 | 51 | 203 | 63 | 253 | 143 | 178 | 214 | 267 | 356 |
| | 24 | 432 | 55 | 221 | 69 | 276 | 156 | 194 | 233 | 292 | 389 |
| | 26 | 468 | 60 | 240 | 75 | 300 | 168 | 211 | 253 | 316 | 421 |
| 20 | 20 | 400 | 51 | 205 | 64 | 256 | 144 | 180 | 216 | 270 | 360 |
| | 22 | 440 | 56 | 225 | 70 | 282 | 158 | 198 | 238 | 297 | 396 |
| | 24 | 480 | 61 | 246 | 77 | 307 | 173 | 216 | 259 | 324 | 432 |
| | 26 | 520 | 67 | 266 | 83 | 333 | 187 | 234 | 281 | 351 | 468 |
| | 28 | 560 | 72 | 287 | 90 | 356 | 202 | 252 | 302 | 378 | 504 |
| 22 | 22 | 484 | 62 | 248 | 77 | 310 | 174 | 218 | 261 | 327 | 436 |
| | 24 | 528 | 68 | 270 | 84 | 338 | 190 | 238 | 285 | 356 | 475 |
| | 26 | 572 | 73 | 293 | 92 | 366 | 206 | 257 | 309 | 386 | 515 |
| | 28 | 616 | 79 | 315 | 99 | 394 | 222 | 277 | 333 | 416 | 554 |
| 24 | 24 | 576 | 74 | 295 | 92 | 369 | 207 | 259 | 311 | 389 | 518 |
| | 26 | 624 | 80 | 319 | 100 | 399 | 225 | 281 | 337 | 421 | 562 |
| | 28 | 672 | 86 | 344 | 108 | 430 | 242 | 302 | 363 | 454 | 605 |
| 26 | 26 | 676 | 87 | 346 | 108 | 433 | 243 | 304 | 365 | 456 | 608 |
| | 28 | 728 | 93 | 373 | 116 | 466 | 262 | 328 | 393 | 491 | 655 |
| 28 | 28 | 784 | 100 | 401 | 125 | 502 | 282 | 353 | 423 | 529 | 706 |
| 30 | 30 | 900 | 115 | 461 | 144 | 576 | 324 | 405 | 486 | 608 | 810 |
| 32 | 32 | 1024 | 131 | 524 | 164 | 655 | 369 | 461 | 553 | 691 | 922 |
| 34 | 34 | 1156 | 148 | 592 | 185 | 740 | 416 | 520 | 624 | 780 | 1040 |
| — | — | 1000 | 128 | 512 | 160 | 640 | 360 | 450 | 540 | 675 | 900 |

## Part 2. Load on Bars (kips) $= 0.8 f_s A_s \div 1000$

Intermediate Grade: $f_s = 16{,}000$

| Bar Size | Number of Bars: 4 | 6 | 8 | 10 | 12 | 14 | 16 | 18 | 20 | 22 |
|---|---|---|---|---|---|---|---|---|---|---|
| ⅝ φ | 16 | 24 | 32 | 40 | 48 | 56 | 63 | 71 | 79 | 87 |
| ¾ φ | 23 | 34 | 45 | 56 | 68 | 79 | 90 | 101 | 113 | 124 |
| ⅞ φ | 31 | 46 | 61 | 77 | 92 | 108 | 123 | 138 | 154 | 169 |
| 1 φ | 40 | 61 | 81 | 101 | 121 | 142 | 162 | 182 | 202 | 223 |
| 1 □ | 51 | 77 | 102 | 128 | 154 | 179 | 205 | 230 | 256 | 282 |
| 1⅛ □ | 65 | 98 | 130 | 163 | 195 | 228 | 260 | 293 | 325 | 358 |
| 1¼ □ | 80 | 120 | 160 | 200 | 240 | 280 | 320 | 360 | 400 | 440 |

Rail or Hard Grade: $f_s = 20{,}000$

| Bar Size | Number of Bars: 4 | 6 | 8 | 10 | 12 | 14 | 16 | 18 | 20 | 22 |
|---|---|---|---|---|---|---|---|---|---|---|
| ⅝ φ | 20 | 30 | 40 | 50 | 60 | 69 | 79 | 89 | 99 | 109 |
| ¾ φ | 28 | 42 | 56 | 70 | 85 | 99 | 113 | 127 | 141 | 155 |
| ⅞ φ | 38 | 58 | 77 | 96 | 115 | 134 | 154 | 173 | 192 | 211 |
| 1 φ | 51 | 76 | 101 | 126 | 152 | 177 | 202 | 227 | 253 | 278 |
| 1 □ | 64 | 96 | 128 | 160 | 192 | 224 | 256 | 288 | 320 | 352 |
| 1⅛ □ | 81 | 122 | 163 | 203 | 244 | 285 | 325 | 366 | 407 | 447 |
| 1¼ □ | 100 | 150 | 200 | 250 | 300 | 349 | 399 | 449 | 499 | 549 |

# Table 19. Tied Columns; American Concrete Institute Code 1936

## Part 1. $P$ (kips) = $(0.154 f'_c A_g + 0.7 f_s A_s) \div 1000$

| Column Size | | Gross Area $A_g$ | Load on Bars (Min.: $0.007 f_s A_g \div 1000$; Max.: $0.028 f_s A_g \div 1000$) | | | | Load on Concrete $0.154 f'_c A_g \div 1000$ | | | | |
|---|---|---|---|---|---|---|---|---|---|---|---|
| | | | $f_s = 16{,}000$ | | $f_s = 20{,}000$ | | $f'_c$ | | | | |
| | | | Min. | Max. | Min. | Max. | 2000 | 2500 | 3000 | 3750 | 5000 |
| 10 | 12 | 120 | 13 | 54 | 17 | 67 | 37 | 46 | 55 | 69 | 92 |
| | 14 | 140 | 16 | 63 | 20 | 78 | 43 | 54 | 65 | 81 | 108 |
| | 16 | 160 | 18 | 72 | 22 | 90 | 49 | 62 | 74 | 92 | 123 |
| | 18 | 180 | 20 | 81 | 25 | 101 | 55 | 69 | 83 | 104 | 139 |
| 12 | 12 | 144 | 16 | 65 | 20 | 81 | 44 | 55 | 67 | 83 | 111 |
| | 14 | 168 | 19 | 75 | 24 | 94 | 52 | 65 | 78 | 97 | 129 |
| | 16 | 192 | 22 | 86 | 27 | 108 | 59 | 74 | 89 | 111 | 148 |
| | 18 | 216 | 24 | 97 | 30 | 121 | 67 | 83 | 100 | 125 | 166 |
| | 20 | 240 | 27 | 108 | 34 | 134 | 74 | 92 | 111 | 139 | 185 |
| 14 | 14 | 196 | 22 | 88 | 27 | 110 | 60 | 75 | 91 | 113 | 151 |
| | 16 | 224 | 25 | 100 | 31 | 126 | 69 | 86 | 104 | 129 | 173 |
| | 18 | 252 | 28 | 113 | 35 | 141 | 78 | 97 | 116 | 146 | 194 |
| | 20 | 280 | 31 | 126 | 39 | 157 | 86 | 108 | 129 | 162 | 216 |
| | 22 | 308 | 34 | 138 | 43 | 173 | 95 | 119 | 142 | 178 | 237 |
| 16 | 16 | 256 | 29 | 115 | 36 | 143 | 79 | 99 | 118 | 148 | 197 |
| | 18 | 288 | 32 | 129 | 40 | 161 | 89 | 111 | 133 | 166 | 222 |
| | 20 | 320 | 36 | 143 | 45 | 179 | 99 | 123 | 148 | 185 | 246 |
| | 22 | 352 | 39 | 158 | 49 | 197 | 108 | 136 | 163 | 203 | 271 |
| | 24 | 384 | 43 | 172 | 54 | 215 | 118 | 148 | 177 | 222 | 296 |
| 18 | 18 | 324 | 36 | 145 | 45 | 182 | 100 | 125 | 150 | 187 | 250 |
| | 20 | 360 | 40 | 161 | 50 | 202 | 111 | 139 | 166 | 208 | 277 |
| | 22 | 396 | 44 | 178 | 55 | 222 | 122 | 153 | 183 | 229 | 305 |
| | 24 | 432 | 48 | 194 | 60 | 242 | 133 | 166 | 200 | 250 | 333 |
| | 26 | 468 | 52 | 210 | 66 | 262 | 144 | 180 | 216 | 270 | 360 |
| 20 | 20 | 400 | 45 | 179 | 56 | 224 | 123 | 154 | 185 | 231 | 308 |
| | 22 | 440 | 49 | 197 | 62 | 247 | 136 | 169 | 203 | 254 | 339 |
| | 24 | 480 | 54 | 215 | 67 | 269 | 148 | 185 | 222 | 277 | 370 |
| | 26 | 520 | 58 | 233 | 73 | 292 | 160 | 200 | 240 | 300 | 400 |
| | 28 | 560 | 63 | 251 | 78 | 313 | 173 | 216 | 259 | 323 | 431 |
| 22 | 22 | 484 | 54 | 217 | 68 | 271 | 149 | 186 | 224 | 280 | 373 |
| | 24 | 528 | 59 | 237 | 74 | 296 | 163 | 203 | 244 | 305 | 407 |
| | 26 | 572 | 64 | 256 | 80 | 320 | 176 | 220 | 264 | 330 | 440 |
| | 28 | 616 | 69 | 276 | 86 | 345 | 190 | 237 | 285 | 356 | 474 |
| 24 | 24 | 576 | 65 | 258 | 81 | 323 | 178 | 222 | 266 | 333 | 443 |
| | 26 | 624 | 70 | 280 | 87 | 349 | 192 | 240 | 288 | 360 | 480 |
| | 28 | 672 | 75 | 301 | 94 | 376 | 207 | 260 | 310 | 388 | 517 |
| 26 | 26 | 676 | 76 | 303 | 95 | 379 | 208 | 260 | 312 | 390 | 520 |
| | 28 | 728 | 82 | 326 | 102 | 408 | 224 | 280 | 336 | 420 | 560 |
| 28 | 28 | 784 | 88 | 351 | 110 | 439 | 242 | 302 | 362 | 453 | 604 |
| 30 | 30 | 900 | 101 | 403 | 126 | 504 | 278 | 346 | 415 | 520 | 693 |
| 32 | 32 | 1024 | 115 | 459 | 143 | 574 | 316 | 394 | 473 | 591 | 788 |
| 34 | 34 | 1156 | 129 | 518 | 162 | 648 | 356 | 445 | 534 | 668 | 891 |
| — | — | 1000 | 112 | 448 | 140 | 560 | 308 | 385 | 462 | 578 | 770 |

## Part 2. Load on Bars (kips) = $0.7 f_s A_s \div 1000$

| Bar Size | Number of Bars | | | | | | | | | | Bar Size | Number of Bars | | | | | | | | | |
|---|---|---|---|---|---|---|---|---|---|---|---|---|---|---|---|---|---|---|---|---|---|
| | 4 | 6 | 8 | 10 | 12 | 14 | 16 | 18 | 20 | 22 | | 4 | 6 | 8 | 10 | 12 | 14 | 16 | 18 | 20 | 22 |
| | Intermediate Grade: $f_s = 16{,}000$ | | | | | | | | | | | Rail or Hard Grade: $f_s = 20{,}000$ | | | | | | | | | |
| $\frac{5}{8}\phi$ | 14 | 21 | 28 | 35 | 42 | 49 | 56 | 63 | 69 | 76 | $\frac{5}{8}\phi$ | 17 | 26 | 35 | 43 | 52 | 61 | 69 | 78 | 87 | 95 |
| $\frac{3}{4}\phi$ | 20 | 30 | 39 | 49 | 59 | 69 | 79 | 89 | 99 | 108 | $\frac{3}{4}\phi$ | 25 | 37 | 49 | 62 | 74 | 86 | 99 | 111 | 123 | 136 |
| $\frac{7}{8}\phi$ | 27 | 40 | 54 | 67 | 81 | 94 | 108 | 121 | 134 | 148 | $\frac{7}{8}\phi$ | 34 | 50 | 67 | 84 | 101 | 118 | 134 | 151 | 168 | 185 |
| $1\phi$ | 35 | 53 | 71 | 88 | 106 | 124 | 142 | 159 | 177 | 195 | $1\phi$ | 44 | 66 | 89 | 111 | 133 | 155 | 177 | 199 | 221 | 243 |
| 1 □ | 45 | 67 | 90 | 112 | 134 | 157 | 179 | 202 | 224 | 247 | 1 □ | 56 | 84 | 112 | 140 | 168 | 196 | 224 | 252 | 280 | 308 |
| $1\frac{1}{8}$ □ | 57 | 85 | 114 | 142 | 171 | 199 | 228 | 256 | 284 | 313 | $1\frac{1}{8}$ □ | 71 | 107 | 142 | 178 | 213 | 249 | 285 | 320 | 356 | 391 |
| $1\frac{1}{4}$ □ | 70 | 105 | 140 | 175 | 210 | 245 | 280 | 315 | 349 | 384 | $1\frac{1}{4}$ □ | 87 | 131 | 175 | 218 | 262 | 306 | 350 | 393 | 437 | 480 |

# Table 20. Tied Columns; American Concrete Institute Code 1928

## Part 1. $P$ (kips) = $[0.225 f'_c A_g + (6750 - 0.225 f'_c) A_s] \div 1000$

| Column Size | | Gross Area $A_g$ | Min. Load on Column: $(0.224 f'_c + 33.75) A_g \div 1000$ | | | | Max. Load on Column: $(0.2205 f'_c + 135) A_g \div 1000$ | | | | Load on Concrete Only: $0.225 f'_c A_g \div 1000$ | | | |
|---|---|---|---|---|---|---|---|---|---|---|---|---|---|---|
| | | | $f'_c$ | | | | $f'_c$ | | | | $f'_c$ | | | |
| | | | 2000 | 2500 | 3000 | 3750 | 2000 | 2500 | 3000 | 3750 | 2000 | 2500 | 3000 | 3750 |
| 10 | 12 | 120 | 58 | 71 | 85 | 105 | 69 | 82 | 96 | 115 | 54 | 68 | 81 | 101 |
| | 14 | 140 | 67 | 83 | 99 | 122 | 81 | 96 | 111 | 135 | 63 | 79 | 95 | 118 |
| | 16 | 160 | 77 | 95 | 113 | 140 | 92 | 110 | 127 | 154 | 72 | 90 | 108 | 135 |
| | 18 | 180 | 87 | 107 | 127 | 157 | 104 | 124 | 143 | 173 | 81 | 101 | 122 | 152 |
| 12 | 12 | 144 | 69 | 85 | 102 | 126 | 83 | 99 | 115 | 138 | 65 | 81 | 97 | 122 |
| | 14 | 168 | 81 | 100 | 119 | 147 | 97 | 115 | 134 | 162 | 76 | 95 | 113 | 142 |
| | 16 | 192 | 93 | 114 | 135 | 168 | 111 | 132 | 153 | 185 | 86 | 108 | 130 | 162 |
| | 18 | 216 | 104 | 128 | 152 | 189 | 124 | 148 | 172 | 208 | 97 | 122 | 146 | 182 |
| | 20 | 240 | 116 | 142 | 169 | 210 | 138 | 165 | 191 | 231 | 108 | 135 | 162 | 203 |
| 14 | 14 | 196 | 94 | 116 | 138 | 171 | 113 | 134 | 156 | 188 | 88 | 110 | 132 | 165 |
| | 16 | 224 | 108 | 133 | 158 | 196 | 129 | 154 | 178 | 215 | 101 | 126 | 151 | 189 |
| | 18 | 252 | 121 | 150 | 178 | 220 | 145 | 173 | 201 | 242 | 113 | 142 | 170 | 213 |
| | 20 | 280 | 135 | 166 | 198 | 245 | 161 | 192 | 223 | 269 | 126 | 158 | 189 | 236 |
| | 22 | 308 | 148 | 183 | 217 | 269 | 177 | 211 | 245 | 296 | 139 | 173 | 208 | 260 |
| 16 | 16 | 256 | 123 | 152 | 181 | 224 | 147 | 176 | 204 | 246 | 115 | 144 | 173 | 216 |
| | 18 | 288 | 139 | 171 | 203 | 252 | 166 | 198 | 229 | 277 | 130 | 162 | 194 | 243 |
| | 20 | 320 | 154 | 190 | 226 | 279 | 184 | 220 | 255 | 308 | 144 | 180 | 216 | 270 |
| | 22 | 352 | 170 | 209 | 248 | 307 | 203 | 242 | 280 | 339 | 158 | 198 | 238 | 297 |
| | 24 | 384 | 185 | 228 | 271 | 335 | 221 | 263 | 306 | 369 | 173 | 216 | 259 | 324 |
| 18 | 18 | 324 | 156 | 192 | 229 | 283 | 187 | 222 | 258 | 312 | 146 | 182 | 219 | 273 |
| | 20 | 360 | 173 | 214 | 254 | 314 | 207 | 247 | 287 | 346 | 162 | 203 | 243 | 304 |
| | 22 | 396 | 191 | 235 | 279 | 346 | 228 | 272 | 315 | 381 | 178 | 223 | 267 | 334 |
| | 24 | 432 | 208 | 256 | 305 | 377 | 249 | 297 | 344 | 415 | 194 | 243 | 292 | 365 |
| | 26 | 468 | 225 | 278 | 330 | 409 | 269 | 321 | 372 | 450 | 211 | 263 | 316 | 395 |
| 20 | 20 | 400 | 193 | 237 | 282 | 349 | 230 | 275 | 319 | 385 | 180 | 225 | 270 | 338 |
| | 22 | 440 | 212 | 261 | 310 | 384 | 253 | 302 | 350 | 423 | 198 | 248 | 297 | 371 |
| | 24 | 480 | 231 | 285 | 339 | 419 | 276 | 329 | 382 | 461 | 216 | 270 | 324 | 405 |
| | 26 | 520 | 250 | 309 | 367 | 454 | 299 | 357 | 414 | 500 | 234 | 293 | 351 | 439 |
| | 28 | 560 | 270 | 332 | 395 | 489 | 322 | 384 | 446 | 539 | 252 | 315 | 378 | 473 |
| 22 | 22 | 484 | 233 | 287 | 341 | 423 | 279 | 332 | 385 | 465 | 218 | 272 | 327 | 408 |
| | 24 | 528 | 254 | 313 | 372 | 461 | 304 | 362 | 421 | 508 | 238 | 297 | 356 | 446 |
| | 26 | 572 | 275 | 339 | 404 | 499 | 329 | 393 | 456 | 550 | 257 | 322 | 386 | 483 |
| | 28 | 616 | 297 | 366 | 435 | 538 | 355 | 423 | 491 | 592 | 277 | 347 | 416 | 520 |
| 24 | 24 | 576 | 277 | 342 | 406 | 503 | 332 | 395 | 459 | 554 | 259 | 324 | 389 | 486 |
| | 26 | 624 | 300 | 370 | 440 | 545 | 359 | 428 | 497 | 600 | 281 | 351 | 421 | 527 |
| | 28 | 672 | 324 | 399 | 474 | 587 | 387 | 461 | 535 | 646 | 302 | 378 | 454 | 567 |
| 26 | 26 | 676 | 325 | 401 | 477 | 590 | 389 | 464 | 538 | 650 | 304 | 380 | 456 | 570 |
| | 28 | 728 | 351 | 432 | 514 | 536 | 419 | 500 | 580 | 700 | 328 | 410 | 491 | 614 |
| 28 | 28 | 784 | 378 | 465 | 553 | 684 | 452 | 538 | 624 | 754 | 353 | 441 | 529 | 662 |
| 30 | 30 | 900 | 433 | 534 | 635 | 786 | 518 | 618 | 717 | 866 | 405 | 506 | 608 | 759 |
| 32 | 32 | 1024 | 493 | 608 | 723 | 895 | 590 | 703 | 816 | 984 | 461 | 576 | 691 | 864 |
| 34 | 34 | 1156 | 557 | 686 | 816 | 1010 | 666 | 794 | 921 | 1112 | 520 | 650 | 780 | 975 |
| — | — | 1000 | 482 | 594 | 706 | 874 | 576 | 686 | 797 | 962 | 450 | 563 | 675 | 844 |

## Part 2. Load on Bars (kips) = $(6750 - 0.225 f'_c) A_s \div 1000$

| Bar Size | Number of Bars 4 | 6 | 8 | 10 | 12 | 14 | 16 | 18 | 20 | 22 |
|---|---|---|---|---|---|---|---|---|---|---|
| | $f'_c = 2000$ | | | | | | | | | |
| $\frac{5}{8}\phi$ | 8 | 12 | 16 | 20 | 23 | 27 | 31 | 35 | 39 | 43 |
| $\frac{3}{4}\phi$ | 11 | 17 | 22 | 28 | 33 | 39 | 44 | 50 | 55 | 61 |
| $\frac{7}{8}\phi$ | 15 | 23 | 30 | 38 | 45 | 53 | 61 | 68 | 76 | 83 |
| $1\phi$ | 20 | 30 | 40 | 50 | 60 | 70 | 80 | 90 | 100 | 110 |
| 1 □ | 25 | 38 | 50 | 63 | 76 | 88 | 101 | 113 | 126 | 139 |
| $1\frac{1}{8}$ □ | 32 | 48 | 64 | 80 | 96 | 112 | 128 | 144 | 160 | 176 |
| $1\frac{1}{4}$ □ | 39 | 59 | 79 | 98 | 118 | 138 | 157 | 177 | 196 | 216 |

| Bar Size | Number of Bars 4 | 6 | 8 | 10 | 12 | 14 | 16 | 18 | 20 | 22 |
|---|---|---|---|---|---|---|---|---|---|---|
| | $f'_c = 2500$ | | | | | | | | | |
| $\frac{5}{8}\phi$ | 8 | 12 | 15 | 19 | 23 | 27 | 31 | 35 | 38 | 42 |
| $\frac{3}{4}\phi$ | 11 | 16 | 22 | 27 | 33 | 38 | 44 | 49 | 54 | 60 |
| $\frac{7}{8}\phi$ | 15 | 22 | 30 | 37 | 45 | 52 | 59 | 67 | 74 | 82 |
| $1\phi$ | 20 | 29 | 39 | 49 | 59 | 68 | 78 | 88 | 98 | 108 |
| 1 □ | 25 | 37 | 50 | 62 | 74 | 87 | 99 | 111 | 124 | 136 |
| $1\frac{1}{8}$ □ | 31 | 47 | 63 | 79 | 94 | 110 | 126 | 141 | 157 | 173 |
| $1\frac{1}{4}$ □ | 39 | 58 | 77 | 97 | 116 | 135 | 154 | 174 | 193 | 212 |

| Bar Size | Number of Bars 4 | 6 | 8 | 10 | 12 | 14 | 16 | 18 | 20 | 22 |
|---|---|---|---|---|---|---|---|---|---|---|
| | $f'_c = 3000$ | | | | | | | | | |
| $\frac{5}{8}\phi$ | 8 | 11 | 16 | 19 | 23 | 26 | 30 | 34 | 38 | 41 |
| $\frac{3}{4}\phi$ | 11 | 16 | 21 | 27 | 32 | 37 | 43 | 48 | 53 | 59 |
| $\frac{7}{8}\phi$ | 15 | 22 | 29 | 36 | 44 | 51 | 58 | 66 | 73 | 80 |
| $1\phi$ | 19 | 29 | 38 | 48 | 58 | 67 | 77 | 86 | 96 | 106 |
| 1 □ | 24 | 36 | 49 | 61 | 73 | 85 | 97 | 109 | 121 | 134 |
| $1\frac{1}{8}$ □ | 31 | 46 | 62 | 77 | 93 | 108 | 123 | 139 | 154 | 170 |
| $1\frac{1}{4}$ □ | 38 | 57 | 76 | 95 | 114 | 133 | 152 | 171 | 190 | 209 |

| Bar Size | Number of Bars 4 | 6 | 8 | 10 | 12 | 14 | 16 | 18 | 20 | 22 |
|---|---|---|---|---|---|---|---|---|---|---|
| | $f'_c = 3750$ | | | | | | | | | |
| $\frac{5}{8}\phi$ | 7 | 11 | 15 | 18 | 22 | 26 | 29 | 33 | 37 | 40 |
| $\frac{3}{4}\phi$ | 10 | 16 | 21 | 26 | 31 | 36 | 42 | 47 | 52 | 57 |
| $\frac{7}{8}\phi$ | 14 | 21 | 28 | 35 | 43 | 50 | 57 | 64 | 71 | 78 |
| $1\phi$ | 19 | 28 | 37 | 47 | 56 | 65 | 75 | 84 | 93 | 103 |
| 1 □ | 24 | 35 | 47 | 59 | 71 | 83 | 95 | 106 | 118 | 130 |
| $1\frac{1}{8}$ □ | 30 | 45 | 60 | 75 | 90 | 105 | 120 | 135 | 150 | 165 |
| $1\frac{1}{4}$ □ | 37 | 55 | 74 | 92 | 111 | 129 | 147 | 166 | 184 | 203 |

# Table 21. Tied Columns; New York Code 1938

## Part 1. $P$ (kips) = $(0.25 f'_c A_g + 7500 A_s) \div 1000$

| Column Size | | Gross Area $A_g$ | Min. Load on Column: $(0.25 f'_c + 37.5) A_g \div 1000$ | | | | Max. Load on Column: $(0.25 f'_c + 300) A_g \div 1000$ | | | | Load on Concrete Only: $0.25 f'_c A_g \div 1000$ | | | |
|---|---|---|---|---|---|---|---|---|---|---|---|---|---|---|
| | | | $f'_c$ | | | | $f'_c$ | | | | $f'_c$ | | | |
| | | | 2000 | 2500 | 3000 | 3400 | 2000 | 2500 | 3000 | 3400 | 2000 | 2500 | 3000 | 3400 |
| 12 | 12 | 144 | 77 | 95 | 113 | 128 | 115 | 133 | 151 | 166 | 72 | 90 | 108 | 122 |
| | 14 | 168 | 90 | 111 | 132 | 149 | 134 | 155 | 176 | 193 | 84 | 105 | 126 | 143 |
| | 16 | 192 | 103 | 127 | 151 | 170 | 154 | 178 | 202 | 221 | 96 | 120 | 144 | 163 |
| | 18 | 216 | 116 | 143 | 170 | 192 | 173 | 200 | 227 | 248 | 108 | 135 | 162 | 184 |
| | 20 | 240 | 129 | 159 | 189 | 213 | 192 | 222 | 252 | 276 | 120 | 150 | 180 | 204 |
| 14 | 14 | 196 | 105 | 130 | 154 | 174 | 157 | 181 | 206 | 225 | 98 | 123 | 147 | 167 |
| | 16 | 224 | 120 | 148 | 176 | 199 | 179 | 207 | 235 | 258 | 112 | 140 | 168 | 190 |
| | 18 | 252 | 135 | 167 | 198 | 224 | 202 | 233 | 265 | 290 | 126 | 158 | 189 | 214 |
| | 20 | 280 | 151 | 186 | 221 | 249 | 224 | 259 | 294 | 322 | 140 | 175 | 210 | 238 |
| | 22 | 308 | 166 | 204 | 243 | 273 | 246 | 285 | 323 | 354 | 154 | 193 | 231 | 262 |
| 16 | 16 | 256 | 138 | 170 | 202 | 227 | 205 | 237 | 269 | 294 | 128 | 160 | 192 | 218 |
| | 18 | 288 | 155 | 191 | 227 | 256 | 230 | 266 | 302 | 331 | 144 | 180 | 216 | 245 |
| | 20 | 320 | 172 | 212 | 252 | 284 | 256 | 296 | 336 | 368 | 160 | 200 | 240 | 272 |
| | 22 | 352 | 189 | 233 | 277 | 312 | 282 | 326 | 370 | 405 | 176 | 220 | 264 | 299 |
| | 24 | 384 | 206 | 254 | 302 | 341 | 307 | 355 | 403 | 442 | 192 | 240 | 288 | 326 |
| 18 | 18 | 324 | 174 | 215 | 255 | 288 | 259 | 300 | 340 | 373 | 162 | 203 | 243 | 275 |
| | 20 | 360 | 194 | 239 | 284 | 320 | 288 | 333 | 378 | 414 | 180 | 225 | 270 | 306 |
| | 22 | 396 | 213 | 262 | 312 | 351 | 317 | 366 | 416 | 455 | 198 | 248 | 297 | 337 |
| | 24 | 432 | 232 | 286 | 340 | 383 | 346 | 400 | 454 | 497 | 216 | 270 | 324 | 367 |
| | 26 | 468 | 252 | 310 | 369 | 415 | 374 | 433 | 491 | 538 | 234 | 293 | 351 | 398 |
| 20 | 20 | 400 | 215 | 265 | 315 | 355 | 320 | 370 | 420 | 460 | 200 | 250 | 300 | 340 |
| | 22 | 440 | 237 | 292 | 347 | 391 | 352 | 407 | 462 | 506 | 220 | 275 | 330 | 374 |
| | 24 | 480 | 258 | 318 | 378 | 426 | 384 | 444 | 504 | 552 | 240 | 300 | 360 | 408 |
| | 26 | 520 | 280 | 345 | 410 | 462 | 416 | 481 | 546 | 598 | 260 | 325 | 390 | 442 |
| | 28 | 560 | 301 | 371 | 441 | 497 | 448 | 518 | 588 | 644 | 280 | 350 | 420 | 476 |
| 22 | 22 | 484 | 260 | 321 | 381 | 430 | 387 | 448 | 508 | 557 | 242 | 303 | 363 | 411 |
| | 24 | 528 | 284 | 350 | 416 | 469 | 422 | 488 | 554 | 607 | 264 | 330 | 396 | 449 |
| | 26 | 572 | 307 | 379 | 450 | 508 | 458 | 529 | 601 | 658 | 286 | 358 | 429 | 486 |
| | 28 | 616 | 331 | 408 | 485 | 547 | 493 | 570 | 647 | 708 | 308 | 385 | 462 | 524 |
| 24 | 24 | 576 | 310 | 382 | 454 | 511 | 461 | 533 | 605 | 662 | 288 | 360 | 432 | 490 |
| | 26 | 624 | 335 | 413 | 491 | 554 | 499 | 577 | 655 | 718 | 312 | 390 | 468 | 530 |
| | 28 | 672 | 361 | 445 | 529 | 596 | 538 | 622 | 706 | 773 | 336 | 420 | 504 | 571 |
| 26 | 26 | 676 | 363 | 448 | 532 | 600 | 541 | 625 | 710 | 777 | 338 | 423 | 507 | 575 |
| | 28 | 728 | 391 | 482 | 573 | 646 | 582 | 673 | 764 | 837 | 364 | 455 | 546 | 619 |
| 28 | 28 | 784 | 421 | 519 | 617 | 696 | 627 | 725 | 823 | 902 | 392 | 490 | 588 | 666 |
| 30 | 30 | 900 | 484 | 596 | 709 | 799 | 720 | 833 | 945 | 1035 | 450 | 563 | 675 | 765 |
| 32 | 32 | 1024 | 550 | 678 | 806 | 909 | 819 | 947 | 1075 | 1178 | 512 | 640 | 768 | 870 |
| 34 | 34 | 1156 | 621 | 766 | 910 | 1026 | 925 | 1069 | 1214 | 1329 | 578 | 723 | 867 | 983 |
| — | — | 1000 | 538 | 663 | 788 | 888 | 800 | 925 | 1050 | 1150 | 500 | 625 | 750 | 850 |

## Part 2. Load on Bars (kips) = $7500 A_s \div 1000$

| Bar Size | Number of Bars | | | | | | | | | | | | | | | | | | |
|---|---|---|---|---|---|---|---|---|---|---|---|---|---|---|---|---|---|---|---|
| | 4 | 5 | 6 | 7 | 8 | 9 | 10 | 11 | 12 | 13 | 14 | 15 | 16 | 17 | 18 | 19 | 20 | 21 | 22 |
| $\frac{5}{8}\phi$ | 9 | 12 | 14 | 16 | 19 | 21 | 23 | 26 | 28 | 30 | 33 | 35 | 37 | 40 | 42 | 44 | 47 | 49 | 51 |
| $\frac{3}{4}\phi$ | 13 | 17 | 20 | 23 | 26 | 30 | 33 | 36 | 40 | 43 | 46 | 50 | 53 | 56 | 59 | 63 | 66 | 69 | 73 |
| $\frac{7}{8}\phi$ | 18 | 23 | 27 | 32 | 36 | 41 | 45 | 50 | 54 | 59 | 63 | 68 | 72 | 77 | 81 | 86 | 90 | 95 | 99 |
| $1\phi$ | 24 | 30 | 36 | 41 | 47 | 53 | 59 | 65 | 71 | 77 | 83 | 89 | 95 | 101 | 107 | 113 | 118 | 124 | 130 |
| 1 □ | 30 | 38 | 45 | 53 | 60 | 68 | 75 | 83 | 90 | 98 | 105 | 113 | 120 | 128 | 135 | 143 | 150 | 158 | 165 |
| $1\frac{1}{8}$ □ | 38 | 48 | 57 | 67 | 76 | 86 | 95 | 105 | 114 | 124 | 133 | 143 | 152 | 162 | 171 | 181 | 191 | 200 | 210 |
| $1\frac{1}{4}$ □ | 47 | 59 | 70 | 82 | 94 | 105 | 117 | 129 | 140 | 152 | 164 | 175 | 187 | 199 | 211 | 222 | 234 | 246 | 257 |

# Table 22. Tied Columns; Chicago Code 1937

## Part 1. $P$ (kips) $= (0.20 f'_c A_g + 0.9 f_r A_s) \div 1000$

| Column Size | | Gross Area $A_g$ | Load on Bars Min. $0.009 f_r A_g \div 1000$ Max. $0.036 f_r A_g \div 1000$ | | | | Load on Concrete $0.20 f'_c A_g \div 1000$ | | | | |
|---|---|---|---|---|---|---|---|---|---|---|---|
| | | | $f_r = 15{,}000$ | | $f_r = 18{,}000$* | | $f'_c$ | | | | |
| | | | Min. | Max. | Min. | Max. | 2000 | 2500 | 3000 | 3750 | 5000 |
| 10 | 12 | 120 | 16 | 65 | 19 | 78 | 48 | 60 | 72 | 90 | 120 |
| | 14 | 140 | 19 | 76 | 23 | 91 | 56 | 70 | 84 | 105 | 140 |
| | 16 | 160 | 22 | 86 | 26 | 104 | 64 | 80 | 96 | 120 | 160 |
| | 18 | 180 | 24 | 97 | 29 | 117 | 72 | 90 | 108 | 135 | 180 |
| 12 | 12 | 144 | 19 | 78 | 23 | 93 | 58 | 72 | 86 | 108 | 144 |
| | 14 | 168 | 23 | 91 | 27 | 109 | 67 | 84 | 101 | 126 | 168 |
| | 16 | 192 | 26 | 104 | 31 | 124 | 77 | 96 | 115 | 144 | 192 |
| | 18 | 216 | 29 | 117 | 35 | 140 | 86 | 108 | 130 | 162 | 216 |
| | 20 | 240 | 32 | 130 | 39 | 156 | 96 | 120 | 144 | 180 | 240 |
| 14 | 14 | 196 | 26 | 106 | 32 | 127 | 78 | 98 | 118 | 147 | 196 |
| | 16 | 224 | 30 | 121 | 36 | 145 | 90 | 112 | 134 | 168 | 224 |
| | 18 | 252 | 34 | 136 | 41 | 163 | 101 | 126 | 151 | 189 | 252 |
| | 20 | 280 | 38 | 151 | 45 | 181 | 112 | 140 | 168 | 210 | 280 |
| | 22 | 308 | 42 | 166 | 50 | 200 | 123 | 154 | 185 | 231 | 308 |
| 16 | 16 | 256 | 35 | 138 | 41 | 166 | 102 | 128 | 154 | 192 | 256 |
| | 18 | 288 | 39 | 156 | 47 | 187 | 115 | 144 | 173 | 216 | 288 |
| | 20 | 320 | 43 | 173 | 52 | 207 | 128 | 160 | 192 | 240 | 320 |
| | 22 | 352 | 48 | 190 | 57 | 228 | 141 | 176 | 211 | 264 | 352 |
| | 24 | 384 | 52 | 207 | 62 | 249 | 154 | 192 | 230 | 288 | 384 |
| 18 | 18 | 326 | 44 | 175 | 52 | 210 | 130 | 163 | 196 | 245 | 326 |
| | 20 | 360 | 49 | 194 | 58 | 233 | 144 | 180 | 216 | 270 | 360 |
| | 22 | 396 | 53 | 214 | 64 | 257 | 158 | 198 | 238 | 297 | 396 |
| | 24 | 432 | 58 | 233 | 70 | 280 | 173 | 216 | 259 | 324 | 432 |
| | 26 | 468 | 63 | 253 | 76 | 303 | 187 | 234 | 281 | 351 | 468 |
| 20 | 20 | 400 | 54 | 216 | 65 | 259 | 160 | 200 | 240 | 300 | 400 |
| | 22 | 440 | 59 | 238 | 71 | 285 | 176 | 220 | 264 | 330 | 440 |
| | 24 | 480 | 65 | 259 | 78 | 311 | 192 | 240 | 288 | 360 | 480 |
| | 26 | 520 | 70 | 281 | 84 | 337 | 208 | 260 | 312 | 390 | 520 |
| | 28 | 560 | 76 | 302 | 91 | 363 | 224 | 280 | 336 | 420 | 560 |
| 22 | 22 | 484 | 65 | 261 | 78 | 314 | 194 | 242 | 290 | 363 | 484 |
| | 24 | 528 | 71 | 285 | 86 | 342 | 211 | 264 | 317 | 396 | 528 |
| | 26 | 572 | 77 | 309 | 93 | 371 | 229 | 286 | 343 | 429 | 572 |
| | 28 | 616 | 83 | 333 | 100 | 399 | 246 | 308 | 370 | 462 | 616 |
| 24 | 24 | 576 | 78 | 311 | 93 | 373 | 230 | 288 | 346 | 432 | 576 |
| | 26 | 624 | 84 | 337 | 101 | 404 | 250 | 312 | 374 | 468 | 624 |
| | 28 | 672 | 91 | 363 | 109 | 435 | 269 | 336 | 403 | 504 | 672 |
| 26 | 26 | 676 | 91 | 365 | 110 | 438 | 270 | 338 | 406 | 507 | 676 |
| | 28 | 728 | 98 | 393 | 118 | 472 | 291 | 364 | 437 | 546 | 728 |
| 28 | 28 | 784 | 106 | 423 | 127 | 508 | 314 | 392 | 470 | 588 | 784 |
| 30 | 30 | 900 | 122 | 486 | 146 | 583 | 360 | 450 | 540 | 675 | 900 |
| 32 | 32 | 1024 | 138 | 553 | 166 | 664 | 410 | 512 | 614 | 768 | 1024 |
| 34 | 34 | 1156 | 156 | 624 | 187 | 749 | 462 | 578 | 694 | 867 | 1156 |
| — | — | 1000 | 135 | 540 | 162 | 648 | 400 | 500 | 600 | 750 | 1000 |

## Part 2. Load on Bars (kips) $= 0.9 f_r A_s \div 1000$

| Bar Size | Number of Bars | | | | | | | | | |
|---|---|---|---|---|---|---|---|---|---|---|
| | 4 | 6 | 8 | 10 | 12 | 14 | 16 | 18 | 20 | 22 |
| | $f_r = 15{,}000$ | | | | | | | | | |
| ¾φ | 24 | 36 | 48 | 59 | 71 | 83 | 95 | 107 | 119 | 131 |
| ⅞φ | 32 | 49 | 65 | 81 | 97 | 113 | 130 | 146 | 162 | 178 |
| 1φ | 43 | 64 | 85 | 107 | 128 | 149 | 171 | 192 | 213 | 235 |
| 1□ | 54 | 81 | 108 | 135 | 162 | 189 | 216 | 243 | 270 | 297 |
| 1⅛□ | 69 | 103 | 137 | 172 | 206 | 240 | 274 | 309 | 343 | 377 |
| 1¼□ | 84 | 126 | 169 | 211 | 253 | 295 | 337 | 379 | 421 | 464 |

| Bar Size | Number of Bars | | | | | | | | | |
|---|---|---|---|---|---|---|---|---|---|---|
| | 4 | 6 | 8 | 10 | 12 | 14 | 16 | 18 | 20 | 22 |
| | $f_r = 18{,}000$* | | | | | | | | | |
| ¾φ | 29 | 43 | 57 | 71 | 86 | 100 | 114 | 128 | 143 | 157 |
| ⅞φ | 39 | 58 | 78 | 97 | 117 | 136 | 156 | 175 | 194 | 214 |
| 1φ | 51 | 77 | 102 | 128 | 154 | 179 | 205 | 230 | 256 | 282 |
| 1□ | 65 | 97 | 130 | 162 | 194 | 227 | 259 | 292 | 324 | 356 |
| 1⅛□ | 82 | 123 | 165 | 206 | 247 | 288 | 329 | 370 | 411 | 453 |
| 1¼□ | 101 | 152 | 202 | 253 | 303 | 354 | 404 | 455 | 505 | 556 |

*Allowed for steel with yield point of 50,000 psi., provided material is identified by marking rolled into the surface during manufacture.

## Table 23. Spiral Columns; Joint Committee Code 1940 (Proposed)— Load on Gross Section

$$P \text{ (kips)} = (0.225\,f'_c A_g + f_s A_s) \div 1000$$

| | | SQUARE Columns | | | | | | | | | | ROUND Columns | | | | | | | | | |
|---|---|---|---|---|---|---|---|---|---|---|---|---|---|---|---|---|---|---|---|---|---|
| | | Load on Bars | | | | Load on Concrete $0.225\,f'_c A_g \div 1000$ | | | | | | Load on Bars | | | | Load on Concrete $0.225\,f'_c A_g \div 1000$ | | | | |
| Col. Size | Gross Area $A_g$ | $f_s=16{,}000$ | | $f_s=20{,}000$ | | $f'_c$ | | | | | Gross Area $A_g$ | $f_s=16{,}000$ | | $f_s=20{,}000$ | | $f'_c$ | | | | |
| | | *Min. Load | **Max. Load | *Min. Load | **Max. Load | 2000 | 2500 | 3000 | 3750 | 5000 | | *Min. Load | **Max. Load | *Min. Load | **Max. Load | 2000 | 2500 | 3000 | 3750 | 5000 |
| 14 | 196 | 31 | 122 | 39 | 152 | 88 | 110 | 132 | 165 | 221 | 154 | 25 | 122 | 31 | 152 | 69 | 87 | 104 | 130 | 173 |
| 15 | 225 | 36 | 150 | 45 | 187 | 101 | 127 | 152 | 190 | 253 | 177 | 28 | 150 | 35 | 187 | 80 | 99 | 119 | 149 | 199 |
| 16 | 256 | 41 | 150 | 51 | 187 | 115 | 144 | 173 | 216 | 288 | 201 | 32 | 150 | 40 | 187 | 91 | 113 | 136 | 170 | 226 |
| 17 | 289 | 46 | 175 | 58 | 218 | 130 | 163 | 195 | 244 | 325 | 227 | 36 | 175 | 45 | 218 | 102 | 128 | 153 | 192 | 255 |
| 18 | 324 | 52 | 200 | 65 | 250 | 146 | 182 | 219 | 273 | 365 | 254 | 41 | 200 | 51 | 250 | 114 | 143 | 172 | 215 | 286 |
| 19 | 361 | 58 | 200 | 72 | 250 | 162 | 203 | 244 | 305 | 406 | 284 | 45 | 200 | 57 | 250 | 128 | 159 | 191 | 239 | 319 |
| 20 | 400 | 64 | 225 | 80 | 281 | 180 | 225 | 270 | 337 | 450 | 314 | 50 | 225 | 63 | 281 | 141 | 177 | 212 | 265 | 354 |
| 21 | 441 | 71 | 225 | 88 | 281 | 198 | 248 | 298 | 372 | 496 | 346 | 55 | 225 | 69 | 281 | 156 | 195 | 234 | 292 | 390 |
| 22 | 484 | 77 | 250 | 97 | 312 | 218 | 272 | 327 | 408 | 544 | 380 | 61 | 250 | 76 | 312 | 171 | 214 | 257 | 321 | 428 |
| 23 | 529 | 85 | 275 | 106 | 343 | 238 | 298 | 357 | 446 | 595 | 415 | 66 | 275 | 83 | 343 | 187 | 234 | 280 | 350 | 467 |
| 24 | 576 | 92 | 275 | 115 | 343 | 259 | 324 | 389 | 486 | 648 | 452 | 72 | 275 | 90 | 343 | 204 | 254 | 305 | 382 | 509 |
| 25 | 625 | 100 | 300 | 125 | 374 | 281 | 352 | 422 | 527 | 703 | 491 | 79 | 300 | 98 | 374 | 221 | 276 | 331 | 414 | 552 |
| 26 | 676 | 108 | 324 | 135 | 406 | 304 | 380 | 456 | 570 | 760 | 531 | 85 | 324 | 106 | 406 | 239 | 299 | 358 | 448 | 597 |
| 27 | 729 | 117 | 324 | 146 | 406 | 328 | 410 | 492 | 615 | 820 | 573 | 92 | 324 | 115 | 406 | 258 | 322 | 387 | 483 | 644 |
| 28 | 784 | 125 | 349 | 157 | 437 | 353 | 441 | 529 | 661 | 882 | 616 | 98 | 349 | 123 | 437 | 277 | 346 | 416 | 519 | 693 |
| 29 | 841 | 135 | 349 | 168 | 437 | 378 | 473 | 567 | 710 | 946 | 661 | 106 | 349 | 132 | 437 | 297 | 372 | 446 | 557 | 743 |
| 30 | 900 | 144 | 374 | 180 | 468 | 405 | 506 | 608 | 760 | 1013 | 707 | 113 | 374 | 141 | 468 | 318 | 398 | 477 | 596 | 795 |
| 31 | 961 | 154 | 399 | 192 | 499 | 433 | 540 | 648 | 811 | 1081 | 755 | 121 | 399 | 151 | 499 | 340 | 424 | 510 | 637 | 849 |
| 32 | 1024 | 164 | 399 | 205 | 499 | 461 | 576 | 691 | 864 | 1152 | 804 | 129 | 399 | 161 | 499 | 362 | 452 | 543 | 679 | 905 |
| 33 | 1089 | 174 | 424 | 218 | 531 | 490 | 613 | 735 | 919 | 1225 | 855 | 137 | 424 | 171 | 531 | 385 | 481 | 577 | 722 | 962 |

*Minimum area of reinforcement 0.01 $A_g$
**With 1½-in. concrete protection and maximum number of maximum size bars arranged in one outer ring

## Table 24. Spiral Columns; American Concrete Institute Code 1936— Load on Gross Section

$$P \text{ (kips)} = (0.22\,f'_c A_g + f_s A_s) \div 1000$$

| | | SQUARE Columns | | | | | | | | | | ROUND Columns | | | | | | | | | |
|---|---|---|---|---|---|---|---|---|---|---|---|---|---|---|---|---|---|---|---|---|---|
| | | Load on Bars | | | | Load on Concrete $0.22\,f'_c A_g \div 1000$ | | | | | | Load on Bars | | | | Load on Concrete $0.22\,f'_c A_g \div 1000$ | | | | |
| Col. Size | Gross Area $A_g$ | $f_s=16{,}000$ | | $f_s=20{,}000$ | | $f'_c$ | | | | | Gross Area $A_g$ | $f_s=16{,}000$ | | $f_s=20{,}000$ | | $f'_c$ | | | | |
| | | *Min. Load | **Max. Load | *Min. Load | **Max. Load | 2000 | 2500 | 3000 | 3750 | 5000 | | *Min. Load | **Max. Load | *Min. Load | **Max. Load | 2000 | 2500 | 3000 | 3750 | 5000 |
| 14 | 196 | 31 | 122 | 39 | 152 | 86 | 108 | 129 | 162 | 216 | 154 | 25 | 122 | 31 | 152 | 68 | 85 | 102 | 127 | 169 |
| 15 | 225 | 36 | 150 | 45 | 187 | 99 | 124 | 149 | 186 | 248 | 177 | 28 | 150 | 35 | 187 | 78 | 97 | 117 | 146 | 194 |
| 16 | 256 | 41 | 150 | 51 | 187 | 113 | 141 | 169 | 211 | 282 | 201 | 32 | 150 | 40 | 187 | 88 | 111 | 133 | 166 | 221 |
| 17 | 289 | 46 | 175 | 58 | 218 | 127 | 159 | 191 | 238 | 318 | 227 | 36 | 175 | 45 | 218 | 100 | 125 | 150 | 187 | 250 |
| 18 | 324 | 52 | 200 | 65 | 250 | 143 | 178 | 214 | 267 | 356 | 254 | 41 | 200 | 51 | 250 | 112 | 140 | 168 | 210 | 280 |
| 19 | 361 | 58 | 200 | 72 | 250 | 159 | 199 | 238 | 298 | 397 | 284 | 45 | 200 | 57 | 250 | 125 | 156 | 187 | 234 | 312 |
| 20 | 400 | 64 | 225 | 80 | 281 | 176 | 220 | 264 | 330 | 440 | 314 | 50 | 225 | 63 | 281 | 138 | 173 | 207 | 259 | 346 |
| 21 | 441 | 71 | 225 | 88 | 281 | 194 | 242 | 291 | 364 | 485 | 346 | 55 | 225 | 69 | 281 | 152 | 190 | 229 | 286 | 381 |
| 22 | 484 | 77 | 250 | 97 | 312 | 213 | 266 | 319 | 399 | 532 | 380 | 61 | 250 | 76 | 312 | 167 | 209 | 251 | 314 | 418 |
| 23 | 529 | 85 | 275 | 106 | 343 | 233 | 291 | 349 | 436 | 582 | 415 | 66 | 275 | 83 | 343 | 183 | 228 | 274 | 343 | 457 |
| 24 | 576 | 92 | 275 | 115 | 343 | 253 | 317 | 380 | 475 | 634 | 452 | 72 | 275 | 90 | 343 | 199 | 249 | 299 | 373 | 498 |
| 25 | 625 | 100 | 300 | 125 | 374 | 275 | 344 | 412 | 516 | 688 | 491 | 79 | 300 | 98 | 374 | 216 | 270 | 324 | 405 | 540 |
| 26 | 676 | 108 | 324 | 135 | 406 | 297 | 372 | 446 | 558 | 744 | 531 | 85 | 324 | 106 | 406 | 234 | 292 | 350 | 438 | 584 |
| 27 | 729 | 117 | 324 | 146 | 406 | 321 | 401 | 481 | 601 | 802 | 573 | 92 | 324 | 115 | 406 | 252 | 315 | 378 | 472 | 630 |
| 28 | 784 | 125 | 349 | 157 | 437 | 345 | 431 | 518 | 647 | 862 | 616 | 98 | 349 | 123 | 437 | 271 | 338 | 406 | 508 | 677 |
| 29 | 841 | 135 | 349 | 168 | 437 | 370 | 463 | 555 | 694 | 925 | 661 | 106 | 349 | 132 | 437 | 291 | 363 | 436 | 545 | 727 |
| 30 | 900 | 144 | 374 | 180 | 468 | 396 | 495 | 594 | 743 | 990 | 707 | 113 | 374 | 141 | 468 | 311 | 389 | 467 | 583 | 778 |
| 31 | 961 | 154 | 399 | 192 | 499 | 423 | 528 | 634 | 792 | 1057 | 755 | 121 | 399 | 151 | 499 | 332 | 415 | 498 | 622 | 830 |
| 32 | 1024 | 164 | 399 | 205 | 499 | 451 | 563 | 676 | 845 | 1126 | 804 | 129 | 399 | 161 | 499 | 354 | 442 | 531 | 664 | 885 |
| 33 | 1089 | 174 | 424 | 218 | 531 | 479 | 599 | 719 | 898 | 1198 | 855 | 137 | 424 | 171 | 531 | 376 | 470 | 564 | 705 | 940 |

*Minimum area of reinforcement 0.01 $A_g$
**With 1½-in. concrete protection and maximum number of maximum size bars arranged in one outer ring

# Table 25. Spiral Columns; Joint Committee Code 1940 (Proposed) and American Concrete Institute Code 1936—Load on Bars

## Load on Bars, $A_s$ (kips) $= f_s A_s \div 1000$ (Max. $A_s = 0.08\,A_g$)

| Bar Size | Number of Bars | | | | | | | | | | | | | | | | | | | | |
|---|---|---|---|---|---|---|---|---|---|---|---|---|---|---|---|---|---|---|---|---|---|
| | 6 | 7 | 8 | 9 | 10 | 11 | 12 | 13 | 14 | 15 | 16 | 17 | 18 | 19 | 20 | 21 | 22 | 23 | 24 | 25 | 26 |
| | Intermediate Grade: $f_s = 16{,}000$ | | | | | | | | | | | | | | | | | | | | |
| ⅝φ | 30 | 35 | 40 | 45 | 50 | 55 | 60 | 64 | 69 | 74 | 79 | 84 | 89 | 94 | 99 | 104 | 109 | 114 | 119 | 124 | 129 |
| ¾φ | 42 | 49 | 56 | 63 | 70 | 77 | 84 | 92 | 99 | 106 | 113 | 120 | 127 | 134 | 141 | 148 | 155 | 162 | 169 | 176 | 183 |
| ⅞φ | 58 | 67 | 77 | 86 | 96 | 106 | 115 | 125 | 134 | 144 | 154 | 163 | 173 | 182 | 192 | 202 | 211 | 221 | 230 | 240 | 250 |
| 1φ | 76 | 88 | 101 | 114 | 126 | 139 | 152 | 164 | 177 | 190 | 202 | 215 | 228 | 240 | 253 | 266 | 278 | 291 | 303 | 316 | 329 |
| 1□ | 96 | 112 | 128 | 144 | 160 | 176 | 192 | 208 | 224 | 240 | 256 | 272 | 288 | 304 | 320 | 336 | 352 | 368 | 384 | 400 | 416 |
| 1⅛□ | 122 | 142 | 163 | 183 | 203 | 224 | 244 | 264 | 285 | 305 | 325 | 346 | 366 | 386 | 406 | 427 | 447 | 467 | 488 | 508 | 528 |
| 1¼□ | 150 | 175 | 200 | 225 | 250 | 275 | 300 | 324 | 349 | 374 | 399 | 424 | 449 | 474 | 499 | 524 | 549 | 574 | 599 | 624 | 649 |
| | Rail or Hard Grade: $f_s = 20\,000$ | | | | | | | | | | | | | | | | | | | | |
| ⅝φ | 37 | 43 | 50 | 56 | 62 | 68 | 74 | 81 | 87 | 93 | 99 | 105 | 112 | 118 | 124 | 130 | 136 | 143 | 149 | 155 | 161 |
| ¾φ | 53 | 62 | 70 | 79 | 88 | 97 | 106 | 114 | 123 | 132 | 141 | 150 | 158 | 167 | 176 | 185 | 194 | 202 | 211 | 220 | 229 |
| ⅞φ | 72 | 84 | 96 | 108 | 120 | 132 | 144 | 156 | 168 | 180 | 192 | 204 | 216 | 228 | 240 | 252 | 264 | 276 | 288 | 300 | 312 |
| 1φ | 95 | 111 | 126 | 142 | 158 | 174 | 190 | 205 | 221 | 237 | 253 | 269 | 284 | 300 | 316 | 332 | 348 | 364 | 379 | 395 | 411 |
| 1□ | 120 | 140 | 160 | 180 | 200 | 220 | 240 | 260 | 280 | 300 | 320 | 340 | 360 | 380 | 400 | 420 | 440 | 460 | 480 | 500 | 520 |
| 1⅛□ | 152 | 178 | 203 | 229 | 254 | 279 | 305 | 330 | 356 | 381 | 406 | 432 | 457 | 483 | 508 | 534 | 559 | 584 | 610 | 635 | 660 |
| 1¼□ | 187 | 218 | 250 | 281 | 312 | 343 | 374 | 406 | 437 | 468 | 499 | 531 | 562 | 593 | 624 | 655 | 686 | 718 | 749 | 780 | 811 |

## Maximum Number of Bars in Outer Ring, *O*, and in Inner Ring, *I*

| Bar Size | Ring | *d*: Diameter of Core | | | | | | | | | | | | | | | | | | | | |
|---|---|---|---|---|---|---|---|---|---|---|---|---|---|---|---|---|---|---|---|---|---|---|
| | | 10 | 11 | 12 | 13 | 14 | 15 | 16 | 17 | 18 | 19 | 20 | 21 | 22 | 23 | 24 | 25 | 26 | 27 | 28 | 29 | 30 |
| ⅝φ | *O* | **9** | **10** | **11** | **13** | **14** | **15** | **16** | **17** | **18** | **19** | **21** | **22** | **23** | **24** | **25** | **26** | **27** | **29** | **30** | **31** | **32** |
| | *I* | 4 | 5 | 7 | 8 | 9 | 10 | 11 | 12 | 13 | 15 | 16 | 17 | 18 | 19 | 20 | 21 | 23 | 24 | 25 | 26 | 27 |
| ¾φ | *O* | **8** | **9** | **10** | **11** | **12** | **13** | **14** | **16** | **17** | **18** | **19** | **20** | **21** | **22** | **23** | **24** | **25** | **26** | **27** | **28** | **29** |
| | *I* | — | 5 | 6 | 7 | 8 | 9 | 10 | 11 | 12 | 13 | 14 | 15 | 16 | 17 | 18 | 19 | 20 | 21 | 22 | 23 | 24 |
| ⅞φ | *O* | **7** | **8** | **9** | **10** | **11** | **12** | **13** | **14** | **15** | **16** | **17** | **18** | **19** | **20** | **21** | **22** | **23** | **24** | **25** | **26** | **27** |
| | *I* | — | 4 | 5 | 6 | 7 | 8 | 9 | 10 | 11 | 11 | 12 | 13 | 14 | 15 | 16 | 17 | 18 | 19 | 20 | 21 | 22 |
| 1φ | *O* | **7** | **8** | **9** | **9** | **10** | **11** | **12** | **13** | **14** | **15** | **16** | **17** | **18** | **18** | **19** | **20** | **21** | **22** | **23** | **24** | **25** |
| | *I* | — | — | 4 | 5 | 6 | 7 | 8 | 8 | 9 | 10 | 11 | 12 | 13 | 14 | 15 | 16 | 17 | 17 | 18 | 19 | 20 |
| 1□ | *O* | **6** | **7** | **7** | **8** | **9** | **10** | **11** | **11** | **12** | **13** | **14** | **14** | **15** | **16** | **17** | **18** | **18** | **19** | **20** | **21** | **22** |
| | *I* | — | — | — | — | 4 | 5 | 6 | 7 | 7 | 8 | 9 | 10 | 11 | 11 | 12 | 13 | 14 | 14 | 15 | 16 | 17 |
| 1⅛□ | *O* | — | **6** | **6** | **7** | **8** | **9** | **9** | **10** | **11** | **11** | **12** | **13** | **13** | **14** | **15** | **16** | **16** | **17** | **18** | **18** | **19** |
| | *I* | — | — | — | — | — | 4 | 5 | 5 | 6 | 7 | 7 | 8 | 9 | 9 | 10 | 11 | 11 | 12 | 13 | 14 | 14 |
| 1¼□ | *O* | — | — | **6** | **6** | **7** | **8** | **8** | **9** | **9** | **10** | **11** | **11** | **12** | **13** | **13** | **14** | **14** | **15** | **16** | **16** | **17** |
| | *I* | — | — | — | — | — | — | — | 4 | 5 | 5 | 6 | 7 | 7 | 8 | 8 | 9 | 10 | 10 | 11 | 12 | 12 |

Note referring to page 89: The spirals in Table 26 conform to the requirement that $p' \geqq 0.0075$ for cold drawn rods and $p' \geqq 0.0112$ for hot rolled rods. These limits were lowered in the Joint Committee Code 1940 after Table 26 went to press. Spirals in Table 26 are in some cases heavier than required by J. C. Code 1940

# Table 26. Spiral Columns; Joint Committee Code 1940 (Proposed) and American Concrete Institute Code 1936—Size and Pitch of Spirals**

| Column Size | Core Diameter | SQUARE Columns 2000 | SQUARE 2500 | SQUARE 3000 | SQUARE 3750 | SQUARE 5000 | ROUND Columns 2000 | ROUND 2500 | ROUND 3000 | ROUND 3750 | ROUND 5000 |
|---|---|---|---|---|---|---|---|---|---|---|---|
| | | Hot Rolled. 1½-in. Concrete Protection | | | | | | | | | |
| 14 | 11 | * | * | * | * | * | ⅜-1¾ | ⅜-1¾ | ⅜-1¾ | * | * |
| 15 | 12 | ½-2 | ½-2 | * | * | * | ⅜-2 | ⅜-2 | ⅜-1¾ | ½-2 | ½-2 |
| 16 | 13 | ½-2 | ½-2 | * | * | * | ⅜-2 | ⅜-2 | ⅜-1¾ | ½-2 | ½-2 |
| 17 | 14 | ½-2¼ | ½-2¼ | * | * | * | ⅜-2¼ | ⅜-2¼ | ⅜-1¾ | ½-2¼ | ½-2 |
| 18 | 15 | ½-2½ | ½-2¼ | ⅝-2½ | ⅝-2¼ | * | ⅜-2½ | ⅜-2¼ | ⅜-1¾ | ½-2½ | ½-2 |
| 19 | 16 | ½-2½ | ½-2¼ | ⅝-2½ | ⅝-2¼ | * | ⅜-2¼ | ⅜-2¼ | ⅜-1¾ | ½-2½ | ½-2 |
| 20 | 17 | ½-2¾ | ½-2 | ⅝-2¾ | ⅝-2¼ | * | ⅜-2¼ | ⅜-2¼ | ⅜-2 | ½-2¾ | ½-2 |
| 21 | 18 | ½-2½ | ½-2 | ⅝-2¾ | ⅝-2 | * | ⅜-2 | ⅜-2 | ⅜-2 | ½-2¾ | ½-2 |
| 22 | 19 | ½-2½ | ½-2 | ⅝-2¾ | ⅝-2 | * | ⅜-2 | ⅜-2 | ⅜-2 | ½-2¾ | ½-2 |
| 23 | 20 | ½-2½ | ½-2 | ⅝-2½ | ⅝-2 | * | ⅜-1¾ | ⅜-1¾ | ⅜-1¾ | ½-2¾ | ½-2 |
| 24 | 21 | ½-2½ | ½-2 | ⅝-2½ | ⅝-2 | * | ½-3¼ | ½-3¼ | ½-3¼ | ½-2¾ | ½-2 |
| 25 | 22 | ½-2½ | ½-2 | ⅝-2½ | ⅝-2 | * | ½-3¼ | ½-3¼ | ½-3¼ | ½-2¾ | ½-2 |
| 26 | 23 | ½-2¼ | ⅝-3 | ⅝-2½ | ⅝-2 | * | ½-3 | ½-3 | ½-3 | ½-2¾ | ½-2 |
| 27 | 24 | ½-2¼ | ⅝-3 | ⅝-2½ | ⅝-2 | * | ½-2¾ | ½-2¾ | ½-2¾ | ½-2¾ | ½-2 |
| 28 | 25 | ½-2¼ | ⅝-2¾ | ⅝-2¼ | * | * | ½-2¾ | ½-2¾ | ½-2¾ | ½-2¾ | ½-2 |
| 29 | 26 | ½-2¼ | ⅝-2¾ | ⅝-2¼ | * | * | ½-2¾ | ½-2¾ | ½-2¾ | ½-2¾ | ½-2 |
| 30 | 27 | ½-2¼ | ⅝-2¾ | ⅝-2¼ | * | * | ½-2½ | ½-2½ | ½-2½ | ½-2½ | ½-2¼ |
| 31 | 28 | ½-2¼ | ⅝-2¾ | ⅝-2¼ | * | * | ½-2½ | ½-2½ | ½-2½ | ½-2½ | ½-2¼ |
| 32 | 29 | ½-2 | ⅝-2¾ | ⅝-2¼ | * | * | ½-2¼ | ½-2¼ | ½-2¼ | ½-2¼ | ½-2¼ |
| 33 | 30 | ½-2 | ⅝-2½ | ⅝-2¼ | * | * | ½-2¼ | ½-2¼ | ½-2¼ | ½-2¼ | ½-2¼ |
| Column | Core | Cold Drawn. 1½-in. Concrete Protection | | | | | | | | | |
| 14 | 11 | ⅜-1¾ | ⅜-1¾ | * | * | * | ¼-1¾ | ⅜-1¾ | ⅜-1¾ | ⅜-1¾ | * |
| 15 | 12 | ⅜-2 | ⅜-1¾ | ½-2 | ½-2 | * | ¼-1¾ | ⅜-2 | ⅜-2 | ⅜-2 | ⅜-1¾ |
| 16 | 13 | ⅜-2 | ⅜-1¾ | ½-2 | ½-2 | * | ¼-2 | ⅜-2 | ⅜-2 | ⅜-2 | ⅜-1¾ |
| 17 | 14 | ⅜-2¼ | ⅜-1¾ | ½-2¼ | ½-2¼ | * | ¼-1¾ | ⅜-2¼ | ⅜-2¼ | ⅜-2¼ | ⅜-1¾ |
| 18 | 15 | ⅜-2¼ | ⅜-1¾ | ½-2½ | ½-2¼ | ⅝-2½ | ¼-1¾ | ⅜-2½ | ⅜-2½ | ⅜-2¼ | ⅜-1¾ |
| 19 | 16 | ⅜-2¼ | ⅜-1¾ | ½-2½ | ½-2 | ⅝-2½ | ⅜-2½ | ⅜-2½ | ⅜-2½ | ⅜-2¼ | ⅜-1¾ |
| 20 | 17 | ⅜-2¼ | ⅜-1¾ | ½-2¾ | ½-2 | ⅝-2½ | ⅜-2¾ | ⅜-2¾ | ⅜-2¾ | ⅜-2¼ | ⅜-1¾ |
| 21 | 18 | ⅜-2 | ⅜-1¾ | ½-2½ | ½-2 | ⅝-2½ | ⅜-3 | ⅜-3 | ⅜-3 | ⅜-2¼ | ⅜-1¾ |
| 22 | 19 | ⅜-2 | ⅜-1¾ | ½-2½ | ½-2 | ⅝-2¼ | ⅜-3 | ⅜-3 | ⅜-3 | ⅜-2¼ | ⅜-1¾ |
| 23 | 20 | ⅜-2 | ½-3 | ½-2½ | ½-2 | ⅝-2¼ | ⅜-2¾ | ⅜-2¾ | ⅜-2¾ | ⅜-2¼ | ½-3¼ |
| 24 | 21 | ⅜-2 | ½-3 | ½-2½ | ½-2 | ⅝-2¼ | ⅜-2¾ | ⅜-2¾ | ⅜-2¾ | ⅜-2¼ | ½-3¼ |
| 25 | 22 | ⅜-2 | ½-3 | ½-2½ | ½-2 | ⅝-2¼ | ⅜-2½ | ⅜-2½ | ⅜-2½ | ⅜-2¼ | ½-3¼ |
| 26 | 23 | ⅜-2 | ½-2¾ | ½-2¼ | ⅝-3 | ⅝-2¼ | ⅜-2½ | ⅜-2½ | ⅜-2½ | ⅜-2¼ | ½-3¼ |
| 27 | 24 | ⅜-2 | ½-2¾ | ½-2¼ | ⅝-3 | ⅝-2¼ | ⅜-2¼ | ⅜-2¼ | ⅜-2¼ | ⅜-2¼ | ½-3¼ |
| 28 | 25 | ½-3½ | ½-2¾ | ½-2¼ | ⅝-2¾ | ⅝-2 | ⅜-2¼ | ⅜-2¼ | ⅜-2¼ | ⅜-2¼ | ½-3¼ |
| 29 | 26 | ½-3½ | ½-2¾ | ½-2¼ | ⅝-2¾ | ⅝-2 | ⅜-2¼ | ⅜-2¼ | ⅜-2¼ | ⅜-2¼ | ½-3¼ |
| 30 | 27 | ½-3¼ | ½-2¾ | ½-2¼ | ⅝-2¾ | ⅝-2 | ⅜-2 | ⅜-2 | ⅜-2 | ⅜-2 | ½-3¼ |
| 31 | 28 | ½-3¼ | ½-2½ | ½-2¼ | ⅝-2¾ | ⅝-2 | ⅜-2 | ⅜-2 | ⅜-2 | ⅜-2 | ½-3¼ |
| 32 | 29 | ½-3¼ | ½-2½ | ½-2 | ⅝-2¾ | ⅝-2 | ⅜-2 | ⅜-2 | ⅜-2 | ⅜-2 | ½-3¼ |
| 33 | 30 | ½-3¼ | ½-2½ | ½-2 | ⅝-2½ | ⅝-2 | ½-3½ | ½-3½ | ½-3½ | ½-3½ | ½-3¼ |
| Column | Core | Hot Rolled. 2-in. Concrete Protection | | | | | | | | | |
| 14 | 10 | * | * | * | * | * | * | * | * | * | * |
| 15 | 11 | * | * | * | * | * | ⅜-1¾ | * | * | * | * |
| 16 | 12 | ½-2 | * | * | * | * | ⅜-2 | ½-2 | ½-2 | ½-2 | * |
| 17 | 13 | ½-2 | * | * | * | * | ⅜-2 | ½-2 | ½-2 | ½-2 | * |
| 18 | 14 | ½-2¼ | * | * | * | * | ⅜-2 | ½-2¼ | ½-2¼ | ½-2 | * |
| 19 | 15 | ½-2¼ | ⅝-2½ | ⅝-2¼ | * | * | ⅜-2 | ½-2½ | ½-2½ | ½-2 | ⅝-2¼ |
| 20 | 16 | ½-2¼ | ⅝-2½ | ⅝-2¼ | * | * | ⅜-2 | ½-2½ | ½-2½ | ½-2 | ⅝-2¼ |
| 21 | 17 | ½-2 | ⅝-2¾ | ⅝-2¼ | * | * | ⅜-2 | ½-2¾ | ½-2½ | ½-2 | ⅝-2¼ |
| 22 | 18 | ½-2 | ⅝-2½ | ⅝-2¼ | * | * | ⅜-2 | ½-3 | ½-2½ | ½-2 | ⅝-2¼ |
| 23 | 19 | ½-2 | ⅝-2½ | ⅝-2 | * | * | ⅜-2 | ½-3 | ½-2½ | ½-2 | ⅝-2½ |
| 24 | 20 | ½-2 | ⅝-2½ | ⅝-2 | * | * | ½-3¼ | ½-3¼ | ½-2½ | ⅝-3¼ | ⅝-2½ |
| 25 | 21 | ½-2 | ⅝-2½ | ⅝-2 | * | * | ½-3¼ | ½-3¼ | ½-2½ | ⅝-3¼ | ⅝-2½ |
| 26 | 22 | ½-2 | ⅝-2½ | ⅝-2 | * | * | ½-3¼ | ½-3¼ | ½-2½ | ⅝-3¼ | ⅝-2½ |
| 27 | 23 | ½-2 | ⅝-2½ | ⅝-2 | * | * | ½-3 | ½-3 | ½-2½ | ⅝-3¼ | ⅝-2½ |
| 28 | 24 | ½-2 | ⅝-2½ | ⅝-2 | * | * | ½-2¾ | ½-2¾ | ½-2¾ | ⅝-3¼ | ⅝-2½ |
| 29 | 25 | ½-2 | ⅝-2¼ | ⅝-2 | * | * | ½-2¾ | ½-2¾ | ½-2¾ | ⅝-3¼ | ⅝-2½ |
| 30 | 26 | ⅝-3 | ⅝-2¼ | ⅝-2 | * | * | ½-2¾ | ½-2¾ | ½-2¾ | ⅝-3¼ | ⅝-2½ |
| 31 | 27 | ⅝-3 | ⅝-2¼ | ⅝-2 | * | * | ½-2½ | ½-2½ | ½-2½ | ⅝-3¼ | ⅝-2½ |
| 32 | 28 | ⅝-2¾ | ⅝-2¼ | * | * | * | ½-2½ | ½-2½ | ½-2½ | ⅝-3¼ | ⅝-2½ |
| 33 | 29 | ⅝-2¾ | ⅝-2¼ | * | * | * | ½-2¼ | ½-2¼ | ½-2¼ | ⅝-3¼ | ⅝-2½ |
| Column | Core | Cold Drawn. 2-in. Concrete Protection | | | | | | | | | |
| 14 | 10 | * | * | * | * | * | * | * | * | * | * |
| 15 | 11 | ⅜-1¾ | * | * | * | * | ⅜-1¾ | ⅜-1¾ | ⅜-1¾ | * | * |
| 16 | 12 | ⅜-1¾ | ½-2 | ½-2 | * | * | ⅜-2 | ⅜-2 | ⅜-2 | ½-2 | ½-2 |
| 17 | 13 | ⅜-1¾ | ½-2 | ½-2 | * | * | ⅜-2 | ⅜-2 | ⅜-2 | ½-2 | ½-2 |
| 18 | 14 | ⅜-1¾ | ½-2¼ | ½-2¼ | * | * | ⅜-2¼ | ⅜-2¼ | ⅜-2 | ½-2¼ | ½-2¼ |
| 19 | 15 | ⅜-1¾ | ½-2½ | ½-2¼ | ⅝-2½ | ⅝-2 | ⅜-2½ | ⅜-2½ | ⅜-2 | ½-2½ | ½-2¼ |
| 20 | 16 | ⅜-1¾ | ½-2½ | ½-2¼ | ⅝-2½ | ⅝-2 | ⅜-2½ | ⅜-2½ | ⅜-2 | ½-2½ | ½-2¼ |
| 21 | 17 | ⅜-1¾ | ½-2½ | ½-2 | ⅝-2¾ | ⅝-2 | ⅜-2¾ | ⅜-2½ | ⅜-2 | ½-2¾ | ½-2¼ |
| 22 | 18 | ⅜-1¾ | ½-2½ | ½-2 | ⅝-2½ | ⅝-2 | ⅜-3 | ⅜-2½ | ⅜-2 | ½-3 | ½-2¼ |
| 23 | 19 | ⅜-1¾ | ½-2½ | ½-2 | ⅝-2½ | ⅝-2 | ⅜-3 | ⅜-2½ | ⅜-2 | ½-3 | ½-2¼ |
| 24 | 20 | ⅜-1¾ | ½-2½ | ½-2 | ⅝-2½ | * | ⅜-2¾ | ⅜-2½ | ⅜-2 | ½-3¼ | ½-2¼ |
| 25 | 21 | ½-3 | ½-2½ | ½-2 | ⅝-2½ | * | ⅜-2¾ | ⅜-2½ | ⅜-2¼ | ½-3¼ | ½-2¼ |
| 26 | 22 | ½-3 | ½-2¼ | ½-2 | ⅝-2½ | * | ⅜-2½ | ⅜-2½ | ⅜-2¼ | ½-3¼ | ½-2¼ |
| 27 | 23 | ½-3 | ½-2¼ | ⅝-3 | ⅝-2½ | * | ⅜-2½ | ⅜-2½ | ⅜-2¼ | ½-3¼ | ½-2¼ |
| 28 | 24 | ½-3 | ½-2¼ | ⅝-3 | ⅝-2½ | * | ⅜-2¼ | ⅜-2¼ | ⅜-2¼ | ½-3¼ | ½-2¼ |
| 29 | 25 | ½-3 | ½-2¼ | ⅝-3 | ⅝-2¼ | * | ⅜-2¼ | ⅜-2¼ | ⅜-2¼ | ½-3¼ | ½-2¼ |
| 30 | 26 | ½-2¾ | ½-2¼ | ⅝-3 | ⅝-2¼ | * | ⅜-2¼ | ⅜-2¼ | ⅜-2¼ | ½-3¼ | ½-2¼ |
| 31 | 27 | ½-2¾ | ½-2¼ | ⅝-3 | ⅝-2¼ | * | ⅜-2 | ⅜-2 | ⅜-2 | ½-3¼ | ½-2¼ |
| 32 | 28 | ½-2¾ | ½-2¼ | ⅝-2¾ | ⅝-2¼ | * | ⅜-2 | ⅜-2 | ⅜-2 | ½-3¼ | ½-2¼ |
| 33 | 29 | ½-2¾ | ½-2¼ | ⅝-2¾ | ⅝-2¼ | * | ⅜-2 | ⅜-2 | ⅜-2 | ½-3¼ | ½-2½ |

*No spiral column available. Design column with ties
**See footnote on page 88

# Table 27. Spiral Columns; American Concrete Institute Code 1928

## Part 1. Area of Core

| | d: Diameter of Core | | | | | | | | | | | | | | | | | | | | |
|---|---|---|---|---|---|---|---|---|---|---|---|---|---|---|---|---|---|---|---|---|---|
| | 10 | 11 | 12 | 13 | 14 | 15 | 16 | 17 | 18 | 19 | 20 | 21 | 22 | 23 | 24 | 25 | 26 | 27 | 28 | 29 | 30 |
| $A_c$ | 79 | 95 | 113 | 133 | 154 | 177 | 201 | 227 | 254 | 284 | 314 | 346 | 380 | 415 | 452 | 491 | 531 | 573 | 616 | 661 | 707 |

## Part 2. $\frac{P}{A_c}\left(\frac{\text{kips}}{\text{sq.in.}}\right) = [1 + (n - 1)p] \times [300 + (0.1 + 4p)f'_c] \div 1000$*

| $f'_c$ | Percentage of Bars: 100 $p$ | | | | | | | | | | | | | | | | | | | | | | | | | |
|---|---|---|---|---|---|---|---|---|---|---|---|---|---|---|---|---|---|---|---|---|---|---|---|---|---|
| | 1.0 | 1.2 | 1.4 | 1.6 | 1.8 | 2.0 | 2.2 | 2.4 | 2.6 | 2.8 | 3.0 | 3.2 | 3.4 | 3.6 | 3.8 | 4.0 | 4.2 | 4.4 | 4.6 | 4.8 | 5.0 | 5.2 | 5.4 | 5.6 | 5.8 | 6.0 |
| 2000 | 0.66 | 0.70 | 0.73 | 0.77 | 0.81 | 0.84 | 0.88 | 0.92 | 0.97 | 1.01 | 1.05 | 1.09 | 1.14 | 1.19 | 1.23 | 1.28 | 1.33 | 1.38 | 1.43 | 1.48 | 1.53 | 1.58 | 1.64 | 1.69 | 1.75 | 1.80 |
| 2500 | 0.72 | 0.76 | 0.80 | 0.84 | 0.88 | 0.92 | 0.96 | 1.00 | 1.04 | 1.09 | 1.13 | 1.18 | 1.22 | 1.27 | 1.32 | 1.37 | 1.42 | 1.47 | 1.52 | 1.57 | 1.63 | 1.68 | 1.74 | 1.79 | 1.85 | 1.91 |
| 3000 | 0.78 | 0.82 | 0.87 | 0.91 | 0.95 | 0.99 | 1.04 | 1.08 | 1.13 | 1.17 | 1.22 | 1.27 | 1.32 | 1.37 | 1.42 | 1.47 | 1.52 | 1.57 | 1.63 | 1.68 | 1.74 | 1.80 | 1.85 | 1.91 | 1.97 | 2.03 |
| 3750 | 0.88 | 0.93 | 0.97 | 1.02 | 1.06 | 1.11 | 1.16 | 1.21 | 1.26 | 1.31 | 1.36 | 1.41 | 1.47 | 1.52 | 1.58 | 1.63 | 1.69 | 1.75 | 1.80 | 1.86 | 1.92 | 1.98 | 2.05 | 2.11 | 2.17 | 2.24 |
| 5000 | 1.05 | 1.10 | 1.16 | 1.21 | 1.26 | 1.32 | 1.38 | 1.43 | 1.49 | 1.55 | 1.61 | 1.67 | 1.73 | 1.79 | 1.86 | 1.92 | 1.98 | 2.05 | 2.12 | 2.18 | 2.25 | 2.32 | 2.39 | 2.46 | 2.53 | 2.60 |

| $d$ | $A_s = pA_c$ | | | | | | | | | | | | | | | | | | | | | | | | | |
|---|---|---|---|---|---|---|---|---|---|---|---|---|---|---|---|---|---|---|---|---|---|---|---|---|---|
| 10 | | | | 1.3 | 1.4 | 1.6 | 1.7 | 1.9 | 2.0 | 2.2 | 2.4 | 2.5 | 2.7 | 2.8 | 3.0 | 3.1 | 3.3 | 3.5 | 3.6 | 3.8 | 3.9 | 4.1 | 4.2 | 4.4 | 4.6 | 4.7 |
| 11 | | | 1.3 | 1.5 | 1.7 | 1.9 | 2.1 | 2.3 | 2.5 | 2.7 | 2.9 | 3.0 | 3.2 | 3.4 | 3.6 | 3.8 | 4.0 | 4.2 | 4.4 | 4.6 | 4.8 | 4.9 | 5.1 | 5.3 | 5.5 | 5.7 |
| 12 | | 1.4 | 1.6 | 1.8 | 2.0 | 2.3 | 2.5 | 2.7 | 2.9 | 3.2 | 3.4 | 3.6 | 3.8 | 4.1 | 4.3 | 4.5 | 4.8 | 5.0 | 5.2 | 5.4 | 5.7 | 5.9 | 6.1 | 6.3 | 6.6 | 6.8 |
| 13 | 1.3 | 1.6 | 1.9 | 2.1 | 2.4 | 2.7 | 2.9 | 3.2 | 3.5 | 3.7 | 4.0 | 4.2 | 4.5 | 4.8 | 5.0 | 5.3 | 5.6 | 5.8 | 6.1 | 6.4 | 6.6 | 6.9 | 7.2 | 7.4 | 7.7 | 8.0 |
| 14 | 1.5 | 1.8 | 2.2 | 2.5 | 2.8 | 3.1 | 3.4 | 3.7 | 4.0 | 4.3 | 4.6 | 4.9 | 5.2 | 5.5 | 5.9 | 6.2 | 6.5 | 6.8 | 7.1 | 7.4 | 7.7 | 8.0 | 8.3 | 8.6 | 8.9 | 9.2 |
| 15 | 1.8 | 2.1 | 2.5 | 2.8 | 3.2 | 3.5 | 3.9 | 4.2 | 4.6 | 4.9 | 5.3 | 5.7 | 6.0 | 6.4 | 6.7 | 7.1 | 7.4 | 7.8 | 8.1 | 8.5 | 8.8 | 9.2 | 9.5 | 9.9 | 10.2 | 10.6 |
| 16 | 2.0 | 2.4 | 2.8 | 3.2 | 3.6 | 4.0 | 4.4 | 4.8 | 5.2 | 5.6 | 6.0 | 6.4 | 6.8 | 7.2 | 7.6 | 8.0 | 8.4 | 8.9 | 9.3 | 9.7 | 10.1 | 10.5 | 10.9 | 11.3 | 11.7 | 12.1 |
| 17 | 2.3 | 2.7 | 3.2 | 3.6 | 4.1 | 4.5 | 5.0 | 5.4 | 5.9 | 6.4 | 6.8 | 7.3 | 7.7 | 8.2 | 8.6 | 9.1 | 9.5 | 10.0 | 10.4 | 10.9 | 11.3 | 11.8 | 12.3 | 12.7 | 13.2 | 13.6 |
| 18 | 2.5 | 3.1 | 3.6 | 4.1 | 4.6 | 5.1 | 5.6 | 6.1 | 6.6 | 7.1 | 7.6 | 8.1 | 8.7 | 9.2 | 9.7 | 10.2 | 10.7 | 11.2 | 11.7 | 12.2 | 12.7 | 13.2 | 13.7 | 14.2 | 14.8 | 15.3 |
| 19 | 2.8 | 3.4 | 4.0 | 4.5 | 5.1 | 5.7 | 6.2 | 6.8 | 7.4 | 7.9 | 8.5 | 9.1 | 9.6 | 10.2 | 10.8 | 11.3 | 11.9 | 12.5 | 13.0 | 13.6 | 14.2 | 14.7 | 15.3 | 15.9 | 16.4 | 17.0 |
| 20 | 3.1 | 3.8 | 4.4 | 5.0 | 5.7 | 6.3 | 6.9 | 7.5 | 8.2 | 8.8 | 9.4 | 10.1 | 10.7 | 11.3 | 11.9 | 12.6 | 13.2 | 13.8 | 14.5 | 15.1 | 15.7 | 16.3 | 17.0 | 17.6 | 18.2 | 18.9 |
| 21 | 3.5 | 4.2 | 4.8 | 5.5 | 6.2 | 6.9 | 7.6 | 8.3 | 9.0 | 9.7 | 10.4 | 11.1 | 11.8 | 12.5 | 13.2 | 13.9 | 14.5 | 15.2 | 15.9 | 16.6 | 17.3 | 18.0 | 18.7 | 19.4 | 20.1 | 20.8 |
| 22 | 3.8 | 4.6 | 5.3 | 6.1 | 6.8 | 7.6 | 8.4 | 9.1 | 9.9 | 10.6 | 11.4 | 12.2 | 12.9 | 13.7 | 14.4 | 15.2 | 16.0 | 16.7 | 17.5 | 18.2 | 19.0 | 19.8 | 20.5 | 21.3 | 22.1 | 22.8 |
| 23 | 4.2 | 5.0 | 5.8 | 6.6 | 7.5 | 8.3 | 9.1 | 10.0 | 10.8 | 11.6 | 12.5 | 13.3 | 14.1 | 15.0 | 15.8 | 16.6 | 17.4 | 18.3 | 19.1 | 19.9 | 20.8 | 21.6 | 22.4 | 23.3 | 24.1 | 24.9 |
| 24 | 4.5 | 5.4 | 6.3 | 7.2 | 8.1 | 9.1 | 10.0 | 10.9 | 11.8 | 12.7 | 13.6 | 14.5 | 15.4 | 16.3 | 17.2 | 18.1 | 19.0 | 19.9 | 20.8 | 21.7 | 22.6 | 23.5 | 24.4 | 25.3 | 26.2 | 27.1 |
| 25 | 4.9 | 5.9 | 6.9 | 7.9 | 8.8 | 9.8 | 10.8 | 11.8 | 12.8 | 13.7 | 14.7 | 15.7 | 16.7 | 17.7 | 18.6 | 19.6 | 20.6 | 21.6 | 22.6 | 23.6 | 24.5 | 25.5 | 26.5 | 27.5 | 28.5 | 29.5 |
| 26 | 5.3 | 6.4 | 7.4 | 8.5 | 9.6 | 10.6 | 11.7 | 12.7 | 13.8 | 14.9 | 15.9 | 17.0 | 18.1 | 19.1 | 20.2 | 21.2 | 22.3 | 23.4 | 24.4 | 25.5 | 26.5 | 27.6 | 28.7 | 29.8 | 30.8 | |
| 27 | 5.7 | 6.9 | 8.0 | 9.2 | 10.3 | 11.5 | 12.6 | 13.7 | 14.9 | 16.0 | 17.2 | 18.3 | 19.5 | 20.6 | 21.8 | 22.9 | 24.0 | 25.2 | 26.3 | 27.5 | 28.6 | 29.8 | 30.9 | 32.1 | 33.2 | |
| 28 | 6.2 | 7.4 | 8.6 | 9.8 | 11.1 | 12.3 | 13.5 | 14.8 | 16.0 | 17.2 | 18.5 | 19.7 | 20.9 | 22.2 | 23.4 | 24.6 | 25.8 | 27.1 | 28.3 | 29.5 | 30.8 | 32.0 | 33.2 | 34.5 | 35.7 | |
| 29 | 6.6 | 7.9 | 9.2 | 10.6 | 11.9 | 13.2 | 14.5 | 15.9 | 17.2 | 18.5 | 19.8 | 21.1 | 22.5 | 23.8 | 25.1 | 26.4 | 27.7 | 29.1 | 30.4 | 31.7 | 33.0 | 34.4 | 35.7 | | | |
| 30 | 7.1 | 8.5 | 9.9 | 11.3 | 12.7 | 14.1 | 15.5 | 17.0 | 18.4 | 19.8 | 21.2 | 22.6 | 24.0 | 25.4 | 26.9 | 28.3 | 29.7 | 31.1 | 32.5 | 33.9 | 35.3 | 36.8 | 38.2 | | | |
| | 0.25 | 0.30 | 0.35 | 0.40 | 0.45 | 0.50 | 0.55 | 0.60 | 0.65 | 0.70 | 0.75 | 0.80 | 0.85 | 0.90 | 0.95 | 1.00 | 1.05 | 1.10 | 1.15 | 1.20 | 1.25 | 1.30 | 1.35 | 1.40 | 1.45 | 1.50 |
| | Percentage of Spirals: 100 $p'$ | | | | | | | | | | | | | | | | | | | | | | | | | |

## Part 3. Area of Bars, $A_s$

| Bar Size | Number of Bars | | | | | | | | | | | | | | | | | | | | |
|---|---|---|---|---|---|---|---|---|---|---|---|---|---|---|---|---|---|---|---|---|---|
| | 6 | 7 | 8 | 9 | 10 | 11 | 12 | 13 | 14 | 15 | 16 | 17 | 18 | 19 | 20 | 21 | 22 | 23 | 24 | 25 | 26 |
| ½φ | 1.2 | 1.4 | 1.6 | 1.8 | 2.0 | 2.2 | 2.4 | 2.6 | 2.8 | 3.0 | 3.2 | 3.4 | 3.6 | 3.8 | 4.0 | 4.2 | 4.4 | 4.6 | 4.8 | 5.0 | 5.2 |
| ½□ | 1.5 | 1.8 | 2.0 | 2.3 | 2.5 | 2.8 | 3.0 | 3.3 | 3.5 | 3.8 | 4.0 | 4.3 | 4.5 | 4.8 | 5.0 | 5.3 | 5.5 | 5.8 | 6.0 | 6.3 | 6.5 |
| ⅝φ | 1.9 | 2.2 | 2.5 | 2.8 | 3.1 | 3.4 | 3.7 | 4.0 | 4.3 | 4.7 | 5.0 | 5.3 | 5.6 | 5.9 | 6.2 | 6.5 | 6.8 | 7.1 | 7.4 | 7.8 | 8.1 |
| ¾φ | 2.6 | 3.1 | 3.5 | 4.0 | 4.4 | 4.8 | 5.3 | 5.7 | 6.2 | 6.6 | 7.0 | 7.5 | 7.9 | 8.4 | 8.8 | 9.2 | 9.7 | 10.1 | 10.6 | 11.0 | 11.4 |
| ⅞φ | 3.6 | 4.2 | 4.8 | 5.4 | 6.0 | 6.6 | 7.2 | 7.8 | 8.4 | 9.0 | 9.6 | 10.2 | 10.8 | 11.4 | 12.0 | 12.6 | 13.2 | 13.8 | 14.4 | 15.0 | 15.6 |
| 1φ | 4.7 | 5.5 | 6.3 | 7.1 | 7.9 | 8.7 | 9.5 | 10.3 | 11.1 | 11.9 | 12.6 | 13.4 | 14.2 | 15.0 | 15.8 | 16.6 | 17.4 | 18.2 | 19.0 | 19.8 | 20.5 |
| 1□ | 6.0 | 7.0 | 8.0 | 9.0 | 10.0 | 11.0 | 12.0 | 13.0 | 14.0 | 15.0 | 16.0 | 17.0 | 18.0 | 19.0 | 20.0 | 21.0 | 22.0 | 23.0 | 24.0 | 25.0 | 26.0 |
| 1⅛□ | 7.6 | 8.9 | 10.2 | 11.4 | 12.7 | 14.0 | 15.2 | 16.5 | 17.8 | 19.1 | 20.3 | 21.6 | 22.9 | 24.1 | 25.4 | 26.7 | 27.9 | 29.2 | 30.5 | 31.8 | 33.0 |
| 1¼□ | 9.4 | 10.9 | 12.5 | 14.0 | 15.6 | 17.2 | 18.7 | 20.3 | 21.8 | 23.4 | 25.0 | 26.5 | 28.1 | 29.6 | 31.2 | 32.8 | 34.3 | 35.9 | 37.4 | 39.0 | 40.6 |

## Part 4. Maximum Number of Bars in Outer Ring, *O*, and in Inner Ring, *I*

| Bar Size | Ring | d: Diameter of Core | | | | | | | | | | | | | | | | | | | | |
|---|---|---|---|---|---|---|---|---|---|---|---|---|---|---|---|---|---|---|---|---|---|---|
| | | 10 | 11 | 12 | 13 | 14 | 15 | 16 | 17 | 18 | 19 | 20 | 21 | 22 | 23 | 24 | 25 | 26 | 27 | 28 | 29 | 30 |
| ½φ ½□ | *O* | **13** | **14** | **16** | **18** | **19** | **21** | **22** | **24** | **25** | **27** | **29** | **30** | **32** | **33** | **35** | **36** | **38** | **40** | **41** | **43** | **44** |
| | *I* | 5 | 6 | 7 | 8 | 9 | 10 | 11 | 12 | 13 | 14 | 14 | 15 | 16 | 17 | 18 | 19 | 20 | 21 | 22 | 23 | 24 |
| ⅝φ | *O* | **11** | **13** | **14** | **15** | **17** | **18** | **20** | **21** | **22** | **24** | **25** | **27** | **28** | **29** | **31** | **32** | **34** | **35** | **36** | **38** | **39** |
| | *I* | 4 | 5 | 6 | 6 | 7 | 8 | 9 | 10 | 11 | 11 | 12 | 13 | 14 | 15 | 16 | 16 | 17 | 18 | 19 | 20 | 21 |
| ¾φ | *O* | **9** | **11** | **12** | **13** | **14** | **15** | **17** | **18** | **19** | **20** | **21** | **23** | **24** | **25** | **26** | **27** | **29** | **30** | **31** | **32** | **33** |
| | *I* | — | 4 | 4 | 5 | 6 | 6 | 7 | 8 | 9 | 9 | 10 | 11 | 11 | 12 | 13 | 14 | 14 | 15 | 16 | 16 | 17 |
| ⅞φ | *O* | **8** | **9** | **10** | **11** | **12** | **13** | **14** | **15** | **16** | **17** | **18** | **19** | **20** | **21** | **22** | **23** | **24** | **25** | **26** | **27** | **28** |
| | *I* | — | — | — | 4 | 4 | 5 | 6 | 6 | 7 | 8 | 8 | 9 | 9 | 10 | 11 | 11 | 12 | 12 | 13 | 14 | 14 |
| 1φ | *O* | **7** | **8** | **8** | **9** | **10** | **11** | **12** | **13** | **14** | **15** | **16** | **17** | **17** | **18** | **19** | **20** | **21** | **22** | **23** | **24** | **25** |
| | *I* | — | — | — | — | — | 4 | 5 | 5 | 6 | 6 | 7 | 7 | 8 | 8 | 9 | 9 | 10 | 10 | 11 | 12 | 12 |
| 1□ | *O* | **6** | **7** | **7** | **8** | **9** | **10** | **11** | **11** | **12** | **13** | **14** | **14** | **15** | **16** | **17** | **18** | **18** | **19** | **20** | **21** | **22** |
| | *I* | — | — | — | — | — | — | 4 | 4 | 5 | 5 | 6 | 6 | 7 | 7 | 8 | 8 | 9 | 9 | 10 | 10 | 11 |
| 1⅛□ | *O* | — | **6** | **6** | **7** | **8** | **9** | **9** | **10** | **11** | **11** | **12** | **13** | **13** | **14** | **15** | **16** | **16** | **17** | **18** | **18** | **19** |
| | *I* | — | — | — | — | — | — | — | 4 | 4 | 4 | 5 | 5 | 6 | 6 | 7 | 7 | 7 | 8 | 8 | 9 | 9 |
| 1¼□ | *O* | — | — | **6** | **6** | **7** | **8** | **8** | **9** | **9** | **10** | **11** | **11** | **12** | **13** | **13** | **14** | **14** | **15** | **16** | **16** | **17** |
| | *I* | — | — | — | — | — | — | — | — | — | 4 | 4 | 4 | 5 | 5 | 6 | 6 | 6 | 7 | 7 | 7 | 8 |

## Table 27. *(continued)*

### Part 5. Size and Pitch of Spirals

$$\text{Values of } 100\,p' = 400\,\frac{\text{Area of Spiral Rod}}{(\text{Core Diameter}) \times (\text{Pitch})}$$

| Rod Size | Pitch | *d:* Diameter of Core | | | | | | | | | | | | | | | | | | | | |
|---|---|---|---|---|---|---|---|---|---|---|---|---|---|---|---|---|---|---|---|---|---|---|
| | | 10 | 11 | 12 | 13 | 14 | 15 | 16 | 17 | 18 | 19 | 20 | 21 | 22 | 23 | 24 | 25 | 26 | 27 | 28 | 29 | 30 |
| ¼ φ | 1¼ | 1.60 | 1.45 | 1.33 | 1.23 | 1.14 | 1.07 | 1.00 | 0.94 | 0.89 | 0.84 | 0.80 | 0.76 | 0.73 | 0.70 | 0.67 | 0.64 | 0.62 | 0.59 | 0.57 | 0.55 | 0.53 |
| | 1½ | 1.33 | 1.21 | 1.11 | 1.03 | 0.95 | 0.89 | 0.83 | 0.78 | 0.74 | 0.70 | 0.67 | 0.63 | 0.61 | 0.58 | 0.56 | 0.53 | 0.51 | 0.49 | 0.48 | 0.46 | 0.44 |
| | 1¾ | | 1.04 | 0.95 | 0.88 | 0.82 | 0.76 | 0.71 | 0.67 | 0.63 | 0.60 | 0.57 | 0.54 | 0.52 | 0.50 | 0.48 | 0.46 | 0.44 | 0.42 | 0.41 | 0.39 | 0.38 |
| | 2 | | | 0.83 | 0.77 | 0.71 | 0.67 | 0.62 | 0.59 | 0.56 | 0.53 | 0.50 | 0.48 | 0.45 | 0.43 | 0.42 | 0.40 | 0.38 | 0.37 | 0.36 | 0.34 | 0.33 |
| | 2¼ | | | | | 0.63 | 0.59 | 0.56 | 0.52 | 0.49 | 0.47 | 0.44 | 0.42 | 0.40 | 0.39 | 0.37 | 0.36 | 0.34 | 0.33 | 0.32 | 0.31 | 0.30 |
| | 2½ | | | | | | 0.53 | 0.50 | 0.47 | 0.44 | 0.42 | 0.40 | 0.38 | 0.36 | 0.35 | 0.33 | 0.32 | 0.31 | 0.30 | 0.29 | 0.28 | 0.27 |
| | 2¾ | | | | | | | | 0.43 | 0.40 | 0.38 | 0.36 | 0.35 | 0.33 | 0.32 | 0.30 | 0.29 | 0.28 | 0.27 | 0.26 | 0.25 | |
| | 3 | | | | | | | | | 0.37 | 0.35 | 0.33 | 0.32 | 0.30 | 0.29 | 0.28 | 0.27 | 0.26 | 0.25 | | | |
| ⅜ φ | 1½ | 2.93 | 2.67 | 2.44 | 2.26 | 2.09 | 1.95 | 1.83 | 1.72 | 1.63 | 1.54 | 1.47 | 1.40 | 1.33 | 1.27 | 1.22 | 1.17 | 1.13 | 1.09 | 1.05 | 1.01 | 0.98 |
| | 1¾ | | 2.29 | 2.09 | 1.93 | 1.80 | 1.68 | 1.57 | 1.48 | 1.40 | 1.32 | 1.26 | 1.20 | 1.14 | 1.09 | 1.05 | 1.01 | 0.97 | 0.93 | 0.90 | 0.87 | 0.84 |
| | 2 | | | 1.83 | 1.69 | 1.57 | 1.47 | 1.38 | 1.29 | 1.22 | 1.16 | 1.10 | 1.05 | 1.00 | 0.96 | 0.92 | 0.88 | 0.85 | 0.82 | 0.79 | 0.76 | 0.73 |
| | 2¼ | | | | | 1.40 | 1.30 | 1.22 | 1.15 | 1.09 | 1.03 | 0.98 | 0.93 | 0.89 | 0.85 | 0.81 | 0.78 | 0.75 | 0.72 | 0.70 | 0.67 | 0.65 |
| | 2½ | | | | | | 1.17 | 1.10 | 1.03 | 0.98 | 0.93 | 0.88 | 0.84 | 0.80 | 0.76 | 0.73 | 0.70 | 0.68 | 0.65 | 0.63 | 0.61 | 0.59 |
| | 2¾ | | | | | | | | 0.94 | 0.89 | 0.84 | 0.80 | 0.76 | 0.73 | 0.70 | 0.67 | 0.64 | 0.62 | 0.59 | 0.57 | 0.55 | 0.53 |
| | 3 | | | | | | | | | 0.81 | 0.77 | 0.73 | 0.70 | 0.67 | 0.64 | 0.61 | 0.59 | 0.56 | 0.54 | 0.52 | 0.51 | 0.49 |
| ½ φ | 2 | | | 3.33 | 3.08 | 2.86 | 2.67 | 2.50 | 2.35 | 2.22 | 2.11 | 2.00 | 1.90 | 1.82 | 1.74 | 1.67 | 1.60 | 1.54 | 1.48 | 1.43 | 1.38 | 1.33 |
| | 2¼ | | | | | 2.54 | 2.37 | 2.22 | 2.09 | 1.97 | 1.87 | 1.78 | 1.69 | 1.62 | 1.55 | 1.48 | 1.42 | 1.37 | 1.32 | 1.27 | 1.23 | 1.19 |
| | 2½ | | | | | | 2.13 | 2.00 | 1.88 | 1.78 | 1.68 | 1.60 | 1.52 | 1.45 | 1.39 | 1.33 | 1.28 | 1.23 | 1.19 | 1.14 | 1.10 | 1.07 |
| | 2¾ | | | | | | | | 1.71 | 1.62 | 1.53 | 1.45 | 1.38 | 1.32 | 1.26 | 1.21 | 1.16 | 1.12 | 1.08 | 1.04 | 1.00 | 0.97 |
| | 3 | | | | | | | | | 1.48 | 1.40 | 1.33 | 1.27 | 1.21 | 1.16 | 1.11 | 1.07 | 1.03 | 0.99 | 0.95 | 0.92 | 0.89 |
| ⅝ φ | 2¾ | | | | | | | | 2.65 | 2.50 | 2.37 | 2.25 | 2.15 | 2.05 | 1.96 | 1.88 | 1.80 | 1.73 | 1.67 | 1.61 | 1.55 | 1.50 |
| | 3 | | | | | | | | | 2.30 | 2.17 | 2.07 | 1.97 | 1.88 | 1.80 | 1.72 | 1.65 | 1.59 | 1.53 | 1.48 | 1.42 | 1.38 |

*Description of use of Table 27, Part 2:
Compute $P/A_c$
From uppor part of tablo, oolect 100p (poroontago of bar roinforoomont)
From lower part of table, select $A_s = pA_c$ and $100p'$ (percentage of spiral)

# Table 28. Spiral Columns; New York Code 1938

$$\frac{P \text{ (lb.)}}{f_c} = A_c + 15A_s + 50p'A_c^*$$

| $f'_c$ | 2000 | 2500 | 3000 | 3400 |
|---|---|---|---|---|
| $f_c$ | 500 | 625 | 750 | 850 |

## Part 1. Area of Core

| | *d:* Diameter of Core | | | | | | | | | | | | | | | | | | | | |
|---|---|---|---|---|---|---|---|---|---|---|---|---|---|---|---|---|---|---|---|---|---|
| | 10 | 11 | 12 | 13 | 14 | 15 | 16 | 17 | 18 | 19 | 20 | 21 | 22 | 23 | 24 | 25 | 26 | 27 | 28 | 29 | 30 |
| $A_c$ | 79 | 95 | 113 | 133 | 154 | 177 | 201 | 227 | 254 | 284 | 314 | 346 | 380 | 415 | 452 | 491 | 531 | 573 | 616 | 661 | 707 |

## Part 2. Transformed Area of Bars = $15A_s$

| Bar Size | Number of Bars | | | | | | | | | | | | | | | | | | | | |
|---|---|---|---|---|---|---|---|---|---|---|---|---|---|---|---|---|---|---|---|---|---|
| | 6 | 7 | 8 | 9 | 10 | 11 | 12 | 13 | 14 | 15 | 16 | 17 | 18 | 19 | 20 | 21 | 22 | 23 | 24 | 25 | 26 |
| ⅝ϕ | 28 | 33 | 37 | 42 | 47 | 51 | 56 | 60 | 65 | 70 | 74 | 79 | 84 | 88 | 93 | 98 | 102 | 107 | 112 | 116 | 121 |
| ¾ϕ | 40 | 46 | 53 | 59 | 66 | 73 | 79 | 86 | 92 | 99 | 106 | 112 | 119 | 125 | 132 | 139 | 145 | 152 | 158 | 165 | 172 |
| ⅞ϕ | 54 | 63 | 72 | 81 | 90 | 99 | 108 | 117 | 126 | 135 | 144 | 153 | 162 | 171 | 180 | 189 | 198 | 207 | 216 | 225 | 234 |
| 1ϕ | 71 | 83 | 95 | 107 | 119 | 130 | 142 | 154 | 166 | 178 | 190 | 201 | 213 | 225 | 237 | 249 | 261 | 273 | 284 | 296 | 308 |
| 1 □ | 90 | 105 | 120 | 135 | 150 | 165 | 180 | 195 | 210 | 225 | 240 | 255 | 270 | 285 | 300 | 315 | 330 | 345 | 360 | 375 | 390 |
| 1⅛ □ | 114 | 133 | 152 | 171 | 191 | 210 | 229 | 248 | 267 | 286 | 305 | 324 | 343 | 362 | 381 | 400 | 419 | 438 | 457 | 476 | 495 |
| 1¼ □ | 140 | 164 | 187 | 211 | 234 | 257 | 281 | 304 | 328 | 351 | 374 | 398 | 421 | 445 | 468 | 491 | 515 | 538 | 562 | 585 | 608 |

## Part 3. Minimum Transformed Area of Bars = $15 \times 0.0075A_g$; Maximum Transformed Area of Bars = $15 \times 0.04A_g$

| | Outside Dimension of SQUARE Columns | | | | | | | | | | | | | | | | | | | | |
|---|---|---|---|---|---|---|---|---|---|---|---|---|---|---|---|---|---|---|---|---|---|
| | 14 | 15 | 16 | 17 | 18 | 19 | 20 | 21 | 22 | 23 | 24 | 25 | 26 | 27 | 28 | 29 | 30 | 31 | 32 | 33 | 34 |
| Min. | 22 | 25 | 29 | 33 | 36 | 41 | 45 | 50 | 54 | 60 | 65 | 70 | 76 | 82 | 88 | 95 | 101 | 108 | 115 | 123 | 130 |
| Max. | 118 | 135 | 154 | 173 | 194 | 217 | 240 | 265 | 290 | 317 | 346 | 375 | 406 | 437 | 470 | 505 | 540 | 577 | 614 | 653 | 694 |
| | Outside Diameter of ROUND Columns | | | | | | | | | | | | | | | | | | | | |
| | 14 | 15 | 16 | 17 | 18 | 19 | 20 | 21 | 22 | 23 | 24 | 25 | 26 | 27 | 28 | 29 | 30 | 31 | 32 | 33 | 34 |
| Min. | 17 | 20 | 23 | 26 | 29 | 32 | 35 | 39 | 43 | 47 | 51 | 55 | 60 | 64 | 69 | 74 | 80 | 85 | 90 | 96 | 102 |
| Max. | 92 | 106 | 121 | 136 | 153 | 170 | 189 | 208 | 228 | 249 | 271 | 294 | 319 | 344 | 369 | 396 | 424 | 453 | 483 | 513 | 544 |

## Part 4. Maximum Number of Bars in Outer Ring, *O*, and in Inner Ring, *I*

| Bar Size | Ring | *d:* Diameter of Core | | | | | | | | | | | | | | | | | | | | |
|---|---|---|---|---|---|---|---|---|---|---|---|---|---|---|---|---|---|---|---|---|---|---|
| | | 10 | 11 | 12 | 13 | 14 | 15 | 16 | 17 | 18 | 19 | 20 | 21 | 22 | 23 | 24 | 25 | 26 | 27 | 28 | 29 | 30 |
| ⅝ϕ | *O* | **11** | **13** | **14** | **15** | **17** | **18** | **20** | **21** | **22** | **24** | **25** | **27** | **28** | **29** | **31** | **32** | **34** | **35** | **36** | **38** | **39** |
| | *I* | 7 | 8 | 9 | 11 | 12 | 14 | 15 | 16 | 18 | 19 | 21 | 22 | 23 | 25 | 26 | 28 | 29 | 30 | 32 | 33 | 35 |
| ¾ϕ | *O* | **9** | **11** | **12** | **13** | **14** | **15** | **17** | **18** | **19** | **20** | **21** | **23** | **24** | **25** | **26** | **27** | **29** | **30** | **31** | **32** | **33** |
| | *I* | 5 | 6 | 7 | 8 | 10 | 11 | 12 | 13 | 15 | 16 | 17 | 18 | 19 | 21 | 22 | 23 | 24 | 25 | 27 | 28 | 29 |
| ⅞ϕ | *O* | **8** | **9** | **10** | **11** | **12** | **13** | **14** | **15** | **16** | **17** | **18** | **19** | **20** | **21** | **22** | **23** | **24** | **25** | **26** | **27** | **28** |
| | *I* | — | 4 | 5 | 6 | 7 | 8 | 10 | 11 | 12 | 13 | 14 | 15 | 16 | 17 | 18 | 19 | 20 | 21 | 22 | 23 | 24 |
| 1ϕ | *O* | **7** | **8** | **8** | **9** | **10** | **11** | **12** | **13** | **14** | **15** | **16** | **17** | **17** | **18** | **19** | **20** | **21** | **22** | **23** | **24** | **25** |
| | *I* | — | — | 4 | 5 | 6 | 7 | 8 | 9 | 9 | 10 | 11 | 12 | 13 | 14 | 15 | 16 | 17 | 17 | 18 | 19 | 20 |
| 1 □ | *O* | **6** | **7** | **7** | **8** | **9** | **10** | **11** | **11** | **12** | **13** | **14** | **14** | **15** | **16** | **17** | **18** | **18** | **19** | **20** | **21** | **22** |
| | *I* | — | — | — | — | 4 | 5 | 6 | 7 | 7 | 8 | 9 | 10 | 11 | 11 | 12 | 13 | 14 | 14 | 15 | 16 | 17 |
| 1⅛ □ | *O* | — | **6** | **6** | **7** | **8** | **9** | **9** | **10** | **11** | **11** | **12** | **13** | **13** | **14** | **15** | **16** | **16** | **17** | **18** | **18** | **19** |
| | *I* | — | — | — | — | — | 4 | 4 | 5 | 6 | 7 | 7 | 8 | 9 | 9 | 10 | 11 | 11 | 12 | 13 | 14 | 14 |
| 1¼ □ | *O* | — | — | **6** | **6** | **7** | **8** | **8** | **9** | **9** | **10** | **11** | **11** | **12** | **13** | **13** | **14** | **14** | **15** | **16** | **16** | **17** |
| | *I* | — | — | — | — | — | — | — | 4 | 5 | 5 | 6 | 7 | 7 | 8 | 8 | 9 | 10 | 10 | 11 | 12 | 12 |

*$A_g$ to be not less than $\frac{1}{2}\frac{P}{f_c}$

# Table 28. *(continued)*

## Part 5. Transformed Area of Spirals $= 50\,p'A_C$*

Values of $50\pi \times \dfrac{\text{(Area of Spiral Rod)(Core Diameter)}}{\text{Pitch}}$ or $50\,A_C \times 0.02$

| Rod Size | Pitch | *d*: Diameter of Core | | | | | | | | | | | | | | | | | | | | |
|---|---|---|---|---|---|---|---|---|---|---|---|---|---|---|---|---|---|---|---|---|---|---|
| | | 10 | 11 | 12 | 13 | 14 | 15 | 16 | 17 | 18 | 19 | 20 | 21 | 22 | 23 | 24 | 25 | 26 | 27 | 28 | 29 | 30 |
| | 1¼ | 63 | 69 | 75 | 82 | 88 | 94 | 101 | 107 | 113 | 119 | 126 | 132 | 138 | 144 | 151 | 157 | 163 | 170 | 176 | 182 | 188 |
| | 1½ | 52 | 58 | 63 | 68 | 73 | 79 | 84 | 89 | 94 | 100 | 105 | 110 | 115 | 120 | 126 | 131 | 136 | | | | |
| | 1¾ | **45** | 49 | 54 | 58 | 63 | 67 | 72 | 76 | 81 | 85 | 90 | 94 | 99 | | | | | | | | |
| ¼φ | 2 | **39** | **43** | 47 | 51 | 55 | 59 | 63 | 67 | 71 | 75 | 79 | | | | | | | | | | |
| | 2¼ | **35** | **38** | **42** | **45** | 49 | 52 | 56 | 59 | | | | | | | | | | | | | |
| | 2½ | **31** | **35** | **38** | **41** | **44** | 47 | 50 | | | | | | | | | | | | | | |
| | 2¾ | **29** | **31** | **34** | **37** | **40** | | | | | | | | | | | | | | | | |
| | 3 | **26** | **29** | **31** | **34** | | | | | | | | | | | | | | | | | |
| | 1½ | 79 | 95 | 113 | 133 | 154 | 173 | 184 | 196 | 207 | 219 | 230 | 242 | 253 | 265 | 276 | 288 | 300 | 311 | 323 | 334 | 346 |
| | 1¾ | **79** | 95 | 113 | 128 | 138 | 148 | 158 | 168 | 178 | 188 | 198 | 207 | 217 | 227 | 237 | 247 | 257 | 267 | 277 | 286 | 296 |
| | 2 | **79** | **95** | 104 | 112 | 121 | 130 | 138 | 147 | 156 | 164 | 173 | 182 | 190 | 199 | 207 | 216 | 225 | 233 | 242 | 251 | 259 |
| ⅜φ | 2¼ | **77** | **85** | **92** | **100** | 108 | 115 | 123 | 131 | 138 | 146 | 154 | 161 | 169 | 177 | 184 | 192 | 200 | 207 | 215 | 223 | 230 |
| | 2½ | **69** | **76** | **83** | **90** | **97** | 104 | 111 | 118 | 124 | 131 | 138 | 145 | 152 | 159 | 166 | 173 | 180 | 187 | 194 | 200 | 207 |
| | 2¾ | **63** | **69** | **75** | **82** | **88** | **94** | **101** | 107 | 113 | 119 | 126 | 132 | 138 | 145 | 151 | 157 | 163 | 170 | 176 | 182 | 189 |
| | 3 | **58** | **63** | **69** | **75** | **81** | **86** | **92** | **98** | 104 | 109 | 115 | 121 | 127 | 132 | 138 | 144 | 150 | 156 | 161 | 167 | |
| | 3¼ | **53** | **58** | **64** | **69** | **74** | **80** | **85** | **90** | **96** | **101** | 106 | 112 | 117 | 122 | 128 | 133 | 138 | 144 | | | |
| | 1½ | | | 113 | 133 | 154 | 177 | 201 | 227 | 254 | 284 | 314 | 346 | 380 | 415 | 452 | 491 | 531 | 566 | 586 | 607 | 628 |
| | 1¾ | | | 113 | 133 | 154 | 177 | 201 | 227 | 254 | 284 | 314 | 346 | 380 | 413 | 431 | 449 | 467 | 484 | 502 | 520 | 539 |
| | 2 | | | 113 | 133 | 154 | 177 | 201 | 227 | 254 | 284 | 314 | 330 | 346 | 361 | 377 | 393 | 408 | 424 | 440 | 456 | 471 |
| | 2¼ | | | **113** | **133** | 154 | 177 | 201 | 227 | 251 | 265 | 279 | 293 | 307 | 321 | 335 | 349 | 363 | 377 | 391 | 405 | 419 |
| ½φ | 2½ | | | **113** | **133** | **154** | 177 | 201 | 214 | 226 | 239 | 251 | 264 | 277 | 289 | 302 | 314 | 327 | 339 | 352 | 364 | 377 |
| | 2¾ | | | **113** | **133** | **154** | **171** | **183** | 194 | 206 | 217 | 229 | 240 | 251 | 263 | 274 | 286 | 297 | 309 | 320 | 331 | 343 |
| | 3 | | | **113** | **133** | **147** | **157** | **168** | **178** | 188 | 199 | 209 | 220 | 230 | 241 | 251 | 262 | 272 | 283 | 293 | 304 | 314 |
| | 3¼ | | | **113** | **126** | **135** | **145** | **155** | **164** | **174** | **184** | 193 | 203 | 213 | 222 | 232 | 242 | 251 | 261 | 271 | 280 | 290 |
| | 3½ | | | **108** | **117** | **120** | **105** | **144** | **153** | **162** | **171** | **170** | 188 | 197 | 206 | 215 | 224 | 233 | 242 | 251 | 260 | 269 |
| | 2 | | | | | | 177 | 201 | 227 | 254 | 284 | 314 | 346 | 380 | 415 | 452 | 491 | 531 | 573 | 616 | 661 | 707 |
| | 2¼ | | | | | | 177 | 201 | 227 | 254 | 284 | 314 | 346 | 380 | 415 | 452 | 491 | 531 | 573 | 606 | 628 | 650 |
| | 2½ | | | | | | 177 | 201 | 227 | 254 | 284 | 314 | 346 | 380 | 415 | 452 | 487 | 506 | 526 | 546 | 565 | 584 |
| ⅝φ | 2¾ | | | | | | **177** | **201** | 227 | 254 | 284 | 314 | 346 | 380 | 408 | 425 | 443 | 461 | 478 | 496 | 514 | 532 |
| | 3 | | | | | | **177** | **201** | **227** | 254 | 284 | 314 | 341 | 357 | 373 | 390 | 406 | 422 | 438 | 455 | 471 | 487 |
| | 3¼ | | | | | | **177** | **201** | **227** | **254** | **284** | 300 | 315 | 330 | 345 | 360 | 375 | 390 | 405 | 420 | 435 | 450 |
| | 3½ | | | | | | **177** | **201** | **227** | **250** | **264** | **278** | 292 | 306 | 320 | 334 | 348 | 362 | 376 | 390 | 404 | 418 |

*But not less than five-sixths of transformed area of bars

Figures in bold type are for spirals with pitch greater than one-sixth of the core diameter, but the New York Code has no such limit

Minimum core diameter has been taken as 12 in. for ½-in. rd. bars and 15 in. for ⅝-in. rd. bars for all codes

# Table 29. Spiral Columns; Chicago Code 1937

$$P \text{ (kips)} = (0.225 f'_c A_c + f_r A_s + 2 f_r p' A_c) \div 1000$$

**Part 1. Load on Core (kips) = $0.225 f'_c A_c \div 1000$**

| $f'_c$ | d: Diameter of Core | | | | | | | | | | | | | | | | | | | | |
|---|---|---|---|---|---|---|---|---|---|---|---|---|---|---|---|---|---|---|---|---|---|
| | 10 | 11 | 12 | 13 | 14 | 15 | 16 | 17 | 18 | 19 | 20 | 21 | 22 | 23 | 24 | 25 | 26 | 27 | 28 | 29 | 30 |
| 2000 | 35 | 43 | 51 | 60 | 69 | 80 | 91 | 102 | 114 | 128 | 141 | 156 | 171 | 187 | 204 | 221 | 239 | 258 | 277 | 297 | 318 |
| 2500 | 44 | 53 | 64 | 75 | 87 | 99 | 113 | 128 | 143 | 159 | 177 | 195 | 214 | 234 | 254 | 276 | 299 | 322 | 346 | 372 | 398 |
| 3000 | 53 | 64 | 76 | 90 | 104 | 119 | 136 | 153 | 172 | 191 | 212 | 234 | 257 | 280 | 305 | 331 | 358 | 387 | 416 | 446 | 477 |
| 3750 | 66 | 80 | 95 | 112 | 130 | 149 | 170 | 192 | 215 | 239 | 265 | 292 | 321 | 350 | 382 | 414 | 448 | 483 | 519 | 557 | 596 |
| 5000 | 88 | 107 | 127 | 149 | 173 | 199 | 226 | 255 | 286 | 319 | 354 | 390 | 428 | 467 | 509 | 552 | 597 | 644 | 693 | 743 | 795 |

**Part 2.** { **Minimum Load on Bars (kips) = $f_r \times 0.01 A_c \div 1000$** or $f_r \times 6 \times 0.44 \div 1000$
**Maximum Load on Bars (kips) = $f_r \times 0.06 A_c \div 1000$** when stresses are transferred by bond

| | d: Diameter of Core | | | | | | | | | | | | | | | | | | | | |
|---|---|---|---|---|---|---|---|---|---|---|---|---|---|---|---|---|---|---|---|---|---|
| | 10 | 11 | 12 | 13 | 14 | 15 | 16 | 17 | 18 | 19 | 20 | 21 | 22 | 23 | 24 | 25 | 26 | 27 | 28 | 29 | 30 |
| | $f_r$ = 15,000 | | | | | | | | | | | | | | | | | | | | |
| Min. | 40 | 40 | 40 | 40 | 40 | 40 | 40 | 40 | 40 | 43 | 47 | 52 | 57 | 62 | 68 | 74 | 80 | 86 | 92 | 99 | 106 |
| Max. | 71 | 86 | 102 | 120 | 139 | 159 | 181 | 204 | 229 | 255 | 283 | 312 | 342 | 374 | 407 | 442 | 478 | 515 | 554 | 594 | 636 |
| | $f_r$ = 18,000 | | | | | | | | | | | | | | | | | | | | |
| Min. | 48 | 48 | 48 | 48 | 48 | 48 | 48 | 48 | 48 | 51 | 57 | 62 | 68 | 75 | 81 | 88 | 96 | 103 | 111 | 119 | 127 |
| Max. | 85 | 103 | 122 | 143 | 166 | 191 | 217 | 245 | 275 | 306 | 339 | 374 | 411 | 449 | 489 | 530 | 573 | 618 | 665 | 713 | 763 |

**Part 3. Load on Bars (kips) = $15A_s$ or $18A_s$**

| $f_r$ | Bar Size | Number of Bars | | | | | | | | | | | | | | | | | | | | |
|---|---|---|---|---|---|---|---|---|---|---|---|---|---|---|---|---|---|---|---|---|---|---|
| | | 6 | 7 | 8 | 9 | 10 | 11 | 12 | 13 | 14 | 15 | 16 | 17 | 18 | 19 | 20 | 21 | 22 | 23 | 24 | 25 | 26 |
| 15,000 | ¾φ | 40 | 46 | 53 | 59 | 66 | 73 | 79 | 86 | 92 | 99 | 106 | 112 | 119 | 125 | 132 | 139 | 145 | 152 | 158 | 165 | 172 |
| | ⅞φ | 54 | 63 | 72 | 81 | 90 | 99 | 108 | 117 | 126 | 135 | 144 | 153 | 162 | 171 | 180 | 189 | 198 | 207 | 216 | 225 | 234 |
| | 1φ | 71 | 83 | 95 | 107 | 119 | 130 | 142 | 154 | 166 | 178 | 190 | 201 | 213 | 225 | 237 | 249 | 261 | 273 | 284 | 296 | 308 |
| | 1 □ | 90 | 105 | 120 | 135 | 150 | 165 | 180 | 195 | 210 | 225 | 240 | 255 | 270 | 285 | 300 | 315 | 330 | 345 | 360 | 375 | 390 |
| | 1⅛ □ | 114 | 133 | 152 | 171 | 191 | 210 | 229 | 248 | 267 | 286 | 305 | 324 | 343 | 362 | 381 | 400 | 419 | 438 | 457 | 476 | 495 |
| | 1¼ □ | 140 | 164 | 187 | 211 | 234 | 257 | 281 | 304 | 328 | 351 | 374 | 398 | 421 | 445 | 468 | 491 | 515 | 538 | 562 | 585 | 608 |
| 18,000* | ¾φ | 48 | 55 | 63 | 71 | 79 | 87 | 95 | 103 | 111 | 119 | 127 | 135 | 143 | 150 | 158 | 166 | 174 | 182 | 190 | 198 | 206 |
| | ⅞φ | 65 | 76 | 86 | 97 | 108 | 119 | 130 | 140 | 151 | 162 | 173 | 184 | 194 | 205 | 216 | 227 | 238 | 248 | 259 | 270 | 281 |
| | 1φ | 85 | 100 | 114 | 128 | 142 | 156 | 171 | 185 | 199 | 213 | 228 | 242 | 256 | 270 | 284 | 299 | 313 | 327 | 341 | 356 | 370 |
| | 1 □ | 108 | 126 | 144 | 162 | 180 | 198 | 216 | 234 | 252 | 270 | 288 | 306 | 324 | 342 | 360 | 378 | 396 | 414 | 432 | 450 | 468 |
| | 1⅛ □ | 137 | 160 | 183 | 206 | 229 | 251 | 274 | 297 | 320 | 343 | 366 | 389 | 411 | 434 | 457 | 480 | 503 | 526 | 549 | 572 | 594 |
| | 1¼ □ | 168 | 197 | 225 | 253 | 281 | 309 | 337 | 365 | 393 | 421 | 449 | 477 | 505 | 534 | 562 | 590 | 618 | 646 | 674 | 702 | 730 |

**Part 4. Maximum Number of Bars in Outer Ring, *O*, and in Inner Ring, *I***

| Bar Size | Ring | d: Diameter of Core | | | | | | | | | | | | | | | | | | | | |
|---|---|---|---|---|---|---|---|---|---|---|---|---|---|---|---|---|---|---|---|---|---|---|
| | | 10 | 11 | 12 | 13 | 14 | 15 | 16 | 17 | 18 | 19 | 20 | 21 | 22 | 23 | 24 | 25 | 26 | 27 | 28 | 29 | 30 |
| ¾φ | *O* | **10** | **11** | **12** | **14** | **15** | **16** | **17** | **19** | **20** | **21** | **22** | **24** | **25** | **26** | **28** | **29** | **30** | **31** | **33** | **34** | **35** |
| | *I* | — | — | — | 4 | 6 | 7 | 8 | 9 | 11 | 12 | 13 | 14 | 16 | 17 | 18 | 19 | 21 | 22 | 23 | 24 | 26 |
| ⅞φ | *O* | **9** | **10** | **11** | **12** | **13** | **15** | **16** | **17** | **18** | **19** | **20** | **21** | **23** | **24** | **25** | **26** | **27** | **28** | **29** | **31** | **32** |
| | *I* | — | — | — | — | 5 | 6 | 7 | 8 | 9 | 10 | 11 | 13 | 14 | 15 | 16 | 17 | 18 | 19 | 21 | 22 | 23 |
| 1φ | *O* | **8** | **9** | **10** | **11** | **12** | **13** | **14** | **15** | **16** | **17** | **18** | **19** | **20** | **22** | **23** | **24** | **25** | **26** | **27** | **28** | **29** |
| | *I* | — | — | — | — | 4 | 5 | 6 | 7 | 8 | 9 | 10 | 11 | 12 | 13 | 14 | 15 | 16 | 17 | 18 | 19 | 20 |
| 1 □ | *O* | **7** | **8** | **8** | **9** | **10** | **11** | **12** | **13** | **14** | **15** | **16** | **17** | **17** | **18** | **19** | **20** | **21** | **22** | **23** | **24** | **25** |
| | *I* | — | — | — | — | — | 4 | 5 | 6 | 7 | 8 | 8 | 9 | 10 | 11 | 12 | 13 | 14 | 15 | 16 | 17 | 18 |
| 1⅛ □ | *O* | **6** | **7** | **7** | **8** | **9** | **10** | **11** | **11** | **12** | **13** | **14** | **15** | **15** | **16** | **17** | **18** | **19** | **19** | **20** | **21** | **22** |
| | *I* | — | — | — | — | — | — | 4 | 5 | 6 | 6 | 7 | 8 | 9 | 10 | 10 | 11 | 12 | 13 | 14 | 14 | 15 |
| 1¼ □ | *O* | — | **6** | **7** | **7** | **8** | **9** | **9** | **10** | **11** | **12** | **12** | **13** | **14** | **14** | **15** | **16** | **17** | **17** | **18** | **19** | **19** |
| | *I* | — | — | — | — | — | — | — | 4 | 5 | 5 | 6 | 7 | 8 | 8 | 9 | 10 | 10 | 11 | 12 | 13 | 13 |

*Allowed for steel with yield point of 50,000 psi., provided material is identified by marking rolled into the surface during manufacture

## Part 5. Minimum Load on Spirals (kips)

$$\text{Values of } \frac{0.125f'_c}{f_r}\left(\frac{A_g}{A_c}-1\right)\frac{2f_rA_c}{1000}=\frac{\pi}{16{,}000}(6d+9)f'_c$$

$$\text{or } 0.01\,f_rA_c \div 1000$$

| $f'_c$ | d: Diameter of Core 10 | 11 | 12 | 13 | 14 | 15 | 16 | 17 | 18 | 19 | 20 | 21 | 22 | 23 | 24 | 25 | 26 | 27 | 28 | 29 | 30 |
|---|---|---|---|---|---|---|---|---|---|---|---|---|---|---|---|---|---|---|---|---|---|
| | Hot Rolled: $f_r$ = 15,000 | | | | | | | | | | | | | | | | | | | | |
| 2000 | 27 | 29 | 32 | 34 | 37 | 39 | 41 | 44 | 46 | 48 | 51 | 53 | 57 | 62 | 68 | 74 | 80 | 86 | 92 | 99 | 106 |
| 2500 | 34 | 37 | 40 | 43 | 46 | 49 | 52 | 55 | 57 | 60 | 63 | 66 | 69 | 72 | 75 | 78 | 81 | 86 | 92 | 99 | 106 |
| 3000 | 41 | 44 | 48 | 51 | 55 | 58 | 62 | 65 | 69 | 72 | 76 | 80 | 83 | 87 | 90 | 94 | 97 | 101 | 104 | 108 | 111 |
| 3750 | 51 | 55 | 60 | 64 | 69 | 73 | 77 | 82 | 86 | 91 | 95 | 99 | 104 | 108 | 113 | 117 | 122 | 126 | 130 | 135 | 139 |
| 5000 | 68 | 74 | 80 | 85 | 91 | 97 | 103 | 109 | 115 | 121 | 127 | 133 | 138 | 144 | 150 | 156 | 162 | 168 | 174 | 180 | 186 |
| | Cold Drawn: $f_r$ = 20,000 | | | | | | | | | | | | | | | | | | | | |
| 2000 | 27 | 29 | 32 | 34 | 37 | 39 | 41 | 45 | 51 | 57 | 63 | 69 | 76 | 83 | 90 | 98 | 106 | 115 | 123 | 132 | 141 |
| 2500 | 34 | 37 | 40 | 43 | 46 | 49 | 52 | 55 | 57 | 60 | 63 | 69 | 76 | 83 | 90 | 98 | 106 | 115 | 123 | 132 | 141 |
| 3000 | 41 | 44 | 48 | 51 | 55 | 58 | 62 | 65 | 69 | 72 | 76 | 80 | 83 | 87 | 90 | 98 | 106 | 115 | 123 | 132 | 141 |
| 3750 | 51 | 55 | 60 | 64 | 69 | 73 | 77 | 82 | 86 | 91 | 95 | 99 | 104 | 108 | 113 | 117 | 122 | 126 | 130 | 135 | 141 |
| 5000 | 68 | 74 | 80 | 85 | 91 | 97 | 103 | 109 | 115 | 121 | 127 | 133 | 138 | 144 | 150 | 156 | 162 | 168 | 174 | 180 | 186 |

## Part 6. Load on Spirals (kips)

$$\text{Values of } 2\pi\,\frac{\text{(Area of Spiral Rod) (Core Diameter)}}{\text{Pitch}}\times\frac{f_r}{1000}$$

$$\text{or } \pi d^2 f_r \div 100{,}000 \text{ for } p' \geqq 0.02$$

| Rod Size | Pitch | d: Diameter of Core 10 | 11 | 12 | 13 | 14 | 15 | 16 | 17 | 18 | 19 | 20 | 21 | 22 | 23 | 24 | 25 | 26 | 27 | 28 | 29 | 30 |
|---|---|---|---|---|---|---|---|---|---|---|---|---|---|---|---|---|---|---|---|---|---|---|
| | | Hot Rolled: $f_r$ = 15,000. Load on Spiral ÷ Load on Bars ≦ 4/3* or 10/9** | | | | | | | | | | | | | | | | | | | | |
| ¼φ | 1¼ | 38 | 41 | 45 | 49 | 53 | 57 | 60 | 64 | 68 | 72 | 76 | 79 | 83 | 87 | 91 | 94 | 98 | 102 | 106 | 109 | 113 |
| | 1½ | 31 | 35 | 38 | 41 | 44 | 47 | 50 | 53 | 57 | 60 | 63 | 66 | 69 | 72 | 75 | 79 | 82 | | | | |
| | 1¾ | | 30 | 32 | 35 | 38 | 40 | 43 | 46 | 48 | 51 | 54 | 57 | 59 | 62 | | | | | | | |
| ⅜φ | 1½ | 47 | 57 | 68 | 80 | 92 | 104 | 111 | 118 | 124 | 131 | 138 | 145 | 152 | 159 | 166 | 173 | 180 | 187 | 194 | 200 | 207 |
| | 1¾ | | 57 | 68 | 77 | 83 | 89 | 95 | 101 | 107 | 113 | 119 | 124 | 130 | 136 | 142 | 148 | 154 | 160 | 166 | 172 | 178 |
| | 2 | | | 62 | 67 | 73 | 78 | 83 | 88 | 93 | 99 | 104 | 109 | 114 | 119 | 124 | 130 | 135 | 140 | 145 | 150 | 156 |
| | 2¼ | | | | | 65 | 69 | 74 | 78 | 83 | 88 | 92 | 97 | 101 | 106 | 111 | 115 | 120 | 124 | 129 | 134 | 138 |
| | 2½ | | | | | | 62 | 66 | 71 | 75 | 79 | 83 | 87 | 91 | 95 | 100 | 104 | 108 | 112 | 116 | 120 | 124 |
| | 2¾ | | | | | | | | 64 | 68 | 72 | 75 | 79 | 83 | 87 | 91 | 94 | 98 | 102 | 106 | 109 | 113 |
| | 3 | | | | | | | | | 62 | 66 | 69 | 73 | 76 | 79 | 83 | 86 | 90 | 93 | 97 | 100 | |
| ½φ | 1¾ | | | 68 | 80 | 92 | 106 | 121 | 136 | 153 | 170 | 189 | 208 | 228 | 248 | 259 | 269 | 280 | 291 | 302 | 312 | 323 |
| | 2 | | | 68 | 80 | 92 | 106 | 121 | 136 | 153 | 170 | 189 | 198 | 207 | 217 | 226 | 236 | 245 | 254 | 264 | 273 | 283 |
| | 2¼ | | | | | 92 | 106 | 121 | 136 | 151 | 159 | 168 | 176 | 184 | 192 | 201 | 209 | 218 | 226 | 235 | 243 | 251 |
| | 2½ | | | | | | 106 | 121 | 128 | 136 | 143 | 151 | 158 | 166 | 173 | 181 | 189 | 196 | 204 | 211 | 219 | 226 |
| | 2¾ | | | | | | | | 117 | 123 | 130 | 137 | 144 | 151 | 158 | 165 | 171 | 178 | 185 | 192 | 199 | 206 |
| | 3 | | | | | | | | | 113 | 119 | 126 | 132 | 138 | 145 | 151 | 157 | 163 | 170 | 176 | 182 | 189 |
| ⅝φ | 2¼ | | | | | | 106 | 121 | 136 | 153 | 170 | 189 | 208 | 228 | 249 | 272 | 295 | 319 | 344 | 364 | 377 | 390 |
| | 2½ | | | | | | 106 | 121 | 136 | 153 | 170 | 189 | 208 | 228 | 249 | 272 | 292 | 304 | 316 | 327 | 339 | 351 |
| | 2¾ | | | | | | | | 136 | 153 | 170 | 189 | 208 | 228 | 244 | 255 | 266 | 276 | 287 | 298 | 308 | 319 |
| | 3 | | | | | | | | | 153 | 170 | 189 | 205 | 214 | 224 | 234 | 244 | 253 | 263 | 273 | 283 | 292 |
| | | Cold Drawn: $f_r$ = 20,000. Load on Spiral ÷ Load on Bars ≦ 16/9* or 40/27** | | | | | | | | | | | | | | | | | | | | |
| ¼φ | 1¼ | 50 | 55 | 60 | 65 | 70 | 75 | 80 | 85 | 91 | 96 | 101 | 106 | 111 | 116 | 121 | 126 | 131 | 136 | 141 | 146 | 151 |
| | 1½ | 42 | 46 | 50 | 54 | 59 | 63 | 67 | 71 | 75 | 80 | 84 | 88 | 92 | 96 | 101 | 105 | 109 | | | | |
| | 1¾ | | 40 | 43 | 47 | 50 | 54 | 57 | 61 | 65 | 68 | 72 | 75 | 79 | 83 | | | | | | | |
| | 2 | | | 38 | 41 | 44 | 47 | 50 | 53 | 57 | 60 | 63 | | | | | | | | | | |
| | 2¼ | | | | | 39 | 42 | 45 | 47 | | | | | | | | | | | | | |
| ⅜φ | 1½ | 63 | 76 | 90 | 106 | 123 | 138 | 147 | 157 | 166 | 175 | 184 | 193 | 203 | 212 | 221 | 230 | 240 | 249 | 258 | 267 | 276 |
| | 1¾ | | 76 | 90 | 103 | 111 | 118 | 126 | 134 | 142 | 150 | 158 | 166 | 174 | 182 | 190 | 197 | 205 | 213 | 221 | 229 | 237 |
| | 2 | | | 83 | 90 | 97 | 104 | 111 | 117 | 124 | 131 | 138 | 145 | 152 | 159 | 166 | 173 | 180 | 187 | 194 | 200 | 207 |
| | 2¼ | | | | | 86 | 92 | 98 | 104 | 111 | 117 | 123 | 129 | 135 | 141 | 147 | 154 | 160 | 166 | 172 | 178 | 184 |
| | 2½ | | | | | | 83 | 88 | 94 | 100 | 105 | 111 | 116 | 122 | 127 | 133 | 138 | 144 | 149 | 155 | 160 | 166 |
| | 2¾ | | | | | | | | 85 | 90 | 95 | 101 | 106 | 111 | 116 | 121 | 126 | 131 | 136 | 141 | 146 | 151 |
| | 3 | | | | | | | | | 83 | 88 | 92 | 97 | 101 | 106 | 111 | 115 | 120 | 124 | 129 | 134 | |
| ½φ | 1¾ | | | 90 | 106 | 123 | 141 | 161 | 182 | 204 | 227 | 251 | 277 | 304 | 330 | 345 | 359 | 373 | 388 | 402 | 417 | 431 |
| | 2 | | | 90 | 106 | 123 | 141 | 161 | 182 | 204 | 227 | 251 | 264 | 277 | 289 | 302 | 314 | 327 | 339 | 352 | 364 | 377 |
| | 2¼ | | | | | 123 | 141 | 161 | 182 | 201 | 212 | 223 | 235 | 246 | 257 | 268 | 279 | 290 | 302 | 313 | 324 | 335 |
| | 2½ | | | | | | 141 | 161 | 171 | 181 | 191 | 201 | 211 | 221 | 231 | 241 | 251 | 261 | 272 | 282 | 292 | 302 |
| | 2¾ | | | | | | | | 155 | 165 | 174 | 183 | 192 | 201 | 210 | 219 | 229 | 238 | 247 | 256 | 265 | 274 |
| | 3 | | | | | | | | | 151 | 159 | 168 | 176 | 184 | 193 | 201 | 210 | 218 | 226 | 235 | 243 | 251 |
| ⅝φ | 2¼ | | | | | | 141 | 161 | 182 | 204 | 227 | 251 | 277 | 304 | 332 | 362 | 393 | 425 | 458 | 485 | 502 | 520 |
| | 2½ | | | | | | 141 | 161 | 182 | 204 | 227 | 251 | 277 | 304 | 332 | 362 | 390 | 405 | 421 | 437 | 452 | 468 |
| | 2¾ | | | | | | | | 182 | 204 | 227 | 251 | 277 | 304 | 326 | 340 | 354 | 368 | 383 | 397 | 411 | 425 |
| | 3 | | | | | | | | | 204 | 227 | 251 | 273 | 286 | 299 | 312 | 325 | 338 | 351 | 364 | 377 | 390 |

*For bars stressed to 15,000 psi.
**For bars stressed to 18,000 psi.

## Diagram 30. Eccentrically Loaded Rectangular Columns with Ties*

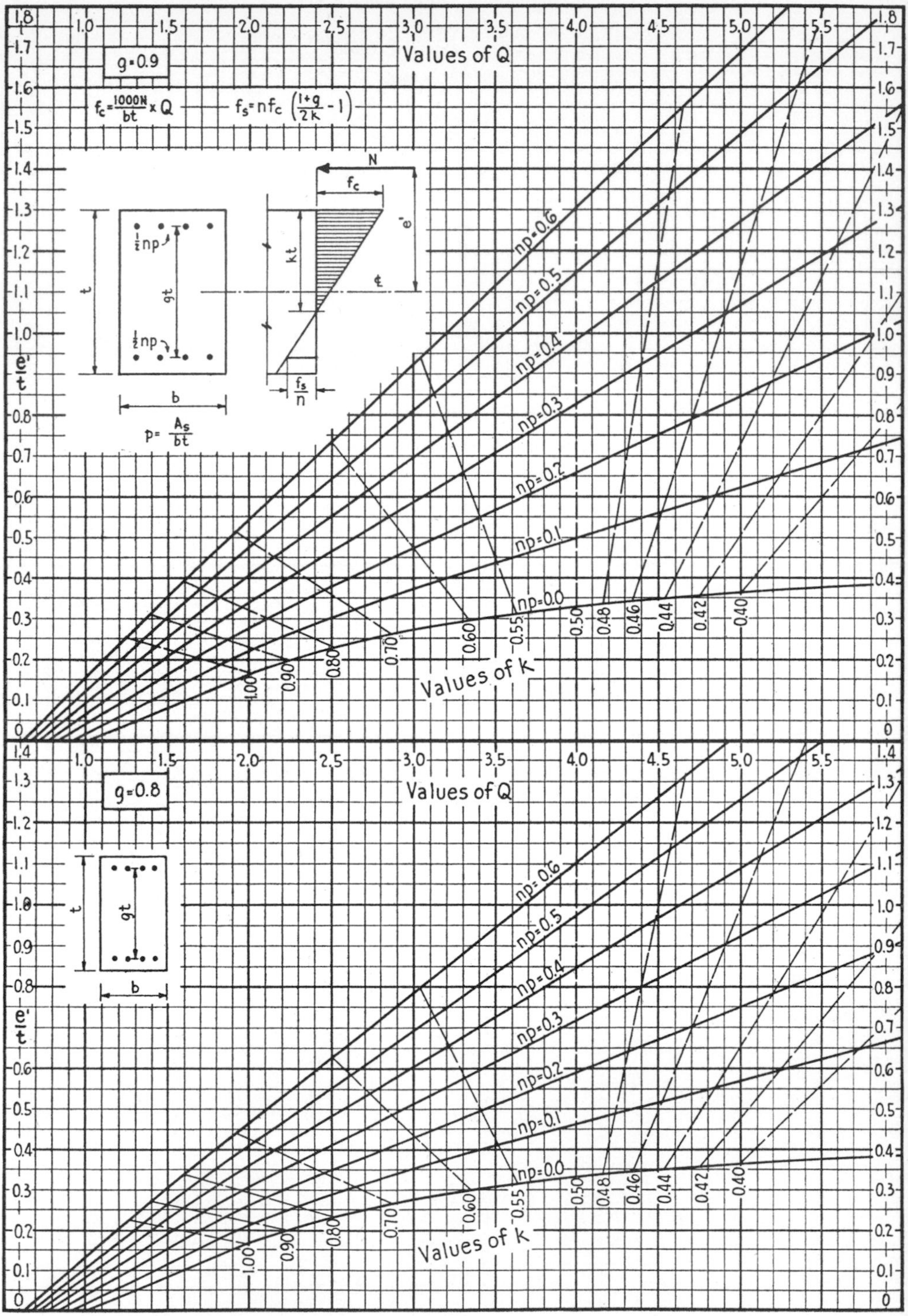


*For application of Diagrams 30, 31 and 32, see Examples 32 to 36.

**Diagram 30. (*continued*)**

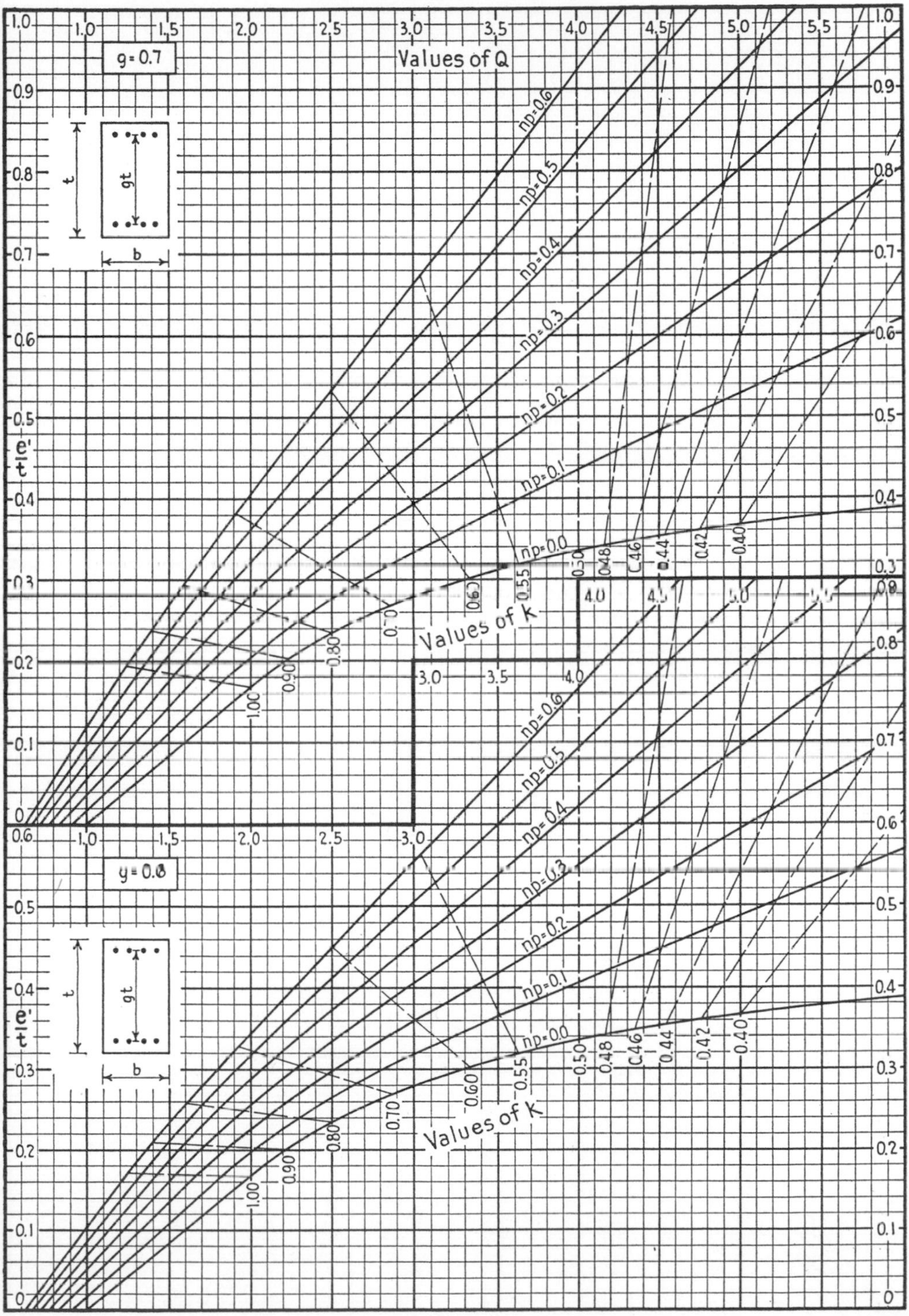

## Diagram 31. Eccentrically Loaded Square Columns with Spirals

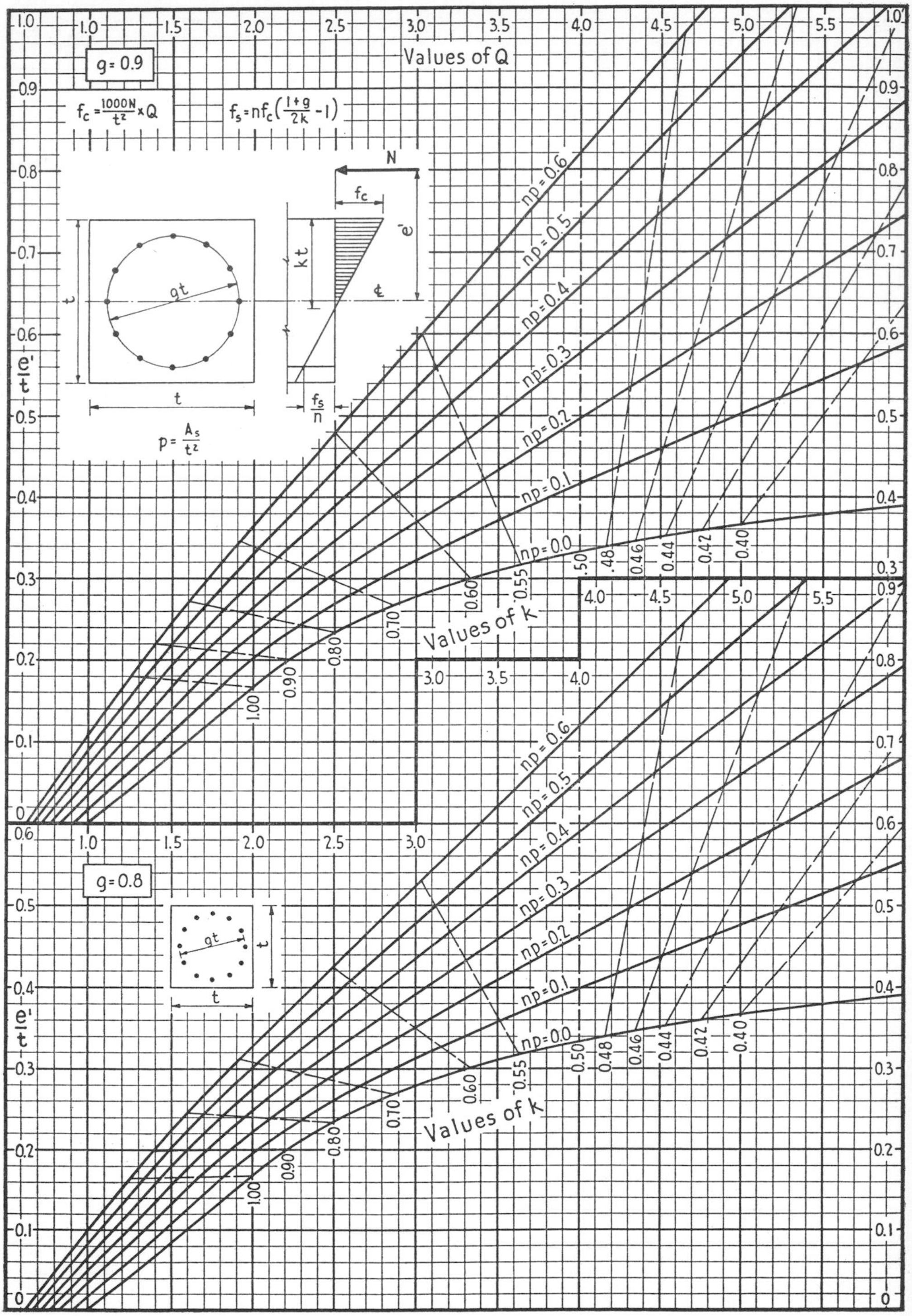

## Diagram 31. (*continued*)

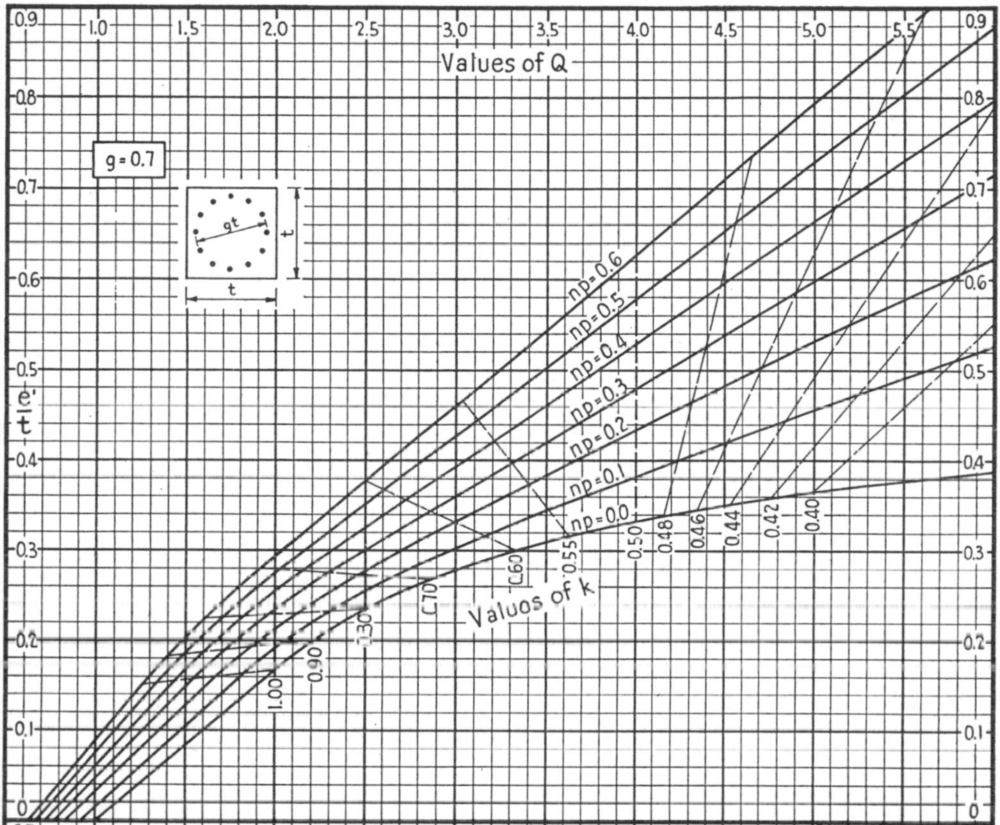


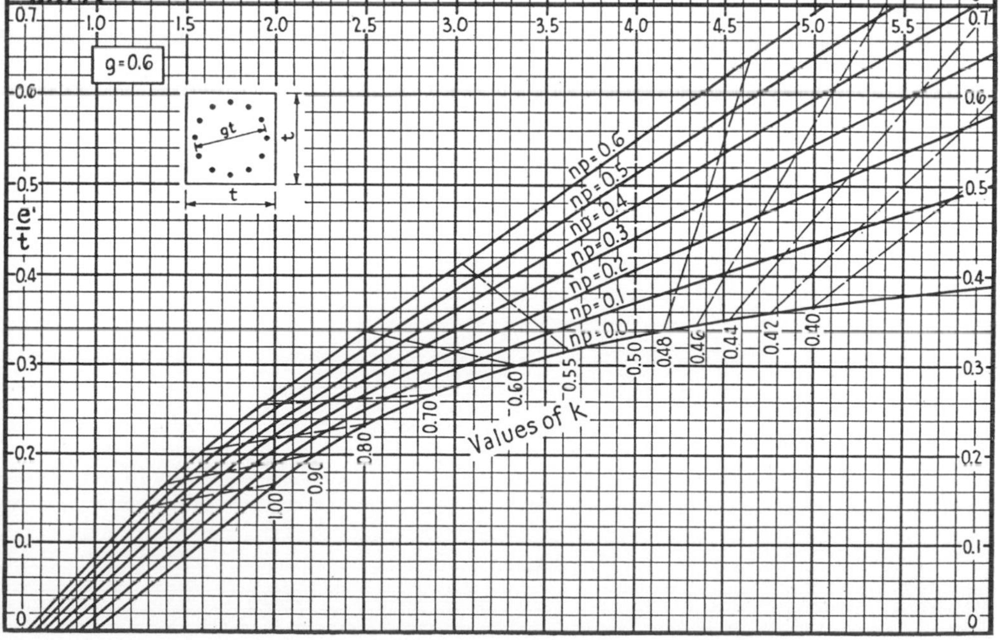

**Diagram 32. Eccentrically Loaded Round Columns with Spirals**

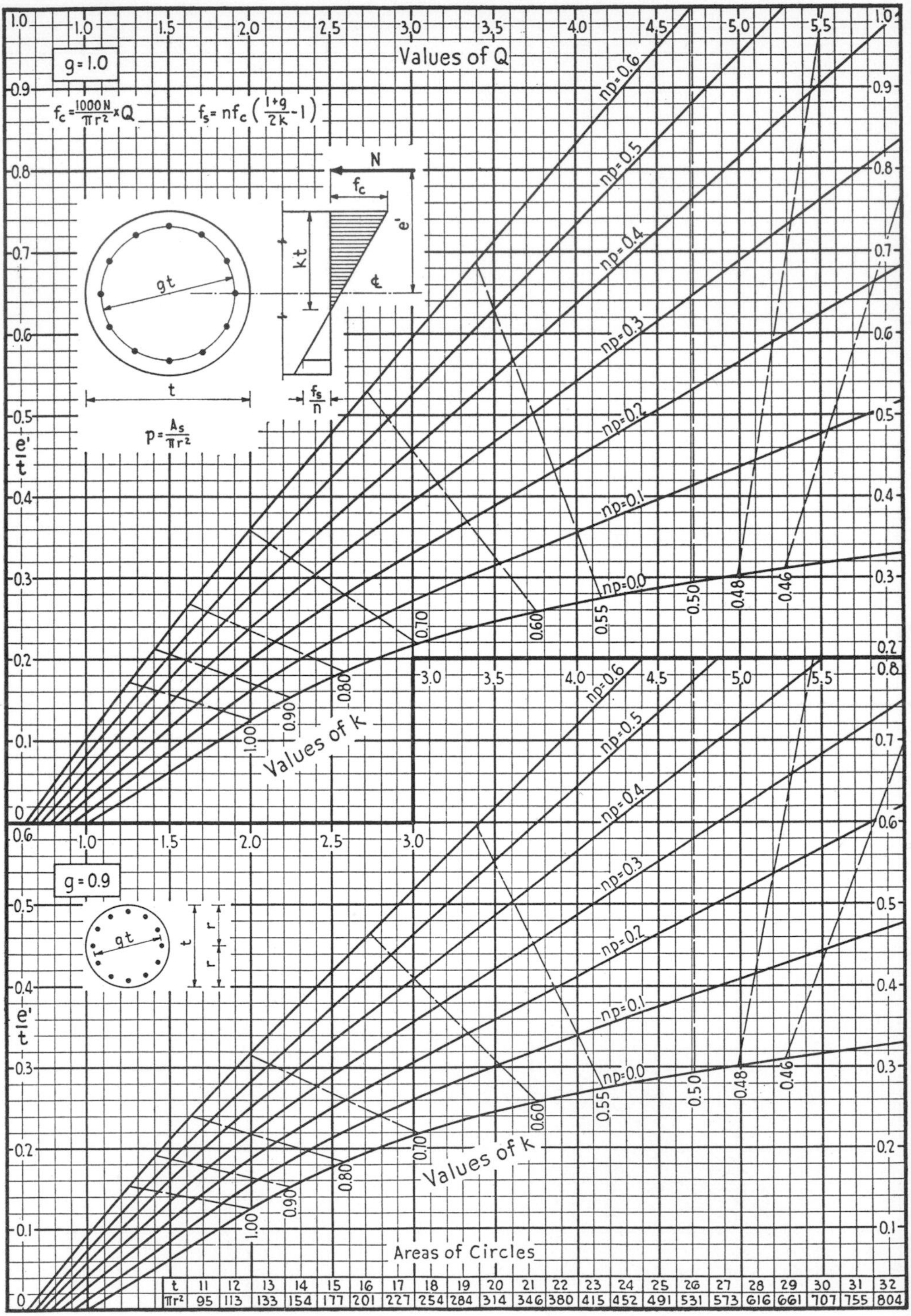

**Diagram 32. (*continued*)**

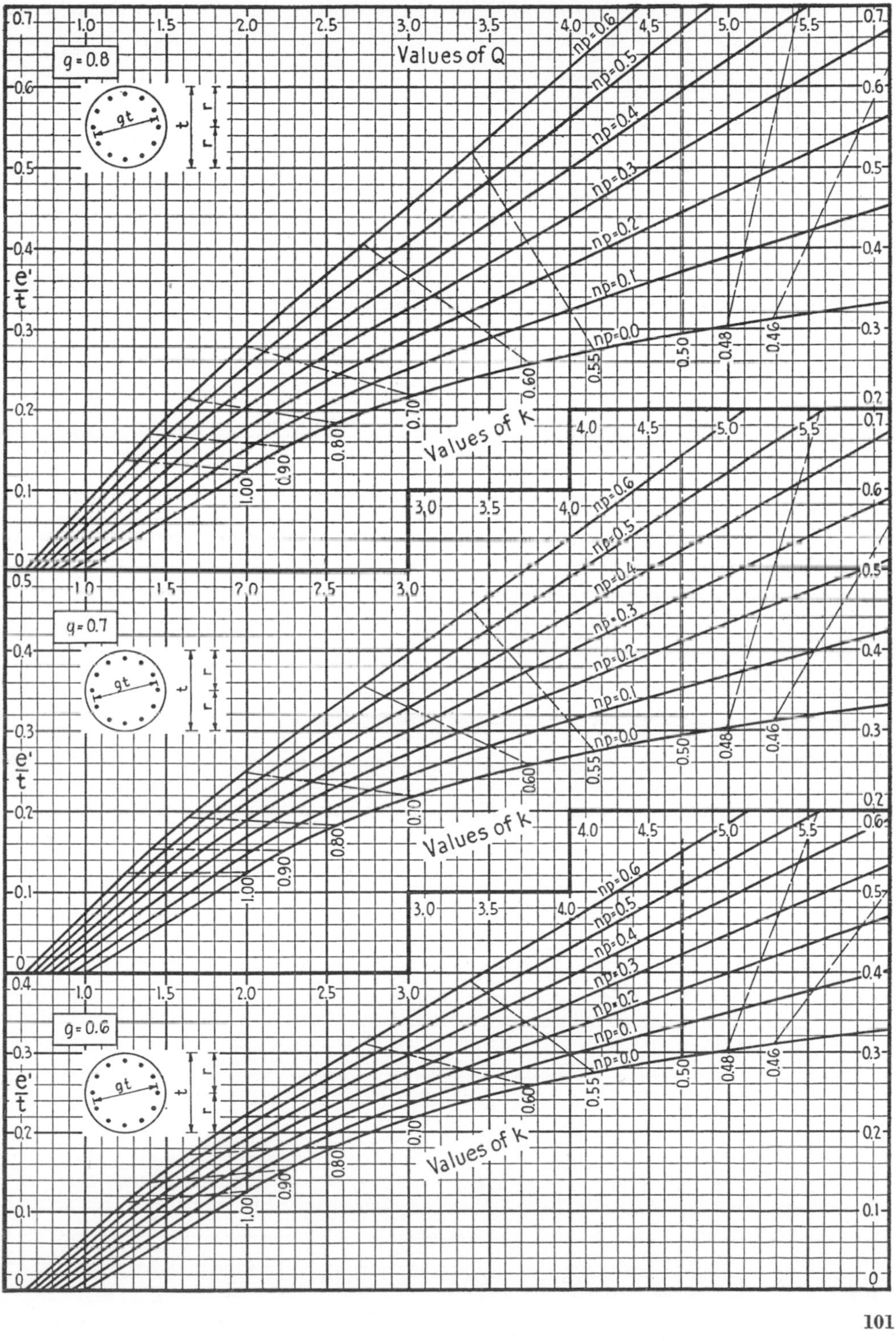

# Table 33. Coefficients ($D$) for Determination of Allowable Stress in Eccentrically Loaded Columns

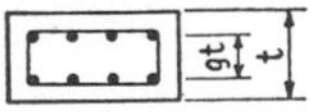


$$D = \frac{1 + (n-1)p}{\frac{1}{6} + \frac{1}{2}(n-1)pg^2}$$

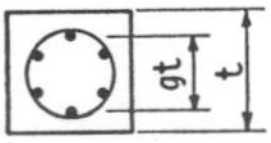


$$D = \frac{1 + (n-1)p}{\frac{1}{6} + \frac{1}{4}(n-1)pg^2}$$

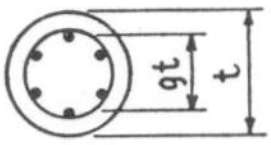


$$D = \frac{1 + (n-1)p}{\frac{1}{8} + \frac{1}{4}(n-1)pg^2}$$

**Values of** $D = \frac{t^2}{2R^2}$

in which $R$ = radius of gyration

$p = \frac{A_s}{A_g}$, in which $A_g$ = gross area of concrete section

All reinforcement is arranged symmetrically

$D$ is used for determination of $f_p$ in eccentrically loaded columns*

| $g$ | $(n-1)p$ | | | | | | | | | | | | | | | | |
|---|---|---|---|---|---|---|---|---|---|---|---|---|---|---|---|---|---|
| | 0.0 | 0.05 | 0.10 | 0.15 | 0.20 | 0.25 | 0.30 | 0.35 | 0.40 | 0.45 | 0.50 | 0.55 | 0.60 | 0.65 | 0.70 | 0.75 | 0.80 |
| | **Rectangular Sections with Ties** | | | | | | | | | | | | | | | | |
| 1.00 | 6.0 | 5.5 | 5.1 | 4.8 | 4.5 | 4.3 | 4.1 | 4.0 | 3.8 | 3.7 | 3.6 | 3.5 | 3.4 | 3.4 | 3.3 | 3.2 | 3.2 |
| 0.95 | 6.0 | 5.5 | 5.2 | 4.9 | 4.7 | 4.5 | 4.3 | 4.2 | 4.0 | 3.9 | 3.8 | 3.7 | 3.7 | 3.6 | 3.5 | 3.5 | 3.4 |
| 0.90 | 6.0 | 5.6 | 5.3 | 5.1 | 4.8 | 4.7 | 4.5 | 4.4 | 4.3 | 4.2 | 4.1 | 4.0 | 3.9 | 3.8 | 3.8 | 3.7 | 3.7 |
| 0.85 | 6.0 | 5.7 | 5.4 | 5.2 | 5.0 | 4.9 | 4.7 | 4.6 | 4.5 | 4.4 | 4.3 | 4.2 | 4.2 | 4.1 | 4.1 | 4.0 | 4.0 |
| 0.80 | 6.0 | 5.7 | 5.5 | 5.4 | 5.2 | 5.1 | 4.9 | 4.8 | 4.7 | 4.7 | 4.6 | 4.5 | 4.5 | 4.4 | 4.3 | 4.3 | 4.3 |
| 0.75 | 6.0 | 5.8 | 5.6 | 5.5 | 5.4 | 5.3 | 5.2 | 5.1 | 5.0 | 4.9 | 4.9 | 4.8 | 4.8 | 4.7 | 4.7 | 4.6 | 4.6 |
| 0.70 | 6.0 | 5.9 | 5.7 | 5.6 | 5.6 | 5.5 | 5.4 | 5.3 | 5.3 | 5.2 | 5.2 | 5.1 | 5.1 | 5.1 | 5.0 | 5.0 | 5.0 |
| 0.65 | 6.0 | 5.9 | 5.9 | 5.8 | 5.7 | 5.7 | 5.6 | 5.6 | 5.6 | 5.5 | 5.5 | 5.5 | 5.4 | 5.4 | 5.4 | 5.4 | 5.4 |
| 0.60 | 6.0 | 6.0 | 6.0 | 5.9 | 5.9 | 5.9 | 5.9 | 5.9 | 5.9 | 5.9 | 5.8 | 5.8 | 5.8 | 5.8 | 5.8 | 5.8 | 5.8 |
| | **Square Sections with Spirals** | | | | | | | | | | | | | | | | |
| 1.00 | 6.0 | 5.9 | 5.7 | 5.6 | 5.5 | 5.5 | 5.4 | 5.3 | 5.3 | 5.2 | 5.1 | 5.1 | 5.1 | 5.0 | 5.0 | 4.9 | 4.9 |
| 0.95 | 6.0 | 5.9 | 5.8 | 5.7 | 5.7 | 5.6 | 5.5 | 5.5 | 5.5 | 5.4 | 5.4 | 5.3 | 5.3 | 5.3 | 5.2 | 5.2 | 5.2 |
| 0.90 | 6.0 | 5.9 | 5.9 | 5.8 | 5.8 | 5.7 | 5.7 | 5.7 | 5.7 | 5.6 | 5.6 | 5.6 | 5.5 | 5.5 | 5.5 | 5.5 | 5.5 |
| 0.85 | 6.0 | 6.0 | 5.9 | 5.9 | 5.9 | 5.9 | 5.9 | 5.9 | 5.9 | 5.8 | 5.8 | 5.8 | 5.8 | 5.8 | 5.8 | 5.8 | 5.8 |
| 0.80 | 6.0 | 6.0 | 6.0 | 6.0 | 6.0 | 6.0 | 6.1 | 6.1 | 6.1 | 6.1 | 6.1 | 6.1 | 6.1 | 6.1 | 6.1 | 6.1 | 6.1 |
| 0.75 | 6.0 | 6.0 | 6.1 | 6.1 | 6.2 | 6.2 | 6.2 | 6.3 | 6.3 | 6.3 | 6.3 | 6.4 | 6.4 | 6.4 | 6.4 | 6.4 | 6.4 |
| 0.70 | 6.0 | 6.1 | 6.1 | 6.2 | 6.3 | 6.3 | 6.4 | 6.4 | 6.5 | 6.5 | 6.6 | 6.6 | 6.7 | 6.7 | 6.7 | 6.8 | 6.8 |
| 0.65 | 6.0 | 6.1 | 6.2 | 6.3 | 6.4 | 6.5 | 6.5 | 6.6 | 6.7 | 6.8 | 6.8 | 6.9 | 7.0 | 7.0 | 7.1 | 7.1 | 7.2 |
| 0.60 | 6.0 | 6.1 | 6.3 | 6.4 | 6.5 | 6.6 | 6.7 | 6.8 | 6.9 | 7.0 | 7.1 | 7.2 | 7.2 | 7.3 | 7.4 | 7.5 | 7.5 |
| | **Round Sections with Spirals** | | | | | | | | | | | | | | | | |
| 1.00 | 8.0 | 7.6 | 7.3 | 7.1 | 6.9 | 6.7 | 6.5 | 6.4 | 6.2 | 6.1 | 6.0 | 5.9 | 5.8 | 5.7 | 5.7 | 5.6 | 5.5 |
| 0.95 | 8.0 | 7.7 | 7.5 | 7.2 | 7.1 | 6.9 | 6.7 | 6.6 | 6.5 | 6.4 | 6.3 | 6.2 | 6.1 | 6.1 | 6.0 | 6.0 | 5.9 |
| 0.90 | 8.0 | 7.8 | 7.6 | 7.4 | 7.3 | 7.1 | 7.0 | 6.9 | 6.8 | 6.7 | 6.6 | 6.6 | 6.5 | 6.4 | 6.4 | 6.3 | 6.3 |
| 0.85 | 8.0 | 7.8 | 7.7 | 7.6 | 7.4 | 7.3 | 7.3 | 7.2 | 7.1 | 7.0 | 7.0 | 6.9 | 6.9 | 6.8 | 6.8 | 6.7 | 6.7 |
| 0.80 | 8.0 | 7.9 | 7.8 | 7.7 | 7.6 | 7.6 | 7.5 | 7.5 | 7.4 | 7.4 | 7.3 | 7.3 | 7.2 | 7.2 | 7.2 | 7.1 | 7.1 |
| 0.75 | 8.0 | 7.9 | 7.9 | 7.9 | 7.8 | 7.8 | 7.8 | 7.7 | 7.7 | 7.7 | 7.7 | 7.7 | 7.6 | 7.6 | 7.6 | 7.6 | 7.6 |
| 0.70 | 8.0 | 8.0 | 8.0 | 8.0 | 8.0 | 8.0 | 8.0 | 8.0 | 8.0 | 8.0 | 8.1 | 8.1 | 8.1 | 8.1 | 8.1 | 8.1 | 8.1 |
| 0.65 | 8.0 | 8.1 | 8.1 | 8.2 | 8.2 | 8.3 | 8.3 | 8.3 | 8.4 | 8.4 | 8.4 | 8.5 | 8.5 | 8.5 | 8.5 | 8.6 | 8.6 |
| 0.60 | 8.0 | 8.1 | 8.2 | 8.3 | 8.4 | 8.5 | 8.6 | 8.6 | 8.7 | 8.8 | 8.8 | 8.9 | 8.9 | 9.0 | 9.0 | 9.1 | 9.1 |

*Note: The $D$-values in this table may be used for investigation of uncracked sections of columns as follows:

$$\text{max. fiber stress: } f_c^{max} = \frac{N}{A_g}\frac{1}{1+(n-1)p}\left(1 + D\frac{e'}{t}\right)$$

$$\text{min. fiber stress: } f_c^{min} = \frac{N}{A_g}\frac{1}{1+(n-1)p}\left(1 - D\frac{e'}{t}\right)$$

## Table 34. Allowable Stress on Eccentrically Loaded Columns Joint Committee Code 1940

$$\text{Values of } D\frac{e'}{t} = \frac{\dfrac{f_p}{f'_c} \times \dfrac{f'_c}{f_a} - 1}{1 - \dfrac{f_p}{f'_c} \times \dfrac{1}{0.45}}$$

Enter table with known value of $\frac{f_a}{f'_c}$; proceed horizontally to the known value of $D\frac{e'}{t}$; select $\frac{f_p}{f'_c}$ or $f_p$

The table is divided into two parts by a line of zeros. The upper part is for $\frac{f_p}{f'_c}$ from 0.44 to 0.23, the lower part is for $\frac{f_p}{f'_c}$ less than 0.23. Values of $D\frac{e'}{t}$ greater than 10 are omitted.

| $f'_c$ | Values of $f_p$ | | | | | | | | | | | | | | | | | | | | | | $f'_c$ |
|---|---|---|---|---|---|---|---|---|---|---|---|---|---|---|---|---|---|---|---|---|---|---|---|
| 2000 | 880 | 860 | 840 | 820 | 800 | 780 | 760 | 740 | 720 | 700 | 680 | 660 | 640 | 620 | 600 | 580 | 560 | 540 | 520 | 500 | 480 | 460 | 2000 |
| 2500 | 1100 | 1075 | 1050 | 1025 | 1000 | 975 | 950 | 925 | 900 | 875 | 850 | 825 | 800 | 775 | 750 | 725 | 700 | 675 | 650 | 625 | 600 | 575 | 2500 |
| 3000 | 1320 | 1290 | 1260 | 1230 | 1200 | 1170 | 1140 | 1110 | 1080 | 1050 | 1020 | 990 | 960 | 930 | 900 | 870 | 840 | 810 | 780 | 750 | 720 | 690 | 3000 |
| 3750 | 1650 | 1613 | 1575 | 1538 | 1500 | 1463 | 1425 | 1388 | 1350 | 1313 | 1275 | 1238 | 1200 | 1163 | 1125 | 1088 | 1050 | 1013 | 975 | 938 | 900 | 863 | 3750 |
| 5000 | 2200 | 2150 | 2100 | 2050 | 2000 | 1950 | 1900 | 1850 | 1800 | 1750 | 1700 | 1650 | 1600 | 1550 | 1500 | 1450 | 1400 | 1350 | 1300 | 1250 | 1200 | 1150 | 5000 |

| $\frac{f_a}{f'_c}$ | Values of $f_p \div f'_c$: 0.44 | 0.43 | 0.42 | 0.41 | 0.40 | 0.39 | 0.38 | 0.37 | 0.36 | 0.35 | 0.34 | 0.33 | 0.32 | 0.31 | 0.30 | 0.29 | 0.28 | 0.27 | 0.26 | 0.25 | 0.24 | 0.23 | $\frac{f_a}{f'_c}$ |
|---|---|---|---|---|---|---|---|---|---|---|---|---|---|---|---|---|---|---|---|---|---|---|---|
| .05 | | | | | | | | | | | | | | | | | | | 9.95 | 9.00 | 8.14 | 7.36 | .05 |
| .06 | | | | | | | | | | | | | | | | | 9.71 | 8.75 | 7.89 | 7.13 | 6.43 | 5.79 | .06 |
| .07 | | | | | | | | | | | | | | | 9.85 | 8.84 | 7.94 | 7.15 | 6.42 | 5.79 | 5.21 | 4.67 | .07 |
| .08 | | | | | | | | | | | | | | 9.24 | 8.25 | 7.38 | 6.62 | 5.94 | 5.32 | 4.78 | 4.29 | 3.84 | .08 |
| .09 | | | | | | | | | | | | | 8.84 | 7.86 | 7.00 | 6.24 | 5.59 | 5.00 | 4.47 | 4.00 | 3.57 | 3.18 | .09 |
| .10 | | | | | | | | | | | 9.82 | 8.62 | 7.61 | 6.75 | 6.00 | 5.35 | 4.77 | 4.25 | 3.79 | 3.37 | 3.00 | 2.66 | .10 |
| .11 | | | | | | | | | | 9.82 | 8.55 | 7.50 | 6.61 | 5.84 | 5.18 | 4.60 | 4.09 | 3.64 | 3.23 | 2.86 | 2.53 | 2.23 | .11 |
| .12 | | | | | | | | | | 8.62 | 7.50 | 6.56 | 5.77 | 5.09 | 4.50 | 3.99 | 3.53 | 3.13 | 2.76 | 2.44 | 2.14 | 1.87 | .12 |
| .13 | | | | | | | | | 8.84 | 7.61 | 6.61 | 5.77 | 5.06 | 4.45 | 3.92 | 3.46 | 3.05 | 2.69 | 2.37 | 2.08 | 1.81 | 1.57 | .13 |
| .14 | | | | | | | | 9.24 | 7.86 | 6.75 | 5.84 | 5.09 | 4.45 | 3.90 | 3.43 | 3.01 | 2.65 | 2.32 | 2.03 | 1.77 | 1.53 | 1.32 | .14 |
| .15 | | | | | | | 9.85 | 8.25 | 7.00 | 6.00 | 5.18 | 4.50 | 3.92 | 3.43 | 3.00 | 2.63 | 2.29 | 2.00 | 1.74 | 1.50 | 1.29 | 1.09 | .15 |
| .16 | | | | | | | 8.84 | 7.38 | 6.24 | 5.35 | 4.60 | 3.99 | 3.46 | 3.01 | 2.63 | 2.29 | 1.99 | 1.72 | 1.48 | 1.27 | 1.07 | 0.89 | .16 |
| .17 | | | | | | 9.71 | 7.94 | 6.62 | 5.59 | 4.77 | 4.09 | 3.53 | 3.05 | 2.65 | 2.29 | 1.99 | 1.71 | 1.47 | 1.25 | 1.06 | 0.88 | 0.72 | .17 |
| .18 | | | | | | 8.75 | 7.15 | 5.94 | 5.00 | 4.25 | 3.64 | 3.13 | 2.69 | 2.32 | 2.00 | 1.72 | 1.47 | 1.25 | 1.05 | 0.88 | 0.71 | 0.57 | .18 |
| .19 | | | | | 9.95 | 7.89 | 6.42 | 5.32 | 4.47 | 3.79 | 3.23 | 2.76 | 2.37 | 2.03 | 1.74 | 1.48 | 1.25 | 1.05 | 0.87 | 0.71 | 0.56 | 0.43 | .19 |
| .20 | | | | | 9.00 | 7.13 | 5.79 | 4.78 | 4.00 | 3.37 | 2.86 | 2.44 | 2.08 | 1.77 | 1.50 | 1.27 | 1.06 | 0.88 | 0.71 | 0.56 | 0.43 | 0.31 | .20 |
| .21 | | | | | 8.14 | 6.43 | 5.21 | 4.29 | 3.57 | 3.00 | 2.53 | 2.14 | 1.81 | 1.53 | 1.29 | 1.07 | 0.88 | 0.71 | 0.56 | 0.43 | 0.31 | 0.19 | .21 |
| .22 | | | | 9.71 | 7.36 | 5.79 | 4.67 | 3.84 | 3.18 | 2.66 | 2.23 | 1.87 | 1.57 | 1.32 | 1.09 | 0.89 | 0.72 | 0.57 | 0.43 | 0.31 | 0.19 | 0.09 | .22 |
| .23 | | | | 8.80 | 6.65 | 5.22 | 4.19 | 3.42 | 2.83 | 2.35 | 1.96 | 1.63 | 1.35 | 1.12 | 0.91 | 0.73 | 0.58 | 0.43 | 0.31 | 0.19 | 0.09 | -0- | .22 |
| .24 | | | | 7.96 | 6.00 | 4.69 | 3.75 | 3.05 | 2.50 | 2.06 | 1.70 | 1.41 | 1.15 | 0.94 | 0.75 | 0.59 | 0.44 | 0.31 | 0.20 | 0.09 | -0- | 0.09 | .21 |
| .25 | | | | 7.20 | 5.40 | 4.20 | 3.34 | 2.70 | 2.20 | 1.80 | 1.47 | 1.20 | 0.97 | 0.77 | 0.60 | 0.45 | 0.32 | 0.20 | 0.09 | -0- | 0.09 | 0.20 | .20 |
| .26 | | | 9.23 | 6.49 | 4.85 | 3.75 | 2.97 | 2.38 | 1.92 | 1.56 | 1.26 | 1.01 | 0.80 | 0.62 | 0.46 | 0.32 | 0.20 | 0.10 | -0- | 0.09 | 0.20 | 0.31 | .19 |
| .27 | | | 8.33 | 5.83 | 4.33 | 3.33 | 2.62 | 2.08 | 1.67 | 1.33 | 1.06 | 0.83 | 0.64 | 0.48 | 0.33 | 0.21 | 0.10 | -0- | 0.10 | 0.20 | 0.31 | 0.43 | .18 |
| .28 | | | 7.50 | 5.22 | 3.86 | 2.95 | 2.30 | 1.81 | 1.43 | 1.13 | 0.88 | 0.67 | 0.49 | 0.34 | 0.21 | 0.10 | -0- | 0.10 | 0.20 | 0.32 | 0.44 | 0.58 | .17 |
| .29 | | | 6.72 | 4.65 | 3.41 | 2.59 | 1.99 | 1.55 | 1.21 | 0.93 | 0.71 | 0.52 | 0.36 | 0.22 | 0.10 | -0- | 0.10 | 0.21 | 0.32 | 0.45 | 0.59 | 0.73 | .16 |
| .30 | | 9.74 | 6.00 | 4.12 | 3.00 | 2.25 | 1.71 | 1.31 | 1.00 | 0.75 | 0.55 | 0.38 | 0.23 | 0.11 | -0- | 0.10 | 0.21 | 0.33 | 0.46 | 0.60 | 0.75 | 0.91 | .15 |
| .31 | | 8.70 | 5.33 | 3.63 | 2.61 | 1.94 | 1.45 | 1.09 | 0.81 | 0.58 | 0.40 | 0.24 | 0.11 | -0- | 0.11 | 0.22 | 0.34 | 0.48 | 0.62 | 0.77 | 0.94 | 1.12 | .14 |
| .32 | | 7.73 | 4.69 | 3.16 | 2.25 | 1.64 | 1.20 | 0.88 | 0.63 | 0.42 | 0.26 | 0.12 | -0- | 0.11 | 0.23 | 0.36 | 0.49 | 0.64 | 0.80 | 0.97 | 1.15 | 1.35 | .13 |
| .33 | | 6.82 | 4.09 | 2.73 | 1.91 | 1.36 | 0.97 | 0.68 | 0.45 | 0.27 | 0.12 | -0- | 0.12 | 0.24 | 0.38 | 0.52 | 0.67 | 0.83 | 1.01 | 1.20 | 1.41 | 1.63 | .12 |
| .34 | | 5.96 | 3.53 | 2.32 | 1.59 | 1.10 | 0.76 | 0.50 | 0.29 | 0.13 | -0- | 0.12 | 0.26 | 0.40 | 0.55 | 0.71 | 0.88 | 1.06 | 1.26 | 1.47 | 1.70 | 1.96 | .11 |
| .35 | | 5.14 | 3.00 | 1.93 | 1.29 | 0.86 | 0.55 | 0.32 | 0.14 | -0- | 0.13 | 0.27 | 0.42 | 0.58 | 0.75 | 0.93 | 1.13 | 1.33 | 1.56 | 1.80 | 2.06 | 2.35 | .10 |
| .36 | | 4.37 | 2.50 | 1.56 | 1.00 | 0.63 | 0.36 | 0.16 | -0- | 0.14 | 0.29 | 0.45 | 0.63 | 0.81 | 1.00 | 1.21 | 1.43 | 1.67 | 1.92 | 2.20 | 2.50 | 2.83 | .09 |
| .37 | 8.51 | 3.65 | 2.03 | 1.22 | 0.73 | 0.41 | 0.17 | -0- | 0.16 | 0.32 | 0.50 | 0.68 | 0.88 | 1.09 | 1.31 | 1.55 | 1.81 | 2.08 | 2.38 | 2.70 | 3.05 | 3.42 | .08 |
| .38 | 7.11 | 2.96 | 1.58 | 0.89 | 0.47 | 0.20 | -0- | 0.17 | 0.36 | 0.55 | 0.76 | 0.97 | 1.20 | 1.45 | 1.71 | 1.99 | 2.30 | 2.62 | 2.97 | 3.34 | 3.75 | 4.19 | .07 |
| .39 | 5.77 | 2.31 | 1.15 | 0.58 | 0.23 | -0- | 0.20 | 0.41 | 0.63 | 0.86 | 1.10 | 1.36 | 1.64 | 1.94 | 2.25 | 2.59 | 2.95 | 3.33 | 3.75 | 4.20 | 4.69 | 5.22 | .06 |
| .40 | 4.50 | 1.69 | 0.75 | 0.28 | -0- | 0.23 | 0.47 | 0.73 | 1.00 | 1.29 | 1.59 | 1.91 | 2.25 | 2.61 | 3.00 | 3.41 | 3.86 | 4.33 | 4.85 | 5.40 | 6.00 | 6.65 | .05 |
| .41 | 3.29 | 1.10 | 0.37 | -0- | 0.28 | 0.58 | 0.89 | 1.22 | 1.56 | 1.93 | 2.32 | 2.73 | 3.16 | 3.63 | 4.12 | 4.65 | 5.22 | 5.83 | 6.49 | 7.20 | 7.96 | 8.80 | .04 |
| .42 | 2.14 | 0.54 | -0- | 0.37 | 0.75 | 1.15 | 1.58 | 2.03 | 2.50 | 3.00 | 3.53 | 4.09 | 4.69 | 5.33 | 6.00 | 6.72 | 7.50 | 8.33 | 9.23 | | | | .03 |
| .43 | 1.05 | -0- | 0.54 | 1.10 | 1.69 | 2.31 | 2.96 | 3.65 | 4.37 | 5.14 | 5.96 | 6.82 | 7.73 | 8.70 | 9.74 | | | | | | | | .02 |
| .44 | -0- | 1.05 | 2.14 | 3.29 | 4.50 | 5.77 | 7.11 | 8.51 | | | | | | | | | | | | | | | .01 |
| | Values of $f_p \div f'_c$: 0.01 | 0.02 | 0.03 | 0.04 | 0.05 | 0.06 | 0.07 | 0.08 | 0.09 | 0.10 | 0.11 | 0.12 | 0.13 | 0.14 | 0.15 | 0.16 | 0.17 | 0.18 | 0.19 | 0.20 | 0.21 | 0.22 | |

| $f'_c$ | Values of $f_p$ | | | | | | | | | | | | | | | | | | | | | | $f'_c$ |
|---|---|---|---|---|---|---|---|---|---|---|---|---|---|---|---|---|---|---|---|---|---|---|---|
| 2000 | 20 | 40 | 60 | 80 | 100 | 120 | 140 | 160 | 180 | 200 | 220 | 240 | 260 | 280 | 300 | 320 | 340 | 360 | 380 | 400 | 420 | 440 | 2000 |
| 2500 | 25 | 50 | 75 | 100 | 125 | 150 | 175 | 200 | 225 | 250 | 275 | 300 | 325 | 350 | 375 | 400 | 425 | 450 | 475 | 500 | 525 | 550 | 2500 |
| 3000 | 30 | 60 | 90 | 120 | 150 | 180 | 210 | 240 | 270 | 300 | 330 | 360 | 390 | 420 | 450 | 480 | 510 | 540 | 570 | 600 | 630 | 660 | 3000 |
| 3750 | 38 | 75 | 113 | 150 | 188 | 225 | 263 | 300 | 338 | 375 | 413 | 450 | 488 | 525 | 563 | 600 | 638 | 675 | 713 | 750 | 788 | 825 | 3750 |
| 5000 | 50 | 100 | 150 | 200 | 250 | 300 | 350 | 400 | 450 | 500 | 550 | 600 | 650 | 700 | 750 | 800 | 850 | 900 | 950 | 1000 | 1050 | 1100 | 5000 |

# Table 35. Spread Footings; American Concrete Institute Code 1936

No pedestals are needed for the designs presented

Maximum unit stresses:

$f_s$ = 20,000 psi.
$f'_c$ = 2500 psi.
$n$ = 12
$f_c$ = 1000 psi.
$v$ = 75 psi.
$u$ = 141 psi.

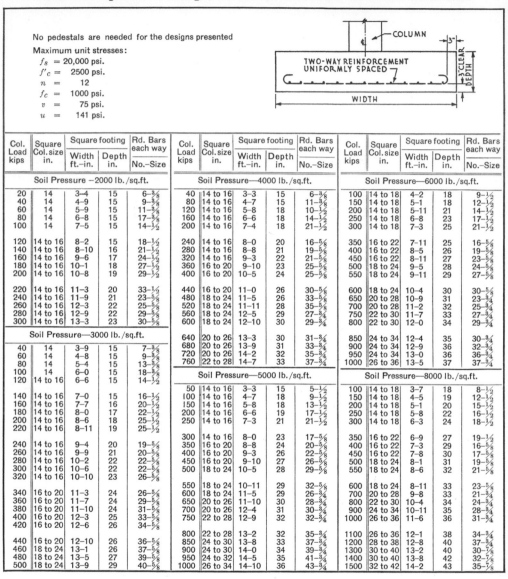

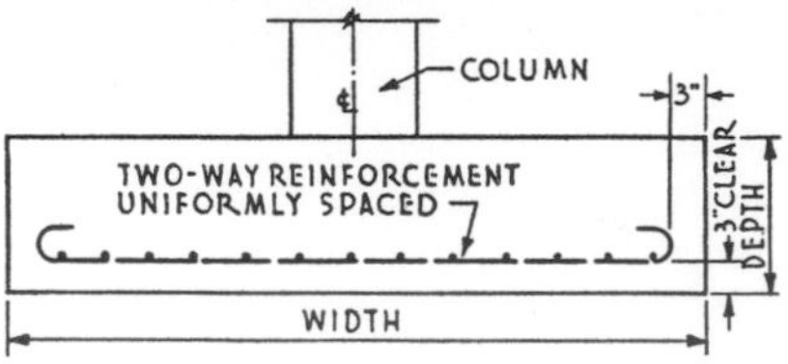


**Soil Pressure—2000 lb./sq.ft.**

| Col. Load kips | Square Col. size in. | Square footing Width ft.–in. | Square footing Depth in. | Rd. Bars each way No.–Size |
|---|---|---|---|---|
| 20 | 14 | 3–4 | 15 | 6–3/8 |
| 40 | 14 | 4–9 | 15 | 9–3/8 |
| 60 | 14 | 5–9 | 15 | 11–3/8 |
| 80 | 14 | 6–8 | 15 | 17–3/8 |
| 100 | 14 | 7–5 | 15 | 14–1/2 |
| 120 | 14 to 16 | 8–2 | 15 | 18–1/2 |
| 140 | 14 to 16 | 8–10 | 16 | 21–1/2 |
| 160 | 14 to 16 | 9–6 | 17 | 24–1/2 |
| 180 | 14 to 16 | 10–1 | 18 | 27–1/2 |
| 200 | 14 to 16 | 10–8 | 19 | 29–1/2 |
| 220 | 14 to 16 | 11–3 | 20 | 33–1/2 |
| 240 | 14 to 16 | 11–9 | 21 | 23–5/8 |
| 260 | 14 to 16 | 12–3 | 22 | 25–5/8 |
| 280 | 14 to 16 | 12–9 | 22 | 29–5/8 |
| 300 | 14 to 16 | 13–3 | 23 | 30–5/8 |

**Soil Pressure—3000 lb./sq.ft.**

| Col. Load kips | Square Col. size in. | Square footing Width ft.–in. | Square footing Depth in. | Rd. Bars each way No.–Size |
|---|---|---|---|---|
| 40 | 14 | 3–9 | 15 | 7–3/8 |
| 60 | 14 | 4–8 | 15 | 9–3/8 |
| 80 | 14 | 5–4 | 15 | 13–3/8 |
| 100 | 14 | 6–0 | 15 | 18–3/8 |
| 120 | 14 to 16 | 6–6 | 15 | 14–1/2 |
| 140 | 14 to 16 | 7–0 | 15 | 16–1/2 |
| 160 | 14 to 16 | 7–7 | 16 | 20–1/2 |
| 180 | 14 to 16 | 8–0 | 17 | 22–1/2 |
| 200 | 14 to 16 | 8–6 | 18 | 25–1/2 |
| 220 | 14 to 16 | 8–11 | 19 | 25–1/2 |
| 240 | 14 to 16 | 9–4 | 20 | 19–5/8 |
| 260 | 14 to 16 | 9–9 | 21 | 20–5/8 |
| 280 | 14 to 16 | 10–2 | 22 | 22–5/8 |
| 300 | 14 to 16 | 10–6 | 22 | 22–5/8 |
| 320 | 14 to 16 | 10–10 | 23 | 26–5/8 |
| 340 | 16 to 20 | 11–3 | 24 | 26–5/8 |
| 360 | 16 to 20 | 11–7 | 24 | 29–5/8 |
| 380 | 16 to 20 | 11–10 | 24 | 31–5/8 |
| 400 | 16 to 20 | 12–3 | 25 | 33–5/8 |
| 420 | 16 to 20 | 12–6 | 26 | 34–5/8 |
| 440 | 16 to 20 | 12–10 | 26 | 36–5/8 |
| 460 | 18 to 24 | 13–1 | 26 | 37–5/8 |
| 480 | 18 to 24 | 13–5 | 27 | 39–5/8 |
| 500 | 18 to 24 | 13–9 | 29 | 40–5/8 |

**Soil Pressure—4000 lb./sq.ft.**

| Col. Load kips | Square Col. size in. | Square footing Width ft.–in. | Square footing Depth in. | Rd. Bars each way No.–Size |
|---|---|---|---|---|
| 40 | 14 to 16 | 3–3 | 15 | 6–3/8 |
| 80 | 14 to 16 | 4–7 | 15 | 11–3/8 |
| 120 | 14 to 16 | 5–8 | 18 | 10–1/2 |
| 160 | 14 to 16 | 6–6 | 18 | 14–1/2 |
| 200 | 14 to 16 | 7–4 | 18 | 21–1/2 |
| 240 | 14 to 16 | 8–0 | 20 | 16–5/8 |
| 280 | 14 to 16 | 8–8 | 21 | 19–5/8 |
| 320 | 14 to 16 | 9–3 | 22 | 21–5/8 |
| 360 | 16 to 20 | 9–10 | 23 | 25–5/8 |
| 400 | 16 to 20 | 10–5 | 24 | 25–5/8 |
| 440 | 16 to 20 | 11–0 | 26 | 30–5/8 |
| 480 | 18 to 24 | 11–5 | 26 | 33–5/8 |
| 520 | 18 to 24 | 11–11 | 28 | 35–5/8 |
| 560 | 18 to 24 | 12–5 | 29 | 27–3/4 |
| 600 | 18 to 24 | 12–10 | 30 | 29–3/4 |
| 640 | 20 to 26 | 13–3 | 30 | 31–3/4 |
| 680 | 20 to 26 | 13–9 | 31 | 33–3/4 |
| 720 | 20 to 26 | 14–2 | 32 | 35–3/4 |
| 760 | 22 to 28 | 14–7 | 33 | 37–3/4 |

**Soil Pressure—5000 lb./sq.ft.**

| Col. Load kips | Square Col. size in. | Square footing Width ft.–in. | Square footing Depth in. | Rd. Bars each way No.–Size |
|---|---|---|---|---|
| 50 | 14 to 16 | 3–3 | 15 | 5–1/2 |
| 100 | 14 to 16 | 4–7 | 18 | 9–1/2 |
| 150 | 14 to 16 | 5–8 | 18 | 13–1/2 |
| 200 | 14 to 16 | 6–6 | 19 | 17–1/2 |
| 250 | 14 to 16 | 7–3 | 21 | 21–1/2 |
| 300 | 14 to 16 | 8–0 | 23 | 17–5/8 |
| 350 | 16 to 20 | 8–8 | 24 | 20–5/8 |
| 400 | 16 to 20 | 9–3 | 26 | 22–5/8 |
| 450 | 16 to 20 | 9–10 | 27 | 26–5/8 |
| 500 | 18 to 24 | 10–5 | 28 | 29–5/8 |
| 550 | 18 to 24 | 10–11 | 29 | 32–5/8 |
| 600 | 18 to 24 | 11–5 | 29 | 26–3/4 |
| 650 | 20 to 26 | 11–10 | 30 | 28–3/4 |
| 700 | 20 to 26 | 12–4 | 31 | 30–3/4 |
| 750 | 22 to 28 | 12–9 | 32 | 32–3/4 |
| 800 | 22 to 28 | 13–2 | 32 | 35–3/4 |
| 850 | 24 to 30 | 13–8 | 33 | 37–3/4 |
| 900 | 24 to 30 | 14–0 | 34 | 39–3/4 |
| 950 | 24 to 32 | 14–5 | 35 | 41–3/4 |
| 1000 | 26 to 34 | 14–10 | 36 | 43–3/4 |

**Soil Pressure—6000 lb./sq.ft.**

| Col. Load kips | Square Col. size in. | Square footing Width ft.–in. | Square footing Depth in. | Rd. Bars each way No.–Size |
|---|---|---|---|---|
| 100 | 14 to 18 | 4–2 | 18 | 9–1/2 |
| 150 | 14 to 18 | 5–1 | 18 | 12–1/2 |
| 200 | 14 to 18 | 5–11 | 21 | 14–1/2 |
| 250 | 14 to 18 | 6–8 | 23 | 17–1/2 |
| 300 | 14 to 18 | 7–3 | 25 | 21–1/2 |
| 350 | 16 to 22 | 7–11 | 25 | 16–5/8 |
| 400 | 16 to 22 | 8–5 | 26 | 19–5/8 |
| 450 | 16 to 22 | 8–11 | 27 | 23–5/8 |
| 500 | 18 to 24 | 9–5 | 28 | 24–5/8 |
| 550 | 18 to 24 | 9–11 | 29 | 27–5/8 |
| 600 | 18 to 24 | 10–4 | 30 | 30–5/8 |
| 650 | 20 to 28 | 10–9 | 31 | 23–3/4 |
| 700 | 20 to 28 | 11–2 | 32 | 25–3/4 |
| 750 | 22 to 30 | 11–7 | 33 | 27–3/4 |
| 800 | 22 to 30 | 12–0 | 34 | 29–3/4 |
| 850 | 24 to 34 | 12–4 | 35 | 30–3/4 |
| 900 | 24 to 34 | 12–9 | 36 | 32–3/4 |
| 950 | 24 to 34 | 13–0 | 36 | 36–3/4 |
| 1000 | 26 to 36 | 13–5 | 37 | 37–3/4 |

**Soil Pressure—8000 lb./sq.ft.**

| Col. Load kips | Square Col. size in. | Square footing Width ft.–in. | Square footing Depth in. | Rd. Bars each way No.–Size |
|---|---|---|---|---|
| 100 | 14 to 18 | 3–7 | 18 | 8–1/2 |
| 150 | 14 to 18 | 4–5 | 19 | 12–1/2 |
| 200 | 14 to 18 | 5–1 | 20 | 15–1/2 |
| 250 | 14 to 18 | 5–8 | 22 | 16–1/2 |
| 300 | 14 to 18 | 6–3 | 24 | 18–1/2 |
| 350 | 16 to 22 | 6–9 | 27 | 19–1/2 |
| 400 | 16 to 22 | 7–3 | 29 | 16–5/8 |
| 450 | 16 to 22 | 7–8 | 30 | 17–5/8 |
| 500 | 18 to 24 | 8–1 | 31 | 19–5/8 |
| 550 | 18 to 24 | 8–6 | 32 | 21–5/8 |
| 600 | 18 to 24 | 8–11 | 33 | 23–5/8 |
| 700 | 20 to 28 | 9–8 | 33 | 21–3/4 |
| 800 | 22 to 30 | 10–4 | 34 | 24–3/4 |
| 900 | 24 to 34 | 10–11 | 35 | 28–3/4 |
| 1000 | 26 to 36 | 11–6 | 36 | 31–3/4 |
| 1100 | 26 to 36 | 12–1 | 38 | 34–3/4 |
| 1200 | 28 to 38 | 12–8 | 40 | 37–3/4 |
| 1300 | 30 to 40 | 13–2 | 40 | 30–7/8 |
| 1400 | 30 to 40 | 13–8 | 42 | 32–7/8 |
| 1500 | 32 to 42 | 14–2 | 43 | 35–7/8 |

# Table 36. Pile Footings; American Concrete Institute Code 1936

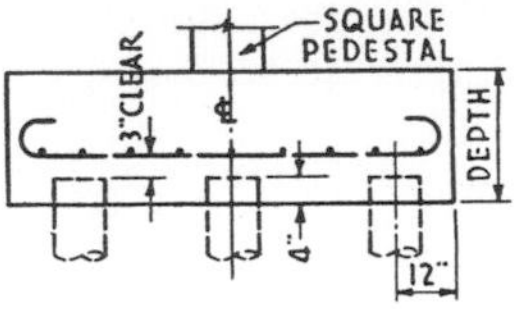


$f_s$ = 20,000 psi. $n$ = 12
$f'_c$ = 2500 psi. $v$ = 75 psi.
$f_c$ = 1000 psi. $u$ = 141 psi.
3′-0″ center to center of piles

Notation:
Wt. = Weight of footing per pile.
$P$ = Maximum allowable load per pile
$A_s$ = Required area of steel one way per kip of pile load
$\Sigma o$ = Required perimeter of steel one way per kip of pile load

Two-way reinforcement:
$A_{sl}$ and $\Sigma o_l$ denote reinforcement the long way.
$A_{ss}$ and $\Sigma o_s$ denote reinforcement the short way.

4 Piles

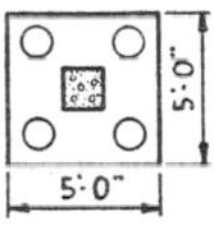


| Depth ft.-in. | Wt. kips | | Pedestal Size—in. 14 | 16 | 18 | 20 |
|---|---|---|---|---|---|---|
| 1-8 | 1.6 | $P$ | 20.5 | 22.0 | 23.6 | 25.2 |
| | | $A_s$ | .052 | .048 | .043 | .038 |
| | | $\Sigma o$ | 0.67 | 0.67 | 0.67 | 0.67 |
| 2-0 | 1.9 | $P$ | 31.5 | 33.5 | 35.6 | * |
| | | $A_s$ | .039 | .036 | .032 | .029 |
| | | $\Sigma o$ | 0.51 | 0.51 | 0.51 | 0.51 |

5 Piles

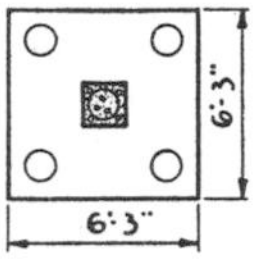


| Depth ft.-in. | Wt. kips | | Pedestal Size—in. 14 | 16 | 18 | 20 |
|---|---|---|---|---|---|---|
| 1-8 | 2.0 | $P$ | 20.5 | 22.0 | 23.6 | 25.2 |
| | | $A_s$ | .088 | .083 | .079 | .074 |
| | | $\Sigma o$ | 0.67 | 0.67 | 0.67 | 0.67 |
| 2-0 | 2.3 | $P$ | 31.5 | 33.5 | 35.6 | 37.7 |
| | | $A_s$ | .066 | .063 | .059 | .055 |
| | | $\Sigma o$ | 0.51 | 0.51 | 0.51 | 0.51 |
| 2-4 | 2.7 | $P$ | 44.6 | 47.2 | 49.8 | 52.4 |
| | | $A_s$ | .053 | .050 | .047 | .044 |
| | | $\Sigma o$ | 0.41 | 0.41 | 0.41 | 0.41 |

6 Piles

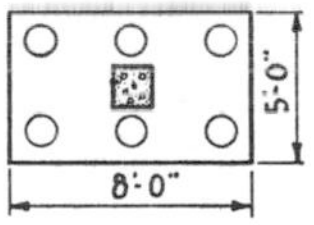


| Depth ft.-in. | Wt. kips | | Pedestal Size—in. 14 | 16 | 18 | 20 |
|---|---|---|---|---|---|---|
| 2-0 | 2.0 | $P$ | 21.0 | 22.4 | 23.8 | 25.2 |
| | | $A_{sl}$ | .155 | .150 | .144 | .139 |
| | | $\Sigma o_l$ | 0.76 | 0.76 | 0.76 | 0.76 |
| | | $A_{ss}$ | .059 | .054 | .048 | 0.43 |
| | | $\Sigma o_s$ | 0.76 | 0.76 | 0.76 | 0.76 |
| 2-4 | 2.3 | $P$ | 29.7 | 31.5 | 33.2 | 35.0 |
| | | $A_{sl}$ | .124 | .120 | .116 | .111 |
| | | $\Sigma o_l$ | 0.61 | 0.61 | 0.61 | 0.61 |
| | | $A_{ss}$ | .047 | .043 | .038 | .034 |
| | | $\Sigma o_s$ | 0.61 | 0.61 | 0.61 | 0.61 |

7 Piles

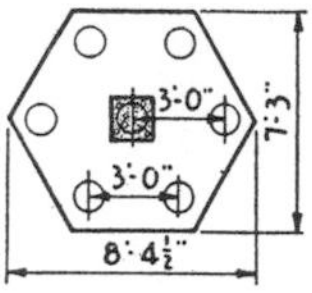


| Depth ft.-in. | Wt. kips | | Pedestal Size—in. 14 | 16 | 18 | 20 |
|---|---|---|---|---|---|---|
| 2-0 | 2.0 | $P$ | 21.0 | 22.3 | 23.7 | 25.2 |
| | | $A_{sl}$ | .127 | .121 | .116 | .110 |
| | | $\Sigma o_l$ | 0.81 | 0.81 | 0.81 | 0.81 |
| | | $A_{ss}$ | .121 | .116 | .111 | .106 |
| | | $\Sigma o_s$ | 0.71 | 0.71 | 0.71 | 0.71 |
| 2-4 | 2.3 | $P$ | 29.7 | 31.5 | 33.2 | 34.9 |
| | | $A_{sl}$ | .102 | .097 | .093 | .088 |
| | | $\Sigma o_l$ | 0.65 | 0.65 | 0.65 | 0.65 |
| | | $A_{ss}$ | .097 | .093 | .089 | .085 |
| | | $\Sigma o_s$ | 0.57 | 0.57 | 0.57 | 0.57 |
| 2-8 | 2.6 | $P$ | 39.9 | 42.0 | 44.1 | 46.2 |
| | | $A_{sl}$ | .085 | .081 | .077 | .074 |
| | | $\Sigma o_l$ | 0.54 | 0.54 | 0.54 | 0.54 |
| | | $A_{ss}$ | .081 | .078 | .074 | .071 |
| | | $\Sigma o_s$ | 0.47 | 0.47 | 0.47 | 0.47 |

8 Piles

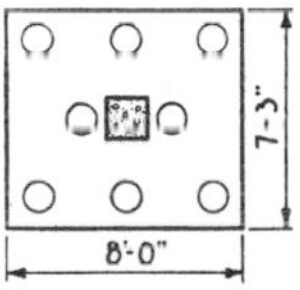


| Depth ft.-in. | Wt. kips | | Pedestal Size—in. 14 | 16 | 18 | 20 |
|---|---|---|---|---|---|---|
| 2-0 | 2.2 | $P$ | 15.7 | 16.8 | 17.8 | 18.9 |
| | | $A_{sl}$ | .153 | .146 | .138 | .131 |
| | | $\Sigma o_l$ | 1.07 | 1.07 | 1.07 | 1.07 |
| | | $A_{ss}$ | .164 | .157 | .150 | .144 |
| | | $\Sigma o_s$ | 0.96 | 0.96 | 0.96 | 0.96 |
| 2-4 | 2.5 | $P$ | 22.3 | 23.6 | 24.9 | 26.2 |
| | | $A_{sl}$ | .122 | .117 | .110 | .105 |
| | | $\Sigma o_l$ | 0.85 | 0.85 | 0.85 | 0.85 |
| | | $A_{ss}$ | .131 | .126 | .120 | .115 |
| | | $\Sigma o_s$ | 0.77 | 0.77 | 0.77 | 0.77 |
| 2-8 | 2.9 | $P$ | 29.9 | 31.5 | 33.0 | 34.6 |
| | | $A_{sl}$ | .102 | .097 | .092 | .087 |
| | | $\Sigma o_l$ | 0.71 | 0.71 | 0.71 | 0.71 |
| | | $A_{ss}$ | .109 | .105 | .100 | .096 |
| | | $\Sigma o_s$ | 0.64 | 0.64 | 0.64 | 0.64 |

*Any load for which the pile is designed, but not more than 315 kips

## Table 36. (*continued*)

### 9 Piles

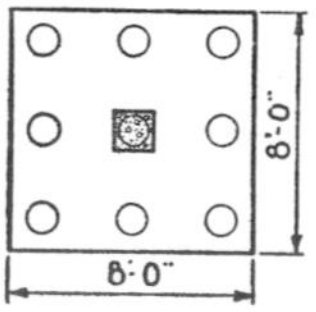


| Depth ft.-in. | Wt. kips | | Pedestal Size—in. 14 | 16 | 18 | 20 |
|---|---|---|---|---|---|---|
| 2-0 | 2.1 | $P$ | 15.7 | 16.8 | 17.8 | 18.9 |
| | | $A_s$ | .207 | .200 | .193 | .186 |
| | | $\Sigma o$ | 1.01 | 1.01 | 1.01 | 1.01 |
| 2-4 | 2.5 | $P$ | 22.3 | 23.6 | 24.9 | 26.2 |
| | | $A_s$ | .166 | .160 | .154 | .149 |
| | | $\Sigma o$ | 0.81 | 0.81 | 0.81 | 0.81 |
| 2-8 | 2.9 | $P$ | 29.9 | 31.5 | 33.0 | 34.6 |
| | | $A_s$ | .138 | .133 | .129 | .124 |
| | | $\Sigma o$ | 0.67 | 0.67 | 0.67 | 0.67 |

### 10 Piles

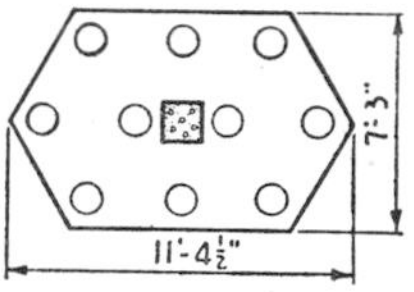


| Depth ft.-in. | Wt. kips | | Pedestal Size—in. 16 | 18 | 20 | 22 |
|---|---|---|---|---|---|---|
| 2-4 | 2.3 | $P$ | 22.5 | 23.7 | 25.0 | 26.2 |
| | | $A_{sl}$ | .248 | .239 | .230 | .221 |
| | | $\Sigma o_l$ | 0.85 | 0.85 | 0.85 | 0.85 |
| | | $A_{ss}$ | .126 | .121 | .115 | .110 |
| | | $\Sigma o_s$ | 0.77 | 0.77 | 0.77 | 0.77 |
| 2-8 | 2.7 | $P$ | 30.0 | 31.6 | 33.0 | 34.5 |
| | | $A_{sl}$ | .207 | .198 | .192 | .184 |
| | | $\Sigma o_l$ | 0.71 | 0.71 | 0.71 | 0.71 |
| | | $A_{ss}$ | .105 | .101 | .096 | .092 |
| | | $\Sigma o_s$ | 0.64 | 0.64 | 0.64 | 0.64 |
| 3-0 | 3.0 | $P$ | 38.5 | 40.3 | 42.0 | 44.8 |
| | | $A_{sl}$ | .177 | .171 | .164 | .158 |
| | | $\Sigma o_l$ | 0.61 | 0.61 | 0.61 | 0.61 |
| | | $A_{ss}$ | .090 | .086 | .082 | .079 |
| | | $\Sigma o_s$ | 0.55 | 0.55 | 0.55 | 0.55 |

### 11 Piles

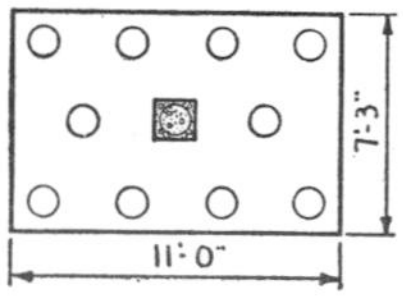


| Depth ft.-in. | Wt. kips | | Pedestal Size—in. 16 | 18 | 20 | 22 |
|---|---|---|---|---|---|---|
| 2-8 | 2.9 | $P$ | 27.0 | 28.4 | 29.7 | 31.0 |
| | | $A_{sl}$ | .227 | .220 | .213 | .206 |
| | | $\Sigma o_l$ | 0.99 | 0.99 | 0.99 | 0.99 |
| | | $A_{ss}$ | .114 | .109 | .104 | .099 |
| | | $\Sigma o_s$ | 0.70 | 0.70 | 0.70 | 0.70 |
| 3-0 | 3.3 | $P$ | 34.6 | 36.2 | 37.7 | 39.3 |
| | | $A_{sl}$ | .195 | .189 | .183 | .177 |
| | | $\Sigma o_l$ | 0.85 | 0.85 | 0.85 | 0.85 |
| | | $A_{ss}$ | .098 | .094 | .089 | .085 |
| | | $\Sigma o_s$ | 0.60 | 0.60 | 0.60 | 0.60 |
| 3-4 | 3.6 | $P$ | 43.2 | 45.0 | 46.8 | 48.6 |
| | | $A_{sl}$ | .170 | .165 | .160 | .155 |
| | | $\Sigma o_l$ | 0.75 | 0.75 | 0.75 | 0.75 |
| | | $A_{ss}$ | .085 | .082 | .078 | .074 |
| | | $\Sigma o_s$ | 0.53 | 0.53 | 0.53 | 0.53 |

### 12 Piles

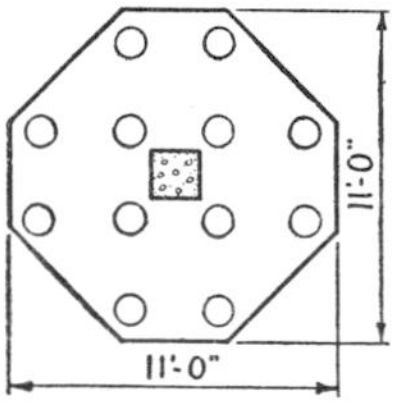


| Depth ft.-in. | Wt. kips | | Pedestal Size—in. 16 | 18 | 20 | 22 |
|---|---|---|---|---|---|---|
| 2-4 | 2.9 | $P$ | 23.6 | 24.9 | 26.2 | 27.5 |
| | | $A_s$ | .291 | .283 | .274 | .266 |
| | | $\Sigma o$ | 1.21 | 1.21 | 1.21 | 1.21 |
| 2-8 | 3.3 | $P$ | 31.5 | 33.0 | 34.6 | 36.2 |
| | | $A_s$ | .242 | .236 | .228 | .222 |
| | | $\Sigma o$ | 1.01 | 1.01 | 1.01 | 1.01 |
| 3-0 | 3.8 | $P$ | 40.4 | 42.2 | 44.1 | 45.9 |
| | | $A_s$ | .208 | .202 | .196 | .190 |
| | | $\Sigma o$ | 0.87 | 0.87 | 0.87 | 0.87 |

### 13 Piles

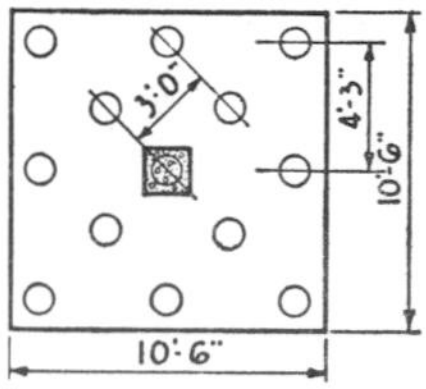


| Depth ft.-in. | Wt. kips | | Pedestal Size—in. 20 | 22 | 24 | 26 |
|---|---|---|---|---|---|---|
| 2-8 | 3.4 | $P$ | 23.1 | 24.1 | 25.2 | 26.2 |
| | | $A_s$ | .232 | .225 | .218 | .211 |
| | | $\Sigma o$ | 1.01 | 1.01 | 1.01 | 1.01 |
| 3-0 | 3.8 | $P$ | 29.3 | 30.5 | 47.7 | 49.5 |
| | | $A_s$ | .199 | .193 | .187 | .181 |
| | | $\Sigma o$ | 0.87 | 0.87 | 0.87 | 0.87 |
| 3-4 | 4.2 | $P$ | 54.5 | 56.6 | 58.7 | 60.8 |
| | | $A_s$ | .174 | .169 | .164 | .158 |
| | | $\Sigma o$ | 0.76 | 0.76 | 0.76 | 0.76 |

### 14 Piles

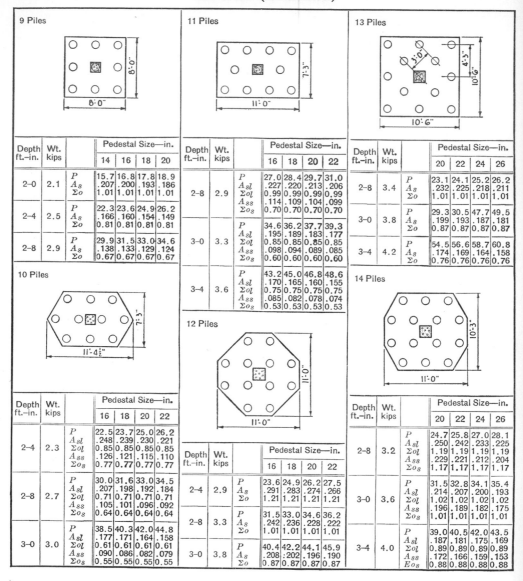

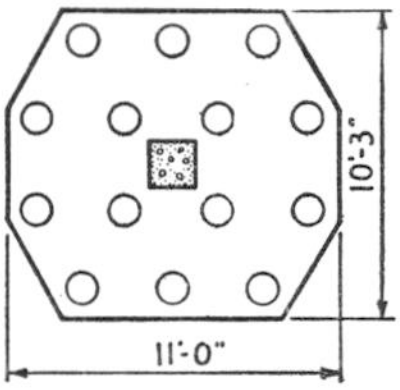


| Depth ft.-in. | Wt. kips | | Pedestal Size—in. 20 | 22 | 24 | 26 |
|---|---|---|---|---|---|---|
| 2-8 | 3.2 | $P$ | 24.7 | 25.8 | 27.0 | 28.1 |
| | | $A_{sl}$ | .250 | .242 | .233 | .225 |
| | | $\Sigma o_l$ | 1.19 | 1.19 | 1.19 | 1.19 |
| | | $A_{ss}$ | .229 | .221 | .212 | .204 |
| | | $\Sigma o_s$ | 1.17 | 1.17 | 1.17 | 1.17 |
| 3-0 | 3.6 | $P$ | 31.5 | 32.8 | 34.1 | 35.4 |
| | | $A_{sl}$ | .214 | .207 | .200 | .193 |
| | | $\Sigma o_l$ | 1.02 | 1.02 | 1.02 | 1.02 |
| | | $A_{ss}$ | .196 | .189 | .182 | .175 |
| | | $\Sigma o_s$ | 1.01 | 1.01 | 1.01 | 1.01 |
| 3-4 | 4.0 | $P$ | 39.0 | 40.5 | 42.0 | 43.5 |
| | | $A_{sl}$ | .187 | .181 | .175 | .169 |
| | | $\Sigma o_l$ | 0.89 | 0.89 | 0.89 | 0.89 |
| | | $A_{ss}$ | .172 | .166 | .159 | .153 |
| | | $Eo_s$ | 0.88 | 0.88 | 0.88 | 0.88 |

## Table 36. (*continued*)

### 15 Piles

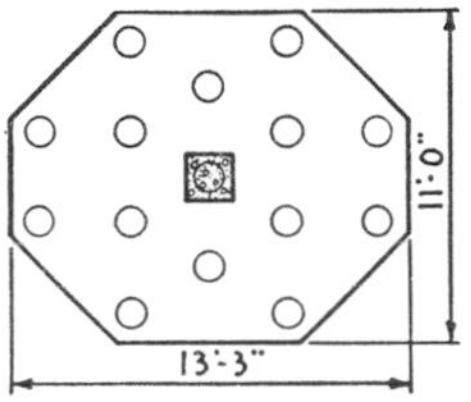


| Depth ft.-in. | Wt. kips | | Pedestal Size—in. 20 | 22 | 24 | 26 |
|---|---|---|---|---|---|---|
| 3–0 | 3.7 | $P$ | 22.0 | 22.9 | 23.9 | 24.8 |
| | | $A_{sl}$ | .295 | .288 | .280 | .272 |
| | | $\Sigma o_l$ | 1.12 | 1.12 | 1.12 | 1.12 |
| | | $A_{ss}$ | .187 | .181 | .174 | .168 |
| | | $\Sigma o_s$ | 0.91 | 0.91 | 0.91 | 0.91 |
| 3–4 | 4.1 | $P$ | 27.1 | 28.3 | 29.3 | 30.4 |
| | | $A_{sl}$ | .258 | .252 | .245 | .238 |
| | | $\Sigma o_l$ | 0.98 | 0.98 | 0.98 | 0.98 |
| | | $A_{ss}$ | .164 | .158 | .152 | .147 |
| | | $\Sigma o_s$ | 0.79 | 0.79 | 0.79 | 0.79 |
| 3–8 | 4.5 | $P$ | 33.0 | 34.2 | 35.4 | 36.6 |
| | | $A_{sl}$ | .230 | .224 | .210 | .211 |
| | | $\Sigma o_l$ | 0.87 | 0.87 | 0.87 | 0.87 |
| | | $A_{ss}$ | .145 | .141 | .135 | .131 |
| | | $\Sigma o_s$ | 0.71 | 0.71 | 0.71 | 0.71 |

### 16 Piles

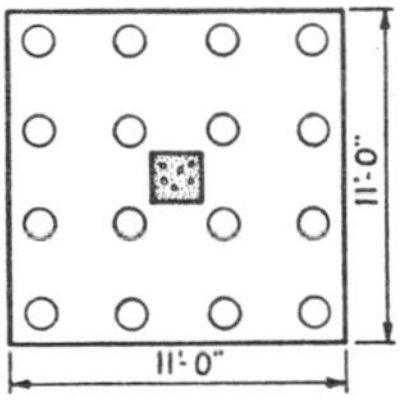


| Depth ft.-in. | Wt. kips | | Pedestal Size—in. 22 | 24 | 26 | 28 |
|---|---|---|---|---|---|---|
| 2–8 | 3.0 | $P$ | 24.1 | 25.2 | 26.2 | 27.3 |
| | | $A_s$ | .324 | .314 | .305 | .295 |
| | | $\Sigma o$ | 1.35 | 1.35 | 1.35 | 1.35 |
| 3–0 | 3.4 | $P$ | 30.5 | 31.7 | 33.0 | 34.2 |
| | | $A_s$ | .278 | .269 | .262 | .253 |
| | | $\Sigma o$ | 1.16 | 1.16 | 1.16 | 1.16 |
| 3–4 | 3.8 | $P$ | 37.7 | 39.1 | 40.5 | 41.9 |
| | | $A_s$ | .243 | .235 | .229 | .221 |
| | | $\Sigma o$ | 1.01 | 1.01 | 1.01 | 1.01 |

### 17 Piles

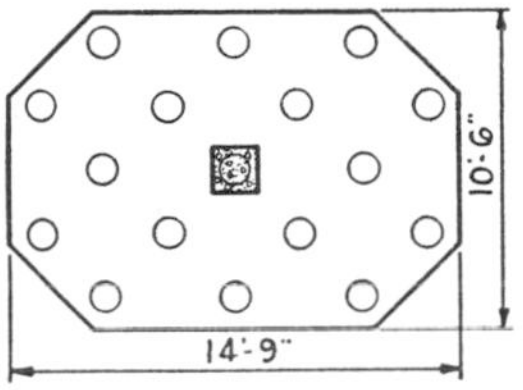


| Depth ft.-in. | Wt. kips | | Pedestal Size—in. 24 | 26 | 28 | 30 |
|---|---|---|---|---|---|---|
| 3–0 | 3.8 | $P$ | 26.2 | 27.2 | 28.2 | 29.2 |
| | | $A_{sl}$ | .404 | .394 | .385 | .375 |
| | | $\Sigma o_l$ | 1.35 | 1.35 | 1.35 | 1.35 |
| | | $A_{ss}$ | .196 | .189 | .183 | .176 |
| | | $\Sigma o_s$ | 0.97 | 0.97 | 0.97 | 0.97 |
| 3–4 | 4.2 | $P$ | 32.2 | 33.5 | 34.7 | 35.9 |
| | | $A_{sl}$ | .354 | .345 | .337 | .328 |
| | | $\Sigma o_l$ | 1.18 | 1.18 | 1.18 | 1.18 |
| | | $A_{ss}$ | .171 | .165 | .160 | .154 |
| | | $\Sigma o_s$ | 0.85 | 0.85 | 0.85 | 0.85 |
| 3–8 | 4.6 | $P$ | 38.8 | 40.3 | 41.8 | 43.3 |
| | | $A_{sl}$ | .314 | .306 | .299 | .292 |
| | | $\Sigma o_l$ | 1.05 | 1.05 | 1.05 | 1.05 |
| | | $A_{ss}$ | .152 | .147 | .142 | .137 |
| | | $\Sigma o_s$ | 0.75 | 0.75 | 0.75 | 0.75 |

### 18 Piles

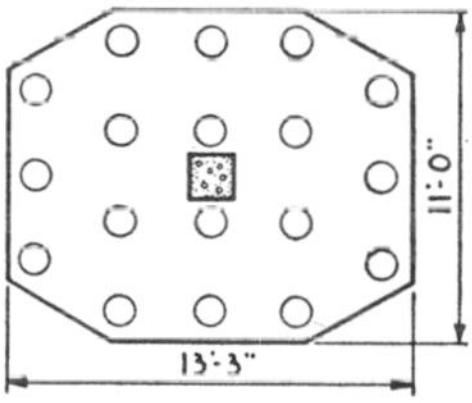


| Depth ft.-in. | Wt. kips | | Pedestal Size—in. 26 | 28 | 30 | 32 |
|---|---|---|---|---|---|---|
| 3–0 | 3.4 | $P$ | 19.8 | 20.6 | 21.3 | 22.0 |
| | | $A_{sl}$ | .376 | .367 | .357 | .347 |
| | | $\Sigma o_l$ | 1.38 | 1.38 | 1.38 | 1.38 |
| | | $A_{ss}$ | .233 | .224 | .215 | .207 |
| | | $\Sigma o_s$ | 1.23 | 1.23 | 1.23 | 1.23 |
| 3–4 | 3.7 | $P$ | 24.3 | 25.2 | 26.0 | 26.9 |
| | | $A_{sl}$ | .329 | .321 | .312 | .304 |
| | | $\Sigma o_l$ | 1.21 | 1.21 | 1.21 | 1.21 |
| | | $A_{ss}$ | .204 | .196 | .188 | .181 |
| | | $\Sigma o_s$ | 1.07 | 1.07 | 1.07 | 1.07 |
| 3–8 | 4.1 | $P$ | 29.2 | 30.2 | 31.1 | 32.1 |
| | | $A_{sl}$ | .292 | .285 | .278 | .270 |
| | | $\Sigma o_l$ | 1.07 | 1.07 | 1.07 | 1.07 |
| | | $A_{ss}$ | .181 | .174 | .167 | .161 |
| | | $\Sigma o_s$ | 0.95 | 0.95 | 0.95 | 0.95 |

### 19 Piles

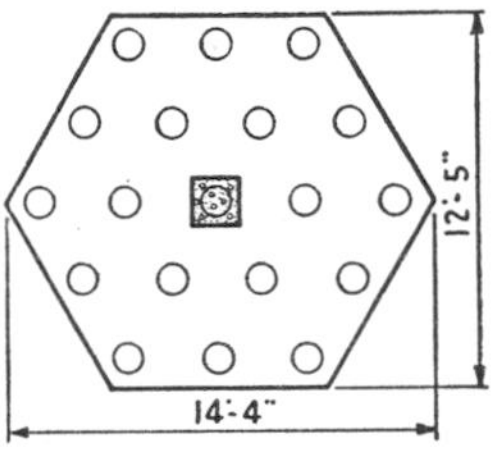


| Depth ft.-in. | Wt. kips | | Pedestal Size—in. 26 | 28 | 30 | 32 |
|---|---|---|---|---|---|---|
| 3–0 | 3.2 | $P$ | 21.9 | 22.7 | 23.5 | 24.4 |
| | | $A_s$ | .319 | .309 | .300 | .291 |
| | | $\Sigma o$ | 1.32 | 1.32 | 1.32 | 1.32 |
| 3–4 | 3.5 | $P$ | 26.9 | 27.8 | 28.7 | 29.7 |
| | | $A_s$ | .279 | .270 | .263 | .255 |
| | | $\Sigma o$ | 1.15 | 1.15 | 1.15 | 1.15 |
| 3–8 | 3.9 | $P$ | 36.5 | 37.7 | 38.9 | 40.0 |
| | | $A_s$ | .248 | .240 | .233 | .227 |
| | | $\Sigma o$ | 1.03 | 1.03 | 1.03 | 1.03 |

### 20 Piles

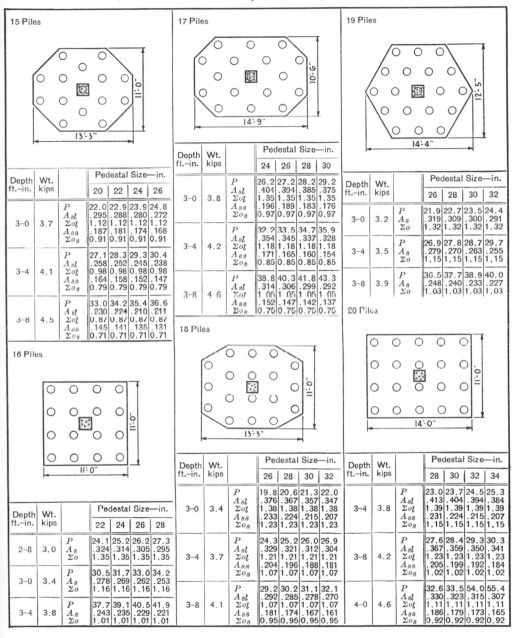

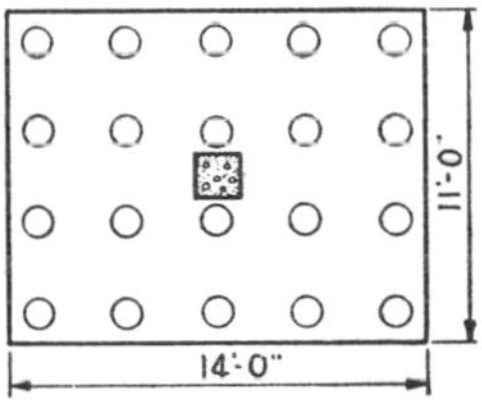


| Depth ft.-in. | Wt. kips | | Pedestal Size—in. 28 | 30 | 32 | 34 |
|---|---|---|---|---|---|---|
| 3–4 | 3.8 | $P$ | 23.0 | 23.7 | 24.5 | 25.3 |
| | | $A_{sl}$ | .413 | .404 | .394 | .384 |
| | | $\Sigma o_l$ | 1.39 | 1.39 | 1.39 | 1.39 |
| | | $A_{ss}$ | .231 | .224 | .215 | .207 |
| | | $\Sigma o_s$ | 1.15 | 1.15 | 1.15 | 1.15 |
| 3–8 | 4.2 | $P$ | 27.6 | 28.4 | 29.3 | 30.3 |
| | | $A_{sl}$ | .367 | .359 | .350 | .341 |
| | | $\Sigma o_l$ | 1.23 | 1.23 | 1.23 | 1.23 |
| | | $A_{ss}$ | .205 | .199 | .192 | .184 |
| | | $\Sigma o_s$ | 1.02 | 1.02 | 1.02 | 1.02 |
| 4–0 | 4.6 | $P$ | 32.6 | 33.5 | 54.0 | 55.4 |
| | | $A_{sl}$ | .330 | .323 | .315 | .307 |
| | | $\Sigma o_l$ | 1.11 | 1.11 | 1.11 | 1.11 |
| | | $A_{ss}$ | .186 | .179 | .173 | .165 |
| | | $\Sigma o_s$ | 0.92 | 0.92 | 0.92 | 0.92 |

## Table 37. Percentage and Weight of Column Spirals*

**Percentage:** $100p' = 400 \dfrac{\text{(Area of Spiral Rod)}}{\text{(Core Dia.)} \times \text{(Pitch)}}$ **Weight:** in lb. per ft. of column $= \dfrac{\pi \text{ (Core Dia.) (Weight per ft. of Rod)}}{\text{Pitch}}$

Values of $100p'$ in bold type (top); weights in light type (bottom)

| Rod Size | Pitch | d: Diameter of Core 10 | 11 | 12 | 13 | 14 | 15 | 16 | 17 | 18 | 19 | 20 | 21 | 22 | 23 | 24 | 25 | 26 | 27 | 28 | 29 | 30 |
|---|---|---|---|---|---|---|---|---|---|---|---|---|---|---|---|---|---|---|---|---|---|---|
| ¼φ | 1¼ | **1.60** | **1.45** | **1.33** | **1.23** | **1.14** | **1.07** | **1.00** | **0.94** | **0.89** | **0.84** | **0.80** | **0.76** | **0.73** | **0.70** | **0.67** | **0.64** | **0.62** | **0.59** | **0.57** | **0.55** | **0.53** |
| | | 4.20 | 4.62 | 5.04 | 5.46 | 5.88 | 6.30 | 6.72 | 7.14 | 7.56 | 7.98 | 8.40 | 8.82 | 9.24 | 9.65 | 10.1 | 10.5 | 10.9 | 11.3 | 11.8 | 12.2 | 12.6 |
| | 1½ | **1.33** | **1.21** | **1.11** | **1.03** | **0.95** | **0.89** | **0.83** | **0.78** | **0.74** | **0.70** | **0.67** | **0.63** | **0.61** | **0.58** | **0.56** | **0.53** | **0.51** | **0.49** | **0.48** | **0.46** | **0.44** |
| | | 3.50 | 3.85 | 4.19 | 4.54 | 4.90 | 5.25 | 5.60 | 5.94 | 6.29 | 6.64 | 7.00 | 7.34 | 7.69 | 8.04 | 8.39 | 8.74 | 9.09 | 9.44 | 9.79 | 10.1 | 10.5 |
| | 1¾ | **1.14** | **1.04** | **0.95** | **0.88** | **0.82** | **0.76** | **0.71** | **0.67** | **0.63** | **0.60** | **0.57** | **0.54** | **0.52** | **0.50** | **0.48** | **0.46** | **0.44** | **0.42** | **0.41** | **0.39** | **0.38** |
| | | 3.00 | 3.30 | 3.60 | 3.90 | 4.20 | 4.50 | 4.80 | 5.10 | 5.40 | 5.70 | 6.00 | 6.30 | 6.60 | 6.90 | 7.20 | 7.50 | 7.80 | 8.10 | 8.40 | 8.70 | 8.99 |
| | 2 | **1.00** | **0.91** | **0.83** | **0.77** | **0.71** | **0.67** | **0.62** | **0.59** | **0.56** | **0.53** | **0.50** | **0.48** | **0.45** | **0.43** | **0.42** | **0.40** | **0.38** | **0.37** | **0.36** | **0.34** | **0.33** |
| | | 2.62 | 2.88 | 3.15 | 3.41 | 3.67 | 3.94 | 4.20 | 4.46 | 4.72 | 4.98 | 5.25 | 5.51 | 5.77 | 6.03 | 6.30 | 6.56 | 6.82 | 7.08 | 7.34 | 7.60 | 7.87 |
| | 2¼ | **0.89** | **0.81** | **0.74** | **0.68** | **0.63** | **0.59** | **0.56** | **0.52** | **0.49** | **0.47** | **0.44** | **0.42** | **0.40** | **0.39** | **0.37** | **0.36** | **0.34** | **0.33** | **0.32** | **0.31** | **0.30** |
| | | 2.33 | 2.56 | 2.80 | 3.03 | 3.26 | 3.50 | 3.73 | 3.96 | 4.20 | 4.43 | 4.66 | 4.90 | 5.13 | 5.36 | 5.60 | 5.83 | 6.06 | 6.30 | 6.53 | 6.77 | 7.00 |
| | 2½ | **0.80** | **0.73** | **0.67** | **0.62** | **0.57** | **0.53** | **0.50** | **0.47** | **0.44** | **0.42** | **0.40** | **0.38** | **0.36** | **0.35** | **0.33** | **0.32** | **0.31** | **0.30** | **0.29** | **0.28** | **0.27** |
| | | 2.10 | 2.31 | 2.52 | 2.73 | 2.94 | 3.15 | 3.36 | 3.56 | 3.78 | 3.98 | 4.20 | 4.41 | 4.62 | 4.83 | 5.04 | 5.25 | 5.46 | 5.67 | 5.88 | 6.09 | 6.30 |
| | 2¾ | **0.73** | **0.66** | **0.61** | **0.56** | **0.52** | **0.48** | **0.45** | **0.43** | **0.40** | **0.38** | **0.36** | **0.35** | **0.33** | **0.32** | **0.30** | **0.29** | **0.28** | **0.27** | **0.26** | **0.25** | **0.24** |
| | | 1.91 | 2.10 | 2.29 | 2.48 | 2.67 | 2.86 | 3.05 | 3.24 | 3.43 | 3.62 | 3.82 | 4.01 | 4.20 | 4.39 | 4.58 | 4.77 | 4.96 | 5.15 | 5.34 | 5.53 | 5.72 |
| | 3 | **0.67** | **0.61** | **0.56** | **0.51** | **0.48** | **0.44** | **0.42** | **0.39** | **0.37** | **0.35** | **0.33** | **0.32** | **0.30** | **0.29** | **0.28** | **0.27** | **0.26** | **0.25** | **0.24** | **0.23** | **0.22** |
| | | 1.75 | 1.92 | 2.10 | 2.27 | 2.45 | 2.62 | 2.80 | 2.97 | 3.15 | 3.32 | 3.50 | 3.67 | 3.85 | 4.02 | 4.20 | 4.37 | 4.55 | 4.72 | 4.90 | 5.07 | 5.25 |
| ⅜φ | 1½ | **2.93** | **2.67** | **2.44** | **2.26** | **2.09** | **1.95** | **1.83** | **1.72** | **1.63** | **1.54** | **1.47** | **1.40** | **1.33** | **1.27** | **1.22** | **1.17** | **1.13** | **1.09** | **1.05** | **1.01** | **0.98** |
| | | 7.87 | 8.66 | 9.45 | 10.2 | 11.0 | 11.8 | 12.6 | 13.4 | 14.2 | 14.9 | 15.7 | 16.5 | 17.3 | 18.1 | 18.9 | 19.7 | 20.4 | 21.2 | 22.0 | 22.8 | 23.6 |
| | 1¾ | **2.51** | **2.29** | **2.09** | **1.93** | **1.80** | **1.68** | **1.57** | **1.48** | **1.40** | **1.32** | **1.26** | **1.20** | **1.14** | **1.09** | **1.05** | **1.01** | **0.97** | **0.93** | **0.90** | **0.87** | **0.84** |
| | | 6.75 | 7.43 | 8.10 | 8.78 | 9.45 | 10.1 | 10.8 | 11.5 | 12.1 | 12.8 | 13.5 | 14.2 | 14.8 | 15.5 | 16.2 | 16.9 | 17.5 | 18.2 | 18.9 | 19.6 | 20.2 |
| | 2 | **2.20** | **2.00** | **1.83** | **1.69** | **1.57** | **1.47** | **1.38** | **1.29** | **1.22** | **1.16** | **1.10** | **1.05** | **1.00** | **0.96** | **0.92** | **0.88** | **0.85** | **0.82** | **0.79** | **0.76** | **0.73** |
| | | 5.91 | 6.50 | 7.09 | 7.68 | 8.27 | 8.85 | 9.44 | 10.0 | 10.6 | 11.2 | 11.8 | 12.4 | 13.0 | 13.6 | 14.2 | 14.8 | 15.4 | 15.9 | 16.5 | 17.1 | 17.7 |
| | 2¼ | **1.96** | **1.78** | **1.63** | **1.50** | **1.40** | **1.30** | **1.22** | **1.15** | **1.09** | **1.03** | **0.98** | **0.93** | **0.89** | **0.85** | **0.81** | **0.78** | **0.75** | **0.72** | **0.70** | **0.67** | **0.65** |
| | | 5.25 | 5.78 | 6.31 | 6.84 | 7.35 | 7.87 | 8.39 | 8.92 | 9.44 | 9.97 | 10.5 | 11.0 | 11.5 | 12.1 | 12.6 | 13.1 | 13.6 | 14.2 | 14.7 | 15.2 | 15.7 |
| | 2½ | **1.76** | **1.60** | **1.47** | **1.35** | **1.26** | **1.17** | **1.10** | **1.03** | **0.98** | **0.93** | **0.88** | **0.84** | **0.80** | **0.76** | **0.73** | **0.70** | **0.68** | **0.65** | **0.63** | **0.61** | **0.59** |
| | | 4.73 | 5.20 | 5.67 | 6.14 | 6.62 | 7.08 | 7.55 | 8.02 | 8.50 | 8.97 | 9.44 | 9.92 | 10.4 | 10.9 | 11.3 | 11.8 | 12.3 | 12.7 | 13.2 | 13.7 | 14.2 |
| | 2¾ | **1.60** | **1.46** | **1.33** | **1.23** | **1.14** | **1.07** | **1.00** | **0.94** | **0.89** | **0.84** | **0.80** | **0.76** | **0.73** | **0.70** | **0.67** | **0.64** | **0.62** | **0.59** | **0.57** | **0.55** | **0.53** |
| | | 4.30 | 4.73 | 5.16 | 5.59 | 6.02 | 6.44 | 6.87 | 7.30 | 7.73 | 8.15 | 8.59 | 9.02 | 9.45 | 9.88 | 10.3 | 10.7 | 11.2 | 11.6 | 12.0 | 12.5 | 12.9 |
| | 3 | **1.47** | **1.33** | **1.22** | **1.13** | **1.05** | **0.98** | **0.92** | **0.86** | **0.81** | **0.77** | **0.73** | **0.70** | **0.67** | **0.64** | **0.61** | **0.59** | **0.56** | **0.54** | **0.52** | **0.51** | **0.49** |
| | | 3.94 | 4.33 | 4.73 | 5.12 | 5.52 | 5.91 | 6.30 | 6.69 | 7.08 | 7.48 | 7.87 | 8.26 | 8.66 | 9.05 | 9.45 | 9.84 | 10.2 | 10.6 | 11.0 | 11.4 | 11.8 |
| | 3¼ | **1.35** | **1.23** | **1.13** | **1.04** | **0.97** | **0.90** | **0.85** | **0.80** | **0.75** | **0.71** | **0.68** | **0.64** | **0.62** | **0.59** | **0.56** | **0.54** | **0.52** | **0.50** | **0.48** | **0.47** | **0.45** |
| | | 3.64 | 4.00 | 4.37 | 4.73 | 5.09 | 5.46 | 5.82 | 6.19 | 6.55 | 6.92 | 7.28 | 7.64 | 8.00 | 8.36 | 8.72 | 9.09 | 9.45 | 9.81 | 10.2 | 10.5 | 10.9 |
| ½φ | 1½ | **5.33** | **4.85** | **4.44** | **4.10** | **3.81** | **3.56** | **3.33** | **3.14** | **2.96** | **2.81** | **2.67** | **2.54** | **2.42** | **2.32** | **2.22** | **2.13** | **2.05** | **1.98** | **1.90** | **1.84** | **1.78** |
| | | 14.0 | 15.4 | 16.8 | 18.2 | 19.6 | 21.0 | 22.4 | 23.8 | 25.2 | 26.6 | 28.0 | 29.4 | 30.8 | 32.2 | 33.6 | 35.0 | 36.4 | 37.8 | 39.2 | 40.6 | 42.0 |
| | 1¾ | **4.57** | **4.16** | **3.81** | **3.52** | **3.27** | **3.05** | **2.86** | **2.69** | **2.54** | **2.41** | **2.29** | **2.18** | **2.08** | **1.99** | **1.90** | **1.83** | **1.76** | **1.69** | **1.63** | **1.58** | **1.52** |
| | | 12.0 | 13.2 | 14.4 | 15.6 | 16.8 | 18.0 | 19.2 | 20.4 | 21.6 | 22.8 | 24.0 | 25.2 | 26.4 | 27.6 | 28.8 | 30.0 | 31.2 | 32.4 | 33.6 | 34.8 | 36.0 |
| | 2 | **4.00** | **3.64** | **3.33** | **3.08** | **2.86** | **2.67** | **2.50** | **2.35** | **2.22** | **2.11** | **2.00** | **1.90** | **1.82** | **1.74** | **1.67** | **1.60** | **1.54** | **1.48** | **1.43** | **1.38** | **1.33** |
| | | 10.5 | 11.5 | 12.6 | 13.6 | 14.7 | 15.7 | 16.8 | 17.8 | 18.9 | 20.0 | 21.0 | 22.0 | 23.1 | 24.1 | 25.2 | 26.2 | 27.3 | 28.3 | 29.4 | 30.4 | 31.5 |
| | 2¼ | **3.55** | **3.23** | **2.96** | **2.73** | **2.54** | **2.37** | **2.22** | **2.09** | **1.97** | **1.87** | **1.78** | **1.69** | **1.62** | **1.55** | **1.48** | **1.42** | **1.37** | **1.32** | **1.27** | **1.23** | **1.19** |
| | | 9.34 | 10.2 | 11.2 | 12.1 | 13.0 | 14.0 | 14.9 | 15.9 | 16.8 | 17.7 | 18.6 | 19.6 | 20.5 | 21.4 | 22.4 | 23.3 | 24.3 | 25.2 | 26.1 | 27.1 | 28.1 |
| | 2½ | **3.20** | **2.91** | **2.67** | **2.46** | **2.29** | **2.13** | **2.00** | **1.88** | **1.78** | **1.68** | **1.60** | **1.52** | **1.45** | **1.39** | **1.33** | **1.28** | **1.23** | **1.19** | **1.14** | **1.10** | **1.07** |
| | | 8.38 | 9.24 | 10.1 | 10.9 | 11.7 | 12.6 | 13.4 | 14.3 | 15.1 | 16.0 | 16.8 | 17.6 | 18.5 | 19.3 | 20.2 | 21.0 | 21.8 | 22.7 | 23.5 | 24.4 | 25.2 |
| | 2¾ | **2.91** | **2.64** | **2.42** | **2.24** | **2.08** | **1.94** | **1.82** | **1.71** | **1.62** | **1.53** | **1.45** | **1.38** | **1.32** | **1.26** | **1.21** | **1.16** | **1.12** | **1.08** | **1.04** | **1.00** | **0.97** |
| | | 7.63 | 8.40 | 9.16 | 9.92 | 10.7 | 11.4 | 12.2 | 13.0 | 13.7 | 14.5 | 15.3 | 16.0 | 16.8 | 17.6 | 18.3 | 19.1 | 19.9 | 20.6 | 21.4 | 22.2 | 22.9 |
| | 3 | **2.67** | **2.43** | **2.23** | **2.05** | **1.91** | **1.78** | **1.67** | **1.57** | **1.48** | **1.40** | **1.33** | **1.27** | **1.21** | **1.16** | **1.11** | **1.07** | **1.03** | **0.99** | **0.95** | **0.92** | **0.89** |
| | | 7.00 | 7.70 | 8.40 | 9.10 | 9.78 | 10.5 | 11.2 | 11.9 | 12.6 | 13.3 | 14.0 | 14.7 | 15.4 | 16.1 | 16.8 | 17.5 | 18.2 | 18.9 | 19.6 | 20.3 | 21.0 |
| | 3¼ | **2.46** | **2.24** | **2.05** | **1.89** | **1.76** | **1.64** | **1.54** | **1.45** | **1.37** | **1.30** | **1.23** | **1.17** | **1.12** | **1.07** | **1.03** | **0.98** | **0.95** | **0.91** | **0.88** | **0.85** | **0.82** |
| | | 6.46 | 7.10 | 7.75 | 8.39 | 9.04 | 9.69 | 10.3 | 11.0 | 11.6 | 12.3 | 12.9 | 13.6 | 14.2 | 14.9 | 15.5 | 16.1 | 16.8 | 17.4 | 18.1 | 18.7 | 19.4 |
| | 3½ | **2.28** | **2.08** | **1.90** | **1.76** | **1.63** | **1.52** | **1.43** | **1.34** | **1.27** | **1.20** | **1.14** | **1.09** | **1.04** | **0.99** | **0.95** | **0.91** | **0.88** | **0.85** | **0.82** | **0.79** | **0.76** |
| | | 6.00 | 6.60 | 7.20 | 7.80 | 8.40 | 9.00 | 9.60 | 10.2 | 10.8 | 11.4 | 12.0 | 12.6 | 13.2 | 13.8 | 14.4 | 15.0 | 15.6 | 16.2 | 16.8 | 17.4 | 18.0 |
| ⅝φ | 2 | **6.20** | **5.64** | **5.17** | **4.77** | **4.44** | **4.13** | **3.88** | **3.65** | **3.45** | **3.26** | **3.10** | **2.95** | **2.82** | **2.70** | **2.59** | **2.48** | **2.39** | **2.30** | **2.21** | **2.14** | **2.07** |
| | | 16.4 | 18.0 | 19.7 | 21.3 | 22.9 | 24.6 | 26.2 | 27.9 | 29.5 | 31.1 | 32.8 | 34.4 | 36.0 | 37.7 | 39.3 | 41.0 | 42.6 | 44.2 | 45.9 | 47.5 | 49.2 |
| | 2¼ | **5.51** | **5.01** | **4.59** | **4.24** | **3.94** | **3.68** | **3.45** | **3.24** | **3.06** | **2.90** | **2.76** | **2.63** | **2.51** | **2.40** | **2.30** | **2.21** | **2.12** | **2.04** | **1.97** | **1.90** | **1.84** |
| | | 14.6 | 16.0 | 17.5 | 18.9 | 20.4 | 21.8 | 23.3 | 24.8 | 26.2 | 27.7 | 29.1 | 30.6 | 32.0 | 33.5 | 35.0 | 36.4 | 37.9 | 39.3 | 40.8 | 42.2 | 43.7 |
| | 2½ | **4.96** | **4.51** | **4.13** | **3.82** | **3.54** | **3.31** | **3.10** | **2.92** | **2.76** | **2.61** | **2.48** | **2.36** | **2.26** | **2.16** | **2.07** | **1.98** | **1.91** | **1.84** | **1.77** | **1.71** | **1.65** |
| | | 13.1 | 14.4 | 15.7 | 17.0 | 18.4 | 19.7 | 21.0 | 22.3 | 23.6 | 24.9 | 26.2 | 27.5 | 28.8 | 30.1 | 31.5 | 32.8 | 34.1 | 35.4 | 36.7 | 38.0 | 39.3 |
| | 2¾ | **4.51** | **4.10** | **3.76** | **3.47** | **3.22** | **3.01** | **2.82** | **2.65** | **2.51** | **2.37** | **2.25** | **2.15** | **2.05** | **1.96** | **1.88** | **1.80** | **1.73** | **1.67** | **1.61** | **1.55** | **1.50** |
| | | 11.9 | 13.1 | 14.3 | 15.5 | 16.7 | 17.9 | 19.1 | 20.3 | 21.4 | 22.6 | 23.8 | 25.0 | 26.2 | 27.4 | 28.6 | 29.8 | 31.0 | 32.2 | 33.4 | 34.6 | 35.7 |
| | 3 | **4.13** | **3.76** | **3.45** | **3.18** | **2.95** | **2.76** | **2.58** | **2.43** | **2.30** | **2.18** | **2.07** | **1.97** | **1.88** | **1.80** | **1.72** | **1.65** | **1.59** | **1.53** | **1.48** | **1.43** | **1.38** |
| | | 10.9 | 12.0 | 13.1 | 14.2 | 15.3 | 16.4 | 17.5 | 18.6 | 19.7 | 20.8 | 21.8 | 22.9 | 24.0 | 25.1 | 26.2 | 27.3 | 28.4 | 29.5 | 30.6 | 31.7 | 32.8 |
| | 3¼ | **3.81** | **3.47** | **3.18** | **2.94** | **2.73** | **2.55** | **2.38** | **2.25** | **2.12** | **2.01** | **1.91** | **1.82** | **1.74** | **1.66** | **1.59** | **1.53** | **1.47** | **1.41** | **1.36** | **1.32** | **1.27** |
| | | 10.1 | 11.1 | 12.1 | 13.1 | 14.1 | 15.1 | 16.1 | 17.2 | 18.2 | 19.2 | 20.2 | 21.2 | 22.2 | 23.2 | 24.2 | 25.2 | 26.2 | 27.2 | 28.2 | 29.2 | 30.2 |
| | 3½ | **3.54** | **3.22** | **2.95** | **2.73** | **2.53** | **2.36** | **2.21** | **2.09** | **1.97** | **1.86** | **1.77** | **1.69** | **1.61** | **1.54** | **1.48** | **1.42** | **1.36** | **1.31** | **1.27** | **1.22** | **1.18** |
| | | 9.37 | 10.3 | 11.2 | 12.2 | 13.1 | 14.1 | 15.0 | 15.9 | 16.9 | 17.8 | 18.7 | 19.7 | 20.6 | 21.5 | 22.5 | 23.4 | 24.3 | 25.3 | 26.2 | 27.2 | 28.1 |

*The weights given include wire for regular loops only. Weight must be added for 1½ turns top and bottom required for embedment equivalent to one-half the tabular weight for 2-in. pitch. Weight of spacers must also be added. A ⅞-in. channel spacer weighs ¾ lb. per lin. ft. Two or more spacers are required for each spiral. Type, weight and number of spacers may vary with local conditions and requirements.

## Table 38. Areas, Weights and Perimeters of Reinforcing Bars and Spiral Rods

**Reinforcing Bars**

| Size—in. Plain | Size—in. Deformed | Area* sq.in. | Weight** lb. per lin.ft. | Perimeter in. |
|---|---|---|---|---|
| ¼φ | — | 0.05 | 0.167 | 0.785 |
| — | ⅜φ | 0.11 | 0.376 | 1.178 |
| — | ½φ | 0.20 | 0.668 | 1.571 |
| — | ½ □ | 0.25 | 0.850 | 2.000 |
| — | ⅝φ | 0.31 | 1.043 | 1.963 |
| — | ¾φ | 0.44 | 1.502 | 2.356 |
| — | ⅞φ | 0.60 | 2.044 | 2.749 |
| — | 1φ | 0.79 | 2.670 | 3.142 |
| — | 1 □ | 1.00 | 3.400 | 4.000 |
| — | 1⅛ □ | 1.27 | 4.303 | 4.500 |
| — | 1¼ □ | 1.56 | 5.313 | 5.000 |

**Spiral Rods**

| Size—in. Plain | Area* sq.in. | Weight** lb. per lin.ft. | Perimeter in. |
|---|---|---|---|
| ¼φ | 0.05 | 0.167 | 0.785 |
| ⅜φ | 0.11 | 0.376 | 1.178 |
| ½φ | 0.20 | 0.668 | 1.571 |
| ⅝φ | 0.25 | 1.043 | 1.963 |

*Areas are as recommended by the Division of Simplified Practice of the U.S. Department of Commerce in its *Bulletin No. 26* effective September 15, 1930 (reinforcing bars) and *Bulletin No. 53* effective December 15, 1932 (spiral rods).

**Weights are in accordance with standards adopted by the Concrete Reinforcing Steel Institute in 1934.

## Table 39. Standard Styles of Welded Wire Fabric

| Spacing of Wires in. | | Gage of Wires (W&M Gage) | | Sect. Area sq.in. per ft. of Fabric | | Weight lb. per 100 sq.ft. |
|---|---|---|---|---|---|---|
| Longit. | Trans. | Longit. | Trans. | Longit. | Trans. | |
| 2 | 16 | 1 | 7 | .377 | .018 | 140 |
| 2 | 16 | 2 | 8 | .325 | .015 | 119 |
| 2 | 16 | 3 | 8 | .280 | .015 | 104 |
| 2 | 16 | 4 | 9 | .239 | .013 | 89 |
| 3 | 16 | 2 | 8 | .216 | .016 | 83 |
| 2 | 16 | 5 | 10 | .202 | .011 | 75 |
| 3 | 16 | 3 | 8 | .187 | .015 | 72 |
| 2 | 16 | 6 | 10 | .174 | .011 | 65 |
| 3 | 16 | 4 | 9 | .159 | .013 | 61 |
| 2 | 16 | 7 | 11 | .148 | .009 | 55 |
| 4 | 16 | 3 | 8 | .140 | .015 | 56 |
| 3 | 16 | 5 | 10 | .135 | .011 | 52 |
| 4 | 16 | 4 | 9 | .120 | .013 | 48 |
| 3 | 16 | 6 | 10 | .116 | .011 | 45 |
| 4 | 16 | 5 | 10 | .101 | .011 | 40 |
| 3 | 16 | 7 | 11 | .098 | .009 | 38 |
| 4 | 16 | 6 | 10 | .087 | .011 | 35 |
| 3 | 16 | 8 | 12 | .082 | .007 | 32 |
| 4 | 16 | 7 | 11 | .074 | .009 | 30 |
| 4 | 12 | 8 | 12 | .062 | .009 | 26 |
| 4 | 12 | 9 | 12 | .052 | .009 | 22 |
| 4 | 12 | 10 | 12 | .043 | .009 | 19 |
| 4 | 12 | 12 | 12 | .026 | .009 | 13 |
| 4 | 12 | 5 | 5 | .101 | .034 | 48 |
| 4 | 12 | 6 | 6 | .087 | .029 | 42 |
| 4 | 12 | 7 | 7 | .074 | .025 | 35 |
| 4 | 12 | 8 | 8 | .062 | .021 | 30 |
| 6 | 12 | 0 | 6 | .148 | .029 | 65 |
| 6 | 12 | 2 | 2 | .108 | .054 | 59 |
| 6 | 12 | 3 | 3 | .093 | .047 | 51 |
| 6 | 12 | 4 | 4 | .080 | .040 | 44 |
| 6 | 12 | 5 | 5 | .067 | .034 | 37 |
| 6 | 12 | 6 | 6 | .058 | .029 | 32 |
| 6 | 12 | 7 | 7 | .049 | .025 | 27 |
| 6 | 8 | 12 | 12 | .017 | .013 | 11 |
| 6 | 6 | 1 | 1 | .126 | .126 | 91 |
| 6 | 6 | 2 | 2 | .108 | .108 | 78 |
| 6 | 6 | 3 | 3 | .093 | .093 | 68 |
| 6 | 6 | 4 | 4 | .080 | .080 | 58 |
| 6 | 6 | 5 | 5 | .067 | .067 | 49 |
| 6 | 6 | 6 | 6 | .058 | .058 | 42 |
| 6 | 6 | 7 | 7 | .049 | .049 | 36 |
| 6 | 6 | 8 | 8 | .041 | .041 | 30 |
| 6 | 6 | 9 | 9 | .035 | .035 | 25 |
| 6 | 6 | 10 | 10 | .029 | .029 | 21 |
| 4 | 4 | 4 | 4 | .120 | .120 | 85 |
| 4 | 4 | 6 | 6 | .087 | .087 | 62 |
| 4 | 4 | 8 | 8 | .062 | .062 | 44 |
| 4 | 4 | 10 | 10 | .043 | .043 | 31 |
| 4 | 4 | 12 | 12 | .026 | .026 | 19 |
| 4 | 4 | 14 | 14 | .015 | .015 | 11 |
| 2 | 2 | 10 | 10 | .086 | .086 | 60 |
| 2 | 2 | 12 | 12 | .052 | .052 | 37 |
| 2 | 2 | 13 | 13 | .039 | .039 | 28 |
| 2 | 2 | 14 | 14 | .030 | .030 | 21 |

Widths: Multiples of the spacing of longitudinal wire up to a maximum width which varies with the size and spacing of the longitudinals. Approximate maximums: 56 in. to 72 in. for 2-in. spacing, 84 in. to 96 in. for 3-in. or 4-in. spacing, and 96 in. to 120 in for 6-in. spacing.

All widths measured center to center of selvage longitudinals.

The traverse wires extend 1 in. beyond the outside longitudinal wires. Square footage or square yardage will be figured exclusive of these projections.

Length—Rolls: Styles having longitudinals number 3 gage or smaller made regularly in standard lengths 150 ft., 200 ft. and 300 ft. Flat sheets can be furnished when desired. Styles having longitudinals larger than number 3 gage made regularly in straightened and cut sheets only.

Weights: All above weights are based on a width of 60 in. measured from center to center of the outside or selvage longitudinal wires.

# Table 40. Moments in Beams With Fixed Ends (ft.kips)

## 1. Uniform Load

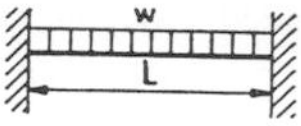


Fixed end moments: Table values $M = \frac{1}{12}wL^2$

Midspan moments: Table values × 0.5 $M = \frac{1}{24}wL^2$

## 2. Concentrated Load at Midspan

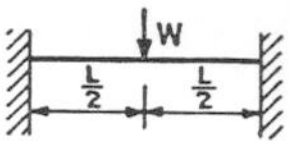


Fixed end moments: Table values $M = \frac{1}{8}WL$

Midspan moments: Table values $M = \frac{1}{8}WL$

| Span $L$ | Uniform Load $w$ in kips per ft. | | | | | | | | | |
|---|---|---|---|---|---|---|---|---|---|---|
| | For following loads use table values directly | | | | | | | | | |
| | 1 | 2 | 3 | 4 | 5 | 6 | 7 | 8 | 9 | 10 |
| | For following loads use table values divided by 10 | | | | | | | | | |
| | 0.1 | 0.2 | 0.3 | 0.4 | 0.5 | 0.6 | 0.7 | 0.8 | 0.9 | 1.0 |
| 5′-0″ | 2.08 | 4.17 | 6.25 | 8.33 | 10.4 | 12.5 | 14.6 | 16.7 | 18.7 | 20.8 |
| 5′-3″ | 2.30 | 4.59 | 6.89 | 9.19 | 11.5 | 13.8 | 16.1 | 18.4 | 20.7 | 23.0 |
| 5′-6″ | 2.52 | 5.04 | 7.56 | 10.1 | 12.6 | 15.1 | 17.6 | 20.2 | 22.7 | 25.2 |
| 5′-9″ | 2.76 | 5.51 | 8.27 | 11.0 | 13.8 | 16.5 | 19.3 | 22.0 | 24.8 | 27.6 |
| 6′-0″ | 3.00 | 6.00 | 9.00 | 12.0 | 15.0 | 18.0 | 21.0 | 24.0 | 27.0 | 30.0 |
| 6′-3″ | 3.26 | 6.51 | 9.77 | 13.0 | 16.3 | 19.5 | 22.8 | 26.0 | 29.3 | 32.6 |
| 6′-6″ | 3.52 | 7.04 | 10.6 | 14.1 | 17.6 | 21.1 | 24.6 | 28.2 | 31.7 | 35.2 |
| 6′-9″ | 3.80 | 7.59 | 11.4 | 15.2 | 19.0 | 22.8 | 26.6 | 30.4 | 34.2 | 38.0 |
| 7′-0″ | 4.08 | 8.17 | 12.3 | 16.3 | 20.4 | 24.5 | 28.6 | 32.7 | 36.8 | 40.8 |
| 7′-3″ | 4.38 | 8.76 | 13.1 | 17.5 | 21.9 | 26.3 | 30.7 | 35.0 | 39.4 | 43.8 |
| 7′-6″ | 4.69 | 9.38 | 14.1 | 18.8 | 23.4 | 28.1 | 32.8 | 37.5 | 42.2 | 46.9 |
| 7′-9″ | 5.01 | 10.0 | 15.0 | 20.0 | 25.0 | 30.0 | 35.0 | 40.0 | 45.0 | 50.1 |
| 8′-0″ | 5.33 | 10.7 | 16.0 | 21.3 | 26.7 | 32.0 | 37.3 | 42.7 | 48.0 | 53.3 |
| 8′-3″ | 5.67 | 11.3 | 17.0 | 22.7 | 28.4 | 34.0 | 39.7 | 45.4 | 51.1 | 56.7 |
| 8′-6″ | 6.02 | 12.0 | 18.1 | 24.1 | 30.1 | 36.1 | 42.2 | 48.2 | 54.2 | 60.2 |
| 8′-9″ | 6.38 | 12.8 | 19.1 | 25.5 | 31.9 | 38.3 | 44.7 | 51.0 | 57.4 | 63.8 |
| 9′-0″ | 6.75 | 13.5 | 20.3 | 27.0 | 33.7 | 40.5 | 47.3 | 54.0 | 60.8 | 67.5 |
| 9′-3″ | 7.13 | 14.3 | 21.4 | 28.5 | 35.6 | 42.8 | 49.9 | 57.0 | 64.2 | 71.3 |
| 9′-6″ | 7.52 | 15.0 | 22.6 | 30.1 | 37.6 | 45.1 | 52.6 | 60.2 | 67.7 | 75.2 |
| 9′-9″ | 7.92 | 15.8 | 23.8 | 31.7 | 39.6 | 47.5 | 55.5 | 63.4 | 71.3 | 79.2 |
| 10′-0″ | 8.33 | 16.7 | 25.0 | 33.3 | 41.7 | 50.0 | 58.3 | 66.7 | 75.0 | 83.3 |
| 10′-6″ | 9.19 | 18.4 | 27.6 | 36.8 | 45.9 | 55.1 | 64.3 | 73.5 | 82.7 | 91.9 |
| 11′-0″ | 10.1 | 20.2 | 30.3 | 40.3 | 50.4 | 60.5 | 70.6 | 80.7 | 90.8 | 101 |
| 11′-6″ | 11.0 | 22.0 | 33.1 | 44.1 | 55.1 | 66.1 | 77.2 | 88.2 | 99.2 | 110 |
| 12′-0″ | 12.0 | 24.0 | 36.0 | 48.0 | 60.0 | 72.0 | 84.0 | 96.0 | 108 | 120 |
| 12′-6″ | 13.0 | 26.0 | 39.1 | 52.1 | 65.1 | 78.1 | 91.2 | 104 | 117 | 130 |
| 13′-0″ | 14.1 | 28.2 | 42.2 | 56.3 | 70.4 | 84.5 | 98.6 | 113 | 127 | 141 |
| 13′-6″ | 15.2 | 30.4 | 45.6 | 60.8 | 75.9 | 91.1 | 106 | 122 | 137 | 152 |
| 14′-0″ | 16.3 | 32.7 | 49.0 | 65.3 | 81.7 | 98.0 | 114 | 131 | 147 | 163 |
| 14′-6″ | 17.5 | 35.0 | 52.6 | 70.1 | 87.6 | 105 | 123 | 140 | 158 | 175 |
| 15′-0″ | 18.8 | 37.5 | 56.3 | 75.0 | 93.8 | 113 | 131 | 150 | 169 | 188 |
| 15′-6″ | 20.0 | 40.0 | 60.1 | 80.1 | 100 | 120 | 140 | 160 | 180 | 200 |
| 16′-0″ | 21.3 | 42.7 | 64.0 | 85.3 | 107 | 128 | 149 | 171 | 192 | 213 |
| 16′-6″ | 22.7 | 45.4 | 68.1 | 90.8 | 113 | 136 | 159 | 182 | 204 | 227 |
| 17′-0″ | 24.1 | 48.2 | 72.2 | 96.3 | 120 | 145 | 169 | 193 | 217 | 241 |
| 17′-6″ | 25.5 | 51.0 | 76.6 | 102 | 128 | 153 | 179 | 204 | 230 | 255 |
| 18′-0″ | 27.0 | 54.0 | 81.0 | 108 | 135 | 162 | 189 | 216 | 243 | 270 |
| 18′-6″ | 28.5 | 57.0 | 85.6 | 114 | 143 | 171 | 200 | 228 | 257 | 285 |
| 19′-0″ | 30.1 | 60.2 | 90.3 | 120 | 150 | 181 | 211 | 241 | 271 | 301 |
| 19′-6″ | 31.7 | 63.4 | 95.1 | 127 | 158 | 190 | 222 | 254 | 285 | 317 |
| 20′-0″ | 33.3 | 66.7 | 100 | 133 | 167 | 200 | 233 | 267 | 300 | 333 |
| 20′-6″ | 35.0 | 70.0 | 105 | 140 | 175 | 210 | 245 | 280 | 315 | 350 |
| 21′-0″ | 36.8 | 73.5 | 110 | 147 | 184 | 221 | 257 | 294 | 331 | 368 |
| 21′-6″ | 38.5 | 77.0 | 116 | 154 | 193 | 231 | 270 | 308 | 347 | 385 |
| 22′-0″ | 40.3 | 80.7 | 121 | 161 | 202 | 242 | 282 | 323 | 363 | 403 |
| 22′-6″ | 42.2 | 84.4 | 127 | 169 | 211 | 253 | 295 | 338 | 380 | 422 |
| 23′-0″ | 44.1 | 88.2 | 132 | 176 | 220 | 264 | 309 | 353 | 397 | 441 |
| 23′-6″ | 46.0 | 92.0 | 138 | 184 | 230 | 276 | 322 | 368 | 414 | 460 |
| 24′-0″ | 48.0 | 96.0 | 144 | 192 | 240 | 288 | 336 | 384 | 432 | 480 |
| 24′-6″ | 50.0 | 100 | 150 | 200 | 250 | 300 | 350 | 400 | 450 | 500 |
| 25′-0″ | 52.1 | 104 | 156 | 208 | 260 | 312 | 365 | 417 | 469 | 521 |
| 25′-6″ | 54.2 | 108 | 163 | 217 | 271 | 325 | 379 | 434 | 488 | 542 |
| 26′-0″ | 56.3 | 113 | 169 | 225 | 282 | 338 | 394 | 451 | 507 | 563 |
| 26′-6″ | 58.5 | 117 | 176 | 234 | 293 | 351 | 410 | 468 | 527 | 585 |
| 27′-0″ | 60.8 | 122 | 182 | 243 | 304 | 365 | 425 | 486 | 547 | 608 |
| 27′-6″ | 63.0 | 126 | 189 | 252 | 315 | 378 | 441 | 504 | 567 | 630 |
| 28′-0″ | 65.3 | 131 | 196 | 261 | 327 | 392 | 457 | 523 | 588 | 653 |
| 28′-6″ | 67.7 | 135 | 203 | 271 | 338 | 406 | 474 | 542 | 609 | 677 |
| 29′-0″ | 70.1 | 140 | 210 | 280 | 350 | 420 | 491 | 561 | 631 | 701 |
| 29′-6″ | 72.5 | 145 | 218 | 290 | 363 | 435 | 508 | 580 | 653 | 725 |
| 30′-0″ | 75.0 | 150 | 225 | 300 | 375 | 450 | 525 | 600 | 675 | 750 |

| Span $L$ | Concentrated Load $W$ in kips | | | | | | | | | |
|---|---|---|---|---|---|---|---|---|---|---|
| | For following loads use table values directly | | | | | | | | | |
| | 10 | 20 | 30 | 40 | 50 | 60 | 70 | 80 | 90 | 100 |
| | For following loads use table values divided by 10 | | | | | | | | | |
| | 1 | 2 | 3 | 4 | 5 | 6 | 7 | 8 | 9 | 10 |
| 5′-0″ | 6.3 | 12.5 | 18.8 | 25.0 | 31.3 | 37.5 | 43.8 | 50.0 | 56.3 | 62.5 |
| 5′-3″ | 6.6 | 13.1 | 19.7 | 26.3 | 32.8 | 39.4 | 45.9 | 52.5 | 59.1 | 65.6 |
| 5′-6″ | 6.9 | 13.8 | 20.6 | 27.5 | 34.4 | 41.3 | 48.1 | 55.0 | 61.9 | 68.8 |
| 5′-9″ | 7.2 | 14.4 | 21.6 | 28.8 | 35.9 | 43.1 | 50.3 | 57.5 | 64.7 | 71.9 |
| 6′-0″ | 7.5 | 15.0 | 22.5 | 30.0 | 37.5 | 45.0 | 52.5 | 60.0 | 67.5 | 75.0 |
| 6′-3″ | 7.8 | 15.6 | 23.4 | 31.3 | 39.1 | 46.9 | 54.7 | 62.5 | 70.3 | 78.1 |
| 6′-6″ | 8.1 | 16.3 | 24.4 | 32.5 | 40.6 | 48.8 | 56.9 | 65.0 | 73.1 | 81.3 |
| 6′-9″ | 8.4 | 16.9 | 25.3 | 33.8 | 42.2 | 50.6 | 59.1 | 67.5 | 75.9 | 84.4 |
| 7′-0″ | 8.8 | 17.5 | 26.3 | 35.0 | 43.8 | 52.5 | 61.3 | 70.0 | 78.8 | 87.5 |
| 7′-3″ | 9.1 | 18.1 | 27.2 | 36.3 | 45.3 | 54.4 | 63.4 | 72.5 | 81.6 | 90.6 |
| 7′-6″ | 9.4 | 18.8 | 28.1 | 37.5 | 46.9 | 56.3 | 65.6 | 75.0 | 84.4 | 93.8 |
| 7′-9″ | 9.7 | 19.4 | 29.1 | 38.8 | 48.4 | 58.1 | 67.8 | 77.5 | 87.2 | 96.9 |
| 8′-0″ | 10.0 | 20.0 | 30.0 | 40.0 | 50.0 | 60.0 | 70.0 | 80.0 | 90.0 | 100 |
| 8′-3″ | 10.3 | 20.6 | 30.9 | 41.3 | 51.6 | 61.9 | 72.2 | 82.5 | 92.8 | 103 |
| 8′-6″ | 10.6 | 21.3 | 31.9 | 42.5 | 53.1 | 63.8 | 74.4 | 85.0 | 95.6 | 106 |
| 8′-9″ | 10.9 | 21.9 | 32.8 | 43.8 | 54.7 | 65.6 | 76.6 | 87.5 | 98.4 | 109 |
| 9′-0″ | 11.3 | 22.5 | 33.8 | 45.0 | 56.3 | 67.5 | 78.8 | 90.0 | 101 | 113 |
| 9′-3″ | 11.6 | 23.1 | 34.7 | 46.3 | 57.8 | 69.4 | 80.9 | 92.5 | 104 | 116 |
| 9′-6″ | 11.9 | 23.8 | 35.6 | 47.5 | 59.4 | 71.3 | 83.1 | 95.0 | 107 | 119 |
| 9′-9″ | 12.2 | 24.4 | 36.6 | 48.8 | 60.9 | 73.1 | 85.3 | 97.5 | 110 | 122 |
| 10′-0″ | 12.5 | 25.0 | 37.5 | 50.0 | 62.5 | 75.0 | 87.5 | 100 | 113 | 125 |
| 10′-6″ | 13.1 | 26.3 | 39.4 | 52.5 | 65.6 | 78.8 | 91.9 | 105 | 118 | 131 |
| 11′-0″ | 13.8 | 27.5 | 41.3 | 55.0 | 68.8 | 82.5 | 96.3 | 110 | 124 | 138 |
| 11′-6″ | 14.4 | 28.8 | 43.1 | 57.5 | 71.9 | 86.3 | 101 | 115 | 129 | 144 |
| 12′-0″ | 15.0 | 30.0 | 45.0 | 60.0 | 75.0 | 90.0 | 105 | 120 | 135 | 150 |
| 12′-6″ | 15.6 | 31.3 | 46.9 | 62.5 | 78.1 | 93.8 | 109 | 125 | 141 | 156 |
| 13′-0″ | 16.3 | 32.5 | 48.8 | 65.0 | 81.3 | 97.5 | 114 | 130 | 146 | 163 |
| 13′-6″ | 16.9 | 33.8 | 50.6 | 67.5 | 84.4 | 101 | 118 | 135 | 152 | 169 |
| 14′-0″ | 17.5 | 35.0 | 52.5 | 70.0 | 87.5 | 105 | 122 | 140 | 157 | 175 |
| 14′-6″ | 18.1 | 36.3 | 54.4 | 72.5 | 90.6 | 109 | 127 | 145 | 163 | 181 |
| 15′-0″ | 18.8 | 37.5 | 56.3 | 75.0 | 93.8 | 112 | 131 | 150 | 169 | 188 |
| 15′-6″ | 19.4 | 38.8 | 58.1 | 77.5 | 96.9 | 116 | 136 | 155 | 174 | 194 |
| 16′-0″ | 20.0 | 40.0 | 60.0 | 80.0 | 100 | 120 | 140 | 160 | 180 | 200 |
| 16′-6″ | 20.6 | 41.3 | 61.9 | 82.5 | 103 | 124 | 144 | 165 | 186 | 206 |
| 17′-0″ | 21.3 | 42.5 | 63.8 | 85.0 | 106 | 128 | 149 | 170 | 191 | 213 |
| 17′-6″ | 21.9 | 43.8 | 65.6 | 87.5 | 109 | 131 | 153 | 175 | 197 | 219 |
| 18′-0″ | 22.5 | 45.0 | 67.5 | 90.0 | 112 | 135 | 158 | 180 | 202 | 225 |
| 18′-6″ | 23.1 | 46.3 | 69.4 | 92.5 | 116 | 139 | 162 | 185 | 208 | 231 |
| 19′-0″ | 23.8 | 47.5 | 71.3 | 95.0 | 119 | 142 | 166 | 190 | 214 | 238 |
| 19′-6″ | 24.4 | 48.8 | 73.1 | 97.5 | 122 | 146 | 171 | 195 | 219 | 244 |
| 20′-0″ | 25.0 | 50.0 | 75.0 | 100 | 125 | 150 | 175 | 200 | 225 | 250 |
| 20′-6″ | 25.6 | 51.3 | 76.9 | 103 | 128 | 154 | 179 | 205 | 231 | 256 |
| 21′-0″ | 26.3 | 52.5 | 78.8 | 105 | 131 | 158 | 184 | 210 | 236 | 263 |
| 21′-6″ | 26.9 | 53.8 | 80.6 | 108 | 134 | 161 | 188 | 215 | 242 | 269 |
| 22′-0″ | 27.5 | 55.0 | 82.5 | 110 | 138 | 165 | 192 | 220 | 248 | 275 |
| 22′-6″ | 28.1 | 56.3 | 84.4 | 113 | 141 | 169 | 197 | 225 | 253 | 281 |
| 23′-0″ | 28.8 | 57.5 | 86.3 | 115 | 144 | 172 | 201 | 230 | 259 | 288 |
| 23′-6″ | 29.4 | 58.8 | 88.1 | 118 | 147 | 176 | 206 | 235 | 264 | 294 |
| 24′-0″ | 30.0 | 60.0 | 90.0 | 120 | 150 | 180 | 210 | 240 | 270 | 300 |
| 24′-6″ | 30.6 | 61.3 | 91.9 | 123 | 153 | 184 | 214 | 245 | 276 | 306 |
| 25′-0″ | 31.3 | 62.5 | 93.8 | 125 | 156 | 188 | 219 | 250 | 281 | 313 |
| 25′-6″ | 31.9 | 63.8 | 95.6 | 128 | 159 | 191 | 223 | 255 | 287 | 319 |
| 26′-0″ | 32.5 | 65.0 | 97.5 | 130 | 162 | 195 | 228 | 260 | 292 | 325 |
| 26′-6″ | 33.1 | 66.3 | 99.4 | 133 | 166 | 199 | 232 | 265 | 298 | 331 |
| 27′-0″ | 33.8 | 67.5 | 101 | 135 | 169 | 202 | 236 | 270 | 304 | 338 |
| 27′-6″ | 34.4 | 68.8 | 103 | 138 | 172 | 206 | 241 | 275 | 309 | 344 |
| 28′-0″ | 35.0 | 70.0 | 105 | 140 | 175 | 210 | 245 | 280 | 315 | 350 |
| 28′-6″ | 35.6 | 71.3 | 107 | 143 | 178 | 214 | 249 | 285 | 321 | 356 |
| 29′-0″ | 36.3 | 72.5 | 109 | 145 | 181 | 218 | 254 | 290 | 326 | 363 |
| 29′-6″ | 36.9 | 73.8 | 111 | 148 | 184 | 221 | 258 | 295 | 332 | 369 |
| 30′-0″ | 37.5 | 75.0 | 113 | 150 | 188 | 225 | 262 | 300 | 338 | 375 |

# Table 40. (*continued*)

## 3. Concentrated Loads at Third Points

Fixed end moments: Table values $M = \frac{1}{9}WL$

Midspan moments: Table values × 0.5 $M = \frac{1}{18}WL$

| Span $L$ | Concentrated Load $W$ in kips — For following loads use table values directly: 10 | 20 | 30 | 40 | 50 | 60 | 70 | 80 | 90 | 100 |
|---|---|---|---|---|---|---|---|---|---|---|
| | For following loads use table values divided by 10: 1 | 2 | 3 | 4 | 5 | 6 | 7 | 8 | 9 | 10 |
| 5′–0″ | 5.6 | 11.1 | 16.7 | 22.2 | 27.8 | 33.3 | 38.9 | 44.4 | 50.0 | 55.6 |
| 5′–3″ | 5.8 | 11.7 | 17.5 | 23.3 | 29.2 | 35.0 | 40.8 | 46.7 | 52.5 | 58.3 |
| 5′–6″ | 6.1 | 12.2 | 18.3 | 24.4 | 30.6 | 36.7 | 42.8 | 48.9 | 55.0 | 61.1 |
| 5′–9″ | 6.4 | 12.8 | 19.2 | 25.6 | 31.9 | 38.3 | 44.7 | 51.1 | 57.5 | 63.9 |
| 6′–0″ | 6.7 | 13.3 | 20.0 | 26.7 | 33.3 | 40.0 | 46.7 | 53.3 | 60.0 | 66.7 |
| 6′–3″ | 6.9 | 13.9 | 20.8 | 27.8 | 34.7 | 41.7 | 48.6 | 55.6 | 62.5 | 69.4 |
| 6′–6″ | 7.2 | 14.4 | 21.7 | 28.9 | 36.1 | 43.3 | 50.6 | 57.8 | 65.0 | 72.2 |
| 6′–9″ | 7.5 | 15.0 | 22.5 | 30.0 | 37.5 | 45.0 | 52.6 | 60.0 | 67.5 | 75.0 |
| 7′–0″ | 7.8 | 15.6 | 23.3 | 31.1 | 38.9 | 46.7 | 54.4 | 62.2 | 70.0 | 77.8 |
| 7′–3″ | 8.1 | 16.1 | 24.2 | 32.2 | 40.3 | 48.3 | 56.4 | 64.4 | 72.5 | 80.6 |
| 7′–6″ | 8.3 | 16.7 | 25.0 | 33.3 | 41.7 | 50.0 | 58.3 | 66.7 | 75.0 | 83.3 |
| 7′–9″ | 8.6 | 17.2 | 25.8 | 34.4 | 43.1 | 51.7 | 60.3 | 68.9 | 77.5 | 86.1 |
| 8′–0″ | 8.9 | 17.8 | 26.7 | 35.6 | 44.4 | 53.3 | 62.2 | 71.1 | 80.0 | 88.9 |
| 8′–3″ | 9.2 | 18.3 | 27.5 | 36.7 | 45.8 | 55.0 | 64.2 | 73.3 | 82.5 | 91.7 |
| 8′–6″ | 9.4 | 18.9 | 28.3 | 37.8 | 47.2 | 56.7 | 66.1 | 75.6 | 85.0 | 94.4 |
| 8′–9″ | 9.7 | 19.4 | 29.2 | 38.9 | 48.6 | 58.3 | 68.1 | 77.8 | 87.5 | 97.2 |
| 9′–0″ | 10.0 | 20.0 | 30.0 | 40.0 | 50.0 | 60.0 | 70.0 | 80.0 | 90.0 | 100 |
| 9′–3″ | 10.3 | 20.6 | 30.8 | 41.1 | 51.4 | 61.7 | 71.9 | 82.2 | 92.5 | 103 |
| 9′–6″ | 10.6 | 21.1 | 31.7 | 42.2 | 52.8 | 63.3 | 73.9 | 84.4 | 95.0 | 106 |
| 9′–9″ | 10.8 | 21.7 | 32.5 | 43.3 | 54.2 | 65.0 | 75.8 | 86.7 | 97.5 | 108 |
| 10′–0″ | 11.1 | 22.2 | 33.3 | 44.4 | 55.6 | 66.7 | 77.8 | 88.9 | 100 | 111 |
| 10′–6″ | 11.7 | 23.3 | 35.0 | 46.7 | 58.3 | 70.0 | 81.7 | 93.3 | 105 | 117 |
| 11′–0″ | 12.2 | 24.4 | 36.7 | 48.9 | 61.1 | 73.3 | 85.6 | 97.8 | 110 | 122 |
| 11′–6″ | 12.8 | 25.6 | 38.3 | 51.1 | 63.9 | 76.7 | 89.4 | 102 | 115 | 128 |
| 12′–0″ | 13.3 | 26.7 | 40.0 | 53.3 | 66.7 | 80.0 | 93.3 | 107 | 120 | 133 |
| 12′–6″ | 13.9 | 27.8 | 41.7 | 55.6 | 69.4 | 83.3 | 97.2 | 111 | 125 | 139 |
| 13′–0″ | 14.4 | 28.9 | 43.3 | 57.8 | 72.2 | 86.7 | 101 | 116 | 130 | 144 |
| 13′–6″ | 15.0 | 30.0 | 45.0 | 60.0 | 75.0 | 90.0 | 105 | 120 | 135 | 150 |
| 14′–0″ | 15.6 | 31.1 | 46.7 | 62.2 | 77.8 | 93.3 | 109 | 124 | 140 | 156 |
| 14′–6″ | 16.1 | 32.2 | 48.3 | 64.4 | 80.6 | 96.7 | 113 | 129 | 145 | 161 |
| 15′–0″ | 16.7 | 33.3 | 50.0 | 66.7 | 83.3 | 100 | 117 | 133 | 150 | 167 |
| 15′–6″ | 17.2 | 34.4 | 51.7 | 68.9 | 86.1 | 103 | 121 | 138 | 155 | 172 |
| 16′–0″ | 17.8 | 35.6 | 53.3 | 71.1 | 88.9 | 107 | 124 | 142 | 160 | 178 |
| 16′–6″ | 18.3 | 36.7 | 55.0 | 73.3 | 91.7 | 110 | 128 | 147 | 165 | 183 |
| 17′–0″ | 18.9 | 37.8 | 56.7 | 75.6 | 94.4 | 113 | 132 | 151 | 170 | 189 |
| 17′–6″ | 19.4 | 38.9 | 58.3 | 77.8 | 97.2 | 117 | 136 | 156 | 175 | 194 |
| 18′–0″ | 20.0 | 40.0 | 60.0 | 80.0 | 100 | 120 | 140 | 160 | 180 | 200 |
| 18′–6″ | 20.6 | 41.1 | 61.7 | 82.2 | 103 | 123 | 144 | 164 | 185 | 206 |
| 19′–0″ | 21.1 | 42.2 | 63.3 | 84.4 | 106 | 127 | 148 | 169 | 190 | 211 |
| 19′–6″ | 21.7 | 43.3 | 65.0 | 86.7 | 108 | 130 | 152 | 173 | 195 | 217 |
| 20′–0″ | 22.2 | 44.4 | 66.6 | 88.8 | 111 | 133 | 156 | 178 | 200 | 222 |
| 20′–6″ | 22.8 | 45.6 | 68.3 | 91.1 | 114 | 137 | 159 | 182 | 205 | 228 |
| 21′–0″ | 23.3 | 46.7 | 70.0 | 93.3 | 117 | 140 | 163 | 187 | 210 | 233 |
| 21′–6″ | 23.9 | 47.8 | 71.7 | 95.6 | 119 | 143 | 167 | 191 | 215 | 239 |
| 22′–0″ | 24.4 | 48.9 | 73.3 | 97.8 | 122 | 147 | 171 | 196 | 220 | 244 |
| 22′–6″ | 25.0 | 50.0 | 75.0 | 100 | 125 | 150 | 175 | 200 | 225 | 250 |
| 23′–0″ | 25.6 | 51.1 | 76.7 | 102 | 128 | 153 | 179 | 204 | 230 | 256 |
| 23′–6″ | 26.1 | 52.2 | 78.3 | 104 | 131 | 157 | 183 | 209 | 235 | 261 |
| 24′–0″ | 26.7 | 53.3 | 80.0 | 107 | 133 | 160 | 187 | 213 | 240 | 267 |
| 24′–6″ | 27.2 | 54.4 | 81.7 | 109 | 136 | 163 | 191 | 218 | 245 | 272 |
| 25′–0″ | 27.8 | 55.6 | 83.3 | 111 | 139 | 167 | 194 | 222 | 250 | 278 |
| 25′–6″ | 28.3 | 56.7 | 85.0 | 113 | 142 | 170 | 198 | 227 | 255 | 283 |
| 26′–0″ | 28.9 | 57.8 | 86.7 | 116 | 144 | 173 | 202 | 231 | 260 | 289 |
| 26′–6″ | 29.4 | 58.9 | 88.3 | 118 | 147 | 177 | 206 | 236 | 265 | 294 |
| 27′–0″ | 30.0 | 60.0 | 90.0 | 120 | 150 | 180 | 210 | 240 | 270 | 300 |
| 27′–6″ | 30.6 | 61.1 | 91.7 | 122 | 153 | 183 | 214 | 244 | 275 | 306 |
| 28′–0″ | 31.1 | 62.2 | 93.3 | 124 | 156 | 187 | 218 | 249 | 280 | 311 |
| 28′–6″ | 31.7 | 63.3 | 95.0 | 127 | 158 | 190 | 222 | 253 | 285 | 317 |
| 29′–0″ | 32.2 | 64.4 | 96.7 | 129 | 161 | 193 | 226 | 258 | 290 | 322 |
| 29′–6″ | 32.8 | 65.6 | 98.3 | 131 | 164 | 197 | 229 | 262 | 295 | 328 |
| 30′–0″ | 33.3 | 66.7 | 100 | 133 | 167 | 200 | 233 | 267 | 300 | 333 |

## 4. Concentrated Loads at Fourth Points

Fixed end moments: Table values $M = \frac{5}{48}WL$

Midspan moments: Table values × 0.6 $M = \frac{3}{48}WL$

| Span $L$ | Concentrated Load $W$ in kips — For following loads use table values directly: 10 | 20 | 30 | 40 | 50 | 60 | 70 | 80 | 90 | 100 |
|---|---|---|---|---|---|---|---|---|---|---|
| | For following loads use table values divided by 10: 1 | 2 | 3 | 4 | 5 | 6 | 7 | 8 | 9 | 10 |
| 5′–0″ | 5.2 | 10.4 | 15.6 | 20.8 | 26.0 | 31.2 | 36.5 | 41.7 | 46.9 | 52.1 |
| 5′–3″ | 5.5 | 10.9 | 16.4 | 21.9 | 27.3 | 32.8 | 38.3 | 43.8 | 49.2 | 54.7 |
| 5′–6″ | 5.7 | 11.5 | 17.2 | 22.9 | 28.6 | 34.4 | 40.1 | 45.8 | 51.6 | 57.3 |
| 5′–9″ | 6.0 | 12.0 | 18.0 | 24.0 | 29.9 | 35.6 | 41.9 | 47.9 | 53.9 | 60.0 |
| 6′–0″ | 6.3 | 12.5 | 18.8 | 25.0 | 31.3 | 37.5 | 43.8 | 50.0 | 56.3 | 62.5 |
| 6′–3″ | 6.5 | 13.0 | 19.5 | 26.0 | 32.6 | 39.1 | 45.6 | 52.1 | 58.6 | 65.1 |
| 6′–6″ | 6.8 | 13.5 | 20.3 | 27.1 | 33.9 | 40.6 | 47.4 | 54.2 | 60.9 | 67.7 |
| 6′–9″ | 7.0 | 14.1 | 21.1 | 28.1 | 35.2 | 42.2 | 49.2 | 56.3 | 63.3 | 70.3 |
| 7′–0″ | 7.3 | 14.6 | 21.9 | 29.2 | 36.5 | 43.8 | 51.0 | 58.3 | 65.6 | 72.9 |
| 7′–3″ | 7.6 | 15.1 | 22.7 | 30.2 | 37.8 | 45.3 | 52.9 | 60.4 | 68.0 | 75.5 |
| 7′–6″ | 7.8 | 15.6 | 23.4 | 31.3 | 39.1 | 46.9 | 54.7 | 62.5 | 70.3 | 78.1 |
| 7′–9″ | 8.1 | 16.1 | 24.2 | 32.3 | 40.4 | 48.4 | 56.5 | 64.6 | 72.7 | 80.7 |
| 8′–0″ | 8.3 | 16.7 | 25.0 | 33.3 | 41.7 | 50.0 | 58.3 | 66.7 | 75.0 | 83.3 |
| 8′–3″ | 8.6 | 17.2 | 25.8 | 34.4 | 43.0 | 51.6 | 60.2 | 68.7 | 77.3 | 85.9 |
| 8′–6″ | 8.9 | 17.7 | 26.6 | 35.4 | 44.3 | 53.1 | 62.0 | 70.8 | 79.7 | 88.5 |
| 8′–9″ | 9.1 | 18.2 | 27.3 | 36.5 | 45.6 | 54.7 | 63.8 | 72.9 | 82.0 | 91.1 |
| 9′–0″ | 9.4 | 18.8 | 28.1 | 37.5 | 46.9 | 56.3 | 65.6 | 75.0 | 84.4 | 93.8 |
| 9′–3″ | 9.6 | 19.3 | 28.9 | 38.5 | 48.2 | 57.8 | 67.4 | 77.1 | 86.7 | 96.4 |
| 9′–6″ | 9.9 | 19.8 | 29.7 | 39.6 | 49.5 | 59.4 | 69.3 | 79.2 | 89.1 | 99.0 |
| 9′–9″ | 10.2 | 20.3 | 30.5 | 40.6 | 50.8 | 60.9 | 71.1 | 81.2 | 91.4 | 102 |
| 10′–0″ | 10.4 | 20.8 | 31.3 | 41.7 | 52.1 | 62.5 | 72.9 | 83.3 | 93.8 | 104 |
| 10′–6″ | 10.9 | 21.9 | 32.8 | 43.8 | 54.7 | 65.6 | 76.6 | 87.5 | 98.4 | 109 |
| 11′–0″ | 11.5 | 22.9 | 34.4 | 45.8 | 57.3 | 68.7 | 80.2 | 91.7 | 103 | 115 |
| 11′–6″ | 12.0 | 24.0 | 35.9 | 47.9 | 59.9 | 71.9 | 83.9 | 95.8 | 108 | 120 |
| 12′–0″ | 12.5 | 25.0 | 37.5 | 50.0 | 62.5 | 75.0 | 87.5 | 100 | 113 | 125 |
| 12′–6″ | 13.0 | 26.0 | 39.1 | 52.1 | 65.1 | 78.1 | 91.1 | 104 | 117 | 130 |
| 13′–0″ | 13.5 | 27.1 | 40.6 | 54.2 | 67.7 | 81.3 | 94.8 | 108 | 122 | 135 |
| 13′–6″ | 14.1 | 28.1 | 42.2 | 56.3 | 70.3 | 84.4 | 98.4 | 113 | 127 | 141 |
| 14′–0″ | 14.6 | 29.2 | 43.7 | 58.3 | 72.9 | 87.5 | 102 | 117 | 131 | 146 |
| 14′–6″ | 15.1 | 30.2 | 45.3 | 60.4 | 75.5 | 90.6 | 106 | 121 | 136 | 151 |
| 15′–0″ | 15.6 | 31.3 | 46.9 | 62.5 | 78.1 | 93.8 | 109 | 125 | 141 | 156 |
| 15′–6″ | 16.1 | 32.3 | 48.4 | 64.6 | 80.7 | 96.9 | 113 | 129 | 145 | 161 |
| 16′–0″ | 16.7 | 33.3 | 50.0 | 66.7 | 83.3 | 100 | 117 | 133 | 150 | 167 |
| 16′–6″ | 17.2 | 34.4 | 51.6 | 68.8 | 85.9 | 103 | 120 | 138 | 155 | 172 |
| 17′–0″ | 17.7 | 35.4 | 53.1 | 70.8 | 88.5 | 106 | 124 | 142 | 159 | 177 |
| 17′–6″ | 18.2 | 36.5 | 54.7 | 72.9 | 91.1 | 109 | 128 | 146 | 164 | 182 |
| 18′–0″ | 18.8 | 37.5 | 56.3 | 75.0 | 93.8 | 113 | 131 | 150 | 169 | 188 |
| 18′–6″ | 19.3 | 38.5 | 57.8 | 77.1 | 96.4 | 116 | 135 | 154 | 173 | 193 |
| 19′–0″ | 19.8 | 39.6 | 59.4 | 79.2 | 99.0 | 119 | 139 | 158 | 178 | 198 |
| 19′–6″ | 20.3 | 40.6 | 60.9 | 81.3 | 102 | 122 | 142 | 163 | 183 | 203 |
| 20′–0″ | 20.8 | 41.7 | 62.5 | 83.3 | 104 | 125 | 146 | 167 | 187 | 208 |
| 20′–6″ | 21.4 | 42.7 | 64.1 | 85.4 | 107 | 128 | 149 | 171 | 192 | 214 |
| 21′–0″ | 21.9 | 43.8 | 65.6 | 87.5 | 109 | 131 | 153 | 175 | 197 | 219 |
| 21′–6″ | 22.4 | 44.8 | 67.2 | 89.6 | 112 | 134 | 157 | 179 | 202 | 224 |
| 22′–0″ | 22.9 | 45.8 | 68.8 | 91.7 | 115 | 138 | 160 | 183 | 206 | 229 |
| 22′–6″ | 23.4 | 46.9 | 70.3 | 93.8 | 117 | 141 | 164 | 188 | 211 | 234 |
| 23′–0″ | 24.0 | 47.9 | 71.9 | 95.8 | 120 | 144 | 168 | 192 | 216 | 240 |
| 23′–6″ | 24.5 | 49.0 | 73.4 | 97.9 | 122 | 147 | 171 | 196 | 220 | 245 |
| 24′–0″ | 25.0 | 50.0 | 75.0 | 100 | 125 | 150 | 175 | 200 | 225 | 250 |
| 24′–6″ | 25.5 | 51.0 | 76.6 | 102 | 128 | 153 | 179 | 204 | 230 | 255 |
| 25′–0″ | 26.0 | 52.1 | 78.1 | 104 | 130 | 156 | 182 | 208 | 234 | 260 |
| 25′–6″ | 26.6 | 53.1 | 79.7 | 106 | 133 | 159 | 186 | 212 | 239 | 266 |
| 26′–0″ | 27.1 | 54.2 | 81.2 | 108 | 135 | 162 | 190 | 217 | 244 | 271 |
| 26′–6″ | 27.6 | 55.2 | 82.8 | 110 | 138 | 166 | 193 | 221 | 248 | 276 |
| 27′–0″ | 28.1 | 56.3 | 84.4 | 112 | 141 | 169 | 197 | 225 | 253 | 281 |
| 27′–6″ | 28.6 | 57.3 | 85.9 | 115 | 143 | 172 | 200 | 229 | 258 | 286 |
| 28′–0″ | 29.2 | 58.3 | 87.5 | 117 | 146 | 175 | 204 | 233 | 262 | 292 |
| 28′–6″ | 29.7 | 59.4 | 89.1 | 119 | 148 | 178 | 208 | 238 | 267 | 297 |
| 29′–0″ | 30.2 | 60.4 | 90.6 | 121 | 151 | 181 | 211 | 242 | 272 | 302 |
| 29′–6″ | 30.7 | 61.5 | 92.2 | 123 | 154 | 184 | 215 | 246 | 277 | 307 |
| 30′–0″ | 31.3 | 62.5 | 93.8 | 125 | 156 | 188 | 219 | 250 | 281 | 313 |

# Table 41. Properties of Sections

Dash-and-dot lines are drawn through centers of gravity

$A$ = Area of section $I$ = Moment of inertia $R$ = Radius of gyration

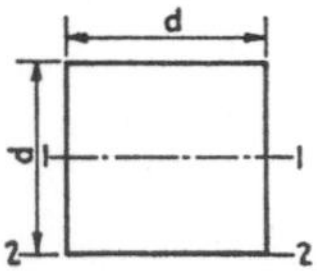


$$A = d^2$$
$$I_1 = \frac{d^4}{12}$$
$$I_2 = \frac{d^4}{3}$$
$$R_1 = 0.2887\,d$$
$$R_2 = 0.5774\,d$$

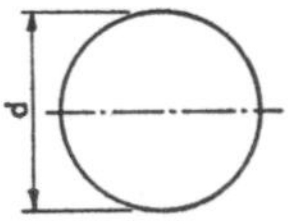


$$A = \frac{\pi d^2}{4} = 0.7854\,d^2$$
$$I = \frac{\pi d^4}{64} = 0.0491\,d^4$$
$$R = \frac{d}{4}$$

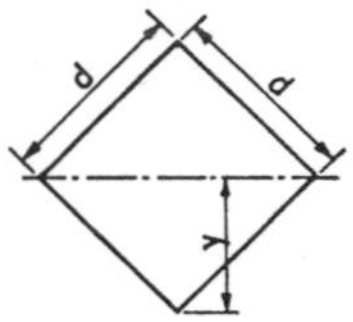


$$A = d^2$$
$$y = 0.7071\,d$$
$$I = \frac{d^4}{12}$$
$$R = 0.2887\,d$$

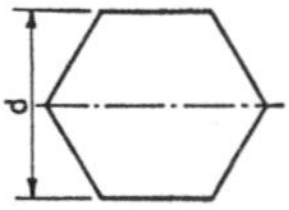


$$A = 0.8660\,d^2$$
$$I = 0.060\,d^4$$
$$R = 0.264\,d$$

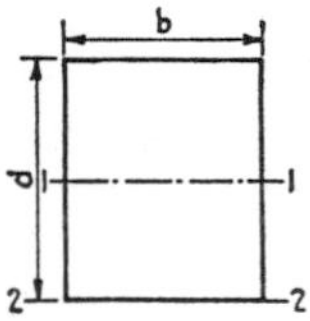


$$A = bd$$
$$I_1 = \frac{bd^3}{12}$$
$$I_2 = \frac{bd^3}{3}$$
$$R_1 = 0.2887\,d$$
$$R_2 = 0.5774\,d$$

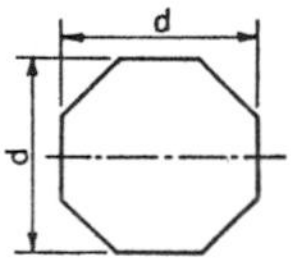


$$A = 0.8284\,d^2$$
$$I = 0.055\,d^4$$
$$R = 0.257\,d$$

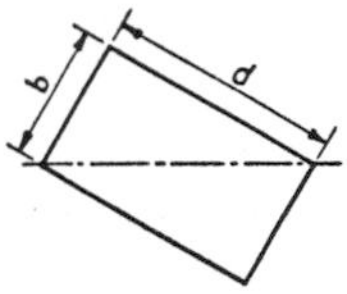


$$A = bd$$
$$y = \frac{bd}{\sqrt{b^2 + d^2}}$$
$$I = \frac{b^3d^3}{6(b^2 + d^2)}$$
$$R = \frac{bd}{\sqrt{6(b^2 + d^2)}}$$

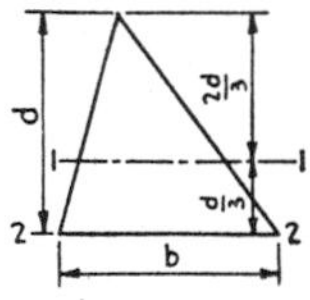


$$A = \frac{bd}{2}$$
$$I_1 = \frac{bd^3}{36}$$
$$I_2 = \frac{bd^3}{12}$$
$$R_1 = 0.236\,d$$
$$R_2 = 0.408\,d$$

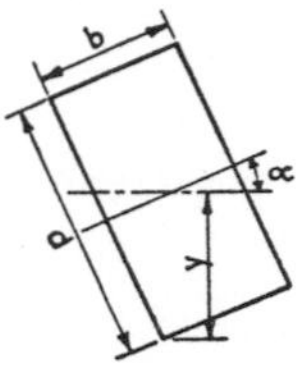


$$A = bd$$
$$y = \frac{b \sin \alpha + d \cos \alpha}{2}$$
$$I = \frac{bd(b^2 \sin^2 \alpha + d^2 \cos^2 \alpha)}{12}$$
$$R = \sqrt{\frac{b^2 \sin^2 \alpha + d^2 \cos^2 \alpha}{12}}$$

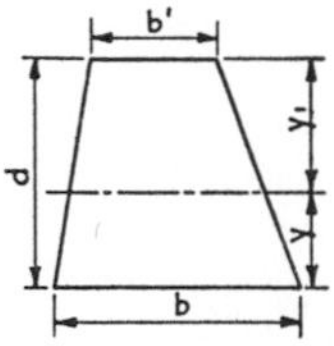


$$A = \frac{d}{2}(b + b')$$
$$y_1 = \frac{d(2b + b')}{3(b + b')}$$
$$y = \frac{d(b + 2b')}{3(b + b')}$$
$$I = \frac{d^3(b^2 + 4bb' + b'^2)}{36(b + b')}$$
$$R = \frac{d}{6(b + b')}\sqrt{2(b^2 + 4bb' + b'^2)}$$

# Table 41. *(continued)*

Dash-and-dot lines are drawn through centers of gravity

$A$ = Area of section $\quad$ $I$ = Moment of inertia $\quad$ $R$ = Radius of gyration

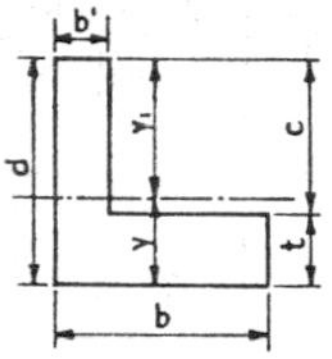


$$A = bt + b'c$$

$$y = \frac{d^2b' + t^2(b - b')}{2(bt + b'c)}$$

$$y_1 = d - y$$

$$I = \frac{b'y_1^3 + by^3 - (b - b')(y - t)^3}{3}$$

$$R = \sqrt{\frac{I}{A}}$$

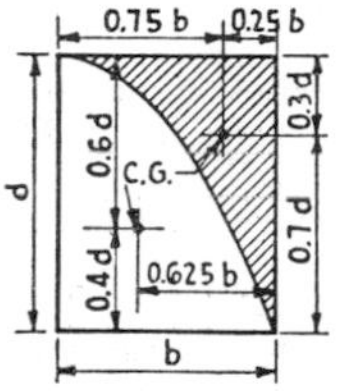


Section of Parabola

Equation:

$$y^2 = \frac{b^2}{d}x$$

$$A \text{ (shaded)} = \frac{bd}{3}$$

$$A \text{ (under curve)} = \frac{2bd}{3}$$

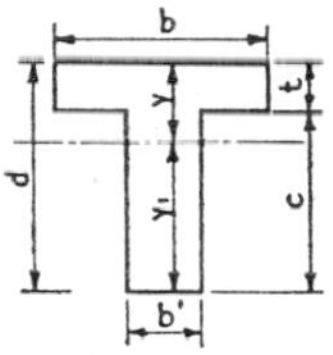


$$A = bt + b'c$$

$$y = \frac{d^2b' + t^2(b - b')}{2(bt + b'c)}$$

$$y_1 = d - y$$

$$I = \frac{b'y_1^3 + by^3 - (b - b')(y - t)^3}{3}$$

$$R = \sqrt{\frac{I}{A}}$$

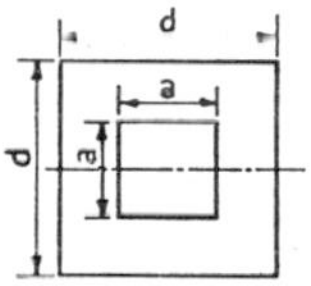


$$A = d^2 - a^2$$

$$I = \frac{d^4 - a^4}{12}$$

$$R = \sqrt{\frac{d^2 + a^2}{12}}$$

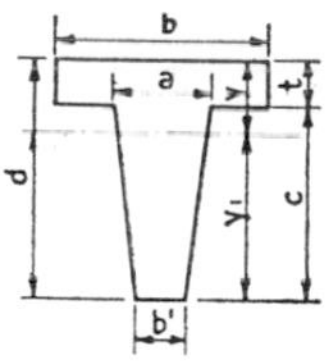


$$A = bt + \frac{c(a + b')}{2}$$

$$y = \frac{6bt^2 + 6b'c(d+t) + 2c(a-b')(c+3t)}{bt + c(a + b')}$$

$$y_1 = d - y$$

$$I = \frac{4bt^3 + c^3(3b' + a)}{12} - A(y - t)^2$$

$$R = \sqrt{\frac{I}{A}}$$

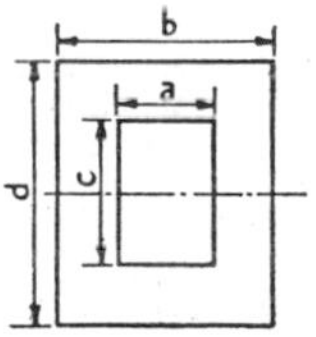


$$A = bd - ac$$

$$I = \frac{bd^3 - ac^3}{12}$$

$$R = \sqrt{\frac{bd^3 - ac^3}{12(bd - ac)}}$$

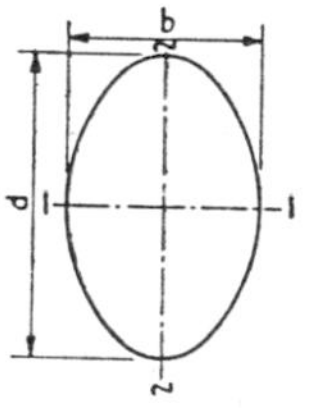


Ellipse

$$A = 0.7854\ bd$$

$$I_1 = \frac{\pi bd^3}{64} = 0.0491\ bd^3$$

$$I_2 = \frac{\pi b^3d}{64} = 0.0491\ b^3d$$

$$R_1 = \frac{d}{4}$$

$$R_2 = \frac{b}{4}$$

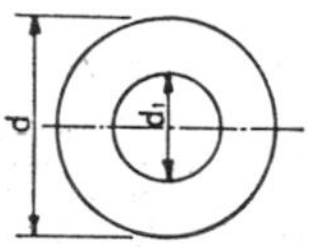


$$A = \frac{\pi(d^2 - d_1^2)}{4} = 0.7854(d^2 - d_1^2)$$

$$I = \frac{\pi(d^4 - d_1^4)}{64} = 0.0491(d^4 - d_1^4)$$

$$R = \tfrac{1}{4}\sqrt{d^2 + d_1^2}$$

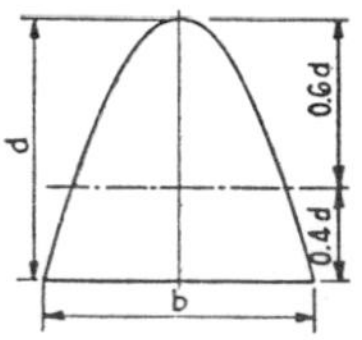


Parabola

Equation:

$$y^2 = \frac{b^2}{4d}x$$

$$A = \frac{2bd}{3}$$

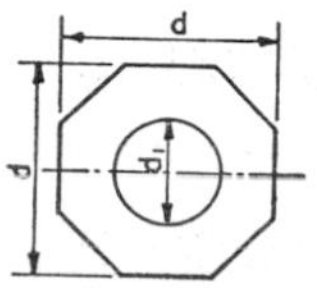

$$A = 0.8284\ d^2 - 0.7854\ d_1^2$$
$$= 0.7854(1.055\ d^2 - d_1^2)$$
$$I = 0.055\ d^4 - 0.0491\ d_1^4$$
$$= 0.0491(1.12\ d^4 - d_1^4)$$
$$R = 0.257\ d - 0.25\ d_1$$
$$= 0.25(1.028\ d - d_1)$$

# Table 42. Live Loads in Pounds Per Square Foot

| Occupancy | Codes: Dept. of Commerce 1924 | Nat. Bd. of Fire Underwriters 1934 | Pacific Coast Bldg. Officials Conference 1937 | New York 1938 | Chicago[20] 1937 | Philadelphia 1929 | Detroit 1936 |
|---|---|---|---|---|---|---|---|
| Dwellings, apartment and tenement houses, hotels, club houses, hospitals and places of detention: | | | | | | | |
| Dwellings, private rooms and apartments | 40[1] | 40 | 40 | 40[11] | 40 | 40 | 40 |
| Public corridors, lobbies and dining rooms | 100 | 100 | 100 | 100 | 100 | 100 | 80 |
| School buildings: | | | | | | | |
| Class rooms and rooms for similar use | 50 | 50 | 40[7] | 60[12] | 50 | 50[25] | 50[25] |
| Corridors and public parts of the building | 100 | 100 | 100 | 100 | 100 | 100 | 80 |
| Theaters, assembly halls and other places of assemblage: | | | | | | | |
| Auditoriums with fixed seats | 50 | 100 | 50 | 75[13] | 75 | 60[26] | 80 |
| Lobbies, passageways, gymnasiums, grandstands, stages and auditoriums or places of assemblage without fixed seats | 100 | 100 | 100[8] | 100 | 100 | 100 | 100[33] |
| Office buildings: | | | | | | | |
| Office space | 50[2,3] | 50[2] | 50[2,3] | 50[11] | 50[21] | 60 | 50[34] |
| Corridors and other public places | 100 | 100 | 100 | 100[14] | 100 | 100 | 125[14] |
| Workshops, factories and mercantile establishments: | | | | | | | |
| Manufacturing—light | 75 | 125[2] | 75 | 120 | 100 | 120[28,27] | 100[35] |
| " —heavy | | | 125 | | 100 | 200[28] | |
| Storage—light | 100 | 125[2] | 125 | 120 | 100 | 150[28,29] | 125[36] |
| " —heavy | 250 | | 250 | | 100 | 200[28] | |
| Stores—retail | 75 | 125[2] | 75 | 75[15] | 100 | 110[28] | 100[35] |
| " —wholesale | 100 | 125[2] | 100 | 120 | 100 | 110[28] | 100[35] |
| Garages: | | | | | | | |
| All types of vehicles | 100 | 125[2] | 100[9] | 175[16] | 100[22] | 100[30] | 150[37] |
| Passenger cars only | 80 | 125[2] | 100 | 75[17] | 50[23] | 100 | 80[38] |
| All stairs and fire escapes, except in private residences | 100 | 100 | 100 | 100 | 100 | 100 | 100[39] |
| Roofs (flat) | 30 | 30 | 20 | 40 | 25 | 30 | 30 |
| Sidewalks | 250[4] | 300 | 250[4] | 300[18] | | 120[31] | 250 |
| Wind | 10–20[5] | 15–30[6] | 15–20[10] | 0–20[19] | 25–35[24] | 20[32] | 20[40] |

Notes:

The classification used in this table is based primarily upon that given in the Report of the Building Code Committee of the U. S. Department of Commerce entitled "Minimum Live Loads Allowable for Use in Design of Buildings."

1. 30 for one and two family dwellings with floors of integral type.
2. Or 2000 on any space 2½ feet square.
3. Additional load equivalent to a single partition placed in any position.
4. Or 800 concentrated.
5. 10 for portions below 40 ft. and 20 for portions above 40 ft.
6. 15 for portions below 40 ft. and 30 for portions above 40 ft.
7. 60 for library reading rooms and 125 for stackrooms.
8. 150 for armories.
9. Or concentrated rear wheel of loaded truck in any position.
10. 15 for portions below 60 ft. and 20 for portions above 60 ft.
11. Including corridors.
12. For rooms with fixed seats or, by special permission, other small rooms. 120 for library stackrooms.
13. 60 for churches.
14. Including entire first floor.
15. 100 for entire first floor.
16. Or 6000 concentrated. Trucking space and driveways, 24,000 concentrated.
17. Or 2000 concentrated.
18. Or 12,000 concentrated for driveways over sidewalks.
19. 25 for structures over 100 ft. high. Special consideration for others.
20. When dead load exceeds live load, specified live loads may be reduced by ratio of live to dead but not to less than two-thirds.
21. Or 2000 concentrated on any space 3 feet square.
22. Or 3000 concentrated on any space 4 feet square.
23. 100 on first and second floors and alternate of 3000 on area 4 feet square.
24. 25 for surfaces less than 275 ft. high with variable above.
25. Only school class rooms with fixed seats.
26. Churches only.
27. 150 for certain occupancies.
28. Every floor beam 4000 concentrated.
29. 110 for storage of household goods.
30. Or 8000 concentrated.
31. Interior courts, sidewalks, etc., not accessible to a driveway.
32. 25 for isolated structures exposed for full height.
33. 125 for dance halls and drill halls.
34. Above first floor including corridors.
35. 125 for first floor.
36. 150 for first floor.
37. Or 2500 concentrated on area 6 inches square with such concentrations spaced alternately 2 ft. 4 in. and 4 ft. 8 in. in one direction and 5 ft. and 10 ft. in the other direction.
38. Only structures with clear head room of 8 ft. 6 in. or less. Or 1500 concentrated spaced as in 37.
39. 50 for dwellings and apartments under 3 stories.
40. For buildings less than 500 ft. high.

# Table 43. Miscellaneous Weights

## Building Materials

| Material | lb./cu.ft. | Material | lb./sq.ft. |
|---|---|---|---|
| Brickwork | 120 | Studs, plates and bridging—2x4 @ 12 in. to 16 in. | 2 |
| Clay tile | 60 | —2x6 @ 12 in. to 16 in. | 3 |
| Concrete—gravel and stone aggregate | 150 | Joists—2x8 @ 20 in. | 2 |
| —lightweight aggregate | 100 | —2x8 @ 14 in. and 2x10 @ 18 in. | 3 |
| —aerated | 50–90 | —2x10 @ 12 in. and 2x12 @ 16 in. | 4 |
| Concrete masonry—gravel and stone aggregate | 80 | —2x12 @ 12 in. | 5 |
| —lightweight aggregate | 50 | Sheathing | 3 |
| Mortar | 120 | Hardwood finish | 4 |
| Sand—dry | 100 | Floor finish of terrazzo, tile, mastic, linoleum, per in. thickness including base | 12 |
| Steel | 490 | Roofing—built up | 2–7 |
| Stone masonry | 160 | —composition shingles | 3 |
| Wood, dry—fir | 32 | —rolled | 1 |
| —oak | 48 | —wood shingles | 2 |
| —yellow pine | 42 | —tile or slate | 5–20 |
| Insulation—loose fill | 10 | Roof slabs of precast concrete or gypsum | 15 |
| | | Plaster on masonry—one side | 5 |
| | | Plaster and lath | 8 |
| | | Suspended ceiling—metal lath and plaster | 10 |
| | | Stucco | 10 |

## Concrete Joist Floors—2½-in. Slab—lb./sq.ft.

| Depth of joist only | 20-In. Pans | | | | 30-in. Pans | | | 12-in. Units | | | 16-in. Units | | |
|---|---|---|---|---|---|---|---|---|---|---|---|---|---|
| | Width of Joist | | | | | | | | | | | | |
| | 4 | 5 | 6 | 7 | 5 | 6 | 7 | 4 | 5 | 6 | 4 | 5 | 6 |
| 4 | .. | .. | .. | .. | .. | .. | .. | 55 | 57 | 59 | 54 | 55 | 56 |
| 6 | 44 | 46 | 48 | .. | 41 | 43 | .. | 66 | 68 | 71 | 61 | 62 | 64 |
| 8 | 49 | 52 | 55 | .. | 46 | 48 | .. | 70 | 81 | 84 | 67 | 70 | 72 |
| 10 | 54 | 58 | 62 | .. | 50 | 53 | .. | 88 | 93 | 96 | 74 | 77 | 81 |
| 12 | 60 | 65 | 69 | 73 | 55 | 58 | 61 | 98 | 103 | 107 | 80 | 85 | 89 |
| 14 | .. | 71 | 76 | 81 | 60 | 63 | 67 | .. | .. | .. | .. | | |

## Masonry Walls and Partitions—lb./sq.ft.

| Material | Thickness—in. | | | | | |
|---|---|---|---|---|---|---|
| | 2 | 3 | 4 | 6 | 8 | 12 |
| Brick | .. | .. | 38 | .. | 80 | 120 |
| Clay tile—walls | .. | .. | 22 | 32 | 39 | 56 |
| —partitions | 16 | 17 | 18 | 28 | 34 | 44 |
| Concrete units—gravel and stone aggregate | .. | .. | 31 | 44 | 54 | 80 |
| —lightweight aggregate | .. | .. | 20 | 28 | 34 | 50 |
| Gypsum tile | 10 | 12 | 13 | 19 | .. | .. |
| Glass block | .. | .. | 18 | .. | 19 | 20 |

# Appendix

## Determination of Moments In Building Frames*

Designers are required by modern codes to analyze building frames as continuous structures. A method of analysis is presented here which permits direct design of members in frames where only centerline dimensions and loads are known. This is not generally possible with other methods.

Simplifications in analysis as permitted by codes are based on recognition of the fact that design moments in frames are not sensitive to small changes in stiffness of members or to loads on non-adjacent spans. These simplifications permit a great timesaving in analysis, yet affect accuracy but little.

The following method** meets the requirements of the A.C.I. Code and affords a quick, sufficiently accurate solution for maximum moments in building frames by the use of two tables. Unimportant and unjustifiable refinements in analysis have been ignored, the purpose being to obtain moments directly with a degree of accuracy consistent with limitations imposed by uncertain loading and indeterminate "constants".

### General Procedure

Table 1A contains design moment coefficients at ends and midspan of beams in ideal frames having various ratios of uniform live to dead load and various ratios of column to beam stiffness. Basic assumptions are taken from the American Concrete Institute Code 1936, Section 702.

Table 2A gives correction coefficients to be added to coefficients of Table 1A when span lengths and loading vary from those assumed in Table 1A.

Through use of the tables, maximum moment coefficients are recorded, based on the load ratio and stiffness ratio chosen to represent the unit frame, after which corrections for variation in load and span length are made, span by span. The designer may design a single beam in a frame, or he may determine design moments for an entire level, as will be illustrated by examples.

### Sign Convention

Signs of beam moments are automatically taken care of in the tables, each moment coefficient and correction coefficient being recorded with its proper sign. The usual convention for signs is followed—negative moments produce tension in top face of beam and positive moments produce tension in bottom face.

### Procedure for Concentrated Loads

Table 2A is divided into several sections so that correction coefficients may be obtained directly where spans have either uniform load, a single

*For symbols and notation, see page 132.

**For a more detailed presentation, reference is made to the paper "Design Coefficients for Building Frames," by A. J. Boase and J. T. Howell, *Journal of the American Concrete Institute*, September, 1939

load at midspan, two equal loads at third-points, or three equal loads at quarter-points.* The procedure is to tabulate coefficients from Table 1A assuming all spans equal and uniform loads throughout, and then to correct the moments in a span by selecting coefficients from the part of Table 2A that deals with the actual type of loading on the span. The various sections of Table 2A have been arranged so that the variables are stiffness ratio of frame $\left(\frac{\Sigma K_{col.}}{K_{beam}}\right)$ and a span-load factor designated as $a\sqrt{\frac{w_{aL}}{w_L}}$ or $a\sqrt{\frac{p_{aL}}{w_L}}$.

The variable $a\sqrt{\frac{w_{aL}}{w_L}}$ includes the effect of span length and variations in uniform loading. Similarly for spans having concentrated loads, $a\sqrt{\frac{p_{aL}}{w_L}}$ includes effect of span length and ratios of "equivalent" uniform load of span to uniform load of standard span. "Equivalent" uniform load, $p_{aL}$, may be total concentrated dead plus live load on span divided by span length, or total concentrated *dead* load on span divided by span length.

## Column Moments

When moment is included in the design of columns, it is in combination with direct load including maximum load from levels above and live load on certain spans at the level under consideration. Theoretically, maximum column moments are obtained by placing live load in a checker-board arrangement on the frame. To obtain maximum axial load, however, all spans adjacent to the column above the section considered must have live load. Except in the case of exterior columns, the loading patterns are different and it is therefore impossible to get maximum load and maximum moment simultaneously. The logic of designing interior columns using maximum direct load and maximum moment is therefore questionable.

Since columns receive moment indirectly, through the rotation of ends of beams, plastic flow and redistribution of stress act to reduce column moment. As a result, actual column moments are smaller than the theoretical maximum moments. For any level, a loading pattern is adopted which produces maximum column load and also a reasonable column moment. This loading is live load on the two spans adjacent to the column under consideration and live load also on alternate spans therefrom. The columns are considered fixed above and below the floor where the moment is computed. The loading pattern is identical with the pattern used for maximum negative moments at beam ends adjacent to the column. It should be noted that for exterior columns where moments are more important, moments based on the above assumptions are maximum.

If the columns above and below are identical, the column design moment is the difference between maximum beam moments at the column, divided by two. If the column above the joint is different from the one below, each column moment is equal to the difference in beam moments multiplied by a ratio equal to the stiffness of the column divided by the total stiffness of both columns.

*In the original paper, Table 2 was intended only for correction of spans having uniform loads. Concentrated loads were reduced to an equivalent form and adjusted so that the one correction table could serve for the various types of loadings. For analyses involving a high percentage of concentrated loads, the use of separate correction tables is considered to be quicker.

Moment in a column above a joint tends to produce tension on the side of the larger beam moment, and moment in the column below produces compression on that side.

### Shear

For design of interior beams the simple beam shear is commonly used, shear due to frame continuity being ignored. At the interior support of exterior beams, however, the shear due to frame continuity is often included as it may be quite large. The design shear at such points is usually estimated to be 1.20 times the simple beam shear.

If a more accurate determination of shear is necessary, shear due to continuity is calculated by placing live load on the frame in a pattern to produce maximum shear, determining end moments for the span in question, and dividing the difference in end moments by the span length.

Since the loading pattern for maximum moment at a beam end is the same as the pattern for maximum shear, the maximum end moments are available for shear determination. Smaller, non-maximum moments at opposite ends of beams are needed also, but since they are not available, other relations between moments and loads must be used.

The following rule allows shear calculation to be made satisfactorily in one step after maximum design moments have been determined.

Beam design shear at any interior* support is equal to the sum of *numerical* values of maximum moment at that end of the beam and maximum midspan moment in the same beam, divided by the span length, plus three-eighths** of the total load on the span.

### Limitations of Procedures

Procedures involving use of Tables 1A and 2A apply with satisfactory accuracy to design of building frames of fairly regular types having uniform and/or symmetrical concentrated loads. For frames having very little support restraint and widely varying beam stiffnesses, or for frames having unsymmetrically loaded spans, more exhaustive analyses may be necessary.

### Steps in the Determination of Beam Moments

(*See Examples 1A to 5A*)

1. Sketch outline of frame and record span lengths and loads.
2. Select as standard span and loading either
   a. The span and loading most repeated in the unit frame, or
   b. A span and loading determined by averaging, roughly, lengths and loading of all spans.
3. Compute the live to dead load ratio, $\frac{w_{live}}{w_{dead}}$, to be used as a constant in Table 1A.

*At an *exterior* support, the simple beam shear is nearly always larger than the shear that includes the effect of continuity.

**For more accurate results use:

- 3/8 for uniform load;
- 1/3 for equal concentrated loads at quarter-points of span;
- 1/3 for equal concentrated loads at third-points of span;
- 1/4 for a single concentrated load at midspan; and
- 1/3 for combinations of uniform and concentrated loads.

4. Estimate the stiffness ratio, $\frac{\Sigma K_{col.}}{K_{beam}}$, of the frame based on the standard span and the columns. If data on stiffnesses are lacking, use the following ratios:
   a. For continuous slabs on beam supports, or for roofs when supporting columns are very slender, use ratio of *one-half.*
   b. For upper floors and slender columns use ratio equal to *one.*
   c. For lower floors and medium sized columns use ratio of *two.*
   d. For lower floors of tall buildings, involving very heavy columns, use a ratio of *four* or more.
5. Using standard span length, $L$, calculate $a$-values for all spans.
6. For each span having concentrated load, determine total "equivalent" uniform load, $p_{TaL}$, by dividing total concentrated load on span by span length.
7. Calculate $a\sqrt{\frac{w_{TaL}}{w_{TL}}}$ or $a\sqrt{\frac{p_{TaL}}{w_{TL}}}$ for all spans.
8. Enter Table 1A with constants from *3* and *4*, and record coefficients in space below the sketched frame.
9. Enter Table 2A with the stiffness ratio from *4* and with proper values of $a\sqrt{\frac{w_{TaL}}{w_{TL}}}$ or $a\sqrt{\frac{p_{TaL}}{w_{TL}}}$ from *7*. In selecting correction coefficients for a span use the section of Table 2A that deals with the type of loading on *that* span. For each span, record the correction coefficients at the near ends of the adjacent spans and for the span itself.
10. Add recorded coefficients algebraically, to obtain final coefficients.
11. Multiply all coefficients by one constant, $w_{TL}L^2$. Results are maximum moments at ends and midspans of beams.

## EXAMPLES

**Example 1A.** Determine maximum end and midspan moments in a frame having four unequal spans and constant uniform live and dead loads.

Given: Dimensions and loads as shown in the sketch. Stiffness of columns equals stiffness of beams.

Determine constants for use in Tables 1A and 2A.

$$\frac{w_{live}}{w_{dead}} = \frac{3}{1} = 3 \qquad \frac{\Sigma K_{col.}}{K_{beam}} = \frac{1+1}{1} = 2$$

Assume, temporarily, that all spans are equal and select the left span ($L$ = 18 ft. 0 in.) as the standard span. Coefficients from Table 1A may now be recorded, but calculate first the constant for use in Table 2A. This constant, $a\sqrt{\frac{w_{TaL}}{w_{TL}}}$, represents the effect of variation in length and loading of a span as compared with the ideal case set up for use in Table 1A: $L$ = 18 ft. 0 in., $w_{TL}$ = 4 kips per ft. Since the total load per foot is the same for all spans, $w_{TaL} = w_{TL} = 4$, and $a\sqrt{\frac{w_{TaL}}{w_{TL}}}$ reduces to $a$.

## Example 1A. Unsymmetrical Frame, Uniform Loads, Constant Load Ratio

| | | | | | | | | | | | | |
|---|---|---|---|---|---|---|---|---|---|---|---|---|
| Spans: | 18'-0" | | | 21'-6" | | | 15'-0" | | | 17'-0" | | |
| Load in kips per foot: $w_{live}$: | 3 | | | 3 | | | 3 | | | 3 | | |
| $w_{dead}$: | 1 | | | 1 | | | 1 | | | 1 | | |
| $w_{total}$: | 4 | | | 4 | | | 4 | | | 4 | | |

**Standard Span Data:** $L = 18'\text{-}0''$ $\qquad \dfrac{w_{live}}{w_{dead}} = 3$

(Select left span) $\qquad \dfrac{\Sigma K_{col.}}{K_{beam}} = 2$

Multiplier $= w_{TL}L^2 = 4 \times 18^2 = 1296$ ft.kips

| | | | | | | | | | | | | |
|---|---|---|---|---|---|---|---|---|---|---|---|---|
| $a$: | | 1.00 | | | 1.19 | | | 0.83 | | | 0.94 | |
| $a\sqrt{\dfrac{w_{TaL}}{w_{TL}}} = a$: | | 1.00 | | | 1.19 | | | 0.83 | | | 0.94 | |
| | EXTERIOR SPAN | | | 1st INTERIOR SPAN | | | 1st INTERIOR SPAN | | | EXTERIOR SPAN | | |
| Table 1A: | −.064 | +.055 | −.096 | −.094 | +.051 | −.091 | −.091 | +.051 | −.094 | −.096 | +.055 | −.064 |
| Table 2A: | | | −.010 | −.029 | +.023 | −.029<br>+.007 | −.010<br>+.022 | −.016 | +.022<br>+.003 | +.007<br>+.008 | −.007 | +.007 |
| Final Coefficients: | −.064 | +.055 | −.106 | −.123 | +.074 | −.113 | −.079 | +.035 | +.069 | −.081 | +.048 | −.057 |
| Maximum Moments: (ft.kips) | −83 | +71 | −137 | −159 | +96 | −146 | −102 | +45 | −89 | −105 | +62 | −74 |

Coefficients from the proper row in Table 1A are now recorded beneath the sketched frame, care being taken to enter the part of the table entitled "Four or More Span Frames". Ignore values of minimum midspan moments (marked Min.+) as they are not needed in this example. Since the frame being designed is first considered as an ideal frame consisting of four standard spans, the second interior column is the symmetry line, and coefficients for the right half of frame are repeated in reverse order in the sketch.

Correction coefficients from Table 2A are now to be recorded, starting with the first interior span from the left, there being no correction, of course, for the standard span. With values of $\dfrac{\Sigma K_{col.}}{K_{beam}} = 2$ and $a\sqrt{\dfrac{w_{TaL}}{w_{TL}}} = 1.19$, enter the section of Table 2A headed "Uniform Load," under the subheading entitled "Interior Spans", and record values in their indicated positions with respect to the span being considered. Similarly for other spans, enter the uniform load section of the table with respective values of $a\sqrt{\dfrac{w_{TaL}}{w_{TL}}}$ and the constant stiffness ratio, and record corrections. It is necessary for best accuracy to interpolate roughly for the correction coefficients of these spans. Note that the correction coefficients for the right span are taken from "Exterior Spans" in Table 2A.

The final coefficients are computed by adding algebraically the coefficients taken from both tables. Maximum moments are now determined by multiplying all final coefficients by the multiplier, $w_{TL}L^2$, which is based on the standard span and load and is recorded in the box.

**Example 2A.** Determine maximum end and midspan moments in a frame having four unequal spans, in which uniform live and dead loads vary from span to span.

Given: Dimensions and loads as shown in the sketch. Column stiffness is about one-half the beam stiffness. Therefore $\frac{\Sigma K_{col.}}{K_{beam}} = \frac{0.5 + 0.5}{1} = 1$

Compute standard span data by selecting left span and loads as typical for the frame, since 19 ft. is about the average span length and the loads

## Example 2A. Unsymmetrical Frame, Variable Uniform Loads

| Spans: | 19'-0" | 14'-10" | 17'-8" | 22'-0" |
|---|---|---|---|---|
| Load in kips per foot: $w_{live}$: | 0.60 | 0.85 | 0.45 | 0.60 |
| $w_{dead}$: | 1.20 | 1.05 | 1.15 | 1.40 |
| $w_{total}$: | 1.80 | 1.90 | 1.60 | 2.00 |

**Standard Span Data:** $L = 19'\text{-}0'$ (Select left span and loads)

Multiplier $= w_{TL}L^2 = 1.80 \times 19^2 = 650$ ft.kips

$\frac{w_{live}}{w_{dead}} = 0.5$ $\quad \frac{\Sigma K_{col.}}{K_{beam}} = 1$

| | | | | | | | | | | | | |
|---|---|---|---|---|---|---|---|---|---|---|---|---|
| $a$: | | 1.00 | | | 0.78 | | | 0.93 | | | 1.16 | |
| $a\sqrt{\frac{w_{TaL}}{w_{TL}}}$: | | $1.00\sqrt{\frac{1.80}{1.80}} = 1.00$ | | | $0.78\sqrt{\frac{1.90}{1.80}} = 0.80$ | | | $0.93\sqrt{\frac{1.60}{1.80}} = 0.88$ | | | $1.16\sqrt{\frac{2.00}{1.80}} = 1.22$ | |
| | | EXTERIOR SPAN | | | 1st INTERIOR SPAN | | | 1st INTERIOR SPAN | | | EXTERIOR SPAN | |
| Table 1A: | −.046 | +.058 | −.100 | −.094 | +.047 | −.087 | −.087 | +.047 | −.094 | −.100 | +.058 | −.046 |
| Table 2A: | 0 | 0 | 0 | 0 | | | | | | | | |
| | | | +.011 | +.024 | −.021 | +.024 | +.011 | | −.017 | −.035 | +.031 | −.025 |
| | | | | | | +.007 | +.015 | −.013 | +.015 | +.007 | | |
| Final Coefficients: | −.046 | +.058 | −.089 | −.070 | +.026 | −.056 | −.061 | +.034 | −.096 | −.128 | +.089 | −.071 |
| Maximum Moments: (ft.kips) | −30 | +38 | −58 | −46 | +17 | −36 | −40 | +22 | −62 | −83 | +58 | −46 |

Minimum Midspan Moments: (In short interior spans)

| | | | | |
|---|---|---|---|---|
| $a\sqrt{\frac{w_{DaL}}{w_{DL}}}$: | | $0.78\sqrt{\frac{1.05}{1.20}} = 0.73$ | $0.93\sqrt{\frac{1.15}{1.20}} = 0.91$ | |
| Table 1A: (Min.+) | | +.019 | +.019 | |
| Table 2A: | | −.027 | −.010 | |
| Table 2A: $\times \frac{w_{DL}}{w_{TL}}$ | $\left(\frac{w_{DL}}{w_{TL}} = \frac{1.20}{1.80} = \frac{2}{3}\right)$ | −.018 | −.007 | |
| Final Coefficients: | | +.001 | +.012 | |
| Minimum Midspan Moments: (Multiplier = 650) | | +1 | +8 | |

Alternate Design: (Assuming that 17'–8" span and its total load were selected as standard)

Data: $L = 17'\text{–}8''$ $\quad w_{TL} = 1.6$ $\quad$ Multiplier $= 1.60 \times 17.67^2 = 500$

| | | | | | | | | | | | | |
|---|---|---|---|---|---|---|---|---|---|---|---|---|
| Maximum Moments: | −31 | +39 | −59 | −47 | +19 | −38 | −41 | +23 | −63 | −84 | +59 | −47 |

$\left(\text{Based on } \frac{w_{live}}{w_{dead}} = 0.5 \text{ and new values of } a\sqrt{\frac{w_{TaL}}{1.60}}\right)$

are about average. The last part of the example will illustrate the freedom of choice the designer has in this respect.

Determine values of $a$ and $a\sqrt{\frac{w_{TaL}}{w_{TL}}}$, noting that both spans and loads influence the latter factors. Coefficients from Table 1A are recorded in their proper positions beneath the frame and correction coefficients from Table 2A are taken for each non-standard span. Final coefficients and maximum moments are computed as in Example 1A.

The presence of one or more short spans in the frame makes it desirable to determine *minimum* midspan moments. The procedure is to record "Min. +" coefficients from Table 1A and to use correction coefficients from Table 2A based on relations between dead loads instead of total loads. Use span-load factor $a\sqrt{\frac{w_{DaL}}{w_{DL}}}$, where $w_{DaL}$ is the dead load per foot on the $aL$-span and $w_{DL}$ is the dead load on the standard $L$-span. With these constants, take midspan coefficients from Table 2A. Before adding to original coefficients, multiply each value by the ratio of standard span dead load to standard span total load, $\frac{w_{DL}}{w_{TL}}$.

For a comparison between maximum moments determined under two assumptions, assume that the 17 ft. 8 in. span and its loads are selected as standards. Coefficients from Table 1A will remain unchanged (for $\frac{w_{live}}{w_{dead}} = 0.5$, average), but Table 2A and final coefficients will be different. Computations are omitted, but maximum moments in this case are little different from those first computed.

**Example 3A.** Determine maximum moments in a frame having spans loaded with either uniform or concentrated loads as shown in sketch. Stiffness of columns equals two times stiffness of beams.

Compute standard span data based on selection of left interior span and loads. The live to dead load ratio is taken as two, which is an approximate average including both uniform and concentrated loads for the entire level.

Spans having concentrated loads are handled as before except that concentrated loads are reduced to an "equivalent" uniform load, $p_{TaL}$, by dividing the total load on the span by the span length. The span-load factor becomes $a\sqrt{\frac{p_{TaL}}{w_{TL}}}$ instead of $a\sqrt{\frac{w_{TaL}}{w_{TL}}}$, and a different section of Table 2A is used, depending upon the type of loading.

In this example compute values of $a$ for all spans and then the respective values of $a\sqrt{\frac{w_{TaL}}{w_{TL}}}$ or $a\sqrt{\frac{p_{TaL}}{w_{TL}}}$. Record coefficients from Table 1A across the frame without regard to difference in span or loading. Coefficients from

## Example 3A. Unsymmetrical Frame, Spans with Uniform or Concentrated Loads

| | | | | | | | | | | | | | | | |
|---|---|---|---|---|---|---|---|---|---|---|---|---|---|---|---|
| Spans: | 21'-0" (7'-0", 7'-0", 7'-0") | | | 20'-0" | | | 16'-0" (8'-0", 8'-0") | | | 22'-0" | | | 24'-0" (6'-0", 6'-0", 6'-0", 6'-0") | | |
| Load in kips or kips per foot: L.L.: | 10, 10 | | | 1.0 | | | 19 | | | 0.9 | | | 5.5, 5.5, 5.5 | | |
| D.L.: | 4, 4 | | | 0.5 | | | 8 | | | 0.4 | | | 3.0, 3.0, 3.0 | | |
| T.L.: | 28 | | | 1.5 | | | 27 | | | 1.3 | | | 25.5 | | |
| $p_{TaL} = \frac{P_{Total}}{Span}$ | 1.33 | | | | | | 1.69 | | | | | | 1.06 | | |
| $a$: | 1.05 | | | 1.00 | | | 0.80 | | | 1.10 | | | 1.20 | | |
| $a\sqrt{\frac{w_{TaL}}{w_{TL}}}$ or $a\sqrt{\frac{p_{TaL}}{w_{TL}}}$ | $1.05\sqrt{\frac{1.33}{1.5}}$ = 0.99 | | | $1.00\sqrt{\frac{1.5}{1.5}}$ = 1.00 | | | $0.80\sqrt{\frac{1.69}{1.5}}$ = 0.85 | | | $1.10\sqrt{\frac{1.3}{1.5}}$ = 1.02 | | | $1.20\sqrt{\frac{1.06}{1.5}}$ = 1.01 | | |
| | EXTERIOR SPAN | | | 1st INTERIOR SPAN | | | 2nd INTERIOR SPAN | | | 1st INTERIOR SPAN | | | EXTERIOR SPAN | | |
| Table 1A: | –.071 | +.049 | –.091 | –.089 | +.047 | –.088 | –.088 | +.047 | –.088 | –.088 | +.047 | –.089 | –.091 | +.049 | –.071 |
| Table 2A: | –.022 | +.016 | –.023 | –.005 | | | | | | | | –.004 | –.021 | +.024 | –.020 |
| | | | 0 | 0 | 0 | 0 | 0 | | –.001 | –.003 | +.002 | –.003 | –.001 | | |
| | | | | | | –.001 | –.006 | +.010 | .006 | .001 | | | | | |
| Final Coefficients: | –.093 | +.065 | –.114 | –.094 | +.047 | –.089 | –.094 | +.096 | –.095 | –.092 | +.049 | –.096 | –.113 | +.073 | –.091 |
| Maximum Moments: (ft.kips) | –56 | +39 | –68 | –56 | +28 | –53 | –56 | +58 | –57 | –55 | +29 | –58 | –68 | +44 | –55 |

**Standard Span Data:** $L = 20'\text{-}0''$ $w_{live} = 1.0$ $\frac{w_{live}}{w_{dead}} = 2$

(Select left interior span and loads) $w_{dead} = 0.5$ $\frac{\Sigma K_{col.}}{K_{beam}} = 4$

Multiplier $= w_{TL}L^2 = 1.5 \times 20^2 = 600$ $w_{TL} = 1.5$

Minimum Midspan Moment in 16-ft. Span: $a\sqrt{\frac{p_{DaL}}{w_{DL}}} = 0.80\sqrt{\frac{\frac{8}{16}}{0.5}} = 0.80$

Table 1A: ("Min. +" value of 2nd interior span) +.008

Table 2A: Midspan loading (midspan correction) +.038

$$\frac{w_{DL}}{w_{TL}} \times (+.038) = \frac{0.5}{1.5} \times (+.038) = +.013$$

Final Coefficient: +.021

Minimum Midspan Moment: (Multiplier = 600) +13 ft.kips

Table 2A are next recorded using the constant stiffness ratio, $\frac{\Sigma K_{col.}}{K_{beam}}$, for the frame and the proper value of $a\sqrt{\frac{w_{TaL}}{w_{TL}}}$ for each span having uniform load and the proper value of $a\sqrt{\frac{p_{TaL}}{w_{TL}}}$ for each span having concentrated load. The type of concentrated loading determines which section of Table 2A should be entered for correction coefficients. As a final step add up the maximum moment coefficients and multiply throughout by the multiplier: $w_{TL}L^2 = 1.5 \times 20^2 = 600$

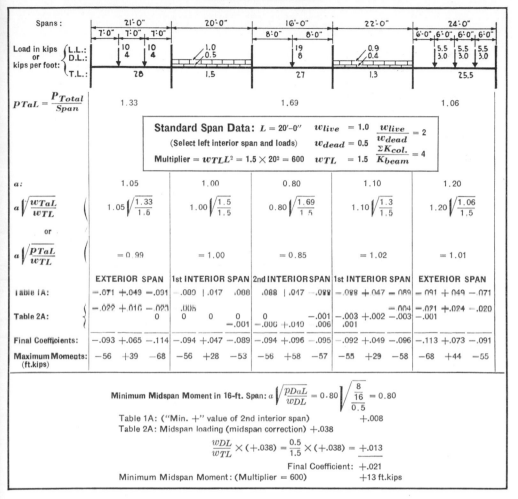

To determine the *minimum* midspan moment in the short 16-ft. span, calculate the span-load factor based on dead loads instead of total loads:

$$a\sqrt{\frac{p_{DaL}}{w_{DL}}} = 0.8\sqrt{\frac{8/16}{0.5}} = 0.8$$

Record minimum midspan coefficient (Min.+) for second interior span from Table 1A and obtain the midspan correction coefficient from Table 2A, using $\frac{\Sigma K_{col.}}{K_{beam}}$ equal to 4, and $a\sqrt{\frac{p_{aL}}{w_L}}$ (in this case $a\sqrt{\frac{p_{DaL}}{w_{DL}}}$) equal to 0.8. The section in Table 2A under "Midspan Loading" and "Interior Spans" is used. Multiply the correction coefficient, +.038, by ratio of standard span dead load to standard span total load before adding to coefficient of Table 1A.

The minimum midspan moment of the 16-ft. span is equal to +.021 × 600 = +13 ft.kips.

**Example 4A.** Determine maximum moments in a frame having uniform and concentrated loads combined as shown in sketch. Stiffness of columns equals stiffness of beams.

## Example 4A. General Case, Uniform and Concentrated Loads Combined

| Spans: | 23'-4" | 14'-0" | 22'-8" | 18'-0" |
|---|---|---|---|---|
| | 5'-10", 5'-10", 5'-10", 5'-10" | 7'-0", 7'-0" | 5'-8", 5'-8", 5'-8", 5'-8" | 6'-0", 6'-0", 6'-0" |
| Load in kips or kips per foot: L.L.: | 0.5; 8, 8, 8 | 0.4; 20 | 0.5; 8, 8, 8 | 0.4; 14, 14 |
| D.L.: | 0.4; 10, 10, 10 | 0.3; 18 | 0.3; 8, 8, 8 | 0.4; 12, 12 |
| T.L.: | 0.9; 54 | 0.7; 38 | 0.8; 48 | 0.8; 52 |
| $p_{TaL} = \frac{P_{Total}}{Span}$: | 2.31 | 2.71 | 2.12 | 2.89 |

**Standard Span Data:** $L = 19'\text{-}6''$
(Select average span, say 19'-6") Average equivalent loads $w_{LL} = 1.7$, $w_{DL} = 1.7$, $w_{TL} = 3.4$; $\frac{w_{live}}{w_{dead}} = 1$; $\frac{\Sigma K_{col.}}{K_{beam}} = 2$
Multiplier $= w_{TL}L^2 = 3.4 \times 19.5^2 = 1293$ ft.kips

| | | | | | | | | | | | | |
|---|---|---|---|---|---|---|---|---|---|---|---|---|
| $a$: | | 1.20 | | | 0.72 | | | 1.16 | | | 0.92 | |
| $a\sqrt{\frac{p_{TaL}+w_{TaL}}{w_{TL}}}$: | | $1.20\sqrt{\frac{2.31+0.9}{3.4}} = 1.17$ | | | $0.72\sqrt{\frac{2.71+0.7}{3.4}} = 0.72$ | | | $1.16\sqrt{\frac{2.12+0.8}{3.4}} = 1.07$ | | | $0.92\sqrt{\frac{2.89+0.8}{3.4}} = 0.96$ | |
| Table 1A: | −.061 | +.053 | −.095 | −.091 | +.048 | −.088 | −.088 | +.048 | −.091 | −.095 | +.053 | −.061 |
| Table 2A: Concentrated Load Sections: | | | | | | | | | | | | |
| Coeff. × $\frac{p_{TaL}}{p_{TaL}+w_{TaL}}$: | −.033 | +.039 | −.038<br>+.004 | −.012<br>+.013 | +.016 | −.007<br>+.013 | −.023<br>+.004 | +.025 | −.023<br>−.005 | −.007<br>−.014 | +.010 | −.012 |
| Uniform Load Section: | | | | | | | | | | | | |
| Coeff. × $\frac{w_{TaL}}{p_{TaL}+w_{TaL}}$: | −.007 | +.006 | −.008<br>+.002 | −.003<br>+.007 | −.005 | −.001<br>+.007 | −.003<br>+.002 | +.002 | −.003<br>0 | −.001<br>+.001 | −.001 | +.001 |
| Final Coefficients: | −.101 | +.098 | −.135 | −.086 | +.059 | −.076 | −.108 | +.075 | −.122 | −.116 | +.062 | −.072 |
| Maximum Moments: (ft.kips) | −131 | +127 | −175 | −111 | +76 | −98 | −140 | +97 | −158 | −150 | +80 | −93 |

There is no "typical" span and loading in this frame, so standard span data must be based upon length and loading estimated as being average. This could have been done in previous examples as well. Only approximate values are necessary in the choice of $L$ and $w_{TL}$ since they are used in the multiplier, $w_{RL}L^2$, and are used also to determine the span-load factors, $a\sqrt{\frac{w_{TaL}}{w_{TL}}}$ or $a\sqrt{\frac{p_{TaL}}{w_{TL}}}$. If large values are chosen, $w_{TL}L^2$ is large, but correction coefficients are altered automatically so that the effect upon the final moments is small. Re-calculation of preceding examples using different standard span lengths and loads will indicate the designer's freedom in making the selections.

In this example, average roughly the span lengths and take $L = 19$ ft. 6 in. Divide the total concentrated load on each span by its span length and record as values of $p_{TaL}$. Add the values of $p_{TaL}$ and $w_{TaL}$ for each span and then average the resulting total uniform loads for all the spans. This determines $w_{TL}$ equal to about 3.4. Live loads approximately equal dead loads, so estimate $w_{live} = 1.7$ and $w_{dead} = 1.7$.

The span-load factors for combined uniform and concentrated load take the form $a\sqrt{\frac{p_{TaL} + w_{TaL}}{w_{TL}}}$. No correction coefficient tables are presented for various combinations of $p_{TaL}$ and $w_{TaL}$, but it is conservative to use the concentrated load sections of Table 2A when loads are combinations of concentrated and uniform loads, since final moments will always be on the safe side. More accurate results will be obtained, however, by separate use of the respective concentrated load section and uniform load section of Table 2A for each span, as follows:

> For any span, enter the proper concentrated load section with value of $a\sqrt{\frac{p_{TaL} + w_{TaL}}{w_{TL}}}$ and record correction coefficients multiplied by the ratio, $\frac{p_{TaL}}{p_{TaL} + w_{TaL}}$ which involves loads on that span only. Next, enter the uniform load section with the same value of $a\sqrt{\frac{p_{TaL} + w_{TaL}}{w_{TL}}}$ and record correction coefficients multiplied by the ratio, $\frac{w_{TaL}}{p_{TaL} + w_{TaL}}$, which is seen to be equal to $1 - \frac{p_{TaL}}{p_{TaL} + w_{TaL}}$.

Correction coefficients in Example 4A have been computed by the procedure just described. The refinement involved in this example may not always be justified when the concentrated load is the major part of the total load on a span and particularly if an arbitrary division of load into uniform and concentrated loads has been made.

**Example 5A.** Determine maximum moments in a frame having spans and loads as shown in the sketch. Ratio of column stiffnesses to beam stiffnesses is variable.

Maximum moments are not sensitive to changes in column stiffness and it is usually sufficient for design, in frames having variable column stiffness, to use the average column stiffness. An estimate of the stiffness ratio for use in the tables may then be made by comparison with the stiffness of the standard span.

This example illustrates the determination of moments in a frame having relatively slender exterior columns compared with interior columns. Under such circumstances it is best to compute moments in exterior spans for a stiffness ratio based on exterior columns, and moments in interior spans for a stiffness ratio based on interior columns. For this example take coefficients for a stiffness ratio of two for exterior spans and a ratio of four for interior spans. Loads and dimensions are the same as in Example 1A to permit a comparison of maximum moments to be made. It is seen that doubling the stiffnesses of interior columns does not change the moments materially.

## Example 5A. Unequal Column Stiffnesses

| | | | | | | | | | | | | |
|---|---|---|---|---|---|---|---|---|---|---|---|---|
| Spans: | | 18'-0" | | | 21'-6" | | | 15'-0" | | | 17'-0" | |
| | | K col. = K beam | | | K col. = 2K beam | | | K col. = 2K beam | | | K col. = K beam | |
| Load in kips per foot: L.L.: | | 3 | | | 3 | | | 3 | | | 3 | |
| D.L.: | | 1 | | | 1 | | | 1 | | | 1 | |
| T.L.: | | 4 | | | 4 | | | 4 | | | 4 | |

**Standard Span Data:** $L = 18'\text{-}0''$ (Select left span)

Multiplier $= w_{TL}L^2 = 4 \times 18^2 = 1296$ ft.kips

$w_{live} = 3$, $w_{dead} = 1$, $w_{TL} = 4$, $\frac{w_{live}}{w_{dead}} = 3$, $\frac{\Sigma K_{col.}}{K_{beam}} = 2\&4$

(Loads and spans same as Example 1A)

| | | | | | | | | | | | | |
|---|---|---|---|---|---|---|---|---|---|---|---|---|
| $a\sqrt{\frac{w_{TaL}}{w_{TL}}} = a$: | | 1.00 | | | 1.19 | | | 0.83 | | | 0.94 | |
| | | $\frac{\Sigma K col.}{K beam} = 2$ | | | $\frac{\Sigma K col.}{K beam} = 4$ | | | $\frac{\Sigma K col.}{K beam} = 4$ | | | $\frac{\Sigma K col.}{K beam} = 2$ | |
| Table 1A: | −.064 | +.055 | −.096 | −.090 | +.048 | −.089 | −.089 | +.048 | −.090 | −.096 | +.055 | −.064 |
| Table 2A: | | | * −.010 | −.031 | +.021 | −.031 | −.006 | | | | | |
| | | | | | | +.004 | +.023 | −.015 | +.023 | +.007* | | |
| | | | | | | | | | +.002 | +.008 | −.007 | +.007 |
| Final Coefficients: | −.064 | +.055 | −.106 | −.121 | +.069 | −.116 | −.072 | +.033 | −.065 | −.081 | +.048 | −.057 |
| Maximum Moments: (ft.kips) | −83 | +71 | −137 | −157 | +89 | −150 | −93 | +43 | −84 | −105 | +62 | −74 |

*Based on stiffness ratio of exterior columns and beam.

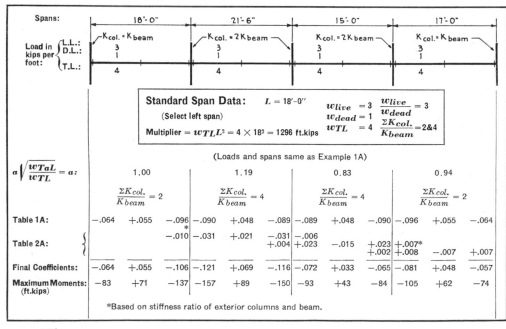

**Example 6A.** *Determination of Column Moments.* The suggested procedure for determination of column moments, as previously described, involves placing live load on the span or spans adjacent to the column under consideration and also on alternate spans therefrom. This is the same live load arrangement as for maximum beam moments at the column. The difference between maximum end moments at a column, therefore, is equal to the total of the two column moments. If the column stiffness below a joint is the same as the one above, the column design moment is equal to the difference between maximum beam moments at the joint, divided by two.

### Example 6A. Column Moments in Frame of Example 2A

Spans:

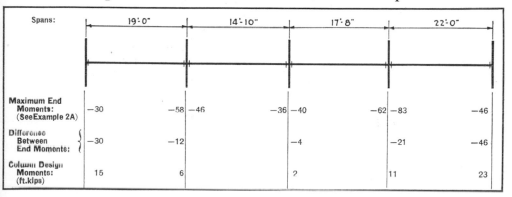

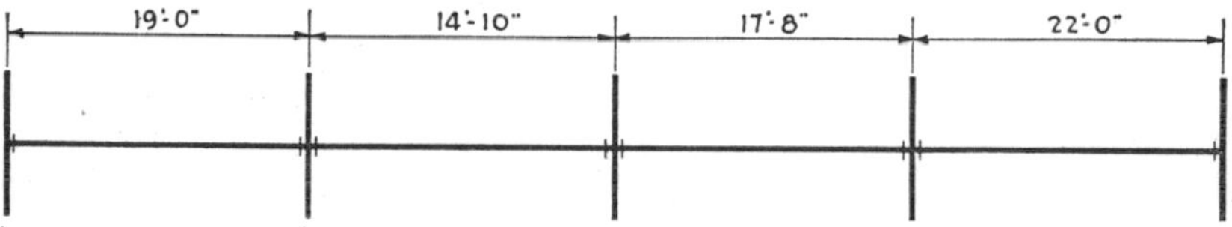


| | | | | | | | | |
|---|---|---|---|---|---|---|---|---|
| Maximum End Moments: (See Example 2A) | −30 | −58 | −46 | −36 | −40 | −62 | −83 | −46 |
| Difference Between End Moments: | −30 | −12 | | | −4 | | −21 | −46 |
| Column Design Moments: (ft.kips) | 15 | 6 | | | 2 | | 11 | 23 |

The frame and the maximum end moments are taken from Example 2A. Column stiffnesses are assumed equal above and below each joint. Moments are calculated mentally and recorded on the frame. It should be noted that moment in a column above a joint tends to produce tension on the side toward the larger beam moment, and moment in the column below —compression on that side.

**Example 7A.** *Determination of Shear.* After maximum moments have been determined, the design shear at ends of beams including shear due to frame continuity may be calculated simply and with fair accuracy by use of the rule:

> Shear at an end of a beam equals the *numerical* sum of maximum moment at that end and maximum midspan moment, divided by the span length, plus 3/8* of the total load on the span.

Referring to the frame and moments of Example 2A, the maximum shear at the interior support of the right span is,

$$V = (83 + 58)\frac{1}{22} + \frac{3}{8}\,(2.00 \times 22.0) = 23\ \textit{kips}$$

*Factor equals 3/8 only for uniform loads on the span. Use:
1/3 for quarter-point or third-point loading.
1/4 for midspan loading, and
1/3 for mixed uniform and concentrated loads.

# Table 1A. Coefficients for Bending Moments in Building Frames

## Maximum Moment Coefficients, $C_1$

$$M = C_1(w_{dead} + w_{live})L^2 \quad \text{where:} \quad \begin{cases} M & = \text{Moment in ft.kips} \\ w_{dead} & = \text{Uniform dead load in kips per ft.} \\ w_{live} & = \text{Uniform live load in kips per ft.} \\ L & = \text{Span in ft.} \end{cases}$$

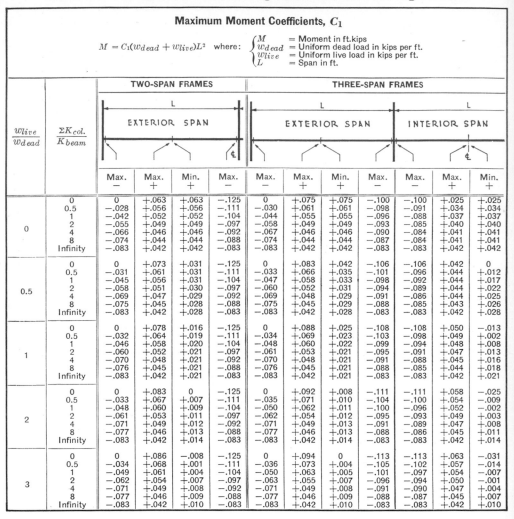

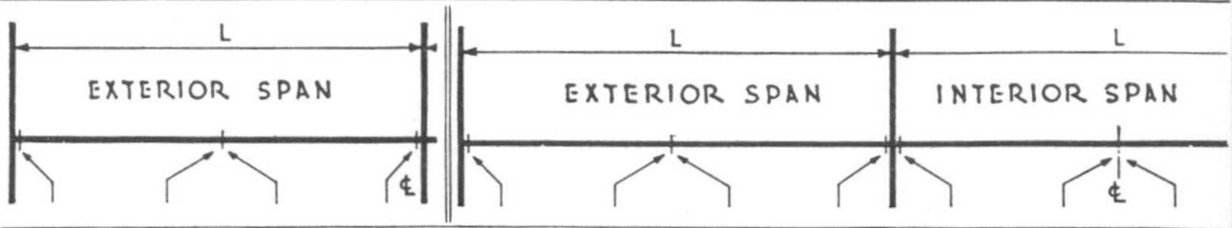


| $\frac{w_{live}}{w_{dead}}$ | $\frac{\Sigma K_{col.}}{K_{beam}}$ | TWO-SPAN FRAMES, EXTERIOR SPAN: Max. − | Max. + | Min. + | Max. − | THREE-SPAN FRAMES, EXTERIOR SPAN: Max. − | Max. + | Min. + | Max. − | INTERIOR SPAN: Max. − | Max. + | Min. + |
|---|---|---|---|---|---|---|---|---|---|---|---|---|
| 0 | 0 | 0 | +.063 | +.063 | −.125 | 0 | +.075 | +.075 | −.100 | −.100 | +.025 | +.025 |
| | 0.5 | −.028 | +.056 | +.056 | −.111 | −.030 | +.061 | +.061 | −.098 | −.091 | +.034 | +.034 |
| | 1 | −.042 | +.052 | +.052 | −.104 | −.044 | +.055 | +.055 | −.096 | −.088 | +.037 | +.037 |
| | 2 | −.055 | +.049 | +.049 | −.097 | −.058 | +.049 | +.049 | −.093 | −.085 | +.040 | +.040 |
| | 4 | −.066 | +.046 | +.046 | −.092 | −.067 | +.046 | +.046 | −.090 | −.084 | +.041 | +.041 |
| | 8 | −.074 | +.044 | +.044 | −.088 | −.074 | +.044 | +.044 | −.087 | −.084 | +.041 | +.041 |
| | Infinity | −.083 | +.042 | +.042 | −.083 | −.083 | +.042 | +.042 | −.083 | −.083 | +.042 | +.042 |
| 0.5 | 0 | 0 | +.073 | +.031 | −.125 | 0 | +.083 | +.042 | −.106 | −.106 | +.042 | 0 |
| | 0.5 | −.031 | +.061 | +.031 | −.111 | −.033 | +.066 | +.035 | −.101 | −.096 | +.044 | +.012 |
| | 1 | −.045 | +.056 | +.031 | −.104 | −.047 | +.058 | +.033 | −.098 | −.092 | +.044 | +.017 |
| | 2 | −.058 | +.051 | +.030 | −.097 | −.060 | +.052 | +.031 | −.094 | −.089 | +.044 | +.022 |
| | 4 | −.069 | +.047 | +.029 | −.092 | −.069 | +.048 | +.029 | −.091 | −.086 | +.044 | +.025 |
| | 8 | −.075 | +.045 | +.028 | −.088 | −.075 | +.045 | +.029 | −.088 | −.085 | +.043 | +.026 |
| | Infinity | −.083 | +.042 | +.028 | −.083 | −.083 | +.042 | +.028 | −.083 | −.083 | +.042 | +.028 |
| 1 | 0 | 0 | +.078 | +.016 | −.125 | 0 | +.088 | +.025 | −.108 | −.108 | +.050 | −.013 |
| | 0.5 | −.032 | +.064 | +.019 | −.111 | −.034 | +.069 | +.023 | −.103 | −.098 | +.049 | +.002 |
| | 1 | −.046 | +.058 | +.020 | −.104 | −.048 | +.060 | +.022 | −.099 | −.094 | +.048 | +.008 |
| | 2 | −.060 | +.052 | +.021 | −.097 | −.061 | +.053 | +.021 | −.095 | −.091 | +.047 | +.013 |
| | 4 | −.070 | +.048 | +.021 | −.092 | −.070 | +.048 | +.021 | −.091 | −.088 | +.045 | +.016 |
| | 8 | −.076 | +.045 | +.021 | −.088 | −.076 | +.045 | +.021 | −.088 | −.085 | +.044 | +.018 |
| | Infinity | −.083 | +.042 | +.021 | −.083 | −.083 | +.042 | +.021 | −.083 | −.083 | +.042 | +.021 |
| 2 | 0 | 0 | +.083 | 0 | −.125 | 0 | +.092 | +.008 | −.111 | −.111 | +.058 | −.025 |
| | 0.5 | −.033 | +.067 | +.007 | −.111 | −.035 | +.071 | +.010 | −.104 | −.100 | +.054 | −.009 |
| | 1 | −.048 | +.060 | +.009 | −.104 | −.050 | +.062 | +.011 | −.100 | −.096 | +.052 | −.002 |
| | 2 | −.061 | +.053 | +.011 | −.097 | −.062 | +.054 | +.012 | −.095 | −.093 | +.049 | +.003 |
| | 4 | −.071 | +.049 | +.012 | −.092 | −.071 | +.049 | +.013 | −.091 | −.089 | +.047 | +.008 |
| | 8 | −.077 | +.046 | +.013 | −.088 | −.077 | +.046 | +.013 | −.088 | −.086 | +.045 | +.011 |
| | Infinity | −.083 | +.042 | +.014 | −.083 | −.083 | +.042 | +.014 | −.083 | −.083 | +.042 | +.014 |
| 3 | 0 | 0 | +.086 | −.008 | −.125 | 0 | +.094 | 0 | −.113 | −.113 | +.063 | −.031 |
| | 0.5 | −.034 | +.068 | +.001 | −.111 | −.036 | +.073 | +.004 | −.105 | −.102 | +.057 | −.014 |
| | 1 | −.049 | +.061 | +.004 | −.104 | −.050 | +.063 | +.005 | −.101 | −.097 | +.054 | −.007 |
| | 2 | −.062 | +.054 | +.007 | −.097 | −.063 | +.055 | +.007 | −.096 | −.094 | +.050 | −.001 |
| | 4 | −.071 | +.049 | +.008 | −.092 | −.071 | +.049 | +.008 | −.091 | −.090 | +.047 | +.004 |
| | 8 | −.077 | +.046 | +.009 | −.088 | −.077 | +.046 | +.009 | −.088 | −.087 | +.045 | +.007 |
| | Infinity | −.083 | +.042 | +.010 | −.083 | −.083 | +.042 | +.010 | −.083 | −.083 | +.042 | +.010 |

Table 1A is a tabulation of design moment coefficients at ends and midspan of beams in ideal frames having the following characteristics:

1. Equal span lengths and constant beam or slab stiffnesses.
2. Far ends of columns above and below the floor under consideration assumed to be fixed and columns or supports of equal stiffnesses.
3. Uniform loads, and arrangement of live load to produce maximum end moments and maximum or minimum midspan moments.

The limits of the table are values of live to dead load ratio, $\frac{w_{live}}{w_{dead}}$, between 0 and 3, and total column stiffness to beam stiffness, $\frac{\Sigma K_{col.}}{K_{beam}}$, from 0 to infinity, corresponding to point supports and fixed supports, respectively.

# Table 1A. (*continued*)

## Maximum Moment Coefficients, $C_1$

$M = C_1(w_{dead} + w_{live})L^2$ where: $M$ = Moment in ft.kips; $w_{dead}$ = Uniform dead load in kips per ft.; $w_{live}$ = Uniform live load in kips per ft.; $L$ = Span in ft.

**FOUR OR MORE SPAN FRAMES**

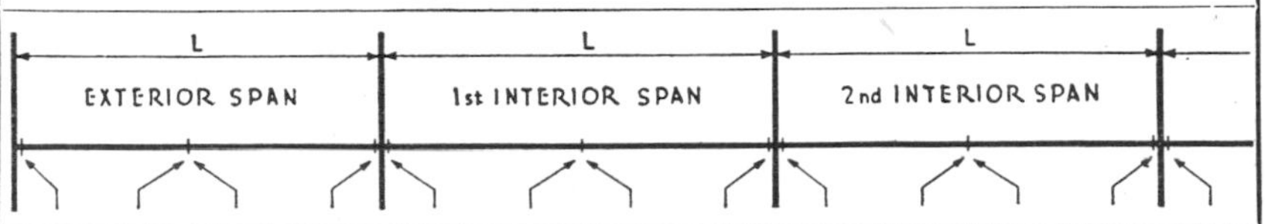


| $\frac{w_{live}}{w_{dead}}$ | $\frac{\Sigma K_{col.}}{K_{beam}}$ | Exterior Span Max. − | Exterior Span Max. + | Exterior Span Min. + | Exterior Span Max. − | 1st Interior Span Max. − | 1st Interior Span Max. + | 1st Interior Span Min. + | 1st Interior Span Max. − | 2nd Interior Span Max. − | 2nd Interior Span Max. + | 2nd Interior Span Min. + | 2nd Interior Span Max. − | Max. − |
|---|---|---|---|---|---|---|---|---|---|---|---|---|---|---|
| 0 | 0 | 0 | +.072 | +.072 | −.106 | −.106 | +.034 | +.034 | −.077 | −.077 | +.044 | +.044 | −.085 | −.085 |
| | 0.5 | −.030 | +.060 | +.060 | −.101 | −.095 | +.038 | +.038 | −.080 | −.081 | +.043 | +.043 | −.084 | −.084 |
| | 1 | −.044 | +.054 | +.054 | −.098 | −.090 | +.039 | +.039 | −.081 | −.082 | +.042 | +.042 | −.084 | −.084 |
| | 2 | −.057 | +.050 | +.050 | −.094 | −.087 | +.041 | +.041 | −.082 | −.083 | +.042 | +.042 | −.083 | −.083 |
| | 4 | −.067 | +.046 | +.046 | −.090 | −.085 | +.042 | +.042 | −.083 | −.083 | +.042 | +.042 | −.083 | −.083 |
| | 8 | −.074 | +.044 | +.044 | −.087 | −.084 | +.042 | +.042 | −.083 | −.083 | +.042 | +.042 | −.083 | −.083 |
| | Infinity | −.083 | +.042 | +.042 | −.083 | −.083 | +.042 | +.042 | −.083 | −.083 | +.042 | +.042 | −.083 | −.083 |
| 0.5 | 0 | 0 | +.081 | +.039 | −.110 | −.110 | +.049 | +.007 | −.088 | −.088 | +.057 | +.016 | −.094 | −.094 |
| | 0.5 | −.033 | +.065 | +.035 | −.104 | −.099 | +.048 | +.016 | −.087 | −.088 | +.052 | +.019 | −.091 | −.091 |
| | 1 | −.046 | +.058 | +.033 | −.100 | −.094 | +.047 | +.019 | −.087 | −.088 | +.049 | +.021 | −.089 | −.089 |
| | 2 | −.060 | +.052 | +.031 | −.095 | −.090 | +.045 | +.022 | −.086 | −.087 | +.047 | +.023 | −.087 | −.087 |
| | 4 | −.069 | +.048 | +.029 | −.091 | −.087 | +.044 | +.025 | −.085 | −.086 | +.044 | +.025 | −.086 | −.086 |
| | 8 | −.076 | +.045 | +.029 | −.088 | −.085 | +.043 | +.026 | −.085 | −.085 | +.043 | +.026 | −.085 | −.085 |
| | Infinity | −.083 | +.042 | +.028 | −.083 | −.083 | +.042 | +.028 | −.083 | −.083 | +.042 | +.028 | −.083 | −.083 |
| 1 | 0 | 0 | +.085 | +.023 | −.113 | −.113 | +.056 | −.006 | −.094 | −.094 | +.063 | +.002 | −.099 | −.099 |
| | 0.5 | −.034 | +.068 | +.022 | −.105 | −.101 | +.052 | +.004 | −.091 | −.092 | +.057 | +.008 | −.095 | −.095 |
| | 1 | −.048 | +.060 | +.022 | −.100 | −.096 | +.050 | +.009 | −.090 | −.091 | +.052 | +.011 | −.092 | −.092 |
| | 2 | −.061 | +.053 | +.021 | −.095 | −.091 | +.048 | +.013 | −.088 | −.089 | +.049 | +.014 | −.089 | −.089 |
| | 4 | −.070 | +.048 | +.021 | −.091 | −.088 | +.046 | +.016 | −.087 | −.087 | +.046 | +.017 | −.087 | −.087 |
| | 8 | −.076 | +.045 | +.021 | −.088 | −.086 | +.044 | +.018 | −.085 | −.085 | +.044 | +.018 | −.085 | −.085 |
| | Infinity | −.083 | +.042 | +.021 | −.083 | −.083 | +.042 | +.021 | −.083 | −.083 | +.042 | +.021 | −.083 | −.083 |
| 2 | 0 | 0 | +.090 | +.007 | −.115 | −.115 | +.064 | −.019 | −.099 | −.099 | +.070 | −.011 | −.104 | −.104 |
| | 0.5 | −.035 | +.070 | +.009 | −.106 | −.103 | +.057 | −.007 | −.095 | −.096 | +.061 | −.004 | −.098 | −.098 |
| | 1 | −.050 | +.062 | +.011 | −.101 | −.098 | +.054 | −.001 | −.093 | −.094 | +.056 | 0 | −.095 | −.095 |
| | 2 | −.063 | +.054 | +.013 | −.096 | −.093 | +.050 | +.004 | −.090 | −.091 | +.051 | +.005 | −.091 | −.091 |
| | 4 | −.071 | +.049 | +.013 | −.091 | −.089 | +.047 | +.008 | −.088 | −.088 | +.047 | +.008 | −.088 | −.088 |
| | 8 | −.077 | +.046 | +.013 | −.088 | −.086 | +.045 | +.011 | −.086 | −.086 | +.045 | +.011 | −.086 | −.086 |
| | Infinity | −.083 | +.042 | +.014 | −.083 | −.083 | +.042 | +.014 | −.083 | −.083 | +.042 | +.014 | −.083 | −.083 |
| 3 | 0 | 0 | +.092 | −.002 | −.116 | −.116 | +.068 | −.026 | −.102 | −.102 | +.073 | −.018 | −.106 | −.106 |
| | 0.5 | −.036 | +.071 | +.003 | −.107 | −.104 | +.060 | −.012 | −.097 | −.098 | +.063 | −.010 | −.100 | −.100 |
| | 1 | −.050 | +.063 | +.005 | −.101 | −.099 | +.055 | −.006 | −.094 | −.095 | +.057 | −.005 | −.096 | −.096 |
| | 2 | −.064 | +.055 | +.007 | −.096 | −.094 | +.051 | 0 | −.091 | −.092 | +.052 | 0 | −.092 | −.092 |
| | 4 | −.072 | +.049 | +.008 | −.091 | −.090 | +.048 | +.004 | −.089 | −.089 | +.048 | +.004 | −.089 | −.089 |
| | 8 | −.077 | +.046 | +.009 | −.088 | −.087 | +.045 | +.007 | −.086 | −.087 | +.045 | +.007 | −.087 | −.087 |
| | Infinity | −.083 | +.042 | +.010 | −.083 | −.083 | +.042 | +.010 | −.083 | −.083 | +.042 | +.010 | −.083 | −.083 |

$\frac{w_{live}}{w_{dead}} = 1$, $\frac{\Sigma K_{col.}}{K_{beam}} = 2$

| MAX. − | MAX. + | MIN. + | MAX. − | MAX. − | MAX. + | MIN. + | MAX. − | MAX. − | MAX. + | MIN. + | MAX. − | MAX. − |
|---|---|---|---|---|---|---|---|---|---|---|---|---|
| -.061 | +.053 | +.021 | -.095 | -.091 | +.048 | +.013 | -.088 | -.089 | +.049 | +.014 | -.089 | -.089 |

Design Moment Coefficients in a Frame as Tabulated for the Given Case from Table 1A

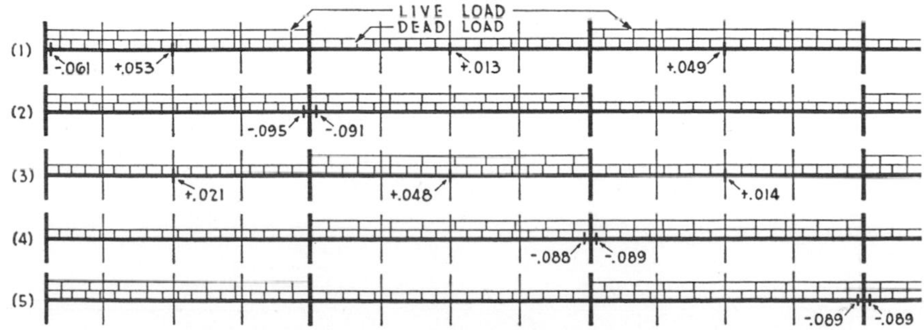


(1) to (5) Arrangomont of Live Load Used to Compute the Design Coefficients Shown

# Table 2A. Corrections to Moment Coefficients of Table 1A

**Values of $C_2$**

For use when spans or loads vary

$$M = C(w_{dead} + w_{live})L^2$$

$$C = C_1 \text{ (from Table 1A)} + C_2 \text{ (from Table 2A)}$$

| $\frac{\Sigma K_{col.}}{K_{beam}}$ | * $a\sqrt{\frac{w_{aL}}{w_L}}$ or $a\sqrt{\frac{p_{aL}}{w_L}}$ | UNIFORM LOAD | | | | | | | | | QUARTER-POINT LOADING | | | | | | | | |
|---|---|---|---|---|---|---|---|---|---|---|---|---|---|---|---|---|---|---|---|
| | | Interior Spans | | | | | Exterior Spans | | | | Interior Spans | | | | | Exterior Spans | | | |
| | | aL 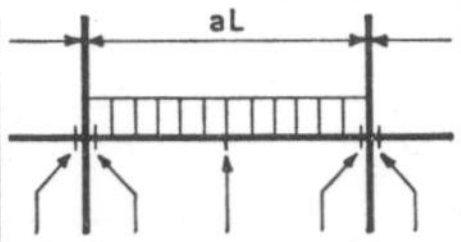 | | | | | aL 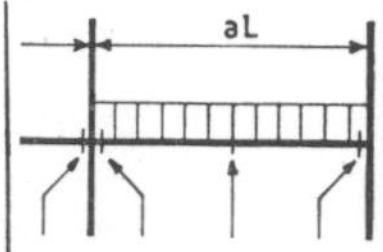 | | | | aL 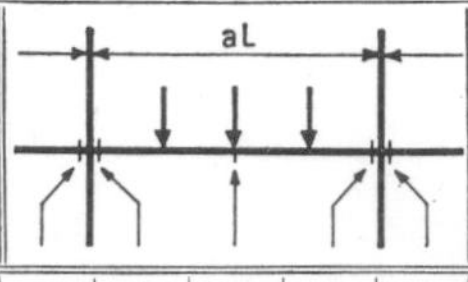 | | | | | aL 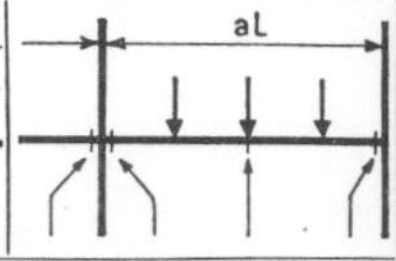 | | | |
| | 1.4 | −.050 | −.050 | +.069 | −.050 | −.050 | −.061 | −.061 | +.090 | 0 | −.076 | −.076 | +.126 | −.076 | −.076 | −.091 | −.091 | +.156 | 0 |
| | 1.3 | −.036 | −.036 | +.050 | −.036 | −.036 | −.044 | −.044 | +.065 | 0 | −.058 | −.058 | +.098 | −.058 | −.058 | −.070 | −.070 | +.122 | 0 |
| | 1.2 | −.023 | −.023 | +.032 | −.023 | −.023 | −.028 | −.028 | +.041 | 0 | −.042 | −.042 | +.073 | −.042 | −.042 | −.050 | −.050 | +.090 | 0 |
| | 1.1 | −.011 | −.011 | +.015 | −.011 | −.011 | −.013 | −.013 | +.020 | 0 | −.027 | −.027 | +.050 | −.027 | −.027 | −.032 | −.032 | +.060 | 0 |
| 0 | 1.0 | 0 | 0 | 0 | 0 | 0 | 0 | 0 | 0 | 0 | −.013 | −.013 | +.029 | −.013 | −.013 | −.016 | −.016 | +.034 | 0 |
| | .9 | +.010 | +.010 | −.014 | +.010 | +.010 | +.012 | +.012 | −.018 | 0 | −.001 | −.001 | +.009 | −.001 | −.001 | −.001 | −.001 | +.010 | 0 |
| | .8 | +.019 | +.019 | −.026 | +.019 | +.019 | +.023 | +.023 | −.034 | 0 | +.010 | +.010 | −.008 | +.010 | +.010 | +.013 | +.013 | −.012 | 0 |
| | .7 | +.027 | +.027 | −.037 | +.027 | +.027 | +.032 | +.032 | −.048 | 0 | +.020 | +.020 | −.023 | +.020 | +.020 | +.024 | +.024 | −.031 | 0 |
| | .6 | +.034 | +.034 | −.046 | +.034 | +.034 | +.041 | +.041 | −.060 | 0 | +.029 | +.029 | −.036 | +.029 | +.029 | +.035 | +.035 | −.048 | 0 |
| | 1.4 | −.037 | −.059 | +.061 | −.059 | −.037 | −.041 | −.066 | +.070 | −.035 | −.057 | −.088 | +.113 | −.088 | −.057 | −.062 | −.100 | +.126 | −.052 |
| | 1.3 | −.027 | −.042 | +.044 | −.042 | −.027 | −.030 | −.048 | +.050 | −.025 | −.043 | −.068 | +.089 | −.068 | −.043 | −.048 | −.077 | +.098 | −.040 |
| | 1.2 | −.017 | −.027 | +.028 | −.027 | −.017 | −.019 | −.030 | +.032 | −.016 | −.031 | −.049 | +.066 | −.049 | −.031 | −.034 | −.055 | +.073 | −.029 |
| | 1.1 | −.008 | −.013 | +.013 | −.013 | −.008 | −.009 | −.014 | +.015 | −.008 | −.020 | −.031 | +.045 | −.031 | −.020 | −.022 | −.035 | +.050 | −.019 |
| 0.5 | 1.0 | 0 | 0 | 0 | 0 | 0 | 0 | 0 | 0 | 0 | −.010 | −.015 | +.026 | −.015 | −.010 | −.011 | −.017 | +.029 | −.009 |
| | .9 | +.007 | +.012 | −.012 | +.012 | +.007 | +.008 | +.013 | −.014 | +.007 | −.001 | −.001 | +.009 | −.001 | −.001 | −.001 | −.001 | +.009 | 0 |
| | .8 | +.014 | +.022 | −.023 | +.022 | +.014 | +.015 | +.025 | −.026 | +.013 | +.008 | +.012 | −.006 | +.012 | +.008 | +.009 | +.014 | −.008 | +.007 |
| | .7 | +.020 | +.031 | −.033 | +.031 | +.020 | +.022 | +.035 | −.037 | +.018 | +.015 | +.024 | −.020 | +.024 | +.015 | +.017 | +.027 | −.023 | +.014 |
| | .6 | +.025 | +.039 | −.041 | +.039 | +.025 | +.028 | +.044 | −.046 | +.023 | +.021 | +.034 | −.031 | +.034 | +.021 | +.024 | +.038 | −.036 | +.020 |
| | 1.4 | −.030 | −.063 | +.057 | −.063 | −.030 | −.032 | −.068 | +.061 | −.049 | −.046 | −.096 | +.106 | −.096 | −.046 | −.048 | −.103 | +.113 | −.074 |
| | 1.3 | −.022 | −.046 | +.041 | −.046 | −.022 | −.023 | −.049 | +.044 | −.035 | −.035 | −.073 | +.083 | −.073 | −.035 | −.037 | −.079 | +.089 | −.057 |
| | 1.2 | −.014 | −.029 | +.026 | −.029 | −.014 | −.015 | −.031 | +.028 | −.022 | −.025 | −.053 | +.062 | −.053 | −.025 | −.026 | −.057 | +.066 | −.041 |
| | 1.1 | −.007 | −.014 | +.012 | −.014 | −.007 | −.007 | −.015 | +.013 | −.011 | −.016 | −.034 | +.043 | −.034 | −.016 | −.017 | −.036 | +.046 | −.026 |
| 1 | 1.0 | 0 | 0 | 0 | 0 | 0 | 0 | 0 | 0 | 0 | −.008 | −.017 | +.025 | −.017 | −.008 | −.008 | −.018 | +.027 | −.013 |
| | .9 | +.006 | +.013 | −.011 | +.013 | +.006 | +.006 | +.013 | −.012 | +.010 | 0 | −.001 | +.009 | −.001 | 0 | 0 | −.001 | +.009 | −.001 |
| | .8 | +.011 | +.024 | −.021 | +.024 | +.011 | +.012 | +.026 | −.023 | +.018 | +.006 | +.013 | −.005 | +.013 | +.006 | +.007 | +.014 | −.006 | +.010 |
| | .7 | +.016 | +.034 | −.030 | +.034 | +.016 | +.017 | +.036 | −.033 | +.026 | +.012 | +.025 | −.018 | +.025 | +.012 | +.013 | +.027 | −.020 | +.020 |
| | .6 | +.020 | +.042 | −.038 | +.042 | +.020 | +.021 | +.045 | −.041 | +.033 | +.017 | +.036 | −.029 | +.036 | +.017 | +.018 | +.039 | −.031 | +.028 |
| | 1.4 | −.022 | −.068 | +.052 | −.068 | −.022 | −.023 | −.071 | +.054 | −.061 | −.033 | −.103 | +.099 | −.103 | −.033 | −.034 | −.107 | +.102 | −.093 |
| | 1.3 | −.016 | −.049 | +.037 | −.049 | −.016 | −.016 | −.051 | +.039 | −.044 | −.025 | −.079 | +.078 | −.079 | −.025 | −.026 | −.082 | +.080 | −.071 |
| | 1.2 | −.010 | −.031 | +.024 | −.031 | −.010 | −.010 | −.033 | +.025 | −.028 | −.018 | −.057 | +.058 | −.057 | −.018 | −.019 | −.059 | +.060 | −.051 |
| | 1.1 | −.005 | −.015 | +.011 | −.015 | −.005 | −.005 | −.016 | +.012 | −.013 | −.012 | −.036 | +.040 | −.036 | −.012 | −.012 | −.038 | +.041 | −.033 |
| 2 | 1.0 | 0 | 0 | 0 | 0 | 0 | 0 | 0 | 0 | 0 | −.006 | −.018 | +.024 | −.018 | −.006 | −.006 | −.019 | +.024 | −.016 |
| | .9 | +.004 | +.014 | −.010 | +.014 | +.004 | +.005 | +.014 | −.011 | +.012 | 0 | −.001 | +.009 | −.001 | 0 | 0 | −.001 | +.009 | −.001 |
| | .8 | +.008 | +.026 | −.019 | +.026 | +.008 | +.009 | +.027 | −.020 | +.023 | +.005 | +.014 | −.004 | +.014 | +.005 | +.005 | +.015 | −.005 | +.013 |
| | .7 | +.011 | +.036 | −.028 | +.036 | +.011 | +.012 | +.038 | −.029 | +.033 | +.009 | +.027 | −.016 | +.027 | +.009 | +.009 | +.029 | −.017 | +.025 |
| | .6 | +.014 | +.045 | −.035 | +.045 | +.014 | +.015 | +.047 | −.036 | +.041 | +.012 | +.039 | −.026 | +.039 | +.012 | +.013 | +.041 | −.027 | +.035 |
| | 1.4 | −.014 | −.073 | +.047 | −.073 | −.014 | −.014 | −.074 | +.048 | −.070 | −.021 | −.110 | +.092 | −.110 | −.021 | −.021 | −.112 | +.093 | −.106 |
| | 1.3 | −.010 | −.052 | +.034 | −.052 | −.010 | −.010 | −.053 | +.035 | −.050 | −.016 | −.085 | +.072 | −.085 | −.016 | −.016 | −.086 | +.073 | −.081 |
| | 1.2 | −.006 | −.033 | +.022 | −.033 | −.006 | −.007 | −.034 | +.022 | −.032 | −.012 | −.061 | +.054 | −.061 | −.012 | −.012 | −.062 | +.055 | −.058 |
| | 1.1 | −.003 | −.016 | +.010 | −.016 | −.003 | −.003 | −.016 | +.011 | −.015 | −.007 | −.039 | +.038 | −.039 | −.007 | −.008 | −.040 | +.038 | −.037 |
| 4 | 1.0 | 0 | 0 | 0 | 0 | 0 | 0 | 0 | 0 | 0 | −.004 | −.019 | +.023 | −.019 | −.004 | −.004 | −.019 | +.023 | −.018 |
| | .9 | +.003 | +.014 | −.009 | +.014 | +.003 | +.003 | +.015 | −.010 | +.014 | 0 | −.001 | +.009 | −.001 | 0 | 0 | −.001 | +.009 | −.001 |
| | .8 | +.005 | +.027 | −.018 | +.027 | +.005 | +.005 | +.028 | −.018 | +.026 | +.003 | +.015 | −.003 | +.015 | +.003 | +.003 | +.015 | −.003 | +.015 |
| | .7 | +.007 | +.039 | −.025 | +.039 | +.007 | +.008 | +.039 | −.026 | +.037 | +.006 | +.029 | −.014 | +.029 | +.006 | +.006 | +.030 | −.014 | +.028 |
| | .6 | +.009 | +.049 | −.031 | +.049 | +.009 | +.009 | +.049 | −.032 | +.047 | +.008 | +.042 | −.023 | +.042 | +.008 | +.008 | +.042 | −.024 | +.040 |
| | 1.4 | −.008 | −.076 | +.044 | −.076 | −.008 | −.008 | −.076 | +.044 | −.075 | −.012 | −.115 | +.087 | −.115 | −.012 | −.012 | −.115 | +.088 | −.113 |
| | 1.3 | −.006 | −.055 | +.032 | −.055 | −.006 | −.006 | −.055 | +.032 | −.054 | −.009 | −.088 | +.069 | −.088 | −.009 | −.010 | −.088 | +.070 | −.087 |
| | 1.2 | −.004 | −.035 | +.020 | −.035 | −.004 | −.004 | −.035 | +.020 | −.034 | −.007 | −.063 | +.052 | −.063 | −.007 | −.007 | −.063 | +.052 | −.062 |
| | 1.1 | −.002 | −.017 | +.010 | −.017 | −.002 | −.002 | −.017 | +.010 | −.016 | −.004 | −.041 | +.036 | −.041 | −.004 | −.004 | −.041 | +.037 | −.040 |
| 8 | 1.0 | 0 | 0 | 0 | 0 | 0 | 0 | 0 | 0 | 0 | −.002 | −.020 | +.022 | −.020 | −.002 | −.002 | −.020 | +.022 | −.020 |
| | .9 | +.002 | +.015 | −.009 | +.015 | +.002 | +.002 | +.015 | −.009 | +.015 | 0 | −.001 | +.009 | −.001 | 0 | 0 | −.001 | +.009 | −.001 |
| | .8 | +.003 | +.028 | −.017 | +.028 | +.003 | +.003 | +.028 | −.017 | +.028 | +.002 | +.016 | −.003 | +.016 | +.002 | +.002 | +.016 | −.003 | +.016 |
| | .7 | +.004 | +.040 | −.024 | +.040 | +.004 | +.004 | +.040 | −.024 | +.040 | +.003 | +.031 | −.013 | +.031 | +.003 | +.003 | +.031 | −.013 | +.030 |
| | .6 | +.005 | +.051 | −.029 | +.051 | +.005 | +.005 | +.051 | −.030 | +.050 | +.005 | +.043 | −.022 | +.043 | +.005 | +.005 | +.043 | −.022 | +.043 |
| | 1.4 | 0 | −.080 | +.040 | −.080 | 0 | 0 | −.080 | +.040 | −.080 | 0 | −.121 | +.081 | −.121 | 0 | 0 | −.121 | +.081 | −.121 |
| | 1.3 | 0 | −.057 | +.029 | −.057 | 0 | 0 | −.057 | +.029 | −.057 | 0 | −.093 | +.064 | −.093 | 0 | 0 | −.093 | +.064 | −.093 |
| | 1.2 | 0 | −.037 | +.018 | −.037 | 0 | 0 | −.037 | +.018 | −.037 | 0 | −.067 | +.048 | −.067 | 0 | 0 | −.067 | +.048 | −.067 |
| | 1.1 | 0 | −.017 | +.009 | −.017 | 0 | 0 | −.017 | +.009 | −.017 | 0 | −.043 | +.034 | −.043 | 0 | 0 | −.043 | +.034 | −.043 |
| Infinity | 1.0 | 0 | 0 | 0 | 0 | 0 | 0 | 0 | 0 | 0 | 0 | −.021 | +.021 | −.021 | 0 | 0 | −.021 | +.021 | −.021 |
| | .9 | 0 | +.016 | −.008 | +.016 | 0 | 0 | +.016 | −.008 | +.016 | 0 | −.001 | +.009 | −.001 | 0 | 0 | −.001 | +.009 | −.001 |
| | .8 | 0 | +.030 | −.015 | +.030 | 0 | 0 | +.030 | −.015 | +.030 | 0 | +.017 | −.002 | +.017 | 0 | 0 | +.017 | −.002 | +.017 |
| | .7 | 0 | +.042 | −.021 | +.042 | 0 | 0 | +.042 | −.021 | +.042 | 0 | +.032 | −.011 | +.032 | 0 | 0 | +.032 | −.011 | +.032 |
| | .6 | 0 | +.053 | −.027 | +.053 | 0 | 0 | +.053 | −.027 | +.053 | 0 | +.046 | −.019 | +.046 | 0 | 0 | +.046 | −.019 | +.046 |

*Use $a\sqrt{\frac{w_{aL}}{w_L}}$ in uniform load section, and $a\sqrt{\frac{p_{aL}}{w_L}}$ in quarter-point loading section

# Table 2A. *(continued)*

## Values of $C_2$

For use when spans or loads vary

$$M = C(w_{dead} + w_{live})L^2$$

$C = C_1$ (from Table 1A) $+ C_2$ (from Table 2A)

| $\frac{\Sigma K_{col.}}{K_{beam}}$ | $a\sqrt{\frac{p_aL}{w_L}}$ | THIRD-POINT LOADING | | | | | | | | | MIDSPAN LOADING | | | | | | | | |
|---|---|---|---|---|---|---|---|---|---|---|---|---|---|---|---|---|---|---|---|
| | | Interior Spans | | | | | Exterior Spans | | | | Interior Spans | | | | | Exterior Spans | | | |
| | | 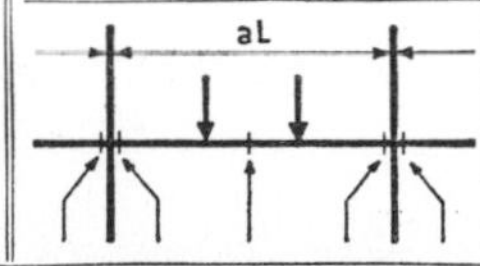 | | | | | 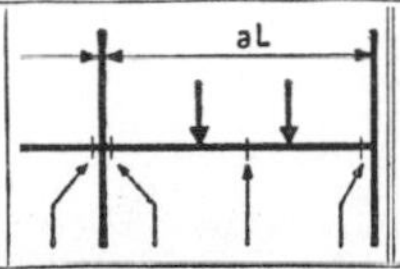 | | | | 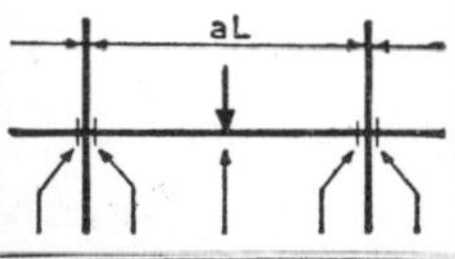 | | | | | 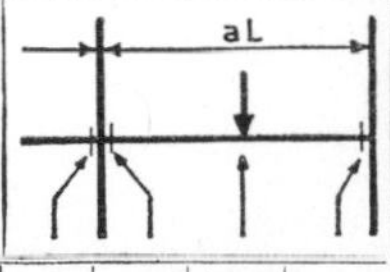 | | | |
| 0 | 1.4 | −.085 | −.085 | +.117 | −.085 | −.085 | −.101 | −.101 | +.151 | 0 | −.102 | −.102 | +.263 | −.102 | −.102 | −.122 | −.122 | +.304 | 0 |
| | 1.3 | −.066 | −.066 | +.091 | −.066 | −.066 | −.079 | −.079 | +.117 | 0 | −.081 | −.081 | +.217 | −.081 | −.081 | −.097 | −.097 | +.249 | 0 |
| | 1.2 | −.048 | −.048 | +.067 | −.048 | −.048 | −.058 | −.058 | +.086 | 0 | −.061 | −.061 | +.174 | −.061 | −.061 | −.073 | −.073 | +.198 | 0 |
| | 1.1 | −.032 | −.032 | +.045 | −.032 | −.032 | −.038 | −.038 | +.057 | 0 | −.043 | −.043 | +.135 | −.043 | −.043 | −.051 | −.051 | +.152 | 0 |
| | 1.0 | −.017 | −.017 | +.024 | −.017 | −.017 | −.021 | −.021 | +.031 | 0 | −.026 | −.026 | +.099 | −.026 | −.026 | −.032 | −.032 | +.109 | 0 |
| | .9 | −.004 | −.004 | +.006 | −.004 | −.004 | −.005 | −.005 | +.007 | 0 | −.011 | −.011 | +.066 | −.011 | −.011 | −.014 | −.014 | +.071 | 0 |
| | .8 | +.008 | +.008 | −.011 | +.008 | +.008 | +.009 | +.009 | −.014 | 0 | +.002 | +.002 | +.037 | +.002 | +.002 | +.003 | +.003 | +.036 | 0 |
| | .7 | +.018 | +.018 | −.025 | +.018 | +.018 | +.022 | +.022 | −.033 | 0 | +.014 | +.014 | +.011 | +.014 | +.014 | +.017 | +.017 | +.006 | 0 |
| | .6 | +.027 | +.027 | −.038 | +.027 | +.027 | +.033 | +.033 | −.049 | 0 | +.024 | +.024 | −.011 | +.024 | +.024 | +.029 | +.029 | −.021 | 0 |
| 0.5 | 1.4 | −.063 | −.098 | +.103 | −.098 | −.063 | −.069 | −.111 | +.117 | −.058 | −.076 | −.118 | +.247 | −.118 | −.076 | −.083 | −.134 | +.263 | −.070 |
| | 1.3 | −.049 | −.076 | +.080 | −.076 | −.049 | −.054 | −.086 | +.091 | −.045 | −.060 | −.094 | +.204 | −.094 | −.060 | −.066 | −.106 | +.217 | −.055 |
| | 1.2 | −.036 | −.056 | +.059 | −.056 | −.036 | −.040 | −.063 | +.067 | −.033 | −.045 | −.071 | +.164 | −.071 | −.045 | −.050 | −.080 | +.174 | −.042 |
| | 1.1 | −.024 | −.037 | +.039 | −.037 | −.024 | −.026 | −.042 | +.045 | −.022 | −.032 | −.050 | +.128 | −.050 | −.032 | −.035 | −.056 | +.135 | −.030 |
| | 1.0 | −.013 | −.020 | +.021 | −.020 | −.013 | −.014 | −.023 | +.024 | −.012 | −.020 | −.031 | +.095 | −.031 | −.020 | −.022 | −.035 | +.099 | −.018 |
| | .9 | −.003 | −.005 | +.005 | −.005 | [illegible] | [illegible] | [illegible] | [illegible] | [illegible] | [illegible] | .013 | +.061 | .013 | [illegible] | [illegible] | −.016 | +.066 | [illegible] |
| | .8 | +.006 | +.009 | −.009 | +.009 | +.006 | +.006 | +.010 | −.011 | +.005 | +.002 | +.002 | +.037 | +.002 | +.002 | +.002 | +.003 | +.037 | +.001 |
| | .7 | +.014 | +.021 | −.022 | +.021 | +.014 | +.015 | +.024 | −.025 | +.013 | +.010 | +.016 | +.014 | +.016 | +.010 | +.011 | +.018 | +.011 | +.010 |
| | .6 | +.020 | +.032 | −.033 | +.032 | +.020 | +.022 | +.036 | −.038 | +.019 | +.018 | +.028 | −.007 | +.028 | +.018 | +.020 | +.032 | −.011 | +.017 |
| 1 | 1.4 | −.051 | −.106 | +.095 | −.106 | −.051 | −.053 | −.114 | +.103 | −.082 | −.061 | −.128 | +.237 | −.128 | −.061 | −.064 | −.138 | +.247 | −.099 |
| | 1.3 | −.039 | −.083 | +.074 | −.083 | −.039 | −.041 | −.089 | +.080 | −.064 | −.049 | −.101 | +.196 | −.101 | −.049 | −.051 | −.109 | +.204 | −.078 |
| | 1.2 | −.029 | −.061 | +.054 | −.061 | −.029 | −.030 | −.065 | +.059 | −.047 | −.037 | −.077 | +.158 | −.077 | −.037 | −.038 | −.082 | +.164 | −.059 |
| | 1.1 | −.019 | −.040 | +.036 | −.040 | −.019 | −.020 | −.043 | +.039 | −.031 | −.026 | −.054 | +.124 | −.054 | −.026 | −.027 | −.058 | +.128 | −.042 |
| | 1.0 | −.010 | −.022 | +.020 | −.022 | −.010 | −.011 | −.023 | +.021 | −.017 | −.016 | −.033 | +.092 | −.033 | −.016 | −.017 | −.036 | +.095 | −.026 |
| | .9 | −.003 | −.005 | +.005 | −.005 | −.003 | −.003 | −.006 | +.005 | −.004 | −.007 | −.014 | +.063 | −.014 | −.007 | −.007 | −.015 | +.065 | −.011 |
| | .8 | +.005 | +.010 | −.009 | +.010 | +.005 | +.005 | +.010 | −.009 | +.007 | +.001 | +.003 | +.038 | +.003 | +.001 | +.001 | +.003 | +.038 | +.002 |
| | .7 | +.011 | +.023 | −.020 | +.023 | +.011 | +.012 | +.025 | −.022 | +.018 | +.008 | +.017 | +.015 | +.017 | +.008 | +.009 | +.019 | +.014 | +.014 |
| | .6 | +.016 | +.034 | −.031 | +.034 | +.016 | +.017 | +.037 | −.033 | +.027 | +.014 | +.030 | −.005 | +.030 | +.014 | +.015 | +.033 | −.007 | +.023 |
| 2 | 1.4 | −.036 | −.114 | +.087 | −.114 | −.036 | −.038 | −.119 | +.090 | −.103 | −.044 | −.138 | +.227 | −.138 | −.044 | −.046 | −.144 | +.231 | −.124 |
| | 1.3 | −.028 | −.089 | +.068 | −.089 | −.028 | −.030 | −.093 | +.070 | −.080 | −.035 | −.109 | +.189 | −.109 | −.035 | −.036 | −.114 | +.192 | −.098 |
| | 1.2 | −.021 | −.065 | +.050 | −.065 | −.021 | −.022 | −.068 | +.052 | −.059 | −.026 | −.082 | +.153 | −.082 | −.026 | −.027 | −.086 | +.155 | −.074 |
| | 1.1 | −.014 | −.043 | +.033 | −.043 | −.014 | −.014 | −.045 | +.034 | −.039 | −.018 | −.058 | +.120 | −.058 | −.018 | −.019 | −.061 | +.121 | −.052 |
| | 1.0 | −.007 | −.024 | +.018 | −.024 | −.007 | −.008 | −.026 | +.019 | −.021 | −.011 | −.036 | +.089 | −.036 | −.011 | −.012 | −.037 | +.091 | −.032 |
| | .9 | −.002 | −.006 | +.004 | −.006 | −.002 | −.002 | −.006 | +.005 | −.005 | −.005 | −.015 | +.062 | −.015 | −.005 | −.005 | −.016 | +.063 | −.014 |
| | .8 | +.003 | +.010 | −.008 | +.010 | +.003 | +.003 | +.011 | −.008 | +.009 | +.001 | +.003 | +.038 | +.003 | +.001 | +.001 | +.003 | +.038 | +.003 |
| | .7 | +.008 | +.025 | −.019 | +.025 | +.008 | +.008 | +.026 | −.019 | +.022 | +.006 | +.019 | +.016 | +.019 | +.006 | +.006 | +.020 | +.016 | +.017 |
| | .6 | +.012 | +.037 | −.028 | +.037 | +.012 | +.012 | +.038 | −.029 | +.033 | +.010 | +.033 | −.002 | +.033 | +.010 | +.011 | +.034 | −.003 | +.029 |
| 4 | 1.4 | −.023 | −.122 | +.079 | −.122 | −.023 | −.024 | −.124 | +.081 | −.118 | −.028 | −.147 | +.218 | −.147 | −.028 | −.029 | −.149 | +.219 | −.142 |
| | 1.3 | −.018 | −.095 | +.062 | −.095 | −.018 | −.019 | −.096 | +.063 | −.091 | −.022 | −.117 | +.181 | −.117 | −.022 | −.023 | −.119 | +.182 | −.112 |
| | 1.2 | −.013 | −.070 | +.045 | −.070 | −.013 | −.014 | −.071 | +.046 | −.067 | −.017 | −.088 | +.147 | −.088 | −.017 | −.017 | −.089 | +.148 | −.085 |
| | 1.1 | −.009 | −.046 | +.030 | −.046 | −.009 | −.009 | −.047 | +.031 | −.045 | −.012 | −.062 | +.116 | −.062 | −.012 | −.012 | −.063 | +.116 | −.060 |
| | 1.0 | −.005 | −.025 | +.016 | −.025 | −.005 | −.005 | −.025 | +.017 | −.024 | −.007 | −.038 | +.087 | −.038 | −.007 | −.007 | −.039 | +.087 | −.037 |
| | .9 | −.001 | −.006 | +.004 | −.006 | −.001 | −.001 | −.006 | +.004 | −.006 | −.003 | −.016 | +.061 | −.016 | −.003 | −.003 | −.017 | +.061 | −.016 |
| | .8 | +.002 | +.011 | −.007 | +.011 | +.002 | +.002 | +.011 | −.007 | +.010 | +.001 | +.003 | +.038 | +.003 | +.001 | +.001 | +.003 | +.038 | +.003 |
| | .7 | +.005 | +.027 | −.017 | +.027 | +.005 | +.005 | +.027 | −.017 | +.026 | +.004 | +.020 | +.018 | +.020 | +.004 | +.004 | +.020 | +.017 | +.019 |
| | .6 | +.008 | +.040 | −.025 | +.040 | +.008 | +.008 | +.040 | −.026 | +.038 | +.007 | +.035 | 0 | +.035 | +.007 | +.007 | +.035 | −.001 | +.033 |
| 8 | 1.4 | −.014 | −.127 | +.074 | −.127 | −.014 | −.014 | −.127 | +.075 | −.126 | −.016 | −.153 | +.212 | −.153 | −.016 | −.017 | −.153 | +.213 | −.151 |
| | 1.3 | −.011 | −.099 | +.058 | −.099 | −.011 | −.011 | −.099 | +.059 | −.098 | −.013 | −.121 | +.176 | −.121 | −.013 | −.013 | −.121 | +.177 | −.120 |
| | 1.2 | −.008 | −.073 | +.042 | −.073 | −.008 | −.008 | −.073 | +.043 | −.072 | −.010 | −.092 | +.143 | −.092 | −.010 | −.010 | −.092 | +.144 | −.090 |
| | 1.1 | −.005 | −.048 | +.028 | −.048 | −.005 | −.005 | −.048 | +.029 | −.048 | −.007 | −.064 | +.113 | −.064 | −.007 | −.007 | −.064 | +.114 | −.064 |
| | 1.0 | −.003 | −.026 | +.015 | −.026 | −.003 | −.003 | −.026 | +.016 | −.026 | −.004 | −.040 | +.086 | −.040 | −.004 | −.004 | −.040 | +.086 | −.039 |
| | .9 | −.001 | −.006 | +.004 | −.006 | −.001 | −.001 | −.006 | +.004 | −.006 | −.002 | −.017 | +.061 | −.017 | −.002 | −.002 | −.017 | +.061 | −.017 |
| | .8 | +.001 | +.012 | −.007 | +.012 | +.001 | +.001 | +.012 | −.007 | +.011 | 0 | +.003 | +.038 | +.003 | 0 | 0 | +.003 | +.038 | +.003 |
| | .7 | +.003 | +.028 | −.016 | +.028 | +.003 | +.003 | +.028 | −.016 | +.027 | +.002 | +.021 | +.018 | +.021 | +.002 | +.002 | +.021 | +.018 | +.021 |
| | .6 | +.004 | +.041 | −.024 | +.041 | +.004 | +.004 | +.041 | −.024 | +.041 | +.004 | +.036 | +.001 | +.036 | +.004 | +.004 | +.036 | +.001 | +.036 |
| Infinity | 1.4 | 0 | −.134 | +.067 | −.134 | 0 | 0 | −.134 | +.067 | −.134 | 0 | −.162 | +.203 | −.162 | 0 | 0 | −.162 | +.203 | −.162 |
| | 1.3 | 0 | −.104 | +.052 | −.104 | 0 | 0 | −.104 | +.052 | −.104 | 0 | −.128 | +.170 | −.128 | 0 | 0 | −.128 | +.170 | −.128 |
| | 1.2 | 0 | −.077 | +.038 | −.077 | 0 | 0 | −.077 | +.038 | −.077 | 0 | −.097 | +.138 | −.097 | 0 | 0 | −.097 | +.138 | −.097 |
| | 1.1 | 0 | −.051 | +.026 | −.051 | 0 | 0 | −.051 | +.026 | −.051 | 0 | −.068 | +.110 | −.068 | 0 | 0 | −.068 | +.110 | −.068 |
| | 1.0 | 0 | −.028 | +.014 | −.028 | 0 | 0 | −.028 | +.014 | −.028 | 0 | −.042 | +.083 | −.042 | 0 | 0 | −.042 | +.083 | −.042 |
| | .9 | 0 | −.007 | +.003 | −.007 | 0 | 0 | −.007 | +.003 | −.007 | 0 | −.018 | +.060 | −.018 | 0 | 0 | −.018 | +.060 | −.018 |
| | .8 | 0 | +.012 | −.006 | +.012 | 0 | 0 | +.012 | −.006 | +.012 | 0 | +.003 | +.038 | +.003 | 0 | 0 | +.003 | +.038 | +.003 |
| | .7 | 0 | +.029 | −.015 | +.029 | 0 | 0 | +.029 | −.015 | +.029 | 0 | +.022 | +.020 | +.022 | 0 | 0 | +.022 | +.020 | +.022 |
| | .6 | 0 | +.043 | −.022 | +.043 | 0 | 0 | +.043 | −.022 | +.043 | 0 | +.038 | +.003 | +.038 | 0 | 0 | +.038 | +.003 | +.038 |

## Symbols and Notation

| | |
|---|---|
| $L$ | : length of standard span; also used as a subscript to refer to standard span, i.e., $w_L$ = uniform load of standard $L$-span |
| $aL$ | : length of a non-standard span; also used as a subscript to refer to a non-standard span, i.e., $w_{aL}$ = uniform load of non-standard $aL$-span |
| $a$ | : ratio of a span length to length of standard span |
| $K_{beam}$ | : stiffness of beam or slab in standard span |
| $\Sigma K_{col.}$ | : total stiffness of columns or support at one end of standard span |
| $w_{dead}$ | : uniform dead load per foot of span |
| $w_{live}$ | : uniform live load per foot of span |
| $w_{TL}$ | : total uniform load per foot of standard span |
| $w_{TaL}$ | : total uniform load per foot of an $aL$-span |
| $p_{TaL}$ | : total concentrated load on an $aL$-span divided by the span length, denoted as total "equivalent" uniform load per foot. |
| $w_{DL}$ | : uniform dead load per foot of standard span |
| $w_{DaL}$ | : uniform dead load per foot of an $aL$-span |
| $p_{DaL}$ | : total concentrated dead load on an $aL$-span divided by the span length, denoted as "equivalent" uniform dead load per foot |

T2—33M—12-39 PRINTED IN U. S. A.